[CONTACTS 2011]

100th edition published by Spotlight, 7 Leicester Place, London WC2H 7RJ
T 020 7437 7631   F 020 7437 5881   E questions@spotlight.com   W www.spotlight.com

What is Contacts?

Contacts is the essential handbook for everyone working or wanting to work in the entertainment industry. It has been published by Spotlight since 1947, once quarterly and then annually, and has now reached its 100th edition. It contains over 5000 listings for companies, services and individuals across all branches of Television, Stage, Film and Radio. These are updated annually to bring you the most accurate information available.

Also watch out for the 'information pages', designed to tell you more about those listed and why you might want to contact them. They include valuable advice from key industry figures - especially helpful if you are just starting out in the industry.

As ever, please send any feedback or suggestions for the next edition to contacts@spotlight.com

How can I / my company appear in the next edition of Contacts?

Contacts is published annually. If you would like to appear in the next edition, either with an advert or a free, text-only listing, please visit: www.contactshandbook.com

How do I buy copies of Contacts?

To purchase additional copies of Contacts,
visit www.contactshandbook.com, e-mail sales@spotlight.com,
or call 020 7440 5026. It is also available from most good bookshops.

Mixed Sources
Product group from well-managed
forests and other controlled sources
www.fsc.org Cert no. SA-COC-1565
© 1996 Forest Stewardship Council
FSC

Printed & bound in Great Britain by MPG Books Group

Contacts 100th Edition
Foreword by Hugh Bonneville

Contacts 1985

Photo: Philip Thorne

One evening in 1985, when I was starting out, I fell into conversation with an actor in a pub in Clapham. "In this profession it's not what you know, it's who you know", declared the sage. "If you haven't got contacts, don't bother".

Instantly I slumped into depression. No, I didn't have any 'contacts'. In fact I didn't know anyone in the industry I had set my heart on joining. But I had recently read about a Hollywood legend getting his first break by smashing up an audition room; he'd taken the bull by the horns and Gone For It. So now it was my turn.

I'd heard rumour of an 'after dinner theatre' tour of the Middle East. I knew the play and there was a part that had my name written all over it. The Director was based at Plymouth Theatre Royal, so off I set from London in my car. I may have had no contacts but hell I had talent, determination and a map.

The Stage Door Keeper looked at me blankly.

I had no appointment and besides, the Director was out getting his laundry so would I please leave. I said I'd wait. She tried to get rid of me several more times but I was in an audition-room trashing mood and refused to budge. When the Director finally appeared two hours later I announced that I'd driven two hundred miles to give him the chance of auditioning me for a role I was born to play.

Wearily he took me into his office. "Sit down" he said. He leaned his elbows on the desk, ran his hands through his hair and groaned. "Look, I cast that part a week ago. Why on earth didn't you ring and find out before driving all that way?"

"I was taking the bull by the, er, y'know, by the horns" I mumbled, crestfallen. "Anyway, I didn't have the phone number."

"Haven't you got Contacts?" he sighed.

"No, none."

He just looked at me, confused by my answer and gobsmacked by my naivety.

I bought my first copy of this publication the next day. The pink cover of my 1985/86 edition has long since faded. Portrait photographers' adverts provide a snapshot of contemporary hairstyles: Bucks Fizz for the women, Simon Le Bon for the men. And

Open Air Theatre, Regent's Park, and took place in a house in South London. As soon as I was in the room, I launched into my Oberon, full of voice and semaphore. I was booming on about oxslips and nodding violets, waving my arms around as if trying to tell a plane

"Haven't you got Contacts?" he sighed.

there's a woman clutching an alligator. There are also the ghosts of the two hundred and fifty addresses I culled from its pages in order to write to agents and theatre companies, announcing the arrival of the best thing since sliced bread, namely Me. I took pains to make each letter personal ("I've often dreamed of performing in Leatherhead...") and was scrupulous about spelling, punctuation and the correct form of address. To the agent Lou Coulson, for example, I wrote "Dear Mr. Coulson".

Strangely, she never got in touch.

However, about one hundred and fifty others did reply, informing me via photocopy that they would keep my details 'on file' and I would be invited to audition when they were next casting or when hell froze over, whichever was the later. For years I kept these rejection letters on a bit of string tied to the toilet roll dispenser in my bathroom; a gesture that combined two-fingered defiance with a nod to recycling before it became fashionable. As time went by my wad of spare loo paper diminished. I think the Churchill Theatre Bromley was the last to go down the pan.

But those two hundred and fifty letters did at least yield two auditions. One was for the

where to park, when Declan Donnellan, who was directing Romeo and Juliet that season, interrupted me, pointing out that I was not on stage at the King's Theatre Glasgow with a need to impress the Upper Circle, but in a cosy sitting room in Putney playing to an audience of one - him - who was all of three feet away. He told me to start again and do it better.

I spent the next six months at the Open Air Theatre, biting my thumb at thee and clutching my newly acquired provisional Equity Card.

So I would qualify the Clapham pub philosopher's wisdom by saying that the breaks come when Luck allows you to put your indisputably talented self in the right place, at the right time and in front of the right person. And to give yourself a better chance of achieving this, you do indeed need Contacts.

Happy 100th Birthday.

SPOTLIGHT

PARTNERS

Nigel Seale, Ben Seale, Emma Smith, Philppa Burton

EDITOR

Kate Poynton

DESIGN & LAYOUT

Kathy Norrish

ACCOUNTS

Nas Fokeerchand - Head of Accounts
Amelia Barnham
Tanya Doganci
Laura Ruocco

CLIENT RELATIONS

Pippa Harrison - Head of Client Relations
Joe Bates
Will Davies
Thom Hammond
Nicholas Peel
Liam Simpson

DATA PROCESSING

Joanna MacLeod - Head of Data Processing
Caroline Taylor
Angie Drake
Amanda Lawrence
Emma Lear
Sharon Mulcahy
Helene Van De Langenberg

EDITORIAL

Cindy Lemmer
Angela Cottrell
Nick Goldfinch
Martin Pavey

HR

Marilyn Peach

IT

Dylan Beattie - Head of IT

IT DEVELOPMENT

Gary Broughton - Development Manager
Dave Clements
Isabelle Kosciusko
Dan Woodhead

IT SYSTEMS

Paul Goldsmith - IT Systems Manager
Christina Kassimatis

MARKETING

Laura Albery - Head of Sales, Marketing & Customer Relations
Sally Barnham
Elaine Compton
Frances Mordue
Joan Queva
Stephanie Rodrigues
Elinor Samuels
Kelly Taylor

PRODUCTION

Neill Kennedy
Hannah Frankel
Louise Fairweather
David McCarthy
Jaime Robb

Contents

Index To Advertisers

[CONTACTS 2011]

G

A

Accountants, Insurance & Law

Agents

Agents & Personal Managers
Children's & Teenagers'
Concert & Concert Promoters
Dance
Literary & Play
Presenters
Voice-Over
Walk-On & Supporting Artists

PMA: For information regarding membership of the Personal Managers' Association please contact
PO Box 63819, London N1P 1HL
T 0845 6027191 W www.thepma.com

CPMA: For information regarding membership of the Co-operative Personal Management Association please contact
The Secretary, CPMA
c/o 62 Foulden Road, London N16 7UR
T 07876 641582 W www.cpma.coop

Members of the above organisations are clearly marked as such in the appropriate listings.

Animals
Arts Centres
Arts Councils

ALEXANDER JAMES & CO
Contact: Andrew Nicholson
Admirals Quarters, Portsmouth Road
Thames Ditton, Surrey KT7 0XA
F 020 8398 9989
E actors@alexanderjames.co.uk
W www.alexanderjames.co.uk
T 020 8398 4447

AON LTD /ALBERT G. RUBEN
Insurance Brokers
Pinewood Studios, Pinewood Road
Iver, Bucks SL0 0NH
F 01753 785861
W www.aon.co.uk
T 01753 785859

ATKINS Chris SERVICES LTD
Accountants & Business Consultants
Astra House, Arklow Road
London SE14 6EB
E info@chrisatkinsservices.co.uk
W www.chrisatkinsservices.co.uk
T 0845 5390227

BLACKMORE Lawrence
Production Accountant
Suite 5, 26 Charing Cross Road
London WC2H 0DG
T 020 7240 1817

BLAKE LAPTHORNE
Solicitors
Watchmaker Court
33 St John's Lane, London EC1M 4DB
F 020 7814 9421
E info@bllaw.co.uk
W www.bllaw.co.uk
T 020 7405 2000

BLINKHORNS
27 Mortimer Street, London W1T 3BL
E joel.trott@blinkhorns.co.uk
W www.blinkhorns.co.uk
T 020 7636 3702

BOWKER ORFORD
Chartered Accountants
15-19 Cavendish Place, London W1G 0DD
F 020 7580 3909
E mail@bowkerorford.com
W www.bowkerorford.com
T 020 7636 6391

BREBNERS
Chartered Accountants
180 Wardour Street, London W1F 8LB
F 020 7287 5315
E partners@brebners.com
W www.brebners.com
T 020 7734 2244

BRECKMAN & COMPANY
Chartered Certified Accountants
49 South Molton Street, London W1K 5LH
W www.breckmanandcompany.co.uk
T 020 7499 2292

CARR Mark & Co LTD
Chartered Accountants
Garrick House, 26-27 Southampton Street
Covent Garden, London WC2E 7RS
T 01273 778802
E mark@markcarr.co.uk
W www.markcarr.co.uk
T 020 7717 8474

CARTER BACKER WINTER
Chartered Accountants, Business Advisers
Enterprise House, 21 Buckle Street
London E1 8NN
F 020 7309 3801
E info@cbw.co.uk
W www.cbw.co.uk
T 020 7309 3800

CENTRE STAGE CHARTERED ACCOUNTANTS
Hampton House, Oldham Road
Middleton, Manchester M24 1GT
E accounts@centrestage-accountants.com
W www.centrestage-accountants.com
T 0161 655 2000

COLLINS & COMPANY
Chartered Accountants
2nd Floor, 116 College Road
Harrow, Middlesex HA1 1BQ
F 020 8863 0068　　　　　　T 020 8427 1888
E hq@collins116.com

COUNT AND SEE LTD
Tax, Accountancy & Book-keeping Services
219 Macmillan Way, London SW17 6AW
F 0845 0043454　　　　　　T 020 8767 7882
E info@countandsee.com
W www.countandsee.com

DUB & CO
7 Torriano Mews, London NW5 2RZ
F 020 7284 8687　　　　　　T 020 7284 8686
E office@dub.co.uk
W www.dub.co.uk

EQUITY INSURANCE SERVICES
131-133 New London Road, Chelmsford, Essex CM2 0QZ
F 01245 491641　　　　　　T 01245 357854
E enquiries@equity-ins-services.com
W www.equity-ins-services.com

FISHER BERGER & ASSOCIATES
Chartered Accountants
Devonshire House
582 Honeypot Lane, Stanmore HA7 1JS
F 020 8732 5500　　　　　　T 020 8732 5501
E nik@fisherberger.com

FORD Jonathan & Co
Chartered Accountants
The Coach House, 31 View Road
Rainhill, Merseyside L35 0LF　　　T 0151 426 4512
E info@jonathanford.co.uk
W www.jonathanford.co.uk

GLOBAL MOBILITY LAW
Contact: Julia de Cadenet. US Legal & Visa Consultancy.
Advice on all aspects of Work Visas and US green cards
for members of performing arts and associated industries.
Advisory work in Media Contracts & Intellectual Property
Matters. Lawyers head offices in London & Paris
T +33 62 62 18 858 (Paris)　　T 07798 695112 (London)
E visas@legalbrain.eu
W www.globalmobilitylaw.com

HARDWICKE BUILDING
Media Law
Lincoln's Inn, London WC2A 3SB
F 020 7691 1234　　　　　　M 07720 294667
E mark.engleman@hardwicke.co.uk
W www.hardwicke.co.uk

HARVEYS LLP
Accountants
The Old Winery, Lamberhurst Vineyard
Lamberhurst, Kent TN3 8EW
F 01892 891892　　　　　　T 01892 890388
E tax@harveysllp.com

HILL DICKINSON LLP
1 St Paul's Square, Old Hall Street
Liverpool L3 9SJ　　　　　　T 0161 817 7200
E mediateam@hilldickinson.com
W www.hilldickinson.com

HOOD Karl LLP
33 Cologne Road, London SW11 2AH　　M 07916 971998
E karl@karlhoodtax.co.uk
W www.karlhoodtax.co.uk

JR CHARTERED ACCOUNTANTS
Chartered Accountants. Entertainment Specialists
E joie@joierisk.com　　　　　T 020 8133 9882
W www.joierisk.com

info**page**

Why might I need this section?

This section contains listings for a number of companies and services which exist to help performers with the day-to-day administration of their working lives. Performers need to manage their business affairs personally, in ways that those in 'normal' jobs do not. For example, unlike most employees, a performer does not have an accounts department to work out their tax and national insurance, or an HR department to take care of contracts or health insurance on their behalf. On top of which, performers can often be away on tour or on set for many months and unable to attend to these matters themselves.

Areas covered in this section include:

Accountants and other financial services

Dedicated companies exist which can help you to manage key financial issues, including national insurance, taxation, benefits, savings and pensions. Specialist mortgage companies also exist for performers and other self-employed workers within the entertainment industry. Specific information about accountancy services is given overleaf. If you are a member of Equity you can also ask them for free financial advice, and an Equity pension scheme exists into which the BBC, ITV, PACT, TV companies and West End Theatre producers will pay when you have a main part with one of them. Similar schemes also exist for dancers and other performers.

Insurance

Performers may often need specialist insurance for specific jobs, as well as the standard life and health insurance policies held by most people. A number of specialist insurers are listed in the pages overleaf. Equity also offers a specialist backstage/accident and public liability insurance policy to all of its members.

Legal

There may be times in a performer's career when he/she needs specialist legal advice or representation. This could be because of a performer's high profile, complicated contractual details, or international employment issues. Legal advisors and solicitors are listed in this section. In addition, as part of their membership, Equity performers can also obtain free legal advice regarding professional engagements or personal injury claims.

How should I use these listings?

As when looking to hire any company or individual, contact a number of different companies and carefully compare the services they offer. Ask others in the industry for recommendations. If you are an Equity member, don't forget to check first that the service isn't already available free of charge, as part of your annual membership.

David Summers & Co is a small, friendly firm of Chartered Accountants who specialise in the self-employed arts / entertainment industry. Their clients benefit from their many useful tax saving tips and advice.

An actor's worst nightmare might be to see his accountant doing stand-up comedy. Well, an accountant's worst nightmare is to see an actor doing his own tax return!

Self Assessment

Whilst tax assessment is not meant to be 'taxing' and can be done by yourself, in practice it takes a qualified accountant to fully understand and complete the form, and even the professionals can struggle with some of the boxes.

Many actors, especially when starting out, choose to complete their own self assessments to cut costs. This can be a foolish path to follow as expenses which can be legitimately claimed are often omitted and expenses which should not appear on the form may be included. Penalties for errors are hard and in these times of austerity the taxman is trying to maximise on these.

It will almost certainly prove beneficial in the long run to use an accountant than to fill in your tax return yourself (and I'm not just saying that because I'm an accountant)!

Choice of Trading Medium

You can carry on business as a sole trader, partnership or as a limited company. Whichever medium you choose will affect the tax you pay and at the end of the day the old saying, "It's not what you earn, it's what you keep," is all too true.

Many actors start out as a sole trader and then convert to a limited company when income rises to about £20,000. This should ensure they end up saving enough tax, even after paying the slightly higher accountancy fees for operating through a limited company. The profits are extracted out of the company by paying a small salary and the balance as dividends which are paid to the shareholders of the company. If some shares were held by your spouse/partner or your parents, a proportion of the profits could be diverted to them, hopefully preventing you becoming a higher rate tax payer.

Perhaps Britain's Got Talent finalist Chandi will be the first dog to own shares in a limited company!

Tax Investigations

The tax return is simply a form with figures in it. It gives the taxman very little detail of the expenses claimed or if the income is fully disclosed. His first action is to accept it at face value and acknowledge he has received it. He then has 12 months to enquire into it if he so wishes.

Enquiries could start for a number of reasons: the return may show insufficient income to live on; the figures may be vastly different to the previous year; the income may not be consistent with other information the taxman holds; or it just may be a purely random enquiry.

It takes skill and knowledge to beat the taxman at his own game, so a tax enquiry should not be handled on your own. Many firms offer insurance to cover the cost of their fees to deal with any tax investigations that arise, and this can be quite inexpensive.

And Finally...

Speaking as an accountant, I would strongly recommend you use one, and I know of the perfect one for you! Joking apart, an accountant will of course cost you money, but probably not as much as you think. It costs nothing to get a quote. The accountant will ensure only the correct expenses are claimed (including some you may not even have thought of) and will keep you out of trouble with the taxman. Just as importantly, he should ensure you deal with things in a timely fashion, thus avoiding the late filing penalties and increasing your risk of a tax investigation.

For further help with accountancy and taxation and a free no obligation fee quote, call David Summers or Chet Haria at David Summers & Co, Chartered Accountants, on 0800 3288741 or visit our website www.dsummers.co.uk. For a free booklet on the accountancy and tax requirements for actors, send an e-mail to dsummersfca@hotmail.com with 'Actors Booklet' as the subject.

The content of this article is intended for general guidance only and no responsibility for loss by any person acting or refraining from action as a result of this article can be accepted. We cannot assume legal liability for any errors or admissions this article may contain.

LACHMAN SMITH ACCOUNTANTS
16B North End Road
Golders Green, London NW11 7PH   T 020 8731 1700
E accounts@lachmansmith.co.uk
W www.lachmansmith.eu

LARK INSURANCE BROKING GROUP
Ibex House, 42-47 Minories, London EC3N 1DY
F 020 7543 2801   T 020 7543 2800
E mailbox@larkinsurance.co.uk
W www.larkinsurance.co.uk

LONGREACH INTERNATIONAL LTD
Specialist Insurance Brokers
20 St Dunstans Hill, London EC3R 8PP
F 020 7929 4884   T 020 7929 4747
E info@longreachint.com
W www.wandp-longreach.com

MACINTYRE HUDSON LLP
Media & Entertainment Accountants
New Bridge Street House
30-34 New Bridge Street
London EC4V 6BJ
F 020 7248 8939   T 020 7429 4100
E entertainment@mhllp.co.uk
W www.macintyrehudson.co.uk

MEDIA INSURANCE BROKERS
3rd Floor, St George's Buildings, Glasgow G1 2DH
F 0141 229 6489   T 0141 229 6480
E david.johnstone@mediainsurance.com
W www.mediainsurance.com

MGM ACCOUNTANCY LTD
3rd Floor
20 Bedford Street, London WC2E 9HP   T 020 7379 9202
E admin@mgmaccountancy.co.uk
W www.mgmaccountancy.co.uk

MONEYWISE INVESTMENTS PLC
Insurance Brokers
440-442 Romford Road
London E7 8DF   T 020 8552 5521
E aadatia@moneywiseplc.co.uk
W www.moneywiseplc.co.uk

NYMAN LIBSON PAUL
Chartered Accountants
Regina House
124 Finchley Road, London NW3 5JS
F 020 7433 2401   T 020 7433 2400
E entertainment@nlpca.co.uk
W www.nlpca.co.uk

PLANISPHERES
Business & Legal Affairs
Sinclair House, 2 Sinclair Gardens
London W14 0AT   T/F 020 7602 2038
E info@planispheres.com
W www.planispheres.com

SLOANE & CO CHARTERED CERTIFIED ACCOUNTANTS
36-38 Westbourne Grove, Newton Road, London W2 5SH
F 020 7229 4810   T 020 7221 3292
E mail@sloane.co.uk
W www.sloane.co.uk

SUMMERS David & COMPANY
Chartered Accountants
Argo House, Kilburn Park Road, London NW6 5LF
F 020 7644 0678   T 0800 3288741
E dsummersfca@hotmail.com   W www.dsummers.co.uk

THEATACCOUNTS LLP
The Oakley, Kidderminster Road, Droitwich Spa
Worcestershire WR9 9AY
F 01905 799856   T 01905 823177
E info@theataccounts.co.uk   W www.theataccounts.co.uk

TODS MURRAY LLP
Contact: Richard Findlay. Entertainment Lawyer
Edinburgh Quay, 133 Fountainbridge, Edinburgh EH3 9AG
F 0131 656 2023   T 0131 656 2000
E richard.findlay@todsmurray.com

VANTIS
Accountants, Business & Tax Advisers
Torrington House, 47 Holywell Hill, St Albans, Herts AL1 1HD
F 01727 861052   T 01727 838255
E stalbans@vantisplc.com
W www.vantisplc.com/stalbanshh

WISE & CO CHARTERED ACCOUNTANTS
Contact: Stephen Morgan
Wey Court West, Union Road
Franham, Surrey GU9 7PT   T 01252 711244
E smo@wiseandco.co.uk   W www.wiseandco.co.uk

Contact: Colin Essex
Room 245, Pinewood Studios
Iver Heath, Bucks SL0 0NH   T 01753 656770
E ces@wiseandco.co.uk

Where culture and talent meet
Multi-cultural representation for Film, TV, Stage and Commercials

Phone 020 7193 4230
info@epmctalent.com
www.epmctalent.com

ASHCROFT
MANAGEMENT
Talent Agency for Actors and Creatives.

www.ashcroftmanagement.co.uk

1984 PERSONAL MANAGEMENT LTD
CPMA Member. Contact: David Meyer. By Post
Accepts Showreels. 26 Performers
Suite 508, Davina House
137 Goswell Road, London EC1V 7ET
F 020 7250 3031   T 020 7251 8046
E info@1984pm.com
W www.1984pm.com

21ST CENTURY ACTORS MANAGEMENT LTD
CPMA Member. Contact: By e-mail. 19 Performers
Commercials. Film. Singers. Stage. Television
206 Panther House, 38 Mount Pleasant
London WC1X 0AN   T 020 7278 3438
E mail@21stcenturyactors.co.uk
W www.21stcenturyactors.co.uk

2MA LTD
Sports. Stunts
Spring Vale, Tutland Road
North Baddesley, Hants SO52 9FL
F 023 8074 1355   T 023 8074 1354
E mo.matthews@2ma.co.uk
W www.2ma.co.uk

A & B PERSONAL MANAGEMENT LTD
Personal Manager. PMA Member. Contact: By Post
PO Box 64671, London NW3 9LH   T 020 7434 4262
E billellis@aandb.co.uk

A & J MANAGEMENT
242A The Ridgeway, Botany Bay
Enfield EN2 8AP   T 020 8342 0542
E info@ajmanagement.co.uk
W www.ajmanagement.co.uk

A-LIST LOOKALIKES & ENTERTAINMENTS LTD
1st Floor, 8 Wharf Street
Leeds LS2 7EQ   T 0113 243 6245
E info@alistlookalikes.co.uk
W www.alistlookalikes.co.uk

AARDVARK CASTING AGENCY
E beth@aardvarkcasting.com   M 07791 839294
W www.aardvarkcasting.com

ABA (ABACUS ADULTS)
The Studio, 4 Bailey Road
Westcott
Dorking, Surrey RH4 3QS
F 01306 877813   T 01306 877144
E aba@abacusagency.co.uk
W www.abacusaba.com

ABAK Chris
47 Chatsworth Road, Stratford
London E15 1RB   M 07986 416540
E chris_abakporo@yahoo.co.uk

ABBOTT June ASSOCIATES
Bowling Green Walk
40 Pitfield Street
London N1 6EU   T 020 7729 7999
E jaa@thecourtyard.org.uk

ACCESS ARTISTE MANAGEMENT LTD
Contact: Sarah Bryan. By Post/e-mail. Accepts Showreels
11-15 Betterton Street
Covent Garden, London WC2H 9BP   T 020 7866 5444
E mail@access-uk.com
W www.access-uk.com

ENDEAVOURING TO SNIFF OUT TALENT THROUGHOUT THE UK

Supplying actors, models, extras and voices, for the entertainment and advertising industries.

www.aardvarkcasting.com
Tel: +44 (0)7791 839294
e mail: beth@aardvarkcasting.com

MARCO WINDHAM 07768 330 027

WWW.FLICKR.COM/PHOTOS/MARCOWINDHAM

infopage

Who are agents and personal managers?

There are hundreds of Agents and Personal Managers in the UK, representing thousands of actors and artists. It is their job to promote their clients to casting opportunities and negotiate contracts on their behalf. In return they take commission ranging from 10-15%. Larger agencies can have hundreds of clients on their books, smaller ones may only have a handful. Agents usually try to represent a good range of artists (age, gender, type) to fill the diverse role types required by casting directors. A personal manager is someone who manages an artist's career on a more one-on-one basis.

What is a co-operative agency?

Co-operative agencies are staffed by actors themselves, who take turns to handle the administrative side of the agency and promote themselves to casting opportunities as a team. If you want more control over your career and can handle the pressures and responsibility that an agent takes away from you, then you might consider joining a co-operative agency. However it is very important that you think carefully about what you are signing up for. You will be responsible for the careers of others as well as yourself, so you must first of all be able to conduct yourself well when speaking to casting professionals. You will also have to commit some of your time to administrative jobs. You must be prepared to deal with finances and forms - all the boring paperwork you usually hand over to your agent! You must also be aware that the other actors in the agency will want to interview you and, if you are successful, to give you a trial period working with them. The Co-operative Personal Management Association (CPMA) offers advice about joining a co-operative agency on their website www.cpma.coop

Why do I need an agent?

A good agent will have contacts and authority in the entertainment industry that you, as an individual actor, would find more difficult to acquire. Agents, if you want them to, can also deal with matters such as Equity and Spotlight membership renewal. They can offer you advice on which headshot would be best to send out to casting directors, what to include or exclude in your CV as you build on your skills and experience, what a particular casting director might expect when you are invited to an audition, and so on.

How should I use these listings?

If you are an actor getting started in the industry, or looking to change your agent, the following pages will supply you with up-to-date contact details for many of the UK's leading agencies. Every company listed is done so by written request to us. Members of the Personal Managers' Association (PMA) and the Co-operative Personal Management Association (CMPA) have indicated their membership status under their name. Some agencies have also chosen to list other information such as relevant contact names, their preferred method of contact from new applicants, whether or not they are happy to receive showreels and/or voicereels with a prospective client's CV and headshot, the number of performers represented by the agency, the number of agents working for the company, and/or a description of the performance areas they cover. Use this information to narrow down your search for a suitable agent.

How do I choose a new agent?

When writing to agencies, try to research the different companies instead of just sending a 'blanket' letter to every single one. This way you can target your approaches to the most suitable agencies and avoid wasting their time (and yours). As well as using the listing information provided here, look at agency websites and ask around for personal recommendations. Unfortunately Spotlight is not able to offer personalised advice on choosing an agent, nor is it in a position to handle any financial or contractual queries or complaints, but we have prepared some useful career advice on our website: www.spotlight.com/artists/advice. Click on our Frequently Asked Questions page for general guidance regarding agents, or you may wish to try consulting our list of Independent Advisory Services if you want one-to-one tailored advice. You can also contact The Agents Association www.agents-uk.com or The Personal Managers' Association (PMA) www.thepma.com. If you are a member of Equity then you can contact their legal and welfare department with general information about issues including commissions, fees and contracts. However, Equity is not able to recommend specific agencies or agents.

How do I approach agencies?

Once you have made a list of suitable agencies, consult the listings again. Some agencies have indicated their preferred method of initial contact, whether by post, e-mail or telephone. Do not e-mail them, for example, if they have stated that they wish to receive your headshot, CV and covering letter by post. If they have not given a preference, you should send your CV by post as this is the traditional method of contacting agents. You should **always** include a stamped-addressed envelope (SAE) big enough to contain your 10 x 8 photo and with sufficient postage. This will increase your chances of getting a reply. Write your name and telephone number on the back of your headshot in case it gets separated from your CV.

Remember that agents receive hundreds of letters each week, so try to keep your communication concise, and be professional at all times. We also recommend that your covering letter has some kind of focus: perhaps you can tell them about your next showcase, or where they can see you currently appearing on stage. Ideally this should be addressed to an individual, not "To whom it may concern" or "Dear Sir or Madam". Some agents have indicated a specific contact to whom you can direct correspondence in their listing.

Some agents have indicated that they are happy to receive a showreel and/or voicereel with your CV, but it would be best to exclude these from your correspondence if they are not mentioned. Point out in your covering letter that one is available and the agent can contact you if they want to find out more.

Should I pay an agent to join their books? Or sign a contract?

Equity (the actors' trade union) does not recommend that artists pay an agent to join their client list. Before signing a contract, you should be very clear about the terms and commitments involved. For advice on both of these issues, or if you experience any problems with a current agent, we recommend that you contact Equity www.equity.org.uk. They also produce the booklet *You and your Agent* which is free to all Equity members and available from their website's members' area.

How do I become an agent?

Budding agents will need to get experience of working in an agent's office; usually this is done by working as an assistant. It can be extremely hard work, and you will be expected to give up a lot of your evenings to attend productions. There are two organisations you may find it useful to contact: the Agents' Association www.agents-uk.com and the Personal Managers' Association www.thepma.com

info**page**

Dolina Logan has been an agent for the last 15 years, previously working as a child actor and later in film production (both features and documentaries). She began working for Pat Lovett Associates in Edinburgh after graduating from the University of Edinburgh, and in 1999 was appointed an associate partner. At this time she moved to London to open and head up their new West End office in Covent Garden, later moving to Regent Street. The agency was renamed Lovett Logan Associates in 2009. Their clients work in all areas, from small-scale theatre touring to West End shows, and from one-off television dramas to big budget Hollywood features.

Finding a good agent can seem like an uphill struggle but it is not impossible! The first thing to do is to research as many as possible. Most agents have their own websites where you can see the type of client list they have as well as the areas they work in (theatre, film, television etc). It is also a good idea to get recommendations from other industry people. Once you have researched various agents, you should be able to narrow down the ones that you wish to approach based on what they can offer. This avoids wasting time writing to musical theatre agents when you only want to work in film, and vice versa.

Your first approach to an agent should be by letter or e-mail, depending on which they prefer. Always address your letter/e-mail to an individual, and if you are e-mailing, send it directly to one agent and don't cc hundreds of other agents. This is a definite 'no no', as is turning up at their office without an appointment! Point out your strengths, any notable credits and what you can offer them as a client. If you spend time on a letter and keep it clear and succinct then it is more likely to be read thoroughly and you are more likely to receive a reply.

Actors should always treat themselves as a business. Having up-to-date, good quality professional photographs is paramount. Sending out photographs to agents which were taken by a friend or are several years out of date suggests that you are not serious about your career. There can be nothing worse than walking into a meeting with an agent or casting director and the first thing they tell you is that you don't look anything like your photograph!

Meeting an agent is a two-way process and is also a time for you to ask any questions you have. Make sure to ask about their contract and commission rates, and be wary of an agent asking for any upfront fees. It is crucial that an agent sees you performing so also be wary of those that offer you representation without ever having seen your work.

When choosing between offers of representation, again ask other actors or industry professionals for their thoughts. You may also want to see if they are members of the PMA (Personal Managers' Association), a professional body with a code of conduct for agents. One of the most important things for me as an agent is that my clients feel they can talk to me. If you don't get that feeling from a prospective agent then they probably aren't the right one for you.

Once you sign with an agent you should feel that you are both working towards the same goal. A good agent is not just finding you the next job, but rather they should always be thinking of the next two or three jobs and how each will help to shape your future career. You should feel supported and informed about what they are doing on your behalf.

Finally, having an agent does not mean it is time to sit back! Successful actors are the ones that remain proactive. Learn new skills and accents, and keep improving the ones you have. Without a doubt, every actor should have a driving licence. So many actors miss out on jobs because they can't drive! Most casting is very last minute so you need to be ready with monologues and songs prepared for when a casting comes up for the next day. It is frustrating for an agent to have pushed for a client to be seen for something, only for that client to turn down the audition because they don't have a piece ready. If you are keen to work with a particular company or director, make sure you see as much of their work as possible so that when you do get a casting with them you are able to talk about it genuinely.

Being prepared and working in partnership with a good agent should see you on the road to a long and successful career. Good luck!

Please visit www.lovettlogan.com for further information.

SHEILA BURNETT
P H O T O G R A P H Y

Simon Pegg

Imelda Staunton

Patsy Palmer

Ewan McGregor

020 7289 3058
www.sheilaburnett-photography.com
Student Rates

ACROBAT PRODUCTIONS
Advisors. Artists
12 Oaklands Court, Hempstead Road
Watford WD17 4LF   T 01923 224938
E roger@acrobatproductions.com
W www.acrobatproductions.com

ACT IN AMERICA LTD
25 Wimpole Street, London   M 07798 695112
E info@actinamerica.com
W www.actinamerica.com

ACTING ASSOCIATES
*Personal Manager. Contact: Fiona Farley. By Post. Accepts
Showreels/Voicereels. 1 Agent represents 40 Performers
Commercials. Corporate. Film. Musicals. Radio. Stage
Television*
71 Hartham Road, London N7 9JJ   T/F 020 7607 3562
E fiona@actingassociates.co.uk
W www.actingassociates.co.uk

ACTOR-MUSICIANS @ ACCESS
*Personal Manager. Contact: Sarah Bryan. By Post/e-mail
Specialises in Actor-Musicians*
c/o Access Artiste Management Ltd
11-15 Betterton Street
Covent Garden, London WC2H 9BP   T 020 7866 5444
E mail@access-uk.com
W www.access-uk.com

ACTORS AGENCY
1 Glen Street, Tollcross, Edinburgh EH3 9JD
F 0131 228 4645   T 0131 228 4040
E info@stivenchristie.co.uk
W www.stivenchristie.co.uk

ACTORS ALLIANCE
*CPMA Member. Contact: By Post. Commercials. Corporate
Film. Stage. Stills. Television*
Disney Place House, 14 Marshalsea Road
London SE1 1HL   T/F 020 7407 6028
E actors@actorsalliance.co.uk
W www.actorsalliance.co.uk

ACTORS' CREATIVE TEAM
CPMA Member
Panther House
38 Mount Pleasant, London WC1X 0AN
F 020 7833 5086   T 020 7278 3388
E office@actorscreativeteam.co.uk
W www.actorscreativeteam.co.uk

ACTORS DIRECT ASSOCIATES
E casting@actorsdirectassociates.net   M 07951 477015
W www.actorsdirectassociates.net

ACTORS DIRECT LTD
Gainsborough House, 109 Portland Street
Manchester M1 6DN   T/F 0161 237 1904
E info@actorsdirect.org.uk
W www.actorsdirect.org.uk

ACTORS FILE THE
Personal Manager. CPMA Member. Contact: By Post/e-mail
Spitfire Studios, 63-71 Collier Street
London N1 9BE   T 020 7278 0087
E mail@theactorsfile.co.uk
W www.theactorsfile.co.uk

ACTORS' GROUP THE (TAG)
Personal Manager. CPMA Member
21-31 Oldham Street, Manchester M1 1JG   T/F 0161 834 4466
E enquiries@theactorsgroup.co.uk
W www.theactorsgroup.co.uk

ACTORS IN SCANDINAVIA
Jääkärinkatu 10, 00150 Helsinki
Finland   T 00 358 4 0054 0640
E laura@actorsinscandinavia.com
W www.actorsinscandinavia.com

ACTORS INTERNATIONAL LTD
The White House
52-54 Kennington Oval
London SE11 5SW
F 020 7820 0990   T 020 3268 0023
E mail@actorsinternational.co.uk

ACTORS IRELAND
Crescent Arts Centre, 2-4 University Road
Belfast BT7 1NH   T 028 9024 8861
E actorsireland@aol.com
W www.actorsireland.net

ACTOR'S TEMPLE THE
13 Warren Street, London W1T 5LG
M 07771 734670   T 020 3004 4537
E info@actorstemple.com
W www.actorstemple.com

ACTORS WORLD CASTING
13 Briarbank Road, London W13 0HH
M 07960 332846   T 020 8998 2579
E katherine@actors-world-production.com
W www.actors-world-production.com

ACTORUM LTD
Personal Manager
9 Bourlet Close, London W1W 7BP
F 020 7636 6975   T 020 7636 6978
E info@actorum.com
W www.actorum.com

AFA ASSOCIATES
Unit 101, Business Design Centre
52 Upper Street, London N1 0QH
E afa-associates@hotmail.com
T 020 7682 3677

AFFINITY MANAGEMENT
The Coach House, Down Park
Turners Hill Road, Crawley Down, West Sussex RH10 4HQ
F 01342 715800
T 01342 715275
E jstephens@affinitymanagement.co.uk

AGENCY LTD THE
Contact: Teri Hayden, Karl Hayden
9 Upper Fitzwilliam Street
Dublin 2, Ireland
F 00 353 1 6766615
T 00 353 1 6618535
E admin1@tagency.ie
W www.the-agency.ie

AHA
See HOWARD Amanda ASSOCIATES LTD

AIM (ASSOCIATED INTERNATIONAL MANAGEMENT)
PMA Member
Fairfax House
Fulwood Place
London WC1V 6HU
F 020 7242 0810
T 020 7831 9709
E info@aimagents.com
W www.aimagents.com

AIRCRAFT CIRCUS ENTERTAINMENT (ACE) AGENCY
7A Melish House
Harrington Way
London SE18 5NR
T 020 8317 8401
E lucy@aircraftcircus.com
W www.aircraftcircus.com

Paris Jefferson PHOTOGRAPHER

london based   parisjefferson.com   07825 047773

ALEXANDER PERSONAL MANAGEMENT LTD
See APM ASSOCIATES

ALL TALENT - THE SONIA SCOTT AGENCY
Contact: Sonia Scott Mackay. By Post/e-mail/Telephone
Accepts Showreels/Voicereels. 2 Agents represent 40
Performers. Film. Modelling. Television. Voice Overs. Walk-on
& Supporting Artists
Unit 325, 95 Morrison Street, Glasgow G5 8BE
M 07971 337074   T 0141 418 1074
E enquiries@alltalentuk.co.uk
W www.alltalentuk.co.uk

ALLEN Debi ASSOCIATES
PMA Member
The Heals Building, 22 Torrington Place
London WC1E 7HP   T 020 7255 6123
E info@debiallenassociates.com
W www.debiallenassociates.com

ALLSORTS AGENCY
Suite 3, Marlborough Business Centre
96 George Lane, London E18 1AD
F 020 8989 5600   T 020 8989 0500
E bookings@allsortsagency.com
W www.allsortsagency.com

ALLSORTS DRAMA FOR CHILDREN
In Association with Sasha Leslie Management
34 Crediton Road, London NW10 3DU   T/F 020 8969 3249
E sasha@allsortsdrama.com

ALLSTARS CASTING
66 Hope Street, Liverpool L1 9BZ
M 07739 359737   T 0151 707 2100
E sylvie@allstarscasting.co.uk
W www.allstarscasting.co.uk

ALPHA PERSONAL MANAGEMENT
Co-operative. CPMA Member
Studio B4, 3 Bradbury Street, London N16 8JN
F 020 7241 2410   T 020 7241 0077
E alpha@alphaactors.com
W www.alphaactors.com

ALPHABET MANAGEMENT
Nice Business Park
19-35 Sylvan Grove, London SE15 1PD
F 020 7252 4341   T 020 7252 4343
E contact@alphabetmanagement.co.uk
W www.alphabetmanagement.co.uk

ALRAUN Anita REPRESENTATION
PMA Member. Contact: By Post only (SAE)
5th Floor, 28 Charing Cross Road
London WC2H 0DB
F 020 7379 6865   T 020 7379 6840
E anita@cjagency.demon.co.uk

ALTARAS Jonathan ASSOCIATES LTD
PMA Member
11 Garrick Street
Covent Garden, London WC2E 9AR
F 020 7836 6066   T 020 7836 8722
E info@jaalondon.com

ALW ASSOCIATES
1 Grafton Chambers, Grafton Place
London NW1 1LN   T 020 7388 7018
E alw_carolpaul@talktalk.net

AMAZON ARTISTS MANAGEMENT
27 Inderwick Road, Crouch End, London N8 9LB
M 07957 358767   T/F 020 8350 4909
E amazonartists@gmail.com

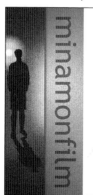

JOHN CLARK

London's leading theatrical photographer
actors - dancers - children

020 8854 4069
07702 627 237
Book online at www.johnclarkphotography.com
info@johnclarkphotography.com

Shivani Ghai: 5 Days
Lucie Jones: X Factor, Les Miserables

Goldy Notay: Sex and the City 2

Matt Di Angelo: The Hustle

Burn Gorman: Cemetery Junction, Layer Cake

Preeya Kalidas: Eastenders

AMBER PERSONAL MANAGEMENT LTD
PMA Member
28 St Margaret's Chambers
5 Newton Street
Manchester M1 1HL
F 0161 228 0235   T 0161 228 0236
E info@amberltd.co.uk
W www.amberltd.co.uk
London   T 020 7734 7887

AMC MANAGEMENT
Contact: Anna McCorquodale, Tricia Howell
31 Parkside, Welwyn, Herts AL6 9DQ
F 01438 718669   T 01438 714652
E anna@amcmanagement.co.uk
W www.amcmanagement.co.uk

AMCK MANAGEMENT LTD
125 Westbourne Studios, 242 Acklam Road
Notting Hill, London W10 5JJ
F 020 7524 7789   T 020 7524 7788
E info@amck.tv
W www.amck.tv

AMERICAN AGENCY THE
Contact: By Post. 3 Agents represent 70-80 Performers
Commercials. Corporate. Film. Musicals. Stage. Television
Voice Overs (American)
14 Bonny Street, London NW1 9PG
F 020 7482 4666   T 020 7485 8883
E americanagency@btconnect.com
W www.americanagency.tv

ANA (Actors Network Agency)
Personal Manager. Co-operative. CPMA Member
55 Lambeth Walk, London SE11 6DX
F 020 7735 8177   T 020 7735 0999
E info@ana-actors.co.uk
W www.ana-actors.co.uk

ANDERSON SAUNDERS ASSOCIATES
4 Geldeston Road, London E5 8RQ   T 020 8806 6361
E belanderson@talktalk.net

ANDREWS Amanda AGENCY
30 Caverswall Road, Blythe Bridge
Stoke-on-Trent, Staffordshire ST11 9BG
M 07711 379770   T/F 01782 393889
E amanda.andrews.agency@tesco.net
W www.amandaandrewsagency.org.uk

ANGEL Susan & FRANCIS Kevin LTD
PMA Member
1st Floor, 12 D'Arblay Street
London W1F 8DU
F 020 7437 1712   T 020 7439 3086
E agents@angelandfrancis.co.uk
W www.angelandfrancis.co.uk

ANTONY Christopher ASSOCIATES
The Old Dairy, 164 Thames Road
London W4 3QS
F 020 8742 8066   T 020 8994 9952
E info@christopherantony.co.uk
W www.christopherantony.co.uk

APM ASSOCIATES
Contact: Linda French
Pinewood Studios, Pinewood Rd, Iver Heath, Bucks SL0 0NH
F 01753 639205   T 01753 639204
E apm@apmassociates.net
W www.apmassociates.net

ARAENA/COLLECTIVE
10 Bramshaw Gardens, South Oxhey
Herts WD19 6XP   T/F 020 8428 0037
E info@collectivedance.co.uk

ARC ENTERTAINMENTS
Contact: By e-mail. 1 Agent represents 300 Active
Performers
10 Church Lane, Redmarshall
Stockton on Tees, Cleveland TS21 1EP   T 01740 631292
E arcents@hotmail.com
W www.arcents.co.uk

ARCADIA ASSOCIATES
18B Vicarage Gate, London W8 4AA   T/F 020 7937 0264
E info.arcadia@btopenworld.com

ARENA ENTERTAINMENT (UK) LTD
Regent's Court, 39 Harrogate Road, Leeds LS7 3PD
F 0113 239 2016   T/F 0113 239 2222
E info@arenaentertainments.co.uk
W www.arenaentertainments.co.uk

ARENA PERSONAL MANAGEMENT LTD
Co-operative
Room 11, East Block, Panther House
38 Mount Pleasant, London WC1X 0AP   T 020 7278 1661
E arenapmltd@aol.com
W www.arenapmltd.co.uk

A R G (ARTISTS RIGHTS GROUP Ltd)
PMA Member
4 Great Portland Street, London W1W 8PA
F 020 7436 6700   T 020 7436 6400
E argall@argtalent.com

ARGYLE ASSOCIATES
Personal Manager. Contact: Richard Argyle. By Post (SAE)
43 Clappers Lane, Fulking
West Sussex BN5 9ND   M 07905 293319
E argyle.associates@me.com

ARTEMIS STUDIOS LTD
30 Charles Square, Bracknell
Berkshire RG12 1AY   T 01344 429403
E agency@artemis-studios.co.uk
W www.agency.artemis-studios.co.uk

ARTIST MANAGEMENT UK LTD
PO Box 96, Liverpool L9 8WY
M 07948 793552   T 0151 523 6222
E chris@artistmanagementuk.com
W www.artistmanagementuk.com

ARUN Jonathan
Personal Manager. PMA Member
Contact: Jonathan Arun, Jeff Guerrera
Studio 9, 33 Stannary Street
London SE11 4AA   T 020 7840 0123
E info@jonathanarun.com   W www.jonathanarun.com

ASHCROFT MANAGEMENT LTD
Dean Clough Mills
Halifax HX3 5AX   T 01422 883090
E info@ashcroftmanagement.co.uk
W www.ashcroftmanagement.co.uk

ASQUITH & HORNER
Consultant: Elspeth Cochrane. Personal Manager
Contact: By Telephone/Post (SAE)
The Studio, 14 College Road
Bromley, Kent BR1 3NS
F 020 8313 0443   T 020 8466 5580

ASSOCIATED ARTS
Designers. Directors. Lighting & Sound Designers
8 Shrewsbury Lane, London SE18 3JF
F 020 8856 8189   T 020 8856 4958
E karen@associated-arts.co.uk
W www.associated-arts.co.uk

ASSOCIATED SPEAKERS
Lecturers & Celebrity Speakers
24A Park Road, Hayes
Middlesex UB4 8JN   T 020 8848 9048

ASTON MANAGEMENT
Aston Farm House, Remenham Lane
Henley on Thames, Oxon RG9 3DE   M 07742 059762
E astonagent@yahoo.co.uk
W www.astonmanagement.org

ASTRAL ACTORS MANAGEMENT
7 Greenway Close, London NW9 5AZ   T 020 8728 2782
E info@astralactors.com
W www.astralactors.com

AVALON MANAGEMENT GROUP LTD
4A Exmoor Street, London W10 6BD
F 020 7598 7300   T 020 7598 8000
E enquiries@avalonuk.com
W www.avalonuk.com

AVENUE ARTISTES LTD
PO Box 1573, Southampton SO16 3XS   T 023 8076 0930
E info@avenueartistes.com
W www.avenueartistes.com

AVIEL TALENT MANAGEMENT INC
1117 St Catherine Street West #718, Montreal
Quebec, Canada H3B 1H9
F 001 (514) 288 0768   T 001 (514) 288 8885
E aviel@canadafilm.com

AWA - ANDREA WILDER AGENCY
23 Cambrian Drive, Colwyn Bay
Conwy LL28 4SL
F 07092 249314   M 07919 202401
E andreawilder@fastmail.fm
W www.awagency.co.uk

AXM (Actors Exchange Management)
Co-operative. PMA Member
308 Panther House, 38 Mount Pleasant
London WC1X 0AN
F 020 7837 7215   T 020 7837 3304
E info@axmgt.com
W www.axmgt.com

BALLROOM, LONDON THEATRE OF
Contact: Paul Harris®. Ballroom/Social Dancers for Film
Stage & Television
24 Montana Gardens, Sutton
Surrey SM1 4FP
M 07958 784462   T 020 8722 8798
E office@londontheatreofballroom.com
W www.londontheatreofballroom.com

B A M ASSOCIATES
Benets, Dolberrow
Churchill, Bristol BS25 5NT   T 01934 852942
E casting@ebam.tv
W www.ebam.tv

BANANAFISH MANAGEMENT
The Arts Village, 20-26 Henry Street
Liverpool L1 5BS
M 07974 206622   T 0151 708 5509
E info@bananafish.co.uk
W www.bananafish.co.uk

BARKER Gavin ASSOCIATES LTD
Contact: Gavin Barker, Michelle Burke
2d Wimpole Street, London W1G 0EB
F 020 7499 3777   T 020 7499 4777
E katie@gavinbarkerassociates.co.uk
W www.gavinbarkerassociates.co.uk

BARR Becca MANAGEMENT
c/o Hamilton Investment
174 New Bond Street
London W1S 4RG   T 020 3137 2980
E info@beccabarrmanagement.co.uk
W www.beccabarrmanagement.co.uk

BASHFORD Simon
See GLOBAL ARTISTS

BEAUS & BELLES
175 Moor Lane, Chessington
Surrey KT9 2AB   T 0844 4142908
E info@beausandbelles.com
W www.beausandbelles.com

BELFAST TALENT AGENCY
The Crescent Arts Centre
2-4 University Road
Belfast, Antrim BT7 1NH   T 028 9024 3324
E info@belfasttalent.com
W www.belfasttalentagency.com

BELFIELD & WARD
PMA Member
4th Floor
80-81 St Martin's Lane
London WC2N 4AA
F 020 3292 9382   T 020 7395 7535
E office@belfieldandward.com

BELFRAGE Julian ASSOCIATES
PMA Member
Adam House
14 New Burlington Street
London W1S 3BQ
F 020 7287 8832   T 020 7287 8544

Graham Cole

Amanda Root

PETER SIMPKIN
PHOTOGRAPHY

t 020 8364 2634
m 07973 224 084
e petersimpkin@aol.com
w www.petersimpkin.co.uk

BELL Olivia MANAGEMENT
PMA Member. Contact: By Post. 2 Agents represent 100
Performers. Commercials. Film. Musicals. Stage. Television
189 Wardour Street, London W1F 8ZD
F 020 7439 4385   T 020 7439 3270
E info@olivia-bell.co.uk
W www.olivia-bell.co.uk

BENJAMIN MANAGEMENT LTD
Cameo House, 11 Bear Street
London WC2H 7AS   M 07921 212360
E agent@benjaminmanagement.co.uk

BERLIN ASSOCIATES
PMA Member. Dramatists & Technicians only
7 Tyers Gate, London SE1 3HX
F 020 7632 5296   T 020 7836 1112
E agents@berlinassociates.com
W www.berlinassociates.com

BETTER CHEMISTRY
1st & 2nd Floors
20 Stansfield Road
Stockwell, London SW9 9RZ   T/F 020 7737 5300
E info@betterchemistry.co.uk
W www.betterchemistry.co.uk

BETTS Jorg ASSOCIATES
PMA Member
Gainsborough House, 81 Oxford Street
London W1D 2EU
F 020 7903 5301   T 020 7903 5300
E agents@jorgbetts.com

BILLBOARD PERSONAL MANAGEMENT
Unit 5, 11 Mowll Street, London SW9 6BG
F 020 7793 0426   T 020 7735 9956
E billboardpm@btconnect.com
W www.billboardpm.com

Alistair McGowan

Rachel Weisz

CAROLE LATIMER Photography
T: 020 7727 9371   www.carolelatimer.com   E: carole@carolelatimer.com

Artist Management
adults   children

Byron's Management
Tel: 020 7242 8096
byronsmanagement@aol.com
www.byronsmanagement.co.uk

BILLY MARSH DRAMA LTD
Actors & Actresses
See MARSH Billy DRAMA LTD

BIRD AGENCY
Personal Performance Manager
The Centre, 27 Station Road, Sidcup, Kent DA15 7EB
F 020 8308 1370   T 020 8269 6862
E birdagency@birdcollege.co.uk
W www.birdcollege.co.uk

BLOND Rebecca ASSOCIATES
PMA Member
69A Kings Road, London SW3 4NX
F 020 7351 4600   T 020 7351 4100
E info@rebeccablondassociates.com

BLOOMFIELDS MANAGEMENT
PMA Member
77 Oxford Street, London W1D 2ES
F 020 7659 2101   T 020 7659 2001
E emma@bloomfieldsmanagement.com
W www.bloomfieldsmanagement.com

BLUE STAR ASSOCIATES
Apartment 8 Shaldon Mansions
132 Charing Cross Road, London WC2H 0LA
F 020 7836 2949   T 020 7836 6220
E hopkinstacey@aol.com

BMA ACTORS & PRESENTERS
Personal Manager. Contact: Fred Haddad. By e-mail. 1200
Performers. Children. Commercials. Corporate. Dancers
Disabled. Film. Modelling. Presenters. Singers. Television
Walk-on & Supporting Artists
346 High Street, Marlow House
Berkhamsted, Hertfordshire HP4 1HT
F 01442 879879   T 01442 878878
E info@bmamodels.com
W www.bmamodels.com

BODENS AGENCY
Personal Manager. Contact: Adam Boden, Katie McCutcheon,
Sarah Holder. By Post/e-mail/Telephone. 3 Agents represent
400 Performers. Children. Commercials. Television. Walk-on
& Supporting Artists
Bodens Studios & Agency, 99 East Barnet Road
New Barnet, Herts EN4 8RF
M 07545 696888   T 020 8447 0909
E info@bodensagency.com
W www.bodensagency.com

BODY LONDON
14 Basil Street, Knightsbridge
London SW3 1AH   T 020 3402 5044
E info@bodylondon.com
W www.bodylondon.com

BODYWORK AGENCY
25-29 Glisson Road, Cambridge CB1 2HA
F 01223 358923   T 01223 309990
E agency@bodyworkds.co.uk

BOSS CREATIVE ENTERTAINMENT
Top Floor, 81 Overhill Road
London SE22 0PQ
F 020 8516 1867   T 020 8299 0478
E enquiries@bosscreativeentertainment.com
W www.bosscreativeentertainment.com

BOSS MODEL MANAGEMENT LTD
Fourways House, 57 Hilton Street
Manchester M1 2EJ   T 0161 237 0100
E info@bossmodels.co.uk
W www.bossmodelmanagement.co.uk

BOYCE Sandra MANAGEMENT
PMA Member
1 Kingsway House, Albion Road, London N16 0TA
F 020 7241 2313   T 020 7923 0606
E info@sandraboyce.com
W www.sandraboyce.com

B P A
Representing Artists of All Ages. Film. Musical Theatre
Specialists. New Media. Stage. Television
174 Clarence Road, Fleet
Hampshire GU51 3XR   T 0845 2260809
E agent@boostpa.co.uk
W www.boostpa.co.uk/agency

BRADLEY Christina MANAGEMENT
19 Jeffrey's Place, Camden
London NW1 9PP   M 07897 794728
E christina@cbmlondon.com
W www.cbmlondon.com

BRAIDMAN Michelle ASSOCIATES LTD
PMA Member
2 Futura House, 169 Grange Road
London SE1 3BN
F 020 7231 4634   T 020 7237 3523
E info@braidman.com
W www.braidman.com

BRAITHWAITE'S THEATRICAL AGENCY
8 Brookshill Avenue, Harrow Weald
Middlesex HA3 6RZ   T 020 8954 5638

BREAK A LEG MANAGEMENT LTD
Units 2/3 The Precinct, Packington Square
London N1 7UP
F 020 7359 3660   T 020 7359 3594
E agency@breakalegman.com
W www.breakalegman.com

NICK BRIMBLE

CATHERINE SHAKESPEARE LANE

PHOTOGRAPHER

020 7226 7694   www.csl-art.co.uk

BRIDGES: THE ACTORS' AGENCY
St George's West
58 Shandwick Place
Edinburgh EH2 4RT   T 0131 226 6433
E admin@bridgesactorsagency.com
W www.bridgesactorsagency.com

BROADCASTING ARTIST MANAGEMENT
3rd Floor, Block A
Morelands, 5-23 Old Street, London EC1V 9HL
F 020 7250 1357   T 020 7490 4225
E info@bcamanagement.co.uk
W www.broadcastingagency.co.uk

BROOD MANAGEMENT
Contact: By e-mail. 1 Agent represents 40 Performers
High Street Buildings, 134 Kirkdale
London SE26 4BB
F 020 8699 8787   T 020 8699 1757
E broodmanagement@aol.com
W www.broodmanagement.com

BROOK Dolly AGENCY
PO Box 5436, Dunmow CM6 1WW
F 01371 875996   T 01371 875767
E dollybrookcasting@btinternet.com

BROOK Jeremy LTD
37 Berwick Street, London W1F 8RS
F 020 7287 8016   T 020 7434 0398
E info@jeremybrookltd.co.uk

BROOK Valerie AGENCY
10 Sandringham Road
Cheadle Hulme, Cheshire SK8 5NH
M 07973 434953   T 0161 486 1631
E colinbrook@freenetname.co.uk

BROOKS Claude ENTERTAINMENTS
19 Sussex Place
Slough, Berks SL1 1NH
F 01753 520424   T 01753 520717

BROWN & SIMCOCKS
PMA Member
1 Bridgehouse Court
109 Blackfriars Road
London SE1 8HW
F 020 7928 1909   T 020 7928 1229
E mail@brownandsimcocks.co.uk

BROWNE STREET Daniel
18 Pinewood Place
Dartford DA2 7WQ   M 07960 322084
E daniel.browne@danielbrownestreet.com
W www.danielbrownestreet.com

BRUNO KELLY LTD
4th Floor, Albany House
324-326 Regent Street, London W1B 3HH
F 020 7183 7332   T 020 7183 7331
E info@brunokelly.com
W www.brunokelly.com

BRUNSKILL MANAGEMENT LTD
Personal Manager. PMA Member. Contact: Aude Powell
By e-mail. Accepts Showreels/Voicereels. Commercials
Corporate. Film. Musicals. Radio. Stage. Television
Voice Overs
Suite 8A, 169 Queen's Gate, London SW7 5HE
F 020 7589 9460   T 020 7581 3388
E contact@brunskill.com

The Courtyard, Edenhall, Penrith, Cumbria CA11 8ST
F 01768 881850   T 01768 881430
E aude@brunskill.com

BSA LTD
See HARRISON Penny BSA LTD

BUCHANAN Bronia ASSOCIATES LTD
PMA Member
First Floor, 23 Tavistock Street, London WC2E 7NX
F 020 7379 5560   T 020 7395 1400
E info@buchanan-associates.co.uk
W www.buchanan-associates.co.uk

BURNETT CROWTHER LTD
PMA Member. Contact: Barry Burnett, Lizanne Crowther
3 Clifford Street, London W1S 2LF
F 020 7287 3239   T 020 7437 8008
E associates@bcltd.org
W www.bcltd.org

BWH AGENCY LTD THE
PMA Member
117 Shaftesbury Avenue, London WC2H 8AD
F 020 7240 2287   T 020 7240 5299
E info@thebwhagency.co.uk
W www.thebwhagency.co.uk

BYRON'S MANAGEMENT
Contact: By Post/e-mail. Accepts Showreels
Commercials. Film. Musicals. Stage. Television
180 Drury Lane, London WC2B 5QF   T 020 7242 8096
E byronsmanagement@aol.com
W www.byronsmanagement.co.uk

C.A. ARTISTES MANAGEMENT
26-28 Hammersmith Grove
London W6 7BA   T 020 8834 1608
E casting@caartistes.com
W www.caartistes.com

CAM
Personal Manager. PMA Member. Contact: By e-mail
1st Floor
55-59 Shaftesbury Avenue
London W1D 6LD
F 020 7734 3205
E reception@cam.co.uk
W www.cam.co.uk
T 020 7292 0600

CAMBELL JEFFREY MANAGEMENT
Set, Costume, Lighting Designers
6 Glenview, Dalmally
Argyll, Scotland PA33 1BE
E cambell@theatricaldesigners.co.uk
T 01838 200707

CAMPBELL Alison MODEL & PROMOTION AGENCY
381 Beersbridge Road
Belfast BT5 5DT
F 028 9080 9808
E info@alisoncampbellmodels.com
W www.alisoncampbellmodels.com
T 028 9080 9809

CAPITAL VOICES
Contact: Anne Skates. Film. Session Singers. Stage. Studio
Television
PO Box 364, Esher
Surrey KT10 9XZ
F 01372 466229
E capvox@aol.com
W www.capitalvoices.com
T 01372 466228

CARAVANSERAI ASSOCIATES LTD
Unit 30, Grand Union Centre
West Row, London W10 5AS
M 07552 162909
E info@cserai.co.uk
T 05601 534892

CAREY Roger ASSOCIATES
Personal Manager. PMA Member
Suite 909
The Old House
Shepperton Film Studios
Studios Road, Shepperton
Middlesex TW17 0QD
F 01932 569602
E info@rogercareyassociates.com
W www.rogercareyassociates.com
T 01932 582890

CARNEY Jessica ASSOCIATES
Personal Manager. PMA Member
4th Floor, 23 Golden Square
London W1F 9JP
F 020 7434 4173
E info@jcarneyassociates.co.uk
W www.jessicacarneyassociates.co.uk
T 020 7434 4143

CAROUSEL EVENTS
Entertainment for Corporate & Private Events
Incentive House
23 Castle Street
High Wycombe, Bucks HP13 6RU
F 01494 511501
E info@carouselentertainments.co.uk
W www.carouselentertainments.co.uk
T 0844 2250465

CARR Norrie AGENCY
Holborn Studios
49-50 Eagle Wharf Road
London N1 7ED
F 020 7253 1772
E info@norriecarr.com
W www.norriecarr.com
T 020 7253 1771

CASA MANAGEMENT
Alison House, 5 Highfield Road
Mellor, Stockport, Cheshire SK6 5AL
F 0161 880 2056
E casamgmt@aol.com
W www.casamanagement.co.uk
T 0161 612 0082

CASAROTTO MARSH LTD
Film Technicians
Waverley House, 7-12 Noel Street
London W1F 8GQ
F 020 7287 9128
E casarottomarsh@casarotto.co.uk
W www.casarotto.co.uk
T 020 7287 4450

CASTAWAY ACTORS AGENCY
30-31 Wicklow Street, Dublin 2, Ireland
F 00 353 1 6719133
E castaway@clubi.ie
W www.irish-actors.com
T 00 353 1 6719264

CASTCALL
Casting & Consultancy Service
106 Wilsden Avenue, Luton LU1 5HR
F 01582 480736
E casting@castcall.co.uk
W www.castcall.co.uk
T 01582 456213

CASTING DEPARTMENT THE
277 Chiswick Village
London W4 3DF
E jillscastingdpt@aol.com
W www.thecastingdept.co.uk
T 020 8582 5523

CAVAT AGENCY
3, 97 Wardour Street, London W1F 0UF
E enquiries@cavatagency.co.uk
W www.cavatagency.co.uk
T 020 8651 1099

Claire Grogan
P h o t o g r a p h y

Lauren Hood

Ben Richards

Lindsey Coulson

Martin Freeman

Abi Hardingham

Duane Henry

Patti Boulaye

Steve McFadden

Gurkiran Kaur

claire@clairegrogan.co.uk
www.clairegrogan.co.uk

Film or Digital

020 7272 1845
07932 635381

C B A INTERNATIONAL
166 Waverley Avenue
Twickenham TW2 6DL M 07789 991032
E cba_office@yahoo.co.uk

Contact: Cindy Brace
c/o C.M.S. Experts Associés
149 Boulevard Malesherbes
75017 Paris, France T 00 33 145 26 33 42
E c_b_a@club-internet.fr
W www.cindy-brace.com

CBL MANAGEMENT
Artistes & Creatives
20 Hollingbury Rise, Brighton
East Sussex BN1 7HJ
M 07956 890307 T 01273 321245
E enquiries@cblmanagement.co.uk
W www.cblmanagement.co.uk

C C A MANAGEMENT
Personal Manager. PMA Member. Contact: By Post
Actors. Technicians
Garden Level, 32 Charlwood Street
London SW1V 2DY
F 020 7630 7376 T 020 7630 6303
E actors@ccamanagement.co.uk
W www.cca-management.co.uk

CCM
CPMA Member
Panther House, 38 Mount Pleasant
London WC1X 0AP T 020 7278 0507
E ccmactors@btconnect.com
W www.ccmactors.co.uk

CDA
PMA Member. Contact: Belinda Wright
125 Gloucester Road, London SW7 4TE
F 020 7373 1110 T 020 7373 3323
E cda@cdalondon.com

CELEBRITY GROUP THE
12 Connaught Square, London W2 2BE T 0871 2501234
E info@celebrity.co.uk
W www.celebrity.co.uk

CENTER STAGE AGENCY
Personal Manager. Contact: By e-mail. Accepts Showreels
55 Performers. Commercials. Film. Singers. Television
7 Rutledge Terrace
South Circular Road
Dublin 8, Ireland T/F 00 353 1 4533599
E geraldinecenterstage@eircom.net
W www.centerstageagency.com

CENTRAL LINE
Personal Manager. Co-operative. CPMA Member
Contact: By Post
11 East Circus Street, Nottingham NG1 5AF T 0115 941 2937
E centralline@btconnect.com
W www.the-central-line.co.uk

CENTURY MODELS MANAGEMENT
United Consortium, 24 Greville Street
Farringdon, London EC1N 8SS
M 07792 339801 T 020 3086 9031
E models@centurym.com
W www.century.com

CHAMBERS MANAGEMENT
Comedians. Comic Actors
39-41 Parker Street, London WC2B 5PQ
F 020 7831 8598 T 020 7796 3588
E hannah@chambersmgt.com
W www.chambersmgt.co.uk

CHAPMAN AGENCY
BSA, Millennium Point, Curzon Street, Birmingham B4 7XG
F 0121 331 7221 T 0121 331 7220
E chapmanagency@bsa.bcu.ac.uk

CHARLESWORTH Peter & ASSOCIATES
67 Holland Park Mews, London W11 3SS
F 020 7792 1893 T 020 7792 4600
E info@petercharlesworth.co.uk

CHATTO & LINNIT LTD
123A Kings Road, London SW3 4PL
F 020 7352 3450 T 020 7352 7722
E info@chattolinnit.com

CHP ARTIST MANAGEMENT
Meadowcroft Barn, Crowbrook Road, Askett
Princes Risborough
Buckinghamshire HP27 9LS T 01844 345630
E contact@chproductions.org.uk
W www.chproductions.org.uk

CHRYSTEL ARTS AGENCY
6 Eunice Grove, Chesham, Bucks HP5 1RL
M 07799 605489 T 01494 773336
E chrystelarts@waitrose.com

CINEL GABRAN MANAGEMENT
Personal Manager. PMA Member. Contact: By Post. Accepts
Showreels. 60 Performers. Commercials. Corporate. Film
Musicals. Presenters. Radio. Stage. Television. Voice Overs
PO Box 5163, Cardiff CF5 9BJ
F 0845 0666601 T 029 2066 6600
E info@cinelgabran.co.uk
W www.cinelgabran.co.uk

Fay Downie

Will C Photography studios
T: **0208 438 0303** M: **07712 669 953** E: billy_snapper@hotmail.com
Special rate of £145 exclusive to Spotlight and Contacts readers

Aliona Adrianova   Jonathan Shotton   Gracy Kamay Lau   Sebastien Louis Blanc   Sir Richard Branson

CINEL GABRAN MANAGEMENT
PMA Member
PO Box 101, Newholm, Whitby, North Yorkshire YO21 3WT
F 0845 0666601   T 0845 0666605
E mail@cinelgabran.co.uk
W www.cinelgabran.co.uk

CIRCUIT PERSONAL MANAGEMENT LTD
Contact: By Post/e-mail. Accepts Showreels. 22 Performers.
Commercials. Corporate. Film. Stage. Television
Suite 71 S.E.C., Bedford Street, Shelton
Stoke-on-Trent, Staffs ST1 4PZ
F 01782 206821   T 01782 285388
E mail@circuitpm.co.uk
W www.circuitpm.co.uk

CIRCUS MANIACS AGENCY
Corporate. Physical Artistes
Unit 62, Basepoint Business Centre, Oakfield Close
Tewkesbury Business Park
Tewkesbury, Gloucestershire GL20 8SD
M 07977 247287   T 01684 854412
E agency@circusmaniacs.com
W www.circusmaniacs.com

CITY ACTORS' MANAGEMENT
Personal Manager. CPMA Member. Contact: Nikki Everson
Oval House, 52-54 Kennington Oval
London SE11 5SW   T 020 7793 9888
E info@cityactors.co.uk
W www.cityactors.co.uk

CLARKE AND JONES LTD
28 Fordwych Court, Shoot Up Hill
London NW2 3PH
F 0870 1313391   T 020 8438 0185
E mail@clarkeandjones.plus.com

CLASS - CARLINE LUNDON ASSOCIATES
25 Falkner Square, Liverpool L8 7NZ   M 07853 248957
E clundon@googlemail.com

CLAYMAN Tony PROMOTIONS LTD
Vicarage House, 58-60 Kensington Church Street
London W8 4DB
F 020 7368 3338   T 020 7368 3336
E tony@tonyclayman.com
W www.tonyclayman.com

CLAYPOLE MANAGEMENT
PO Box 123, DL3 7WA
F 0870 1334784   T 0845 6501777
E info@claypolemanagement.co.uk
W www.claypolemanagement.co.uk

CLIC AGENCY
7 Ffordd Seion, Bangor
Gwynedd LL57 1BS   T 01248 354420
E clic@btinternet.com
W www.clicagency.co.uk

CLOUD NINE AGENCY
96 Tiber Gardens, Treaty Street
London N1 0XE
M 07957 268971   T/F 020 7278 0029
E email@cloudnineagency.co.uk
W www.cloudnineagency.co.uk

COCHRANE Elspeth PERSONAL MANAGEMENT
Existing Clients only. No New Applicants
See ASQUITH & HORNER

COLE KITCHENN PERSONAL MANAGEMENT LTD
PMA Member
212 Strand, London WC2R 1AP
F 020 7353 9650   T 020 7427 5681
E stuart@colekitchenn.com
W www.colekitchenn.com

COLLINS Shane ASSOCIATES
PMA Member
11-15 Betterton Street, Covent Garden
London WC2H 9BP
F 0870 4601983   T 020 7470 8864
E info@shanecollins.co.uk
W www.shanecollins.co.uk

COLLIS MANAGEMENT LTD
PMA Member
182 Trevelyan Road, London SW17 9LW
F 020 8682 0973   T 020 8767 0196
E marilyn@collismanagement.co.uk

COMEDY CLUB LTD THE
2nd Floor, 28-31 Moulsham Street
Chelmsford, Essex CM2 0HX
F 01245 255507   T 0845 4595656
E info@hahaheehee.com
W www.hahaheehee.com

COMIC VOICE MANAGEMENT
2nd Floor, 28-31 Moulsham Street
Chelmsford, Essex CM2 0HX
F 01245 255507   T 0845 4595656
E info@comicvoice.com
W www.comicvoice.com

COMMERCIAL AGENCY THE
See TCA (The Commercial Agency)

CONTI Italia AGENCY LTD
Contact: By Post/Telephone
Italia Conti House, 23 Goswell Road
London EC1M 7AJ
F 020 7253 1430   T 020 7608 7500
E agency@italiaconti.co.uk

Pictures can speak louder than words

Philip Quast

Sheridan Smith

Jaygann Ayeh

Nick James *actors'* photographer

Sally Dexter

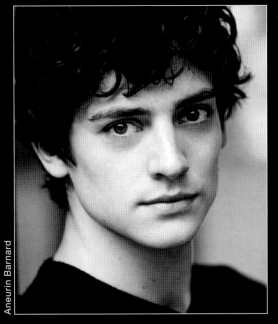

Aneurin Barnard

07961 122 030   nickjamesphotography.co.uk

Paul Merton

Simone Sault

CONWAY Clive CELEBRITY PRODUCTIONS LTD
32 Grove Street, Oxford OX2 7JT
F 01865 514409
T 01865 514830
E info@celebrityproductions.org
W www.celebrityproductions.info

CONWAY VAN GELDER GRANT LTD
Personal Manager. PMA Member
3rd Floor, 8-12 Broadwick Street
London W1F 8HW
T 020 7287 0077
E info@conwayvg.co.uk

COOKE Howard ASSOCIATES
PMA Member. Contact: Howard Cooke. By Post
2 Agents represent 50 Performers
Commercials. Film. Stage. Television
19 Coulson Street, Chelsea
London SW3 3NA
F 020 7591 0155
T 020 7591 0144

COOPER Tommy MAGICAL AGENCY
Comedy. Magicians
21 Streatham Court, Ashley Cross
Poole, Dorset BH14 0EX
M 07860 290437
W www.tommycooperremembered.co.uk

CORNER Clive ASSOCIATES
Contact: Duncan Stratton. By Post. Accepts Showreels
3 Agents represent 80 Performers
Commercials. Film. Musicals. Stage. Television
'The Belenes', 60 Wakeham
Portland DT5 1HN
T 01305 860267
E cornerassociates@aol.com

CORNISH Caroline MANAGEMENT LTD
Technicians only
12 Shinfield Street, London W12 0HN
M 07725 555711
T 020 8743 7337
E carolinecornish@me.com
W www.carolinecornish.co.uk

CORONA MANAGEMENT
3 Thameside Centre
Kew Bridge Road
Brentford, Middlesex TW8 0HF
T 020 8758 2553
E info@coronatheatreschool.com
W www.coronatheatreschool.com

COULSON Lou ASSOCIATES LTD
PMA Member
1st Floor, 37 Berwick Street
London W1F 8RS
F 020 7439 7569
T 020 7734 9633
E info@loucoulson.co.uk

COULTER MANAGEMENT AGENCY LTD
PMA Member. Contact: Anne Coulter
PO Box 2830, Glasgow G61 9BQ
T 0141 357 6666
E coultermanagement@ntlworld.com
W www.coultermanagement.com

COVENT GARDEN MANAGEMENT
5 Denmark Street, London WC2H 8LP
M 07944 283659
E admin@splatsentertainment.com
W www.coventgardenmanagement.com

CPA MANAGEMENT
The Studios, 219B North Street
Romford, Essex RM1 4QA
F 01708 766077
T 01708 766444
E info@cpamanagement.co.uk
W www.cpastudios.co.uk

CRAWFORDS
PO Box 56662, London W13 3BH
T 020 8947 9999
E cr@wfords.com
W www.crawfords.tv

Alice Coulthard

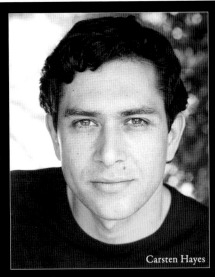

Carsten Hayes

Natasha Merchant
(Formerly Natasha Greenberg)
Photographer

020 8653 5399   www.natashamerchant.com   07932 618 111

CREATIVE BLAST AGENCY
The Office, 12A Meteor Road
Westcliff on Sea, Essex SS0 8DG   M 07545 009830
E info@cbagency.co.uk
W www.cbagency.co.uk

CREATIVE MEDIA MANAGEMENT
PMA Member. No Actors. Film, TV & Theatre Technical
Personnel only
Ealing Studios, Ealing Green, London W5 5EP
F 020 8566 5554   T 020 8584 5363
E enquiries@creativemediamanagement.com
W www.creativemediamanagement.com

CREDITS ACTORS AGENCY LTD
29 Lorn Road
London SW9 0AB   T 020 7737 0735
E credits@actors29.freeserve.co.uk

CRESCENT MANAGEMENT
Personal Manager. Co-operative. CPMA Member
Contact: By Post. Accepts Showreels
10 Barley Mow Passage
Chiswick
London W4 4PH
F 020 8987 0207   T 020 8987 0191
E mail@crescentmanagement.co.uk
W www.crescentmanagement.co.uk

CROI ACTORS AGENCY
Town Hall Theatre
Galway
Co. Galway
Ireland   T 00 353 851420683
E croiactorsagency@yahoo.co.uk
W www.croiproductions.webs.com

Matt Anker photographer   07835 241835
www.mattanker.com   London based   student discounts

CRUICKSHANK CAZENOVE LTD
*PMA Member. Contact: Harriet Cruickshank. By Post. 1 Agent
Choreographers, Designers & Directors only*
97 Old South Lambeth Road, London SW8 1XU
F 020 7582 6405   T 020 7735 2933
E harriet@ccagents.co.uk

CS MANAGEMENT
The Croft, 7 Cannon Road
Southgate, London N14 7HE
F 020 8886 7555   T 020 8886 4264
E carole@csmanagementuk.com
W www.csmanagementuk.com

CS SPORTS PROMOTIONS
*Contact: By e-mail/Telephone. 300+ Performers. Actors
Commercials. Dancers. Modelling. Sports Models*
56 Church Road, Crystal Palace
London SE19 2EZ
F 020 8771 4704   T 020 8771 4700
E agent@sportspromotions.co.uk
W www.sportspromotions.co.uk

C.S.A. (Christina Shepherd Advertising)
4th Floor, 45 Maddox Street
London W1S 2PE
F 020 7499 7535   T 020 7499 7534
E csa@shepherdmanagement.co.uk

CTM
E info@centraltalent.co.uk   T 0845 6045551
W www.centraltalent.co.uk

CURTIS BROWN GROUP LTD
PMA Member
Haymarket House, 28-29 Haymarket
London SW1Y 4SP
F 020 7393 4401   T 020 7393 4400
E actorsagents@curtisbrown.co.uk
W www.curtisbrown.co.uk

DALY David ASSOCIATES
Contact: David Daly, Louisa Clifton
586 King's Road, London SW6 2DX
F 020 7610 9512   T 020 7384 1036
E agent@daviddaly.co.uk
W www.daviddaly.co.uk

DALY David ASSOCIATES (MANCHESTER)
Contact: Mary Ramsay
16 King Street, Knutsford
Cheshire WA16 6DL
F 01565 755334   T 01565 631999
E north@daviddaly.co.uk
W www.daviddaly.co.uk

DALZELL & BERESFORD LTD
26 Astwood Mews, London SW7 4DE
F 020 7341 9412   T 020 7341 9411
E mail@dbltd.co.uk

DANCERS
1 Charlotte Street, London W1T 1RD
F 020 7637 0328   T 020 7636 1473
E info@features.co.uk
W www.features.co.uk

DARRELL Emma MANAGEMENT
Directors. Producers. Writers
Hazelbank, 3 Chalfont Lane
Chorleywood, Herts WD3 5PR   T 01923 284061
E emma.mc@virgin.net

DAVID ARTISTES MANAGEMENT AGENCY LTD THE
26-28 Hammersmith Grove, London W6 7BA   T 020 8834 1615
E casting@davidagency.co.uk
W www.davidagency.co.uk

DAVIS Chris MANAGEMENT LTD
PMA Member
Tenbury House, 36 Teme Street
Tenbury Wells, Worcestershire WR15 8AA
F 01584 819076   T 01584 819005
E info@cdm-ltd.com
W www.cdm-ltd.com

DAVIS Lena, BISHOP John ASSOCIATES
Personal Manager. Contact: By Post. 2 Agents
Cotton's Farmhouse, Whiston Road
Cogenhoe, Northants NN7 1NL   T 01604 891487
E admin@cottonsfarmhouse.org

DEALERS AGENCY BELFAST
Cathedral House, 22-31 Waring Street, Belfast BT1 2DX
M 07834 774330   T 028 9043 6639
E info@dealersagency.co.uk
W www.dealersagency.co.uk

DENMARK STREET MANAGEMENT
Personal Manager. CPMA Member. Contact: By Post (SAE)
Suite 4, Clarendon Buildings
25 Horsell Road, Highbury N5 1XL
F 020 7084 4053   T 020 7700 5200
E mail@denmarkstreet.net
W www.denmarkstreet.net

DEREK'S HANDS AGENCY
Hand & Foot Modelling
26-28 Hammersmith Grove, London W6 7BA   T 020 8834 1609
E casting@derekshands.com
W www.derekshands.com

DEVINE ARTIST MANAGEMENT
Mayfair House, 14 Heddon Street, London W1B 4DA
F 0844 8845083   T 0844 8844578
E mail@devinemanagement.co.uk

de WOLFE Felix
Personal Manager. PMA Member. Contact: By Post. Accepts
Showreels. 3 Agents. Film. Musicals. Radio. Stage. Television
Kingsway House, 103 Kingsway, London WC2B 6QX
F 020 7242 8119   T 020 7242 5066
E info@felixdewolfe.com
W www.felixdewolfe.com

DIAMOND MANAGEMENT
PMA Member
31 Percy Street, London W1T 2DD
F 020 7631 0500   T 020 7631 0400
E agents@diman.co.uk

DIESTENFELD Lily
Personal Manager. Over 50+ ages
No unsolicited Post/e-mails/Calls from Actors
28B Alexandra Grove
London N12 8HG   M 07957 968214
E lilyd@talk21.com

DIRECT PERSONAL MANAGEMENT
Personal Manager. CPMA Member
Contact: Daphne Franks. By e-mail
1 Agent represents, 28 Performers.
Commercials. Corporate. Film. Stage. Television
St John's House
16 St John's Vale
London SE8 4EN   T/F 020 8694 1788
E daphne.franks@directpm.co.uk
W www.directpm.co.uk

DIRECT PERSONAL MANAGEMENT
Personal Manager. CPMA Member
Contact: Daphne Franks. By e-mail
1 Agent represents 28 Performers
Commercials. Corporate. Film. Stage. Television
Park House, 62 Lidgett Lane
Leeds LS8 1PL   T/F 0113 266 4036
E daphne.franks@directpm.co.uk
W www.directpm.co.uk

DJB MANAGEMENT
12 Chiswick Terrace
London W4 5LY   M 07527 870988
E djbmanagement@gmail.com
W www.djbmanagement.moonfruit.com

DOE John MANAGEMENT
123 Hanover Road, London NW10 3DN
M 07957 114175   T 020 8960 2848
E casting@johndoemgt.com
W www.johndoemgt.com

DOTTED LINE
13 Portman House, 136 High Road
London N22 6DF   T 0844 3510223
E info@dotted-line.co.uk
W www.dotted-line.co.uk

DOUBLE ACT CELEBRITY LOOK ALIKES
PO Box 25574, London NW7 3GB
F 020 8201 1795   T 020 8381 0151
E info@double-act.co.uk
W www.double-act.co.uk

DOUBLEFVOICES
Singers
1 Hunters Lodge, Bodiam
East Sussex TN32 5UE
M 07976 927764   T 01580 830071
E rob@doublefvoices.com

DOWNES PRESENTERS AGENCY
96 Broadway, Bexleyheath, Kent DA6 7DE   T 020 8304 0541
E downes@presentersagency.com
W www.presentersagency.com

DP MANAGEMENT
Contact: Danny Pellerini. By Post
Accepts Showreels/Voicereels
1 Agent represents 60 Performers
Argyle House
29-31 Euston Road
London NW1 2SD   M 07837 138892
E danny@dpmanagement.org
W www.dpmanagement.org

DQ MANAGEMENT
27 Ravenswood Park
Northwood
Middlesex HA6 3PR
M 07713 984633   T 01273 721221
E dq.management1@googlemail.com
W www.dqmanagement.com

DRAGON PERSONAL MANAGEMENT
20 Nant-Fawr Road
Cyncoed
Cardiff CF23 6JR
T 020 7183 5362   T 029 2075 4491
E casting@dragon-pm.com
W www.dragon-pm.com

DRAKE Simon MANAGEMENT
9 Golden Square
London W1F 9HZ
F 020 7183 9013   T 020 7183 8995
E admin@simondrakemanagement.co.uk
W www.simondrakemanagement.co.uk

DS PERSONAL MANAGEMENT
St Martin's Theatre, West Street
London WC2N 9NH
M 07711 245848   T 020 8743 7777
E ds@denisesilvey.com

EARLE Kenneth PERSONAL MANAGEMENT
214 Brixton Road, London SW9 6AP
F 020 7274 9529   T 020 7274 1219
E kennethearle@agents-uk.com
W www.entertainment-kennethearle.co.uk

EARNSHAW Susi MANAGEMENT
Personal Manager
The Bull Theatre
68 High Street
Barnet, Herts EN5 5SJ
F 020 8364 9618   T 020 8441 5010
E casting@susiearnshaw.co.uk
W www.susiearnshawmanagement.com

EDEN Shelly ASSOCIATES LTD
The Old Factory
Minus One House
Lyttelton Road, London E10 5NQ   T/F 020 8558 3536
E shellyeden@aol.com

EDLER Debbie MANAGEMENT LTD (DEM)
Little Friars Cottage
Lombard Street
Eynsham, Oxon OX29 4HT   T 01865 884203
E info@demagency.co.uk
W www.demagency.co.uk

EJA ASSOCIATES
Incorporating Simply Singers International
PO Box 63617, London SW9 1AN
M 07891 632946   T 020 7564 2688
E ejaassociates@aol.com

EKA ACTOR MANAGEMENT
Personal Manager. Contact: By Post/e-mail
Accepts Showreels. 6 Agents
Commercials. Film. Television
Voice Overs
The Warehouse Studios, Glaziers Lane
Culcheth, Warrington WA3 4AQ
F 01925 767563   T 01925 761088
E castings@eka-agency.com
W www.eka-agency.com

ELITE TALENT LTD
54 Crosslee Road, Blackley
Manchester M9 6TA   M 07787 342221
E jackie@elite-talent.com
W www.elite-talent.com

ELLIOTT AGENCY LTD THE
10 High Street
Shoreham-by-Sea BN43 5DA   T 01273 454111
E elliottagency@btconnect.com
W www.elliottagency.co.uk

ELLIS Bill LTD
See A & B PERSONAL MANAGEMENT LTD

ELLITE MANAGEMENT
Contact: By Post/e-mail. Accepts Showreels
3 Agents represent 40 Performers. Dancers
'The Dancer'
8 Peterson Road, Wakefield WF1 4EB
M 07957 631510   T 0845 6525361
E enquiries@ellitemanagement.co.uk
W www.elliteproductions.co.uk

EMPTAGE HALLETT
PMA Member
14 Rathbone Place, London W1T 1HT
F 020 7580 2748   T 020 7436 0425
E mail@emptagehallett.co.uk

2nd Floor, 3-5 The Balcony
Castle Arcade, Cardiff CF10 1BU
F 029 2034 4206   T 029 2034 4205
E gemma.mcavoy@emptagehallett.co.uk

ENCORE UK CASTING
PO Box 251
Newton Abbot, Devon TQ12 1AL
F 01626 202989   T 01626 211040
E hannah@encorecasting.co.uk
W www.encorecasting.co.uk

ENGERS Emma ASSOCIATES LTD
56 Russell Court
Woburn Place, London WC1H 0LW
M 07790 011920   T 020 7278 9980
E emma@emmaengersassociates.com
W www.emmaengersassociates.com

ENGLISH Doreen '95
Contact: By Post/Telephone
4 Selsey Avenue, Aldwick, Bognor Regis
West Sussex PO21 2QZ   T/F 01243 825968

ENTERTAINMENT PEOPLE MANAGEMENT
63 Blythe Road, Kensington
London W14 0HP
F 020 7100 6090   T 020 7100 6070
E russell.hawkins@ep-site.com
W www.ep-site.com

EPICA TALENT MANAGEMENT
Personal Manager. Representing Actors in Feature Films,
Television, Theatre & Commercials. Existing Clients only
81 Sutherland Avenue, London W9 2HG
M 07532 158818   T 020 3240 1064
E info@epicatm.co.uk
W www.epicatm.co.uk

EPMC TALENT
Contact: Aldo Arcilla. By e-mail
Accepts Showreels/Voicereels
18 Soho Square
London W1D 3QL
F 0871 6619916
E info@epmctalent.com
W www.epmctalent.com
T 020 7193 4230

EPSTEIN June ASSOCIATES
Contact: By Post/e-mail
Flat 1, 62 Compayne Gardens
London NW6 3RY
F 020 7328 0684
E june@june-epstein-associates.co.uk
T 020 7328 0864

ESSANAY
Personal Manager. PMA Member
Contact: By Post
PO Box 56662, London W13 3BH
E info@essanay.co.uk
T 020 8998 0007

ETHNICS ARTISTE AGENCY
86 Elphinstone Road
Walthamstow, London E17 5EX
F 020 8523 4523
E info@ethnicsaa.co.uk
T 020 8523 4242

EUROKIDS CASTING AGENCY
Contact: Amy Musker. By Post/e-mail. Accepts Showreels
6 Agents. Children. Commercials. Film. Television
Walk-on & Supporting Artists
The Warehouse Studios
Glaziers Lane
Culcheth, Warrington WA3 4AQ
F 01925 767563
E castings@eka-agency.com
W www.eka-agency.com
T 01925 761088

EVANS & REISS
100 Fawe Park Road
London SW15 2EA
E janita@evansandreiss.co.uk
T 020 8871 0788

EVANS Jacque MANAGEMENT LTD
Top Floor Suite
14 Holmesley Road
London SE23 1PJ
F 020 8699 5192
W www.jacqueevansltd.com
T 020 8699 1202

EVANS Stephanie ASSOCIATES
Rivington House
82 Great Eastern Street
London EC2A 3JF
E steph@stephanie-evans.com
W www.stephanie-evans.com
T/F 0870 6092629

EVOLUTION TALENT MANAGEMENT
The Truman Brewery Building
Studio 21, 91 Brick Lane
London E1 6QL
F 020 7375 2752
E info@evolutionmngt.com
W www.evolutionmngt.com
T 020 7770 6128

EXPERTS MANAGEMENT SERVICES LTD
T/A Jane Hughes Management
PO Box 200, Stockport
Cheshire SK12 1GW
M 07766 130604
E gill@jhm.co.uk
T 01625 858556

Lime

Lime Actors Agency & Management Ltd

Nemesis House / 1 Oxford Court / Bishopsgate / Manchester / M2 3WQ
0161 236 0827 / www.limemanagement.tv / georgina@limemanagement.co.uk

EXPRESSIONS CASTING AGENCY
3 Newgate Lane
Mansfield
Nottingham NG18 2LB
F 01623 647337   T 01623 424334
E expressions-uk@btconnect.com
W www.expressionsperformingarts.co.uk

EYE AGENT MANAGEMENT
1st Floor
47 Chatsworth Road
Stratford, London E15 1RB
M 07986 416540   T 020 8534 1554
E chris_abakporo@yahoo.co.uk
W www.eyeagentmanagement.co.uk

EYE MODELS THE
First Floor
92 Commercial Street
Spitalfields
London E1 6LZ   T 020 7377 7500
E bayo@theeyecasting.com
W www.theeyecasting.com

FARINO Paola
Actors
109 St Georges Road
London SE1 6HY   T 020 7207 0858
E info@paolafarino.co.uk
W www.paolafarino.co.uk

FARNES Norma MANAGEMENT
9 Orme Court, London W2 4RL
F 020 7792 2110   T 020 7727 1544

FAWKES Irene MANAGEMENT
Contact: Irene Fawkes. By Post. Accepts Showreels. 1 Agent represents 40 Performers. Commercials. Film. Musicals Stage. Television
2nd Floor, 91A Rivington Street
London EC2A 3AY
F 020 7613 0769   T 020 7729 8559
E irenefawkes@btconnect.com

FBI AGENCY
PO Box 250, Leeds LS1 2AZ
M 07515 567309   M 07050 222747
E casting@fbi-agency.co.uk
W www.fbi-agency.co.uk

FD MANAGEMENT
Contact: By e-mail. Accepts Showreels
1 Agent represents 15 Performers
18C Marine Square, Brighton BN2 1DN   M 07730 800679
E vivienwilde@mac.com

FEA MANAGEMENT (Ferris Entertainment)
London. Belfast. Cardiff
Number 8, 132 Charing Cross Road
London WC2H 0LA   T 0845 4724725
E info@ferrisentertainment.com
W www.ferrisentertainment.com

FEAST MANAGEMENT LTD
PMA Member
1st Floor, 34 Upper Street
London N1 0PN
F 020 7354 8995   T 020 7354 5216
E office@feastmanagement.co.uk

Personal Management

Agents:
Simon Bashford
Michael Garrett
Jessica Jones
Niki Winterson

GLOBAL ARTISTS
23 Haymarket London SW1Y 4DG
Tel: 020 7839 4888 Fax: 020 7839 4555
email: info@globalartists.co.uk
www.globalartists.co.uk
www.theatricalagent.co.uk

Members of the Personal Managers' Association

Michael Garrett Associates Ltd. Registered No. 4404385
Registered Office: 23 Haymarket, London SW1Y 4DG

FEATURED & BACKGROUND CASTING LTD
Contact: Lois Ward, Suzanne Johns
Audley Cottage, High Street
Cookham, Berkshire SL6 9SF
M 07899 898286   T 01628 531475
E info@fabcastingagency.com
W www.fabcastingagency.com

FEATURES
1 Charlotte Street, London W1T 1RD
F 020 7637 0328   T 020 7637 1487
E info@features.co.uk
W www.features.co.uk

FIELD Alan ASSOCIATES
Personal Manager. Contact: By e-mail
Celebrities. Composers. Musicals. Presenters. Singers
3 The Spinney, Bakers Hill
Hadley Common, Herts EN5 5QJ
M 07836 555300   T 020 8441 1137
E alan@alanfield.com

FILM CAST CORNWALL & SW
c/o 3 Church Walk, Truro TR1 1JH   T 01326 311419
E enquiries@filmcastcornwall.co.uk
W www.filmcastcornwall.co.uk

FILM RIGHTS LTD
Personal Manager. Contact: By Post
Suite 306, Belsize Business Centre
258 Belsize Road, London NW6 4BT
F 020 7624 3629   T 020 7316 1837

FINCH & PARTNERS
Top Floor, 29-37 Heddon Street
London W1B 4BR
F 020 7287 6420   T 020 7851 7140
E reception@finchandpartners.com
W www.finchandpartners.com

FIRST CALL MANAGEMENT
29-30 Dame Street, Dublin 2, Ireland
F 00 353 1 679 8353   T 00 353 1 679 8401
E fcm@indigo.ie

FISHER
Studio 125, 77 Beak Street
London W1F 9DB   T 020 7993 6042
E fisher@castinguk.com

FITZGERALD Sheridan MANAGEMENT
Contact: Edward Romfourt. By Post (SAE). No Phone Calls
52C Wells Street, London W1T 3PR   T 0845 5390504

FLAIR TALENT
Cameo House, 13-17 Bear Street
London WC2H 7AS   T 020 8693 8649
E bookings@flairtalent.com
W www.flairtalent.com

FLETCHER ASSOCIATES
Personal Manager. Contact: Francine Fletcher. By Telephone
15 Performers. Corporate. Experts. Radio. Stage. Television
25 Parkway, London N20 0XN
F 020 8361 8866   T 020 8361 8061
W www.fletcherassociates.net

FLETCHER JACOB
Artist Management
92 Commercial Street, London E1 6LZ   T 020 7617 7181
E info@fletcherjacob.co.uk
W www.fletcherjacob.co.uk

FLP
Hurlingham Studios, Unit 19A
Ranelagh Gardens, Fulham, London SW6 3PA
F 020 7731 3422   T 020 7371 0300
E info@formulaliveproductions.com
W www.formulaliveproductions.com

FOSTER Sharon MANAGEMENT
15A Hollybank Road, Birmingham B13 0RF   T 0121 443 4865
E mail@sharonfoster.co.uk
W www.sharonfoster.co.uk

FOX Clare ASSOCIATES
Set, Lighting & Sound Designers
9 Plympton Road, London NW6 7EH   T/F 020 7328 7494
E cimfox@yahoo.co.uk
W www.clarefox.co.uk

Gigi Robarts
Photographer

07908 725 944
gigifoto2@aol.com

headshots | portraits | student rates

FOX Julie ASSOCIATES
Personal Manager
Contact: Julie Fox. By e-mail only
Accepts Showreels/Voicereels.
2 Agents represent 50 Performers
E agent@juliefoxassociates.co.uk   T/F 01628 777853

FRENCH Linda
See APM ASSOCIATES

FRESH AGENTS LTD
Suite 5, Saks House
19 Ship Street
Brighton BN1 1AD   T 0845 4080998
E info@freshagents.co.uk
W www.freshagents.co.uk

FRESH PARTNERS LTD
1 Hardwick's Square, Wandsworth
London SW18 4AW   T 020 7198 8478
E hello@fresh-partners.com
W www.fresh-partners.com

FRONTLINE ACTORS AGENCY DUBLIN
30-31 Wicklow Street, Dublin 2, Ireland   T 00 353 1 6359882
E frontlineactors@eircom.net
W www.frontlineactors.com

FUNKY BEETROOT CELEBRITY MANAGEMENT LTD
Personal Manager. Actors. Television Celebrities
PO Box 143, Faversham, Kent ME13 9LP
F 01227 752300   T 01227 751549
E info@funky-beetroot.com   W www.funky-beetroot.com

w w w . h e r e s l o o k i n g a t y o u . c o . u k

ANDY PARADISE   photographer

t : 0 7 9 5 7   3 9 2 9 8 0   e : a n d y @ h e r e s l o o k i n g a t y o u . c o . u k

GAELFORCE 10 MANAGEMENT
Film City, 401 Govan Road
Glasgow G51 2QJ
F 0871 7146275
E info@gaelforce10.com
W www.gaelforce10.com
T 0845 6031266

GAGAN Hilary ASSOCIATES
Personal Manager. PMA Member
187 Drury Lane, London WC2B 5QD
F 020 7430 1869
E hilary@hgassoc.co.uk
T 020 7404 8794

GALLOWAYS ONE
15 Lexham Mews, London W8 6JW
F 020 7376 2416
E email@gallowaysone.com
W www.gallowaysone.com
T 020 7376 2288

GANNON Kay
Central Chambers
93 Hope Street
Glasgow G2 6LD
E kay@revolutiontalentmanagement.com
W www.revolutiontalentmanagement.com
T/F 0141 221 8622

GARDNER HERRITY LTD
PMA Member. Contact: Andy Herrity
24 Conway Street, London W1T 6BG
F 020 7388 0688
E info@gardnerherrity.co.uk
W www.gardnerherrity.co.uk
T 020 7388 0088

GARRETT Michael
See GLOBAL ARTISTS

GARRICKS
PMA Member
Angel House, 76 Mallinson Road
London SW11 1BN
F 020 7801 0088
E info@garricks.net
T 020 7738 1600

GAY Noel
PMA Member
19 Denmark Street
London WC2H 8NA
F 020 7287 1816
E info@noelgay.com
W www.noelgay.com
T 020 7836 3941

GENESIS PERSONAL MANAGEMENT LTD
6B New Broughton Road, Melksham
Wiltshire SN12 8BS
W www.genesismanagement.co.uk
T 01225 706883

GFI MANAGEMENT
Personal Manager
Green Gables, 47 North Lane
Teddington, Middlesex TW11 0HU
M 07956 646412
E agency@goforitcentre.com
W www.goforitcentre.com
T 020 8943 1120

GILBERT & PAYNE
Room 236, 2nd Floor, Linen Hall
162-168 Regent Street, London W1B 5TB
F 020 7494 3787
E ee@gilbertandpayne.com
T 020 7734 7505

GILLMAN Geraldine ASSOCIATES
Malcolm House
Malcolm Primary School, Malcolm Road
Penge, London SE20 8RH
M 07799 791586
E geraldi.gillma@btconnect.com
T 0844 8005328

GLASS Eric LTD
25 Ladbroke Crescent, Notting Hill
London W11 1PS
F 020 7229 6220
E eglassltd@aol.com
T 020 7229 9500

GLOBAL7
PO Box 56232, London N4 4XP
M 07956 956652
E global7castings@gmail.com
W www.global7casting.com
T/F 020 7281 7679

GLOBAL ARTISTS
PMA Member. Contact: By Post/e-mail
Accepts Showreels/Voicereels. 5 Agents
23 Haymarket, London SW1Y 4DG
F 020 7839 4555
E info@globalartists.co.uk
W www.globalartists.co.uk
T 020 7839 4888

GLYN MANAGEMENT
The Old School House, Brettenham
Ipswich IP7 7QP
F 01449 736117
E glyn.management@tesco.net
T 01449 737695

GO ENTERTAINMENTS LTD
Circus Artistes. Chinese State Circus. Cirque Surreal. Bolshoi Circus "Spirit of The Horse"
The Arts Exchange, Congleton, Cheshire CW12 1LA
F 01260 270777
E info@arts-exchange.com
W www.arts-exchange.com
T 01260 276627

GOLD ARTISTES
1A Ordnance Road
Studio 29
Edgar Myles House
London E16 4BN   M 07981 065728
E goldartistes@live.co.uk

GOLDMANS MANAGEMENT
E casting@shana-goldmans.co.uk   T 01323 472391
W www.shana-goldmans.co.uk

GORDON & FRENCH
PMA Member. Contact: By Post
12-13 Poland Street
London W1F 8QB
F 020 7734 4832   T 020 7734 4818
E mail@gordonandfrench.net

GRAHAM David PERSONAL MANAGEMENT (DGPM)
The Studio, 107A Middleton Road
London E8 4LN   T/F 020 7241 6752
E info@dgpmtheagency.com

GRANT James MEDIA
94 Strand On The Green, Chiswick, London W4 3NN
F 020 8742 4951   T 020 8742 4950
E enquiries@jamesgrant.co.uk
W www.jamesgrant.co.uk

GRANTHAM-HAZELDINE LTD
PMA Member
Suite 315, The Linen Hall
162-168 Regent Street, London W1B 5TD
F 020 7038 3739   T 020 7038 3737
E agents@granthamhazeldine.com

GRAY Darren MANAGEMENT
Specialising in representing/promoting Australian Artists
2 Marston Lane, Portsmouth
Hampshire PO3 5TW
F 023 9267 7227   T 023 9269 9973
E darren.gray1@virgin.net
W www.darrengraymanagement.co.uk

GREEN & UNDERWOOD
Personal Manager. Contact: By Post
PO Box 56662, London W13 3BH   T 020 8998 0007
E info@greenandunderwood.com

GRESHAM Carl GROUP
PO Box 3, Bradford
West Yorkshire BD1 4QN
F 01274 827161   T 01274 735880
E gresh@carlgresham.co.uk
W www.carlgresham.com

GRIDMODELS UK LTD
Contact: Rosie Beasley. By e-mail/Telephone
2 Agents represent 300 Performers. Modelling
45 Garth Close, Morden
Surrey SM4 4NN   T 020 7993 6512
E enquiries@gridmodels.com
W www.gridmodelsfashionandcommercialsagency.com

GRIFFIN Sandra MANAGEMENT LTD
6 Ryde Place
Richmond Road
East Twickenham, Middlesex TW1 2EH
F 020 8744 1812   T 020 8891 5676
E office@sandragriffin.com
W www.sandragriffin.com

GROUNDLINGS THEATRE COMPANY
The Old Beneficial School
Kent Street
Portsea, Hampshire PO1 3BS   T 023 9273 7370
E funkythespians@aol.com
W www.groundlings.co.uk

GROVES Rob PERSONAL MANAGEMENT
Contact: By e-mail. 1 Agent represents 80 Performers
4th Floor, 33 Glasshouse Street
London W1B 5DG
F 07092 873538   T 020 3174 0501
E rob@robgroves.co.uk
W www.robgroves.co.uk

GUBBAY Louise ASSOCIATES
26 Westmore Road, Tatsfield
Kent TN16 2AX   T 01959 573080
E louise@louisegubbay.com
W www.louisegubbay.com

GURNETT J. PERSONAL MANAGEMENT LTD
12 Newburgh Street, London W1F 7RP
F 020 7287 9642   T 020 7440 1850
E mail@jgpm.co.uk
W www.jgpm.co.uk

HALL JAMES PERSONAL MANAGEMENT
PO Box 604, Pinner
Middlesex HA5 9GH
F 020 8868 5825   T 020 8429 8111
E agents@halljames.co.uk
W www.halljames.co.uk

HALLY Yvette MANAGEMENT
121 Grange Road
Rathfarnham
Dublin 14, Ireland
F 00 353 1 4933076   T 00 353 1 4933685
E yhmgt@eircom.net

HAMBLETON Patrick MANAGEMENT
Top Floor
136 Englefield Road
London N1 3LQ   T 020 7226 0947
E patrick@phm.uk.com

HAMILTON HODELL LTD
PMA Member
5th Floor
66-68 Margaret Street
London W1W 8SR
F 020 7636 1226   T 020 7636 1221
E info@hamiltonhodell.co.uk
W www.hamiltonhodell.co.uk

HARRIS AGENCY LTD THE
71 The Avenue, Watford
Herts WD17 4NU   T 01923 211644
E theharrisagency@btconnect.com

HARRISON Penny BSA LTD
Trinity Lodge
25 Trinity Crescent
London SW17 7AG
F 020 8672 8971   T 020 8672 0136
E harrisonbsa@aol.com

HARVEY VOICES
58 Woodlands Road
London N9 8RT   T 020 7952 4361
W www.harveyvoices.co.uk

HAT MANAGEMENT
Contact: Neil Howarth
24 Thornley Rise, Audenshaw
Manchester M34 5JX
M 07775 744438   T 0161 370 8648
E hat.mgmt@hotmail.co.uk

HATTON McEWAN
Personal Manager. Contact: Stephen Hatton, Aileen McEwan,
James Penford. By Post
PO Box 37385, London N1 7XF
F 020 7251 9081   T 020 7253 4770
E mail@hattonmcewan.com
W www.hattonmcewan.com

H C A
See COOKE Howard ASSOCIATES

KAREN SCOTT
PHOTOGRAPHY

student rates
07958 975 950
www.karenscottphotography.com
info@karenscottphotography.com

HCAGENCY
HandE Media Group, Brickfield Business Centre
Thornwood High Road, Epping, Essex CM16 6TH
F 01992 570601   T 01992 570728
E diana@hande-caa.co.uk
W www.hande-caa.co.uk

HEADNOD TALENT AGENCY
63 Redchurch Street, London E2 7DJ   T 020 7502 9478
E info@headnodagency.com
W www.headnodagency.com

**HENRIETTA RABBIT CHILDREN'S ENTERTAINMENT
AGENCY**
*Children's Entertainers. Balloonologists. Close-up Magicians
Clowns. Face Painters. Jugglers. Punch & Judy. Stiltwalkers*
The Warren, 12 Eden Close, York YO24 2RD   T 0800 0965653
E info@henriettarabbit.co.uk
W www.henriettarabbit.co.uk

HENRY'S AGENCY
53 Westbury
Rochford
Essex SS4 1UL   T/F 01702 541413
E info@henrysagency.co.uk
W www.henrysagency.co.uk

HICKS Jeremy ASSOCIATES LTD
Personal Manager
Contact: By Post/e-mail
Accepts Showreels
2 Agents represent 25 Performers
Chefs. Comedians. Presenters. Writers
3 Richmond Buildings
London W1D 3HE
F 020 7734 6302
E info@jeremyhicks.com   T 020 7734 7957
W www.jeremyhicks.com

Rare Talent Actors Management is a dynamic agency with a fresh approach to acting management.

We supply professional actors to all aspects of the industry including television, film, theatre, corporate and commercials.

tanzaro house, ardwick green north, manchester, m12 6fz
t: 0161 273 4004 **f:** 0161 273 4567
info@raretalentactors.com www.raretalentactors.com

HILTON Elinor ASSOCIATES
1 Goodwin's Court, London WC2H 4LL
E info@elinorhilton.com
W www.elinorhilton.com
T 020 7240 2555

HIRED HANDS
12 Cressy Road, London NW3 2LY
E hiredhandsagency@aol.com
W www.hiredhandsmodels.com
T 020 7267 9212

HOBBART & HOBBART
24 Kelvedon Road, London SW6 5BW
E braathen@hobbart.no
W www.hobbart.co.uk
M 07595 260208

HOBBS Liz GROUP LTD
Talent Management
65 London Road, Newark
Notts NG24 1RZ
F 0870 3337009
E casting@lizhobbsgroup.com
W www.lizhobbsgroup.com
T 0870 0702702

HOBSONS ACTORS
62 Chiswick High Road, Chiswick
London W4 1SY
F 020 8996 5350
E actors@hobsons-international.com
W www.hobsons-international.com
T 020 8995 3628

HOLLOWOOD Jane ASSOCIATES LTD
Apartment 17, 113 Newton Street
Manchester M1 1AE
T 020 8291 5702
E janehollowood@ukonline.co.uk
T 0161 237 9141

HOLLY Dave ARTS MEDIA SERVICES
The Annexe, 23 Eastwood Gardens
Felling, Tyne & Wear NE10 0AH
T 0191 438 2711

HOLMES Kim SHOWBUSINESS ENTERTAINMENT AGENCY LTD
8 Charles Close
Ilkeston, Derbyshire DE7 5AF
F 0115 944 0390
E kimholmesshowbiz@hotmail.co.uk
T 0115 930 5088

HOPE Sally ASSOCIATES
PMA Member
108 Leonard Street, London EC2A 4XS
F 020 7613 4848
E casting@sallyhope.biz
W www.sallyhope.biz
T 020 7613 5353

HORSEY Dick MANAGEMENT LTD
Personal Manager. Contact: By Post/e-mail/Telephone
Accepts Showreels/Voicereels. 2 Agents represent 40
Performers. Corporate. Musicals. Stage. Television
Suite 1, Cottingham House
Chorleywood Road
Rickmansworth, Herts WD3 4EP
M 07850 112211
E roger@dhmlimited.co.uk
W www.dhmlimited.co.uk
T 01923 710614

HOWARD Amanda ASSOCIATES LTD
PMA Member. Contact: By Post
21 Berwick Street
London W1F 0PZ
F 020 7287 7785
E mail@amandahowardassociates.co.uk
W www.amandahowardassociates.co.uk
T 020 7287 9277

HOWE Janet CASTING AGENCY
Personal Manager. Agents. Children. Modelling. Television
Walk-on & Supporting Artists
58A High Street
Newcastle Under Lyme
Staffordshire ST5 1QE
E info@janethowe.com
W www.janethowecasting.co.uk
T 01782 661777

The Pie Factory, 101 Broadway
Salford Quays, Manchester M50 2EQ
M 07801 942178
T/F 0161 660 1104

HOWELL Philippa
See PHPM (Philippa Howell Personal Management)

HOXTON STREET CASTING
Hoxton Hall, 130 Hoxton Street
London N1 6SH
E lucy@hoxtonstreetcasting.co.uk
W www.hoxtonstreetcasting.co.uk
T 020 7503 5131

HUDSON Nancy ASSOCIATES LTD
PO Box 1344
High Wycombe North
Bucks HP11 9ER
E agents@nancyhudsonassociates.com
W www.nancyhudsonassociates.com
T 020 7499 5548

HUNTER Bernard ASSOCIATES
13 Spencer Gardens
London SW14 7AH
F 020 8392 9334
T 020 8878 6308

HUNWICK HUGHES LTD
Personal Manager
Suite 2F, 45A George Street
Edinburgh EH2 2HT
F 0131 225 4535
E maryam@hunwickhughes.com
W www.hunwickhughes.com
T 0131 225 3585

I-MAGE CASTINGS
Regent House Business Centre
Suite 22, 24-25 Nutford Place
Marble Arch, London W1H 5YN
F 020 7725 7004
E jane@i-mage.uk.com
W www.i-mage.uk.com
T 020 7725 7003

ICON ACTORS MANAGEMENT
Tanzaro House, Ardwick Green North
Manchester M12 6FZ
F 0161 273 4567
E info@iconactors.net
W www.iconactors.net
T 0161 273 3344

I.M.L.
Personal Manager. CPMA Member
The White House, 52-54 Kennington Oval
London SE11 5SW   T/F 020 7587 1080
E info@iml.org.uk
W www.iml.org.uk

IMPACT INTERNATIONAL MANAGEMENT
Personal Manager. Contact: Cornelia Hefti. By e-mail
Accepts Showreels/Voicereels
1 Agent represents 10 Performers
Cruises. Musical Theatre. Speciality Acts & Events
1st Floor Danceworks, 16-18 Balderton Street
London W1K 6TN
M 07941 269849   T 020 7495 6655
E info@impact-london.co.uk
W www.impact-london.co.uk

IMPERIAL PERSONAL MANAGEMENT LTD
102 Kirkstall Road, Leeds
West Yorkshire LS3 1JA
M 07890 387758   T 0113 244 3222
E katie@ipmcasting.com
W www.ipmcasting.com

IMPERIUM MANAGEMENT
232 Muswell Hill Broadway, London N10 3SH   T 020 8442 1971
E info@imperium-management.com
W www.imperium-management.com

INDEPENDENT TALENT GROUP LTD
Formerly ICM, London. PMA Member
Oxford House, 76 Oxford Street
London W1D 1BS
F 020 7323 0101   T 020 7636 6565
W www.independenttalent.com

INDEPENDENT THEATRE WORKSHOP THE
8 Terminus Mills, Clonskeogh
Dublin 6, Ireland T 00 353 1 2600831
E info@independent-theatre-workshop.com
W www.independent-theatre-workshop.com

INSPIRATION MANAGEMENT
Co-operative. CPMA Member
Room 227, The Aberdeen Centre
22-24 Highbury Grove, London N5 2EA T 020 7704 0440
E mail@inspirationmanagement.eclipse.co.uk
W www.inspirationmanagement.org.uk

INSPIRE ACADEMY
The Attic Studio, 3rd Floor, 46-48 Carrington Street
Nottingham NG1 7FG T 0115 9177 296
E admin@inspireacademy.co.uk
W www.inspireacademy.co.uk

INTER-CITY CASTING
Personal Manager. Contact: By Post. Accepts Showreels
2 Agents represent 60 Performers
27 Wigan Lane, Wigan
Greater Manchester WN1 1XR T/F 01942 321969
E intercitycasting@btconnect.com

INTERNATIONAL ARTISTES LTD
PMA Member
4th Floor, Holborn Hall
193-197 High Holborn, London WC1V 7BD
F 020 7404 9865 T 020 7025 0600
E reception@internationalartistes.com

INTERNATIONAL COLLECTIVE ARTIST MANAGEMENT
9-13 Grape Street, Covent Garden
London WC2H 8ED
F 020 7557 6656 T 020 7557 6650
E mel@internationalcollective.com
W www.internationalcollective.com

INTERNATIONAL MODEL MANAGEMENT LTD
Incorporating Yvonne Paul Management
Elysium Gate, Unit 15, 126-128 New Kings Rd, London SW6 4LZ
F 020 7736 2221 T 020 7610 9111
E info@immmodels.com
W www.immmodels.com

INTERNATIONAL MODELS & TALENT AGENCY
1901 Avenue of The Stars, Suite #200
Century City, CA 90067
F (310) 461 1304 T (310) 461 1550
E int.talent@hotmail.com

IRISH ACTORS LONDON
2 Bloemfontein Road, London W12 7BX T 020 3318 5732
E irishactorslondon@live.co.uk
W www.irishactorslondon.co.uk

IT&M MANAGEMENT
Personal Manager. Contact: Claire Edworthy, Piers Chater
Robinson. By Post/e-mail. Accepts Voicereels. 2 Agents
represent 32 Performers. Dancers. Musicals. Singers. Writers
Garden Studios
11-15 Betterton Street
Covent Garden
London WC2H 9BP
F 020 7379 0801 T 020 7470 8786
E info@it-m.co.uk
W www.it-m.co.uk

JAA
See ALTARAS Jonathan ASSOCIATES LTD

JABBERWOCKY AGENCY
Contact: Christina Yates. By e-mail
4 Agents represent 135 Performers. Children. Teenagers
Glassenbury Hill Farm
Glassenbury Road
Cranbrook, Kent TN17 2QF
F 01580 714346 T 01580 714306
E info@jabberwockyagency.com
W www.jabberwockyagency.com

JAFFREY MANAGEMENT LTD
Personal Manager. Contact: By Post/e-mail
Accepts Showreels/Voicereels (SAE). 2 Agents represent 60
Performers. Commercials. Film. Stage. Television
74 Western Road, Romford
Essex RM1 3LP T 01708 732350
E mail@jaffreyactors.co.uk
W www.jaffreyactors.co.uk

JAM AGENCY
Holborn Hall, 193-197 High Holborn
London WC1V 7BD
F 020 7831 7267 T 020 7269 7923
E info@jamagency.co.uk

JAM2000 AGENCY
The Windmill Studio Centre
106A Pembroke Road
Ruislip, Middlesex HA4 8NW T 01895 624755
E thewindmillstudio@gmail.com
W www.thewindmillstudio.com

JAMES Susan
See SJ MANAGEMENT

JAMESON Joy LTD
Personal Manager
21 Uxbridge Street
Kensington, London W8 7TQ
F 020 7985 0842 T 020 7221 0990
E joy@jote.freeuk.com

JB ASSOCIATES
*Personal Manager. PMA Member. Contact: John Basham
By Post/e-mail. Accepts Showreels/Voicereels. 2 Agents
represent 60 Performers. Commercials. Radio. Stage
Television*
4th Floor, Manchester House, 84-86 Princess Street
Manchester M1 6NG
F 0161 237 1809   T 0161 237 1808
E info@j-b-a.net
W www.j-b-a.net

JEFFREY & WHITE MANAGEMENT LTD
Personal Manager. PMA Member
2 Ladygrove Court, Hitchwood Lane, Preston, Hitchin
Hertfordshire SG4 7SA   T 01462 433752
E info@jeffreyandwhite.co.uk
W www.jeffreyandwhite.co.uk

JERMIN Mark MANAGEMENT
Contact: By Post/e-mail. Accepts Showreels. 2 Agents
8 Heathfield, Swansea SA1 6EJ
F 01792 458844   T 01792 458855
E info@markjermin.co.uk   W www.markjermin.co.uk

J.G.M.
15 Lexham Mews, London W8 6JW
F 020 7376 2416   T 020 7376 2414
E mail@jgmtalent.com   W www.jgmtalent.com

JLM PERSONAL MANAGEMENT
*Personal Manager. PMA Member
Contact: Sharon Henry. By Post. Accepts Showreels
2 Agents. Commercials. Film. Radio. Stage. Television*
4th Flr, Holborn Hall, 193-197 High Holborn, London WC1V 7BD
F 020 7404 9865   T 020 7025 0630
E info@jlmpm.co.uk

Daisy Ward   Robbie Towns   Anna Acton

alexruoccophotography
t: 07732293231 www.alexruoccophotography.co.uk

J.M. MANAGEMENT
Personal representation to a small number of
Actors/Actresses in film work
20 Pembroke Road, North Wembley
Middlesex HA9 7PD   T 020 8908 0502

JOHNSON WHITELEY LTD
12 Argyll Mansions, Hammersmith Road
London W14 8QG
F 020 7348 0164   T/F 020 7348 0163
E johnsonwhiteley@btconnnect.com

JOHNSTON & MATHERS ASSOCIATES LTD
PO Box 3167, Barnet EN5 2WA   T/F 020 8449 4968
E johnstonmathers@aol.com
W www.johnstonandmathers.com

JOYCE Michael MANAGEMENT
4th Floor, 14-18 Heddon Street
London W1B 4DA
F 020 7745 6275   T 020 7745 6274
E info@michaeljoycemanagement.com
W www.michaeljoycemanagement.com

JPA MANAGEMENT
30 Daws Hill Lane, High Wycombe
Bucks HP11 1PW
F 01494 510479   T 01494 520978
E jackie.palmer@btinternet.com
W www.jpamanagement.co.uk

K TALENT ARTIST MANAGEMENT
Personal Manager. Contact: By Post/e-mail. Accepts
Showreels/Voicereels. 4 Agents represent 80 Performers
Children. Commercials. Dancers. Film. Musicals. Singers
Stage. Television
24-25 Macklin Street, Covent Garden
London WC2B 5NN
T 0844 5672470   T 020 7691 8930
E mail@ktalent.co.uk
W www.ktalent.co.uk

KAL MANAGEMENT
Contact: By Post
95 Gloucester Road, Hampton
Middlesex TW12 2UW
F 020 8979 6487   T 020 8783 0039
E kaplan222@aol.com
W www.kaplan-kaye.co.uk

KANAL Roberta AGENCY
82 Constance Road, Twickenham
Middlesex TW2 7JA
T/F 020 8894 7952   T 020 8894 2277
E roberta.kanal@dsl.pipex.com

KEDDIE SCOTT ASSOCIATES LTD
Personal Manager. PMA Member. Contact: By Post. Accepts
Showreels/Voicereels. 4 Agents represent 145 Performers
Commercials. Corporate. Dancers. Film. Musicals. Presenters
Radio. Singers. Stage. Television. Writers
Studio 1, 17 Shorts Gardens
Covent Garden, London WC2H 9AT
F 020 7147 1326   T 020 7836 6802
E fiona@ks-ass.co.uk
W www.ks-ass.co.uk

KSA - SCOTLAND
Personal Manager. PMA Member. Contact: Paul Michael
By Post/e-mail. Accepts Showreels/Voicereels. 2 Agents
represent 45 Performers. Film. Musicals. Stage. Television
(0/1) 430 Tantallon Road, Glasgow G41 3HR
F 020 7147 1326   M 07980 121728
E scotland@ks-ass.co.uk

KSA - WALES
Studio 1, 17 Shorts Gardens
Covent Garden, London WC2H 9AT
M 07917 272298   T 020 7836 6802
E wales@ks-ass.co.uk
W www.ks-ass.co.uk

KELLY MANAGEMENT
PMA Member
10 White Horse Street
Mayfair, London W1J 7LJ
F 020 7499 9388   T 020 7499 8402
E assistant@kelly-management.com
W www.kelly-management.com

KENIS Steve & Co
PMA Member
Royalty House
72-74 Dean Street, London W1D 3SG
F 020 7287 6328   T 020 7434 9055
E sk@sknco.com

KEW PERSONAL MANAGEMENT
PO Box 679, RH1 9BT   T 020 8871 3697
E info@kewpersonalmanagement.com
W www.kewpersonalmanagement.com

KEYLOCK MANAGEMENT
Contact: By Post. Accepts Showreels. 1 Agent represents 64
Performers. Commercials. Film. Stage. Television
5 North Dean Cottages, Speen Road
North Dean, Bucks HP14 4NN
M 07712 579502   T 01494 563142
E mark@keylockmanagement.com
W www.keylockmanagement.com

KIDS MANAGEMENT
35 Truggers, Handcross
West Sussex RH17 6DQ   T 01444 401595
E kidsmanagement@ymail.com
W www.kidsmanagement.co.uk

KING Adrian ASSOCIATES
PMA Member. Contact: Adrian King. By Post/e-mail
Accepts Showreels
33 Marlborough Mansions, Cannon Hill, London NW6 1JS
F 020 7435 4100   T 020 7435 4600
E akassocs@aol.com

K M C AGENCIES
Personal Manager. Commercials. Corporate. Dancers
Musical Theatre
Garden Studios, 11-15 Betterton Street, London WC2H 9BP
F 0870 4421780   T 0845 6602459
E london@kmcagencies.co.uk

K M C AGENCIES
PO Box 122, 48 Great Ancoats Street
Manchester M4 5AB
F 0161 237 9812   T 0161 237 3009
E casting@kmcagencies.co.uk

KNIGHT Nic MANAGEMENT
23 Buckler Court
Eden Grove
London N7 8EF   T 020 3093 5422
E enquiries@nicknightmanagement.com
W www.nicknightmanagement.com

KNIGHT Ray CASTING
21A Lambolle Place
London NW3 4PG
F 020 7722 2322   T 020 7722 1551
E casting@rayknight.co.uk
W www.rayknight.co.uk

KNIGHT AYTON MANAGEMENT
35 Great James Street
London WC1N 3HB
F 020 7831 4455   T 020 7831 4400
E info@knightayton.co.uk
W www.knightayton.co.uk

KNOCK2BAG MANAGEMENT
60 Pasquier Road
London E17 6HB   M 07870 212189
E knock2bagmanagement@knock2bag.co.uk
W www.knock2bag.co.uk

KORT Richard MANAGEMENT LTD
Moat Farm, Norwell Woodhouse
Newark, Notts NG23 6NG
F 01636 636719   T 01636 636686
E richardkort@dial.pipex.com
W www.richardkortassociates.com

KREATE
Unit 232, 30 Great Guildford Street
London SE1 0HS
F 020 7401 3003   T 020 7401 9007
E web@kreate.co.uk

KREMER ASSOCIATES
See MARSH Billy DRAMA LTD

KSA - SCOTLAND
See KEDDIE SCOTT ASSOCIATES LTD

KSA - WALES
See KEDDIE SCOTT ASSOCIATES LTD

KW PROMOTIONS LTD
9 College Road, Alsager
Stoke-on-Trent ST7 2SS   M 07835 316639
E dkeeno1@hotmail.com
W www.kwpromotions.co.uk

L.A. MANAGEMENT
10 Fairoak Close, Kenley
Surrey CR8 5LJ   M 07963 573538
E info@lamanagement.biz
W www.lamanagement.biz

LADA MANAGEMENT
Personal Manager. Contact: Richard Boschetto
By Post/e-mail. Accepts Showreels/Voicereels
2 Agents represent 30 Performers. Film. Musicals
Stage. Television
23 Austin Friars, London EC2N 2QP
F 020 3384 5816   T 020 3384 5815
E management@lada.org.uk
W www.lada.org.uk/agency

Sparkhouse Studios, Rope Walk, Lincoln LN6 7DQ
F 01522 837201   T 01522 837243

LADIDA
Contact: By Post
Accepts Showreels
2 Agents represent 75 Performers
Commercials. Creatives. Film. Musicals. Radio. Stage
Television. Writers
Cambridge Theatre
Earlham Street, London WC2H 9HU
F 020 7379 6198   T 020 7379 6199
E m@ladidagroup.com
W www.ladidagroup.com

LAINE Betty MANAGEMENT
The Studios, East Street
Epsom, Surrey KT17 1HH   T/F 01372 721815
E enquiries@betty-laine-management.co.uk

LAINE MANAGEMENT LTD
Laine House, 131 Victoria Road, Hope, Salford M6 8LF
F 0161 787 7572   T 0161 789 7775
E sam@lainemanagement.co.uk
W www.lainemanagement.co.uk

LANGFORD ASSOCIATES LTD
Personal Manager. Contact: Barry Langford. By Post/e-mail
Commercials. Film. Stage. Television
17 Westfields Avenue
Barnes, London SW13 0AT
F 020 8878 7078   T 020 8878 7148
E barry.langford@btconnect.com
W www.langfordassociates.com

LAWRENCE Tonicha AGENCY
Serenissima, Church Hill, Thorner, Leeds LS14 3EG
M 07766 415996 T/F 0113 289 3433
E agent@tonichalawrence.co.uk
W www.tonichalawrenceagency.com

LE BARS Tessa MANAGEMENT
Existing Clients only
54 Birchwood Road, Petts Wood, Kent BR5 1NZ
M 07860 287255 T 01689 837084
E tessa.lebars@ntlworld.com
W www.galtonandsimpson.com

LEE Wendy MANAGEMENT
2nd Floor, 36 Langham Street
London W1W 7AP T 020 7703 5187
E wendy-lee@btconnect.com

LEHRER Jane ASSOCIATES
Personal Manager. PMA Member
Contact: By Post/e-mail. 2 Agents
100A Chalk Farm Road, London NW1 8EH
F 020 7482 4899 T 020 7482 4898
E jane@janelehrer.co.uk
W www.janelehrer.co.uk

LEIGH Mike ASSOCIATES
37 Marylebone Lane, London W1U 2NW
F 020 7486 5886 T 020 7935 5500
W www.mikeleighassoc.com

LEIGH MANAGEMENT
14 St David's Drive, Edgware
Middlesex HA8 6JH T/F 020 8951 4449
E leighmanagement@aol.com

LESLIE Sasha MANAGEMENT
In Association with Allsorts Drama for Children
34 Crediton Road, London NW10 3DU   T/F 020 8969 3249
E sasha@allsortsdrama.com

LIME ACTORS AGENCY & MANAGEMENT LTD
Contact: Georgina Andrew. By Post. Accepts Showreels
Nemesis House, 1 Oxford Court
Bishopsgate, Manchester M2 3WQ
F 0161 228 6727   T 0161 236 0827
E georgina@limemanagement.co.uk
W www.limemanagement.tv

LINKSIDE AGENCY
Contact: By Post. 2 Agents represent 40 Performers
Dancers. Musicals. Singers. Stage. Television
21 Poplar Road, Leatherhead, Surrey KT22 8SF
F 01372 378398   T 01372 802374
E linkside_agency@yahoo.co.uk

LINTON MANAGEMENT
3 The Rock, Bury BL9 0JP
F 0161 761 1999   T 0161 761 2020
E carol@linton.tv

27-31 Clerkenwell Close, London EC1R 0AT
F 020 7785 7276   T 020 7785 7275
E london@linton.tv

LONDON THEATRICAL
Contact: Paul Pearson
18 Leamore Street, London W6 0JZ   T 020 8748 1478
E agent@londontheatrical.com
W www.londontheatrical.com

LONG Eva AGENTS
Contact: By Post/e-mail. 2 Agents represent 30 Performers
Commercials. Corporate. Film. Musicals. Radio. Singers
Stage. Television. Voice Overs
107 Station Road, Earls Barton
Northants NN6 0NX
F 01604 811921   M 07736 700849
E evalongagents@yahoo.co.uk
W www.evalongagents.co.uk

LONGRUN ARTISTES AGENCY
Contact: Gina Long, Irene Wernli. By e-mail
3 Agents represent 120 Clients
Marylebone Dance Studio
12 Lisson Grove
London NW1 6TS   T 020 8316 6662
E gina@longrunartistes.co.uk
W www.longrunartistes.co.uk

LOOKALIKES
Contact: Susan Scott
106 Tollington Park
London N4 3RB   T 020 7281 8029
E susan@lookalikes.info
W www.lookalikes.info

LOOKS
Contact: By Post/e-mail/Telephone. 200 Performers
Commercials. Corporate. Modelling. Presenters
Walk-on & Supporting Artists
PO Box 42783, London N2 0UF
F 020 8442 9190   T 020 8341 4477
E lookslondonltd@btconnect.com
W www.lookslondon.com

LOVETT LOGAN ASSOCIATES
Formerly PLA. PMA Member
2 York Place, Edinburgh EH1 3EP
F 0131 478 7070   T 0131 478 7878
E edinburgh@lovettlogan.com
W www.lovettlogan.com

40 Margaret Street
London W1G 0JH
F 020 7495 6411   T 020 7495 6400
E london@lovettlogan.com

LSW PROMOTIONS
PO Box 31855, London SE17 3XP   T/F 020 7793 9755
E londonswo@hotmail.com

LUXFACTOR GROUP (UK) THE
Personal Manager. Contact: Michael D. Finch. By e-mail
1 Agent represents 20+ Performers. Creatives. Presenters
Television. Walk-on & Supporting Artists
Fleet Place, 12 Nelson Drive
Petersfield, Hampshire GU31 4SJ
F 0845 3700588   T 0845 3700589
E info@luxfactor.co.uk
W www.luxfactor.co.uk

LYNE Dennis AGENCY
PMA Member
503 Holloway Road, London N19 4DD
F 020 7272 4790   T 020 7272 5020
E info@dennislyne.com

MA9 MODEL MANAGEMENT
New Bond House, 124 New Bond Street
London W1S 1DX   T 020 7096 1191
E info@ma9models.com
W www.ma9models.com

CARL PROCTOR PHOTOGRAPHY
www.carlproctorphotography.com

Jane Horrocks   Peter James   Emma Choy   Craig Blake   Karina Sugden

t: 07956 283340   e: carlphotos@btconnect.com

MACFARLANE CHARD ASSOCIATES LTD
PMA Member
33 Percy Street, London W1T 2DF
F 020 7636 7751   T 020 7636 7750
E enquiries@macfarlane-chard.co.uk
W www.macfarlane-chard.co.uk

MACFARLANE CHARD ASSOCIATES IRELAND
7 Adelaide Street
Dun Laoghaire, Co Dublin, Ireland
F 00 353 1 663 8649   T 00 353 1 663 8646
E derick@macfarlane-chard.ie

MACFARLANE DOYLE ASSOCIATES
125 Hoole Road, Chester CH2 3NW   T/F 01244 347091
E ross.macfarlane@btinternet.com
W www.macfarlanedoyle.com

MACNAUGHTON LORD REPRESENTATION
PMA Member. Choreographers. Composers. Designers
Directors. Lighting Designers. Lyricists. Musical Directors
Writers
Unit 10, The Broomhouse Studios
50 Sulivan Road, London SW6 3DX
F 020 7371 7563   T 020 7384 9517
E info@mlrep.com   W www.mlrep.com

MAIDA VALE SINGERS
Contact: Christopher Dee. Singers for Recordings, Theatre
Film, Radio & Television
7B Lanhill Road, Maida Vale, London W9 2BP
M 07889 153145   T/F 020 7266 1358
E maidavalesingers@cdtenor.freeserve.co.uk
W www.maidavalesingers.co.uk

Claire Foy   John McGuire   Freema Agyeman

SIMON ANNAND
PHOTOGRAPHER

www.simonannand.com   07884 446 776

Concessions available

Author of
THE HALF,
Actors Preparing
to go on Stage

25 years' experience
NT, RSC, Royal Court

NIC KNIGHT MANAGEMENT *in association with* **THE ANNA SCHER THEATRE**

23 Buckler Court
Eden Grove
London N7 8EF
T: +44 (0) 203 093 5422
E: enquiries@nicknightmanagement.com

www.nicknightmanagement.com

Specialist Representation • Film
Television • Theatre • Commercials
*Over 40 Years
drama training
experience (AST)*

www.annaschertheatre.com

MAIN ARTISTS
*Personal Manager. Boutique Agency. Contact: Stephen
Anderson. Commercials. Film. Stage. Television*
1 Union Street
Brighton BN1 1HA
F 0870 1280003   T 01273 724001
E stephen@mainartists.com

MAITLAND MANAGEMENT
Personal Manager. Contact: Anne Skates
21A Harley Place
London W1G 8LZ
F 01372 466229   T 020 7636 7492
E maitmus@aol.com
W www.maitlandmanagement.com

MAMBAB AGENCY
Contact: Nichola D. Hartwell
PO Box 51261, Kennington
London SE11 4SW
M 07868 728132   T 020 7793 4848
E contacts@mrandmissblackandbeautiful.com
W www.mrandmissblackandbeautiful.com

MANAGEMENT 2000
*Contact: Jackey Gerling. By Post
Accepts Showreels
1 Agent represents 40 Performers
Commercials. Film. Radio. Stage. Television*
11 Well Street, Treuddyn
Flintshire CH7 4NH   T/F 01352 771231
E jackey@management-2000.co.uk
W www.management-2000.co.uk

MANS Johnny PRODUCTIONS LTD
PO Box 196, Hoddesdon
Herts EN10 7WG
F 01992 470516   T 01992 470907
E johnnymansagent@aol.com
W www.johnnymansproductions.co.uk

MARCUS & McCRIMMON MANAGEMENT
*Personal Manager. Contact: By Post
Accepts Showreels
3 Agents represent 60 Performers
Film. Musicals. Stage. Television*
1 Heathgate Place
75 Agincourt Road
Hampstead, London NW3 2NU
F 020 3012 3478   T 020 3012 3477
E info@marcusandmccrimmon.com
W www.marcusandmccrimmon.com

MARKHAM AGENCY THE
*PMA Member. Personal Manager. Contact: John Markham
By Post/e-mail. Accepts Showreels/Voicereels*
405 Strand, London WC2R ONE
F 020 7836 4222   T 020 7836 4111
E info@themarkhamagency.com
W www.themarkhamagency.com

MARKHAM, FROGGATT & IRWIN
*Personal Manager. PMA Member
Contact: By Post*
4 Windmill Street, London W1T 2HZ
F 020 7637 5233   T 020 7636 4412
E admin@markhamfroggattirwin.com
W www.markhamfroggattirwin.com

MARLOWES AGENCY
HMS President, Victoria Embankment
Blackfriars, London EC4Y 0HJ   T 020 7193 7227
E miles@marlowes.eu
W www.marlowes.eu

MARLOWES DANCERS & MUSICAL THEATRE AGENCY
HMS President, Victoria Embankment
Blackfriars, London EC4Y 0HJ   T 020 7193 4484
E mitch@marlowes.eu
W www.marlowes.eu

MARSH Billy ASSOCIATES LTD
PMA Member
76A Grove End Road, St John's Wood
London NW8 9ND
F 020 7449 6933   T 020 7449 6930
E talent@billymarsh.co.uk
W www.billymarsh.co.uk

MARSH Billy DRAMA LTD
Actors & Actresses
20 Garrick Street, London WC2E 9BT
F 020 3178 5488   T 020 3178 4748
E info@billymarshdrama.co.uk

MARSHALL Scott PARTNERS LTD
*PMA Member
Contact: Amanda Evans, Suzy Kenway, Manon Palmer*
2nd Floor, 15 Little Portland Street
London W1W 8BW
F 020 7636 9728   T 020 7637 4623
W www.scottmarshall.co.uk

MARTIN Carol PERSONAL MANAGEMENT
19 Highgate West Hill, London N6 6NP
F 020 8340 4868   T 020 8348 0847

MASTERS ENTERTAINMENTS
47 Staunton Street, Portsmouth PO1 4EJ   M 07709 527753
E soniamaster@aol.com
W www.masterentertainments.com

MAY John
46 Golborne Road, London W10 5PR   T 020 8962 1606
E john@johnmaymanagement.co.uk
W www.johnmaymanagement.co.uk

MAYER Cassie LTD
PMA Member
5 Old Garden House, The Lanterns
Bridge Lane, London SW11 3AD
F 020 7350 0890   T 020 7350 0880
E info@cassiemayerltd.co.uk

Scott Harrison-Jones Photography
T. 07885752868

MBA (MAHONEY BANNON ASSOCIATES)
Formerly John Mahoney Management
Concorde House, 18 Margaret Street, Brighton BN2 1TS
F 01273 685971   T 01273 685970
E info@mbagency.co.uk
W www.mbagency.co.uk

McDONAGH Melanie MANAGEMENT (ACADEMY OF PERFORMING ARTS & CASTING AGENCY)
14 Apple Tree Way, Oswaldtwistle
Accrington, Lancashire BB5 0FB
M 07909 831409   T 01254 392560
E mcdonaghmgt@aol.com
W www.mcdonaghmanagement.co.uk

McKINNEY MACARTNEY MANAGEMENT LTD
Technicians
Gable House, 18-24 Turnham Green Terrace
London W4 1QP   T 020 8995 4747
E mail@mckinneymacartney.com
W www.mckinneymacartney.com

McLEAN Bill PERSONAL MANAGEMENT
Personal Manager. Contact: By Post
23B Deodar Road, London SW15 2NP   T 020 8789 8191

McLEAN-WILLIAMS MANAGEMENT
PMA Member
14 Rathbone Place, London W1T 1HT
F 020 7631 3739   T 020 7631 5385
E info@mclean-williams.com
W www.mclean-williams.com

McLEOD AGENCY LTD THE
Unit 9, Bridge View Office Park
Henry Boot Way, Priory Park East, Hull HU4 7DW
F 01482 353635   T 01482 565444
E info@mcleodagency.co.uk
W www.mcleodagency.co.uk

McREDDIE Ken ASSOCIATES LTD
Personal Manager. PMA Member. Contact: By Post only
11 Connaught Place, London W2 2ET
F 020 7734 6530   T 020 7439 1456
E email@kenmcreddie.com
W www.kenmcreddie.com

MCS LTD
47 Dean Street, London W1D 5BE   T 020 7734 9995
E info@mcsagency.co.uk
W www.mediacelebrityservices.co.uk

MEDIA LEGAL
Existing Clients only
Town House, 5 Mill Pond Close
Sevenoaks, Kent TN14 5AW   T 01732 460592

METROPOLITAN MANAGEMENT
24 Beehive Lane
Basildon SS14 2LG   T 020 7193 5978
E info@dan-blumenau.com
W www.dan-blumenau.com

MF MANAGEMENT LTD
Drury House, 34-43 Russell Street
London WC2B 5HA   T 020 3291 2929
E mfmall@mfmanagement.com

MGA MANAGEMENT
1 Warwick Row
London SW1E 5ER   T 020 7808 7094
E management@themgacompany.com
W www.themgacompany.com

The MGA Company
1 St Colme Street
Edinburgh EH11 2RZ   T 0131 466 9392
E info@themgacompany.com

MIME THE GAP
Mime Artistes. Physical Comedy Specialists
23 Manor Place
Staines
Middlesex TW18 1AE   M 07970 685982
E richard@mimethegap.com
W www.mimethegap.com

MINT MANAGEMENT
Upper Chance
Churn Estate, Blewbury
Didcot, Oxon OX11 9HA
M 07792 107644   T 01235 851165
E lisinewent123@btinternet.com

MITCHELL MAAS McLENNAN
MPA Offices
29 Thomas Street
Woolwich, London SE18 6HU
M 07540 995802   T/F 020 8301 8745
E agency@mmm2000.co.uk
W www.mmm2000.co.uk

MLR
See MACNAUGHTON LORD REPRESENTATION

MONDI ASSOCIATES LTD
Personal Manager. Contact: Michelle Sykes
By Post/e-mail
Accepts Showreels/Voicereels
1 Agent represents 60 Clients. Children
Commercials. Corporate. Dancers. Film. Musicals
Presenters. Radio. Singers
Stage. Television. Voice Overs
Unit 3 O, Cooper House
2 Michael Road
London SW6 2AD   M 07817 133349
E info@mondiassociates.com
W www.mondiassociates.com

MONTAGU ASSOCIATES
Ground Floor
13 Hanley Road
London N4 3DU   T 020 7263 3883
E montagus@btconnect.com

 **AM LONDON**   **ACTORS HEADSHOTS**

SIMON PEGG

CONNIE FISHER

SELINA SUFI

John Barrowman headshot
JOHN BARROWMAN

CATHERINE TATE

PETER SERAFINOWICZ

CARINA BIRRELL

CHRIS DALEY

MODEL, DANCE & PERFORMER PORTFOLIOS

WWW.AM-LONDON.COM

 STUDIO: 020 7193 1868   MOBILE: 07974 188 105

MOORE Jakki MANAGEMENT
Halecote, St Lukes Road
Haverigg, Cumbria LA18 4HB
M 07967 612784　　　　　　　　　　　　T 01229 776389
E jakki@jakkimoore.com

MORELLO CHERRY ACTORS AGENCY
T 020 7993 5538
E info@mcaa.co.uk
W www.mcaa.co.uk

MORGAN & GOODMAN
271 Regent Street, London W1B 2ES　　　T 020 7437 1383
E mg1@btinternet.com

MORGAN Lee MANAGEMENT
Cameo House, 11 Bear Street
Leicester Square, London WC2H 7AS
F 020 7839 1900　　　　　　　　　　　　T 020 7766 5234
E leemorganmgnt@aol.com
W www.leemorganmanagement.co.uk

MORRIS Andrew MANAGEMENT
124 Cole Green Lane, Welwyn Garden City
Herts AL7 3JD
M 07918 636775　　　　　　　　　　　　T/F 020 7482 0451
E agentmorris1@yahoo.com

MORSE & du FER MANAGEMENT
17 Thistlefield Close, Bexley
Kent DA5 3GJ　　　　　　　　　　　　　T 020 8752 0172
E morsedufer@hotmail.co.uk
W www.morsedufer.com

MOUTHPIECE MANAGEMENT
PO Box 145, Inkberrow
Worcestershire WR7 4ZG
M 07900 240904　　　　　　　　　　　　T 01527 850149
E karin@mouthpiecemanagement.co.uk
W www.mouthpiecemanagement.co.uk

MPC ENTERTAINMENT
Contact: By e-mail/Telephone
MPC House 15-16 Maple Mews, Maida Vale
London NW6 5UZ
F 020 7624 4220　　　　　　　　　　　　T 020 7624 1184
E mpc@mpce.com
W www.mpce.com

MR MANAGEMENT
PMA Member
29 Belton Road, Brighton BN2 3RE　　　　T/F 01273 232381
E info@mrmanagement.net
W www.mrmanagement.net

MRS JORDAN ASSOCIATES
Contact: By e-mail only. 2 Agents represent 35 Performers
Commercials. Creatives. Film. Stage. Television
Mayfair House, 14-18 Heddon Street
London W1B 4DA   T 020 3151 0710
E info@mrsjordan.co.uk
W www.mrsjordan.co.uk

MUGSHOTS AGENCY
M 07880 896911
E becky@mugshots.co.uk

MURPHY Elaine ASSOCIATES
Suite 1, 50 High Street, London E11 2RJ
F 020 8989 1400   T 020 8989 4122
E elaine@elainemurphy.co.uk

MUSIC INTERNATIONAL
13 Ardilaun Road, London N5 2QR
F 020 7226 9792   T 020 7359 5183
E neil@musicint.co.uk
W www.musicint.co.uk

MV MANAGEMENT
Clients must be graduates of Mountview Academy of
Theatre Arts. Co-operative of 25 Performers
Ralph Richardson Memorial Studios, Kingfisher Place
Clarendon Road, London N22 6XF
F 020 8829 1050   T 020 8889 8231
E theagency@mountview.org.uk

MYERS MANAGEMENT
63 Fairfields Crescent
London NW9 0PR   T/F 020 8204 8941
E judy_hepburn@hotmail.com

MY SPIRIT PRODUCTIONS LTD
Mystics. Psychics
Maidstone TV Studios, Vinters Park
Maidstone ME14 5NZ   T 01634 323376
E info@myspirittv.com
W www.myspiritradio.com

NARROW ROAD COMPANY THE
PMA Member
3rd Floor, 76 Neal Street
London WC2H 9PL
F 020 7379 9777   T 020 7379 9598
E agents@narrowroad.co.uk

182 Brighton Road, Coulsdon
Surrey CR5 2NF
F 020 8763 2558   T 020 8763 9895
E richardireson@narrowroad.co.uk

2nd Floor
Grampian House, 144 Deansgate
Manchester M3 3EE   T/F 0161 833 1605
E manchester@narrowroad.co.uk

NEALON Steve ASSOCIATES
186 Courtlands Avenue
Lee, London SE12 8JD
F 020 8852 2558   T 020 8463 9238
E steve@stevenealonassociates.co.uk
W www.stevenealonassociates.co.uk

NELSON BROWNE MANAGEMENT LTD
40 Bowling Green Lane, London EC1R 0NE
M 07796 891388   T 020 7970 6010
E enquiries@nelsonbrowne.com
W www.nelsonbrowne.com

NEVS AGENCY
Regal House, 198 King's Road
London SW3 5XP
F 020 7352 6068   T 020 7352 4886
E getamodel@nevs.co.uk
W www.nevs.co.uk

NEW CASEY AGENCY
The Annexe, 129 Northwood Way
Northwood HA6 1RF   T 01923 823182

NEW FACES LTD
Personal Manager. Contact: Val Horton, Tania Patti
By Post/e-mail. Accepts Showreels. 3 Agents represent 50
Performers. Children. Commercials. Film. Stage. Television
3rd Floor, The Linen Hall
162-168 Regent Street, London W1B 5TD
F 020 7287 5481   T 020 7439 6900
E info@newfacestalent.co.uk
W www.newfacestalent.co.uk

NFD - THE FILM & TV AGENCY
PO Box 76
Leeds LS25 9AG   T/F 01977 681949
E info@film-tv-agency.com
W www.film-tv-agency.com

NICHOLSON Jackie ASSOCIATES
Personal Manager. Contact: By Post
Suite 44, 2nd Floor
Morley House
320 Regent Street, London W1B 3BD
F 020 7580 4489   T 020 7580 4422
E jnalondon@aol.com

N M MANAGEMENT
16 St Alfege Passage
Greenwich
London SE10 9JS   T 020 8853 4337
E nmmanagement@hotmail.com

NMP MANAGEMENT
Personal Manager. Contact: By e-mail. 2 Agents represent 10
Performers. Comedians. Corporate. Presenters. Television
8 Blenheim Court, Brookway
Leatherhead, Surrey KT22 7NA
F 01372 374417   T 01372 361004
E management@nmp.co.uk
W www.nmpmanagement.co.uk

NMS AGENCY THE
Contact: By e-mail only
10 Oakview Close, Watford
Hertfordshire WD19 4RA   M 07944 854656
E thenmsagency@live.co.uk

NORTH OF WATFORD ACTORS AGENCY
Co-operative
Bridge Mill, Hebden Bridge
West Yorks HX7 8EX
F 01422 846503   T 01422 845361
E info@northofwatford.com
W www.northofwatford.com

NORTH WEST ACTORS - NIGEL ADAMS
Personal Manager. Contact: Nigel Adams. By Post. Accepts
Showreels/Voicereels. Commercials. Film. Radio. Stage
Television
36 Lord Street, Radcliffe
Manchester M26 3BA   T/F 0161 724 6625
E nigel.adams@northwestactors.co.uk
W www.northwestactors.co.uk

NORTHERNALLSTARS.CO.UK
2 Prince's Gardens, Sunderland SR6 8DF   M 07980 507690
E info@northernallstars.co.uk
W www.northernallstars.co.uk

NORTHERN LIGHTS MANAGEMENT LTD
Dean Clough Mills, Halifax
West Yorks HX3 5AX
F 01422 330101   T 01422 382203
E northern.lights@virgin.net

NORTHERN PROFESSIONALS
Action Safety. Boat & Diving Equipment Hire
Casting Technicians
21 Cresswell Avenue
North Shields
Tyne & Wear NE29 9BQ   T 0191 257 8635
E bill@northernprocasting.co.uk
W www.northernprocasting.co.uk

NORTHERN STAR ACTORS AGENCY
332 Royal Exchange
Manchester M2 7BR   T 0161 832 3535
E mark@northernstaractors.co.uk
W www.northernstaractors.co.uk

NORTHONE MANAGEMENT
CPMA Member
HG08 Aberdeen Studios, Highbury Grove
London N5 2EA   T/F 020 7359 9666
E actors@northone.co.uk
W www.northone.co.uk

NS ARTISTES MANAGEMENT
10 Claverdon House, Holly Bank Road
Billesley, Birmingham B13 0QY
M 07870 969577   T 0121 684 5607
E nsmanagement@fsmail.net
W www.nsartistes.co.uk

NSM (Natasha Stevenson Management Ltd)
Personal Manager. PMA Member. Contact: By Post/e-mail/
Telephone. 3 Agents. Commercials. Film. Stage. Television
Studio 7C, Clapham North Arts Centre
Voltaire Road, London SW4 6DH
F 020 7720 5565   T 020 7720 3355
E inbox@natashastevenson.co.uk
W www.natashastevenson.co.uk

NUMBER ONE MODEL AGENCY
The Barn, Pasture Farm
Coventry Road, Solihull B92 0HH   T 01675 443900
E info@numberonemodelagency.co.uk
W www.numberonemodelagency.co.uk

HARRY RAFIQUE PHOTOGRAPHY
07986 679 498
www.hr-photographer.co.uk

NYLAND MANAGEMENT
93 Kinder Road, Hayfield SK22 2LE   T 01663 745629
E casting@nylandmanagement.com
W www.nylandmanagement.com

OBJECTIVE TALENT MANAGEMENT
3rd Floor, Riverside Building
County Hall, Westminster Bridge Road
London SE1 7PB   T/F 020 7202 2300
E info@objectivetalentmanagement.com
W www.objectivetalentmanagement.com

OFF THE KERB PRODUCTIONS
3rd Floor, Hammer House
113-117 Wardour Street, London W1F 0UN
F 020 7437 0647   T 020 7437 0607
E info@offthekerb.co.uk
W www.offthekerb.co.uk

OI OI AGENCY
*2 Agents represent 400 Performers. Adults. Children
Commercials. Corporate. Dancers. Disabled. Film. Modelling
Musicals. Presenters. Radio. Singers. Stage. Television
Voice Overs*
The Coach House, Pinewood Film Studios
Pinewood Road, Iver Heath, Buckinghamshire SL0 0NH
F 01753 655622   T 01753 852326
E info@oioi.org.uk
W www.oioi.org.uk

ONE MAKE UP/ONE PHOTOGRAPHIC LTD
4th Floor, 48 Poland Street
London W1F 7ND
F 020 7287 2313   T 020 7287 2311
E info@onemakeup.com
W www.onemakeup.com

jack ladenburg
photographer

julian rhind-tutt

victoria kruger

07932 053 743

www.jackladenburg.co.uk   info@jackladenburg.co.uk

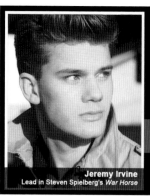

OPERA & CONCERT ARTISTS
Musicals. Opera
75 Aberdare Gardens
London NW6 3AN
F 020 7372 3537   T 020 7328 3097
E enquiries@opera-and-concert-artists.co.uk

ORDINARY PEOPLE
Actors. Modelling
16 Camden Road, London NW1 9DP
F 020 7267 5677   T 020 7267 7007
E info@ordinarypeople.co.uk
W www.ordinarypeople.co.uk

OREN ACTORS MANAGEMENT
CPMA Member
Chapter Arts Centre
Market Road
Cardiff CF5 1QE   T 0845 4591420
E info@orenactorsmanagement.co.uk
W www.orenactorsmanagement.co.uk

ORIENTAL CASTING AGENCY LTD
Contact: Peggy Sirr. By e-mail/Telephone
Accepts Showreels/Voicereels
1 Agent represents 200+ Performers Afro/Asian Artists
22 Wontford Road
Purley, Surrey CR8 4BL   T 020 8660 0101
E peggy.sirr@btconnect.com
W www.orientalcasting.com

ORPIN ASSOCIATES
Studio 54, 77 Beak Street
London W1F 9DB   T 01462 672305
E enquiries@orpinassociates.com
W www.orpinassociates.com

ORR MANAGEMENT AGENCY
1st Floor
147-149 Market Street
Farnworth
Greater Manchester BL4 8EX   T 01204 579842
E barbara@orrmanagement.co.uk
W www.orrmanagement.co.uk

OTTO PERSONAL MANAGEMENT LTD
Personal Manager. CPMA Member
S.I.F., 5 Brown Street
Sheffield S1 2BS
F 0114 279 5225   T 0114 275 2592
E admin@ottopm.co.uk
W www.ottopm.co.uk

O.U.R.
Poplar Dock Marina
Broadwalk Place
London E14 5SH   M 07977 302250
E info@our-company.co.uk
W www.our-company.co.uk

PADBURY David ASSOCIATES
44 Summerlee Avenue
Finchley
London N2 9QP   T/F 020 8883 1277
E info@davidpadburyassociates.com
W www.davidpadburyassociates.com

PAN ARTISTS AGENCY LTD
Cornerways, 34 Woodhouse Lane
Sale, Cheshire M33 4JX
M 07890 715115   T 0800 6349147
E panartists@btconnect.com
W www.panartists.co.uk

PARADIGM ARTIST AGENCY LLP
35 St Josephs Court
Llanelli
Carmarthenshire SA15 1NR
M 07792 761133   M 07814 375320
E info@paradigmartistagency.com
W www.paradigmartistagency.com

PARAMOUNT INTERNATIONAL MANAGEMENT
30 Performers. International Comedians
Talbot House
204-226 Imperial Drive
Harrow, Middlesex HA2 7HH
F 020 8868 6475   T 020 8429 3179
E mail@ukcomedy.com
W www.ukcomedy.com

PARKER Cherry MANAGEMENT (RSM)
See RSM (Cherry Parker Management)

PARSONS Cary MANAGEMENT
Set, Costume & Lighting Designers, Directors &
Choreographers
Goldicote Lodge, Goldicote Road
Loxley, Warwick CV35 9LF   T 01789 840453
E carylparsons@gmail.com

PAYNE MANAGEMENT
Contact: Natalie Payne. Accepts Showreels on request
T 0161 408 6715 (Manchester)   T 020 7193 1156 (London)
E agent@paynemanagement.co.uk
W www.paynemanagement.co.uk

ACTORS
SINGERS
DANCERS
CHILDREN

B/W
COLOUR

RETOUCHING

ONLINE
BOOKING

ONLINE
PORTFOLIO

SAME DAY
TURNAROUND

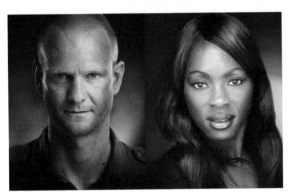

07946323631

KOVAL
STUDIO

www.piotrkowalik.co.uk

P B J MANAGEMENT LTD
Personal Manager. PMA Member. Contact: Janette Linden
By e-mail. Accepts Showreels. 11 Agents represent 115
Performers. Comedians. Commercials. Corporate. Presenters
Radio. Stage. Television. Voice Overs. Walk-on & Supporting
Artists. Writers
5 Soho Square, London W1D 3QA
F 020 7287 1191   T 020 7287 1112
E general@pbjmgt.co.uk
W www.pbjmgt.co.uk

PC THEATRICAL, MODEL & CASTING AGENCY
Large Database of Twins
10 Strathmore Gardens, Edgware, Middlesex HA8 5HJ
F 020 8933 3418   T 020 8381 2229
E twinagy@aol.com
W www.twinagency.com

PELHAM ASSOCIATES
Personal Manager. PMA Member. Contact: Peter Cleall
The Media Centre
9-12 Middle Street, Brighton BN1 1AL
F 01273 202492   T 01273 323010
E petercleall@pelhamassociates.co.uk
W www.pelhamassociates.co.uk

PEMBERTON ASSOCIATES LTD
PMA Member. Contact: Barbara Pemberton. By Post/e-mail
Showreels on request. 5 Agents represent 130 Performers
Film. Musicals. Radio. Singers. Stage. Television. Voice Overs
193 Wardour Street
London W1F 8ZF
F 020 7734 2522   T 020 7734 4144
E general@pembertonassociates.com
W www.pembertonassociates.com

PEMBERTON ASSOCIATES LTD
PMA Member. Contact: Barbara Pemberton. By Post/e-mail
Showreels on request. 5 Agents represent 130 Performers
Film. Musicals. Radio. Singers. Stage. Television. Voice Overs
Express Networks
1 George Leigh Street
Manchester M4 5DL
F 0161 235 8442 T 0161 235 8440
E general@pembertonassociates.com
W www.pembertonassociates.com

PEOPLEMATTER.TV
40 Bowling Green Lane
Clerkenwell, London EC1R 0NE
F 020 7415 7074 T 020 7415 7070
E tony@peoplematter.tv
W www.peoplematter.tv

PEPPERPOT PROMOTIONS
Bands
Suite 20B
20-22 Orde Hall Street
London WC1N 3JW
F 020 7405 6799 T 020 7405 9108
E chris@pepperpot.co.uk

PERFORMANCE ACTORS AGENCY
Co-operative. CPMA Member
137 Goswell Road, London EC1V 7ET
F 020 7251 3974 T 020 7251 5716
E info@performanceactors.co.uk
W www.performanceactors.co.uk

PERFORMING ARTS
Personal Manager. PMA Member. Contact: By Post/e-mail
2 Agents represent 30 Performers
Creative Team
Members only
6 Windmill Street, London W1T 2JB
F 020 7631 4631 T 020 7255 1362
E info@performing-arts.co.uk
W www.performing-arts.co.uk

PERRYMENT Mandy - CAREY Roger ASSOCIATES
M 07790 605191 T 01932 223861
E mail@mandyperryment.com

PERSONAL APPEARANCES
20 North Mount
1147-1161 High Road
Whetstone N20 0PH T/F 020 8343 7748
E patsy@personalappearances.biz
W www.personalappearances.biz

PHD ARTISTS
Contact: Paul Harris® on behalf of Pineapple Agency
24 Montana Gardens
Sutton
Surrey SM1 4FP T/F 020 7241 6601
E office@phdartists.com
W www.phdartists.com

PHILLIPS Frances
Personal Manager. PMA Member
Contact: Frances Zealander-Phillips. By e-mail
2 Agents represent 40 Performers
89 Robeson Way, Borehamwood
Hertfordshire WD6 5RY
M 07957 334328 T 020 8953 0303
E frances@francesphillips.co.uk
W www.francesphillips.co.uk

PHPM (Philippa Howell Personal Management)
Contact: By e-mail only
Commercials. Film. Musicals. Stage. Television
405 The Strand, London WC2R 0NE
M 07790 969024 T020 7836 2837
E philippa@phpm.co.uk
W www.phpm.co.uk

184 Bradway Road
Sheffield S17 4QX T 0114 235 3663

PHYSICK Hilda
Personal Manager. Contact: By Post
78 Temple Sheen Road, London SW14 7RR
F 020 8876 5561 T 020 8876 0073

PICCADILLY MANAGEMENT
Personal Manager
23 New Mount Street
Manchester M4 4DE
F 0161 953 4001 T 0161 953 4057
E info@piccadillymanagement.com
W www.piccadillymanagement.com

PINEAPPLE AGENCY
Montgomery House
159-161 Balls Pond Road, London N1 4BG
F 020 7241 3006 T 020 7241 6601
E pineapple.agency@btconnect.com
W www.pineappleagency.com

PINK OLIVE AGENCY
3 Wigmore Road, Worthing
West Sussex BN14 9HJ T 01903 205898
E lyn@pinkoliveagency.com
W www.pinkoliveagency.com

PLA
See LOVETT LOGAN ASSOCIATES

PLAIN JANE
E info@plain-jane.co.uk M 07813 667319
W www.plain-jane.co.uk

PLATER Janet MANAGEMENT LTD
Contact: Janet Plater. By Post. Accepts Showreels
Commercials. Film. Radio. Stage. Television
D Floor, Milburn House
Dean Street
Newcastle upon Tyne NE1 1LF T 0191 221 2490
E magpie@tynebridge.demon.co.uk
W www.janetplatermanagement.co.uk

edward bennett

charlotte whitaker

ɑɯ HEADSHOTS

professional headshots for actors and performers

contact: alex winn
tel: 07816 317 038
www.awheadshots.com

PLATINUM ARTISTS
Stratford House
Hilton, Bridgnorth WV15 5NZ   T 0120 8914 8410
E mail@platinumartists.co.uk
W www.platinumartists.co.uk

PLUNKET GREENE ASSOCIATES
In conjunction with James Sharkey Associates Ltd
Existing Clients only
PO Box 8365, London W14 0GL
F 020 7603 2221   T 020 7603 2227
E lyndatrapnell@compuserve.com

POLLYANNA MANAGEMENT LTD
1 Knighten Street, Wapping
London E1W 1PH   T/F 020 8530 6722
E aliceharwood@talktalk.net   W www.pollyannatheatre.org

POOLE Gordon AGENCY LTD
The Limes, Brockley, Bristol BS48 3BB
F 01275 462252   T 01275 463222
E agents@gordonpoole.com
W www.gordonpoole.com

PORTABLE COMEDY CLUB THE
14 Dover Street, Mayfair, London W1S 4LY
F 020 7281 6520   M 07808 808080
E enquiries@theportablecomedyclub.co.uk
W www.theportablecomedyclub.co.uk

POWER MODEL MANAGEMENT CASTING AGENCY
PO Box 1198, Salhouse
Norwich NR13 6WD   T 01603 777190
E info@powermodel.co.uk
W www.powermodel.co.uk

Dominic O'Regan
Photography

Location	Headshots
Home	Publicity
Studio	Student Discounts

www.dominicoregan.co.uk   07795 560370   dom@dominicoregan.co.uk

| Robert Kilroy-Silk | Ruth Shephard | Anthony Marsh | Michelle C |

Howard Sayer Photographer

www.howardsayer.com   m: 07860 559891   howard@howardsayer.com

POWER PROMOTIONS
PO Box 61, Liverpool L13 0EF
F 0870 7060202   T 0151 230 0070
E tom@powerpromotions.co.uk
W www.powerpromotions.com

PREGNANT PAUSE AGENCY
Pregnant Models, Dancers, Actresses
11 Matham Road
East Molesey KT8 0SX   T 020 8979 8874
E sandy@pregnantpause.co.uk
W www.pregnantpause.co.uk

PRESTON Morwenna MANAGEMENT
49 Leithcote Gardens, London SW16 2UX   T 020 8835 8147
E info@morwennapreston.com
W www.morwennapreston.com

PRICE GARDNER MANAGEMENT
PO Box 59908, London SW16 5QH
F 020 7381 3288   T 020 7610 2111
E info@pricegardner.co.uk
W www.pricegardner.co.uk

PRINCIPAL ARTISTES
Personal Manager. Contact: By Post
4 Paddington Street, Marylebone
London W1U 5QE
F 020 7486 4668   T 020 7224 3414

PROSPECTS ASSOCIATIONS
Sessions. Singers. Voice Overs for Commercials,
Film & Television
28 Magpie Close, Forest Gate
London E7 9DE   T 020 8555 3628
E wasegun@yahoo.co.uk

PURE ACTORS AGENCY & MANAGEMENT LTD
44 Salisbury Road
Manchester M41 0RB
F 0161 746 9886   T 0161 747 2377
E enquiries@pure-management.co.uk
W www.pure-management.co.uk

PVA MANAGEMENT LTD
County House, St Mary's Street
Worcester WR1 1HB
F 01905 610709   T 01905 616100
E post@pva.co.uk
W www.pva.co.uk

QUICK Nina ASSOCIATES
See TAYLOR Brian ASSOCIATES

RAFFLES Tim ENTERTAINMENTS
Personal Manager. 2 Agents represent 9 Performers
Corporate. Cruise Work. Singers. Television
Victoria House
29 Swaythling Road
West End, Southampton SO30 3AG   T/F 023 8046 5843
E info@timrafflesentertainments.co.uk
W www.timrafflesentertainments.co.uk

RAGE MODELS
Tigris House, 256 Edgware Road
London W2 1DS
F 020 7402 0507   T 020 7262 0515
E ragemodels@ugly.org
W www.ugly.org

RAMA GLOBAL LTD
Contact: Rachael Pacey, Martin Arrowsmith. By Post
Accepts Showreels. 1 Agent represents 10 Performers
Children. Commercials. Film. Stage. Television
Huntingdon House, 278-290 Huntingdon Street
Nottingham NG1 3LY
F 0115 948 3696   T 0845 0540255
E admin@rama-global.co.uk
W www.rama-global.co.uk

RANDALL RICHARDSON ACTORS MANAGEMENT
2nd Floor, 145-157 St John Street
London EC1V 4PY
F 0870 7623212   T 020 7060 1645
E mail@randallrichardson.co.uk
W www.randallrichardson.co.uk

RAPID TALENT LTD
5 Vancouver Road, Eastbourne
East Sussex BN23 5BF
M 07980 899156   T 020 7734 5775
E enquiries@rapidtalent.co.uk
W www.rapidtalent.co.uk

RARE TALENT ACTORS MANAGEMENT
Tanzaro House
Ardwick Green North
Manchester M12 6FZ
F 0161 273 4567   T 0161 273 4004
E info@raretalentactors.com
W www.raretalentactors.com

RAVENSCOURT MANAGEMENT
See CORONA MANAGEMENT

RAW AGENCY LTD
Studio 1, Bizzy House
73A Mayplace Road West
Bexleyheath, Kent DA7 4JL
F 0845 5200401   T 0845 5200400
E clients@rawagencyltd.com
W www.rawagencyltd.com

RAY KNIGHT CASTING
See KNIGHT Ray CASTING

RAZZAMATAZZ MANAGEMENT
Personal Manager. Contact: Jill Shirley. By e-mail/Telephone
1 Agent represents 10 Clients. Children. Dancers
Presenters. Singers
204 Holtye Road
East Grinstead
West Sussex RH19 3ES
M 07836 268292   T 01342 301617
E razzamatazzmanagement@btconnect.com

RbA MANAGEMENT LTD
Personal Manager. CPMA Member. Contact: By e-mail
Accepts Showreels/Voicereels. Approx 25 Performers
37-45 Windsor Street
Liverpool L8 1XE   T 0151 708 7273
E info@rbamanagement.co.uk
W www.rbamanagement.co.uk

RBM ACTORS
3rd Floor, 168 Victoria Street
London SW1E 5LB
F 020 7630 6549   T 020 7630 7733
E info@rbmactors.com
W www.rbmactors.com

RDDC MANAGEMENT AGENCY
52 Bridleway
Waterfoot
Rossendale, Lancashire BB4 9DS
M 07900 840758   T 01706 211161
E info@rddc.co.uk
W www.rddc.co.uk

REACTORS AGENCY
CPMA Member. Contact: By Post/e-mail. Accepts Showreels
Co-operative of 23 Performers
1 Eden Quay, Dublin 1, Ireland
F 00 353 1 8783182   T 00 353 1 8786833
E info@reactors.ie
W www.reactors.ie

REAL PEOPLE, REAL TALENT
Fourways House
57 Hilton Street
Manchester M1 2EJ
F 0161 236 1237   T 0161 237 0101
E info@realpeople4u.com
W www.realpeople4u.com

REANIMATOR MANAGEMENT
PMA Member
Now trading as Gielgud Management
The Old Cinema
1st Floor, 59-61 The Broadway
Haywards Heath
West Sussex RH16 3AS
F 01444 447030   T 01444 447020
E management@gielgud.com
W www.reanimator.co.uk

RED&BLACK
E info@red-black.co.uk   M 07722 887277
W www.red-black.co.uk

RED CANYON MANAGEMENT
M 07939 365578   M 07931 381696
E info@redcanyon.co.uk
W www.redcanyon.co.uk

RED DOOR MANAGEMENT
The Pie Factory, 101 Broadway
Media City, Manchester M50 2EQ   T 0161 425 6495
E mail@the-reddoor.co.uk
W www.the-reddoor.co.uk

RED HOT ENTERTAINMENT
Contact: Nicky Raby. By e-mail
Accepts Showreels/Voicereels
4 Agents represent 35 Performers
Commercials Disabled. Film. Musicals
Stage. Television. Writers
6 Farriers Mews, London SE15 3XP
F 020 7635 8988   T 020 7635 0403
E info@redhotentertainment.biz
W www.redhotentertainment.biz

RED ONION AGENCY
Session Fixer for Stage
806 High Street, Leyton
London E10   T 020 8520 3975
E info@redonion.uk.com
W www.redonion.uk.com

REDDIN Joan
Personal Manager. Contact: By Post
Hazel Cottage, Frogg's Island
Wheeler End Common
Bucks HP14 3NL   T 01494 882729

REDROOFS ASSOCIATES
26 Bath Road, Maidenhead
Berkshire SL6 4JT
T 01628 822982 (Holiday Times)   T 01628 674092
E agency@redroofs.co.uk
W www.redroofs.co.uk

REGAN RIMMER MANAGEMENT
Contact: Debbie Rimmer
17 Dallinger Road, London SE12 0TJ
F 020 8851 1517   T 020 8851 1414
E thegirls@regan-rimmer.co.uk

Contact: Leigh-Ann Regan
Ynyslas Uchaf Farm
Blackmill, Bridgend CF35 6DW
F 01656 841815   T 01656 841841
E regan-rimmer@btconnect.com

REGENCY AGENCY
25 Carr Road, Calverley
Leeds LS28 5NE   T 0113 255 8980

REPRESENTATION UPSON EDWARDS
Voice Coaches only
23 Victoria Park Road
Tunstall, Stoke-on-Trent
Staffs ST6 6DX
F 01782 728004   T 01782 827222
E sarah.upson@voicecoach.tv
W www.voicecoach.tv

REYNOLDS Sandra AGENCY
Contact: By e-mail
8 Agents represent 150 Performers. Children
Commercials. Photographic Modelling. Presenters
Bacon House, 35 St Georges Street
Norwich NR3 1DA
F 01603 219825   T 01603 623842
E info@sandrareynolds.co.uk
W www.sandrareynolds.co.uk

Shakespeare House
168 Lavender Hill
London SW11 5TF
F 020 7387 5848   T 020 7387 5858

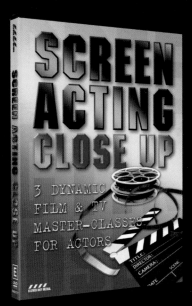
RICHARD STONE PARTNERSHIP THE
See STONE Richard PARTNERSHIP THE

RICHARDS Lisa AGENCY THE
108 Upper Leeson Street, Dublin 4, Ireland
F 00 353 1 6671256   T 00 353 1 6375000
E info@lisarichards.ie
W www.lisarichards.ie

117 Waterloo Road, London SE1 8UL   T 020 7922 5799
E office@lisarichards.co.uk

RICHARDS Stella MANAGEMENT
Contact: Stella Richards, Julia Lintott
Existing Clients only
42 Hazlebury Road, London SW6 2ND
F 020 7731 5082   T 020 7736 7786
E stellagent@aol.com
W www.stellarichards.com

RICHMOND SHARPE AGENCY
Merricourt, Windmill Lane
Appleton, Warrington, Cheshire WA4 5JP   T 0161 858 0049
E info@richmondsharpe.com
W www.richmondsharpe.com

RIDGEWAY MANAGEMENT
Fairley House
Andrews Lane
Cheshunt, Herts EN7 6LB
F 01992 633844   T 01992 633775
E info@ridgewaystudios.co.uk

RISQUE MODEL MANAGEMENT
32 Walter Walk
London HA8 9ES   T 0870 2283890
E info@risquemodel.co.uk
W www.risquemodel.co.uk

ROAR GLOBAL
34-35 Eastcastle Street, London W1W 8DW
F 020 7462 9061   T 020 7462 9060
E info@roarglobal.com
W www.roarglobal.com

ROBERTS Nicola MANAGEMENT
149 Nelson Road, London N8 9RR   T/F 020 8375 5555
E info@nicolarobertsmanagement.com
W www.nicolarobertsmanagement.com

ROGUES & VAGABONDS MANAGEMENT LTD
Personal Manager. CPMA Member
The Print House, 18 Ashwin Street, London E8 3DL
F 020 7249 8564   T 020 7254 8130
E rogues@vagabondsmanagement.com
W www.vagabondsmanagement.com

ROLE MODELS
12 Cressy Road, London NW3 2LY   T 020 7284 4337
E info@rolemodelsagency.com
W www.rolemodelsagency.com

RONAN Lynda PERSONAL MANAGEMENT
Hunters House, 1 Redcliffe Road, London SW10 9NR
F 020 7183 0547   T 020 7183 0017
E lynda@lyndaronan.com
W www.lyndaronan.com

ROOM 3 AGENCY
The Old Chapel, 14 Fairview Drive
Redland, Bristol BS6 6PH
F 0845 5679333   T 0845 5678333
E kate@room3agency.com
W www.room3agency.com

ROSEBERY MANAGEMENT LTD
CPMA Member. Contact: By Post. Accepts Showreels
1 Agent represents 27 Performers
Commercials. Film. Musicals. Stage. Television. Voice Overs
Hoxton Hall, 130 Hoxton Street, London N1 6SH
F 020 7503 0517   T 020 7684 0187
E admin@roseberymanagement.com
W www.roseberymanagement.com

ROSS Frances MANAGEMENT
Personal Manager. Contact: Frances Ross. By e-mail. 1 Agent
represents 20 Performers. Commercials. Corporate. Film
Stage. Television
Higher Leyonne, Golant, Fowey, Cornwall PL23 1LA
M 07918 648330   T/F 01726 832395
E francesross@btconnect.com
W www.francesrossmanagement.co.uk

ROSS BROWN ASSOCIATES
Personal Manager
Rosedale House, Rosedale Road, Richmond, Surrey TW9 2SZ
F 020 8398 4111   T 020 8939 9000
E sandy@rossbrown.eu

ROSSMORE MANAGEMENT
PMA Member
10 Wyndham Place, London W1H 2PU
F 020 7258 0124   T 020 7258 1953
E agents@rossmoremanagement.com
W www.rossmoremanagement.com

ROUGH HANDS AGENCY THE
29 James Street, Epping, Essex, London CM16 6RR
M 07932 573228   T 01992 578835
E roughhandsagency@yahoo.co.uk

ROWE ASSOCIATES
33 Percy Street, London W1T 2DF
M 07887 898220   T/F 01992 308519
E agents@growe.co.uk
W www.growe.co.uk

ROYCE MANAGEMENT
29 Trenholme Road, London SE20 8PP   T/F 020 8778 6861
E office@roycemanagement.co.uk
W www.roycemanagement.co.uk

RPM2
Studio House, Delamare Road, Cheshunt, Herts EN8 9SH
T 0845 3625456   T/F 0845 2415585
E rhino-rpm2@hotmail.com
W www.rhino2-rpm.com

RSM (Cherry Parker Management)
Contact: Cherry Parker
15 The Fairway SS9 4QN
M 07976 547066   T 01702 522647
E info@rsm.uk.net
W www.rsm.uk.net

RUDEYE DANCE AGENCY
The Basement, 73 St John Street
London EC1M 4NJ   T 020 7014 3023
E info@rudeye.com
W www.rudeye.com

SAATCHI MODEL MANAGEMENT LTD
Contact: By Post/e-mail
The Residence, Dale Road, Marple, Cheshire SK6 6NL
E info@saatchimodels.co.uk
W www.saatchimodels.co.uk

www.rosiestillphotography.co.uk
rosie@rosiestillphotography.co.uk
020 8857 6920
07597 946 252

Ami Metcalf

Chris Jarvis

Michael Barber

my own south London studio
very relaxed atmosphere
urgent bookings - no problem
special "Spotlight" and student rates
view your work instantly
whole shoot put onto cd

Christopher Parker

Bella Emberg

SAINOU LTD
PMA Member
10-11 Lower John Street, London W1F 9EB
F 020 7734 1312 T 020 7734 6441
E office@sainou.com W www.sainou.com

SANDERS Loesje LTD
PMA Member. Contact: Loesje Sanders, Jo Probitts. By Post
Choreographers. Designers. Directors. Lighting Designers
Pound Square, 1 North Hill, Woodbridge, Suffolk IP12 1HH
F 01394 388734 T 01394 385260
E loesje@loesjesanders.org.uk W www.loesjesanders.com

SARABAND ASSOCIATES
Contact: Sara Randall, Bryn Newton
265 Liverpool Road, London N1 1LX
F 020 7609 2370 T 020 7609 5313
E brynnewton@btconnect.com

SAROSI Amanda ASSOCIATES
1 Holmbury View, London E5 9EG
F 020 7096 2141 T 020 7993 6008
E amanda@asassociates.biz

SASHAZE TALENT AGENCY
2 Gleannan Close
Omagh, Co. Tyrone BT79 7YA M 07968 762942
E info@sashaze.com W www.sashaze.com

SCA MANAGEMENT
Contact: By Post
Abbey Business Centre
Wellington Way, Brooklands Business Park
Weybridge KT13 0TT
F 01932 268500 T 01932 268375
E agency@sca-management.co.uk
W www.sca-management.co.uk

Theatrical Agents • Actors • Dancers • Singers Models • Presenters • Choreographers

Room 236 Linen Hall 162-168 Regent Street London W1B 5TB
T 020 7734 3356 **F** 020 7494 3787
w www.successagency.co.uk **e** ee@successagency.co.uk

SCHNABL Peter
The Barn House, Cutwell, Tetbury
Gloucestershire GL8 8EB
F 01666 502998   T 01666 502133
E peter.schnabl@virgin.net

SCOTT Russell MANAGEMENT LTD
Cabaret. Jazz. Musical Theatre
PO Box 729, Borehamwood
Herts WD6 9GW   T 0844 5676896
E enquiry@russellscottmanagement.com
W www.russellscottmanagement.com

SCOTT Tim
PO Box 61776, London SW1V 3UX   T/F 020 7828 3824
E timscott@btinternet.com

SCOTT MARSHALL PARTNERS LTD
See MARSHALL Scott PARTNERS LTD

SCOTT-PAUL YOUNG ENTERTAINMENTS LTD
Artists Representation & Promotions
SPY Record Company
Northern Lights House
110 Blandford Road North, Langley
Nr Windsor, Berks SL3 7TA   T/F 01753 693250
E castingdirect@spy-ents.com
W www.spy-artistsworld.com

SCOTT-NIVEN ASSOCIATES
Lower Ground Floor Office
205 Victoria Rise
Clapham, London SW4 0PF   T 020 7884 0375
E theteam@scott-nivenassociates.com
W www.scott-nivenassociates.com

SCRIMGEOUR Donald ARTISTS AGENT
Choreographers. Principal Dancers. Producers
49 Springcroft Avenue, London N2 9JH
F 020 8883 9751   T 020 8444 6248
E vwest@dircon.co.uk
W www.donaldscrimgeour.com

SEARS MANAGEMENT LTD
Melbury House, 34 Southborough Road
Bickley, Kent BR1 2EB
F 01689 862120   T 01689 861859
E linda@searsgroup.co.uk

SECOND SKIN AGENCY
Foxgrove House, School Lane, Seer Green
Beaconsfield, Bucks HP9 2QJ   T/F 01494 730166
E jenny@secondskinagency.com
W www.secondskinagency.com

SEDGWICK Dawn MANAGEMENT
3 Goodwins Court, Covent Garden
London WC2N 4LL
F 020 7240 0415   T 020 7240 0404

SELECT MANAGEMENT
PO Box 748, London NW4 1TT
F 020 8203 8335   M 07956 131494
E mail@selectmanagement.info
W www.selectmanagement.info

SHAPER Susan MANAGEMENT
5 Dovedale Gardens
465 Battersea Park Road
London SW11 4LR
F 020 7350 1802   T 020 7585 1023
E info@susanshapermanagement.com

SHELDRAKE Peter AGENCY
Contact: By e-mail
1 Agent represents 30 Clients
Commercials. Film. Musicals. Stage. Television
139 Lower Richmond Road
London SW14 7HX
M 07758 063663   T 020 8876 9572
E psagent@btinternet.com

SHEPHERD MANAGEMENT LTD
PMA Member
4th Floor, 45 Maddox Street
London W1S 2PE
F 020 7499 7535   T 020 7495 7813
E info@shepherdmanagement.co.uk

SHEPPERD-FOX
5 Martyr Road
Guildford, Surrey GU1 4LF   M 07957 624601
E info@shepperd-fox.co.uk
W www.shepperd-fox.co.uk

SHOWSTOPPERS!
Events Management & Entertainment
42 Foxglove Close
Witham, Essex CM8 2XW
F 01376 510340   T 01376 518486
E mail@showstoppers-group.com
W www.showstoppers-group.com

SHOWTIME CASTINGS
112 Milligan Street
Docklands
London E14 8AS   T 020 7068 6816
E gemma@showtimecastings.com
W www.showtimecastings.com

SIBLEY Claire MANAGEMENT
15 Tweedale WharfMadeley
Shropshire TF7 4EW   T 01952 588951
E info@clairesibleymanagement.co.uk
W www.clairesibleymanagement.co.uk

SIMON & HOW ASSOCIATES
12-18 Hoxton Street, London N1 6NG   T 020 7739 8820
E info@simon-how.com
W www.simon-how.com

SIMPSON FOX ASSOCIATES LTD
PMA Member
Set, Costume and Lighting Designers. Directors
Choreographers
52 Shaftesbury Avenue
London W1D 6LP
F 020 7494 2887   T 020 7434 9167
E info@simpson-fox.com

Mike Cliff *Photography*
www.mikecliffphotography.co.uk 07539 644579
Hoddesdon, Herts. - covering Hertfordshire, Essex, Middlesex & London

SINGER Sandra ASSOCIATES
Personal Manager
Contact: By e-mail
2 Agents represent 60 Performers. Adults. Children
Choreographers. Commercials. Feature Film. Musical Theatre
Television
21 Cotswold Road, Westcliff-on-Sea
Essex SS0 8AA   T 01702 331616
E sandrasingeruk@aol.com
W www.sandrasinger.com

SINGERS INC
9-13 Grape Street, Covent Garden, London WC2H 8ED
F 020 7557 6656   T 020 7557 6650
E chris@inc-space.com
W www.internationalcollective.com

SIRR Peggy
See ORIENTAL CASTING AGENCY LTD

SJ MANAGEMENT
8 Bettridge Road, London SW6 3QD
F 020 7371 0409   T 020 7371 0441
E sj@susanjames.demon.co.uk

SMART MANAGEMENT
Contact: Mario Renzullo
PO Box 64377, London EC1P 1ND   T 020 7837 8822
E smart.management@virgin.net

SMEDLEY Tom MANAGEMENT
28 White House, London SW11 3LJ   M 07515 775220
E tom@tomsmedleymanagement.com
W www.tomsmedleymanagement.com

NOHO STUDIOS

We create you the ultimate ACTOR package you need to sell yourself
We understand how to help you and your agent utilise your skills within your marketing package

Actor headshots, photographs, showreels, voice clips, websites, taping of auditions for US

For competitive prices and a fantastic result please look at our website to see examples of our work

WWW.NOHOSTUDIOS.CO.UK

EMAIL: MICHAEL@NOHOSTUDIOS.CO.UK | TEL: 07889895510

SIMON & HOW ASSOCIATES
LONDON

T - **020 7739 8820**
E - **info@simon-how.com**
W - **www.simon-how.com**

Representing - **Actors** & **Extras for Advertising** | **Theatre** | **Television** | **Film** | **Photographic**

SMILE TALENT
2 Church Walk, Littlebury
Saffron Walden, Essex CB11 4TS
F 01799 529333   T 01799 520000
E info@smiletalent.com
W www.smiletalent.biz

SONGTIME/CHANDLER'S MANAGEMENT
10 Wallis Mews, Leatherhead
Surrey KT22 9DQ   T 01372 372352
E info@songtime.co.uk
W www.songtime.co.uk

SOPHIE'S PEOPLE
Choreographers. Dancers
40 Mexfield Road, London SW15 2RQ
F 0870 7876447   T 0870 7876446
E sophies.people@btinternet.com
W www.sophiespeople.com

S.O.S.
85 Bannerman House, Lawn Lane, London SW8 1UA
M 07740 359770   T 020 7735 5133
E info@sportsofseb.com
W www.sportsofseb.com

SPACE PERSONAL MANAGEMENT
*Personal Manager. Contact: Katherine Stonehouse. By
e-mail. 1 Agent represents 35 Performers. Commercials. Film
Musicals. Stage. Television*
PO Box 64412, London W5 9GU   T 020 8560 7709
E katherine@spacepersonalmanagement.co.uk
W www.spacepersonalmanagement.co.uk

SPEAKERS CIRCUIT LTD THE
After Dinner Speakers
Country Store, The Greer
Frant, East Sussex TN3 9DR
F 01892 750089   T 01892 750131
E speakers-circuit@freenetname.co.uk

SPEAKERS CORNER
*Award Hosts, Comedians, Facilitators & Speakers for
Corporate Events*
207 High Road, London N2 8AN
F 020 8883 7213   T 020 8365 3200
E info@speakerscorner.co.uk
W www.speakerscorner.co.uk

SPLITTING IMAGES LOOKALIKES AGENCY
25 Clissold Court, Greenway Close
London N4 2EZ   T 020 8809 2327
E info@splitting-images.com
W www.splitting-images.com

SPORTS OF SEB LTD
85 Bannerman House, Lawn Lane
London SW8 1UA
M 07740 359770   T 020 7735 5133
E info@sportsofseb.com
W www.sportsofseb.com

SPYKER Paul MANAGEMENT
PO Box 48848, London WC1B 3WZ
F 020 7462 0047   T 020 7462 0046
E belinda@psmlondon.com

SRA PERSONAL MANAGEMENT
Lockhart Road, Cobham
Surrey KT11 2AX   T 01932 863194
E agency@susanrobertsacademy.co.uk

SSA MANAGEMENT
59 Barrington Court, Page's Hill
Muswell Hill, London N10 1QH   M 07904 817229
E shootingstarsacademy@gmail.com
W www.ssamanagement.co.uk

STAFFORD Helen MANAGEMENT
Contact: Helen Stafford
14 Park Avenue, Bush Hill Park
Enfield EN1 2HP
F 020 8372 0611   T 020 8360 6329
E helen.stafford@blueyonder.co.uk

STAGE CENTRE MANAGEMENT LTD
*Co-operative. CPMA Member. Contact: Kelda Holmes
By e-mail. 1 Lead Agent represents 28 Performers
Commercials. Film. Musicals. Stage. Television*
41 North Road, London N7 9DP   T 020 7607 0872
E info@stagecentre.org.uk
W www.stagecentre.org.uk

STAGEWORKS ARTIST MANAGEMENT
32 Brookfield Road, London E9 5AH   T 020 8525 0111

STAGEWORKS WORLDWIDE PRODUCTIONS
*Contact: By e-mail
Cirque Artistes. Corporate. Dancers. Ice-Skaters. Musicals*
525 Ocean Boulevard, Blackpool FY4 1EZ
F 01253 343702   T 01253 342426
E kelly.willars@stageworkswwp.com
W www.stageworkswwp.com

S.T. ARTS MANAGEMENT
Contact: Tarquin Shaw-Young. Actors. Actresses
PO Box 127, Ross On Wye HR9 6WZ
F 0845 4082464   T 0845 4082468
E tarquin@startsmanagement.co.uk
W www.startsmanagement.co.uk

STAR MANAGEMENT LTD
16A Winton Drive
Glasgow G12 0QA — T 0844 8002292
E star@starmanagement.co.uk
W www.starmanagement.co.uk

STENTORIAN
2 Aldersley Avenue
Skipton BD23 2LA — M 07808 353611
E stentorian@btinternet.com
W www.stentorian.freeuk.com

STEVENSON Natasha MANAGEMENT LTD
See NSM (Natasha Stevenson Management Ltd)

STIRLING MANAGEMENT
Contact: Glen Mortimer. By e-mail
Accepts Showreels 3 Agents represent 70 Performers
Commercials. Film Presenters. Stage. Television
490 Halliwell Road
Bolton, Lancashire BL1 8AN
F 0844 4128689 — T 0845 0176500
E admin@stirlingmanagement.co.uk
W www.stirlingmanagement.co.uk

STIVEN CHRISTIE MANAGEMENT
Incorporating The Actors Agency of Edinburgh
1 Glen Street, Tollcross
Edinburgh EH3 9JD
F 0131 228 4645 — T 0131 228 4040
E info@stivenchristie.co.uk
W www.stivenchristie.co.uk

ST. JAMES'S MANAGEMENT
Personal Manager. Existing Clients only
19 Lodge Close, Stoke D'Abernon
Cobham, Surrey KT11 2SG
F 01932 863152 — T 01932 860666
E jlstjames@btconnect.com

STONE Ian ASSOCIATES
Suite 262, Maddison House
226 High Street
Croydon CR9 1DF — T 020 8667 1627

STONE Richard PARTNERSHIP THE
PMA Member
2 Henrietta Street, London WC2E 8PS
F 020 7497 0869 — T 020 7497 0849
E all@thersp.com
W www.thersp.com

STRAIGHT LINE MANAGEMENT
Division of Straight Line Productions
58 Castle Avenue, Epsom
Surrey KT17 2PH
F 020 8393 8079 — T 020 8393 4220
E hilary@straightlinemanagement.co.uk

STRANGE John MANAGEMENT
Film City, 401 Govan Road
Glasgow G51 2DJ
F 0141 440 6769 — T 0141 445 0444
E john@strangemanagement.co.uk
W www.strangemanagement.co.uk

SUCCESS
Room 236, 2nd Floor
Linen Hall, 162-168 Regent Street
London W1B 5TB
F 020 7494 3787 — T 020 7734 3356
E ee@successagency.co.uk
W www.successagency.co.uk

SUMMERS Mark MANAGEMENT
1 Beaumont Avenue, West Kensington
London W14 9LP
T 020 7229 8413
E info@marksummers.com
W www.marksummers.com

SUPERTED
2 Chapel Place, Rivington Street
London EC2A 3DQ
T 05602 406688
E email@superted.com
W www.superted.com

TACT-AGENTS
Zekeringstraat 17, 1014 BM
Amsterdam, The Netherlands
F 00 31 20 570 8989
T 00 31 20 570 8945
E info@tactagents.nl
W www.tactagents.nl

TAKE2 CASTING AGENCY & TALENT MANAGEMENT
28 Beech Park Road
Foxrock, Dublin 18
T 00 353 872563403
E pamela@take2.ie
W www.take2.ie

TALENT4 MEDIA LTD
Studio LG16, Shepherds Building Central
Charecroft Way, London W14 0EH
F 020 7183 4331
T 020 7183 4330
E enquiries@talent4media.com
W www.talent4media.com

TALENT ARTISTS LTD
Contact: Jane Wynn Owen
No Unsolicited Enquiries
59 Sydner Road, London N16 7UF
F 020 7923 2009
T 020 7923 1119
E talent.artists@btconnect.com

TALENT SCOUT THE
19 Edge Road, Dewsbury WF12 0QA
T 01924 464049
E connect@thetalentscout.org
W www.thetalentscout.org

TAVISTOCK WOOD
PMA Member
45 Conduit Street, London W1S 2YN
F 020 7434 2017
T 020 7494 4767
E info@tavistockwood.com
W www.tavistockwood.com

TAYLOR Brian ASSOCIATES
50 Pembroke Road, Kensington
London W8 6NX
F 020 7602 6301
T 020 7602 6141
E briantaylor@nqassoc.freeserve.co.uk

TCA (The Commercial Agency)
12 Evelyn Mansions
Carlisle Place, London SW1P 1NH
F 020 7233 8110
T 020 7233 8100
E mail@thecommercialagency.co.uk
W www.thecommercialagency.co.uk

TCG ARTIST MANAGEMENT LTD
Contact: Kristin Tarry (Director), Johnny Muller, Emma Davidson, Jackie Davis. By Post/e-mail. Accepts Showreels Commercials. Film. Musicals. Stage. Television
14A Goodwin's Court, London WC2N 4LL
F 020 7240 3606
T 020 7240 3600
E info@tcgam.co.uk
W www.tcgam.co.uk

TENNYSON AGENCY THE
10 Cleveland Avenue, Merton Park
London SW20 9EW
T 020 8543 5939
E mail@tennysonagency.co.uk

THOMAS Lisa MANAGEMENT
Contact: By e-mail. 5 Agents represent 30+ Performers
Unit 10, 7 Wenlock Road
London N1 7SL
F 0845 9005522
T 0845 9005511
E lisa@lisathomasmanagement.com
W www.lisathomasmanagement.com

THOMPSON David ASSOCIATES
7 St Peter's Close, London SW17 7UH
M 07889 191093
T 020 8682 3083
E montefioredt@aol.com

THOMSON Mia ASSOCIATES
35 Central Avenue, Polegate
East Sussex BN26 6HA
F 01323 489137
T 01323 486143
E info@miathomsonassociates.co.uk
W www.miathomsonassociates.co.uk

THORNTON AGENCY
Contact: By Post/e-mail/Telephone. 50 Performers. Specialist Agency for Small People. Commercials. Corporate. Film Stage. Television
72 Purley Downs Road
South Croydon CR2 0RB
T/F 020 8660 5588
E jacqui.thorntons@tinyworld.co.uk
W www.diwarfs4hire.com

THRELFALL Katie ASSOCIATES
2A Gladstone Road, London SW19 1QT
F 020 8543 7545
T 020 8543 4344
E info@ktthrelfall.co.uk

THRESH Melody MANAGEMENT ASSOCIATES LTD (MTM)
Quay West at Media City UK
Trafford Wharf Road
Manchester M17 1HH
T 0161 240 2110
E melodythreshmtm@aol.com

TILDSLEY Janice ASSOCIATES
Contact: Kathryn Kirton. By Post
2 Agents represent
80 Performers
47 Orford Road, London E17 9NJ
F 020 8521 1174
T 020 8521 1888
E info@janicetildsleyassociates.co.uk
W www.janicetildsleyassociates.co.uk

TINKER Victoria MANAGEMENT
Non-Acting. Technical
Birchenbridge House
Brighton Road
Mannings Heath, Horsham
West Sussex RH13 6HY   T/F 01403 210653

TOTAL VANITY LTD
15 Walton Way, Aylesbury
Buckinghamshire HP21 7JJ
M 07739 381788   M 07710 780152
E richard.williams@totalvanity.com
W www.totalvanity.com

TRENDS AGENCY & MANAGEMENT LTD
Contact: By e-mail
Commercials. Dancers. Musicals. Singers. Stage
Sullom Lodge, Sullom Side Lane
Garstang PR3 1GH
F 01253 407715   T 0871 2003343
E info@trendsgroup.co.uk
W www.trendsgroup.co.uk

TROIKA
PMA Member
3rd Floor, 74 Clerkenwell Road
London EC1M 5QA
F 020 7490 7642   T 020 7336 7868
E info@troikatalent.com

TTA
59 Belvawney Close
Chelmsford, Essex CM1 2HF   T 01202 526667
E agents@tomorrowstalent.co.uk

TURNSTONE CASTING & ENTERTAINMENT
Hilton Hall, Hilton Lane
Essington, Staffordshire WV11 2BQ
M 07866 211647   T 0845 5570927
E mark_turner85@hotmail.com

TV MANAGEMENTS
Brink House, Avon Castle
Ringwood, Hants BH24 2BL
F 01425 480123   T 01425 475544
E etv@tvmanagements.co.uk

TWINS
See PC THEATRICAL, MODEL & CASTING AGENCY

TWITCH EVENT CHOREOGRAPHY
Contact: By e-mail
Accepts Showreels
2 Agents represent 100 Performers
Circus Performers. Corporate. Dancers. Models
Stage. Television
5 Breakspears Mews, Brockley SE4 1PY
M 07932 656358   M 07747 770816
E info@twitch.uk.com
W www.twitch.uk.com

TWO'S COMPANY
Existing Clients only. Directors. Stage. Writers
244 Upland Road, London SE22 0DN
F 020 8299 3714   T 020 8299 4593
E graham@2scompanytheatre.co.uk

UGLY MODELS
Tigris House, 256 Edgware Road
London W2 1DS
F 020 7402 0507   T 020 7402 5564
E info@ugly.org
W www.ugly.org

lucy-jo hudson

michael pollard
manchester
tel : 0161 456 7470
email : info@michaelpollard.co.uk
website : www.michaelpollard.co.uk
studio/location/student rates

paulcable
photography & design

www.paulcable.com
info@paulcable.com
07958 932 764

'the BIG agency for short & tall actors'

actors from 3ft to 5ft & over 7ft
for films, TV, theatre & advertising

tel: +44 (0)1733 240392 • email: office@willowmanagement.co.uk • on-line casting directory: willowmanagement.co.uk

UNITED AGENTS LTD
Personal Manager. PMA Member
12-26 Lexington Street, London W1F 0LE   T 020 3214 0800
E info@unitedagents.co.uk
W www.unitedagents.co.uk

UPBEAT MANAGEMENT
Theatre Touring & Events. No Actors
Larg House, Woodcote Grove
Coulsdon, Surrey CR5 2QQ   T 020 8668 3332
E info@upbeat.co.uk
W www.upbeat.co.uk

UPSON EDWARDS
See REPRESENTATION UPSON EDWARDS

URBAN HEROES
Lower Ground
124 Boundary Road, London NW8 0RH
F 0870 4792458   T 020 7043 1072
E justin@theurbanheroes.com
W www.theurbanheroes.com

URBAN TALENT
Nemesis House, 1 Oxford Court
Bishopsgate, Manchester M2 3WQ
F 0161 228 6727   T 0161 228 6866
E liz@nmsmanagement.co.uk
W www.urbantalent.tv

UTOPIA MODEL MANAGEMENT
348 Moorside Road
Swinton, Manchester M27 9PW
F 0871 2180843   M 07771 884844
E kya@utopiamodels.co.uk

UVA MANAGEMENT LTD
Contact: By e-mail
Commercials. Film. Presenters. Stage. Television
Pinewood Film Studios, Pinewood Road
Iver Heath, Buckinghamshire SL0 0NH   T 01753 652233
E berko@uvamanagement.com
W www.uvamanagement.com

VACCA Roxanne MANAGEMENT
73 Beak Street, London W1F 9SR
F 020 7734 8086   T 020 7734 8085

VALLÉ ACADEMY THEATRICAL AGENCY THE
The Vallé Academy Studios
Wilton House, Delamare Road
Cheshunt, Herts EN8 9SG
F 01992 622868   T 01992 622861
E agency@valleacademy.co.uk
W www.valleacademy.co.uk

VAMP JAZZ
Bands. Entertainers. Musicians. Singers (not Musical Theatre)
Ealing House, 33 Hanger Lane
London W5 3HJ   T 020 8992 1571
E vampjazz@aol.com

VERBECK Dean PERSONAL MANAGEMENT
c/o Forge Fach Centre
Hebron Road
Swansea SA6 5EJ   T 01792 849565
E dean.dvpm@mail.com
W www.tpfwales.com/site/agency.html

VIDAL-HALL Clare
PMA Member
Choreographers. Composers. Designers. Directors
Lighting Designers
57 Carthew Road, London W6 0DU
F 020 8741 9459   T 020 8741 7647
E info@clarevidalhall.com
W www.clarevidalhall.com

VINE Michael ASSOCIATES
Light Entertainment
1 Stormont Road, London N6 4NS   T 020 8347 2580
E stephen@michaelvineassociates.com

VisABLE PEOPLE
Contact: Louise Dyson
Artists with Disabilities
E louise@visablepeople.com   T 01905 776631
W www.visablepeople.com

VM TALENT LTD (Vic Murray Talent)
PMA Member
185A/B Latchmere Road
London SW11 2JZ   T 020 7924 4453
E info@vmtalent.com
W www.vmtalent.com

VSA LTD
PMA Member. Contact: Andy Charles
186 Shaftesbury Avenue
London WC2H 8JB
F 020 7240 2930   T 020 7240 2927
E info@vsaltd.com
W www.vsaltd.com

W ATHLETIC
The Hub, Fowler Avenue
IQ Farnborough Business Park GU14 7JF   T 01252 302255
E wathletic@me.com
W www.wathletic.com

WADE Suzann
Personal Manager
PMA Member
Contact: By Post only
Accepts Showreels. 2 Agents represent 18 Performers
Film. Musicals. Stage. Television
9 Wimpole Mews
London W1G 8PG
F 020 7486 5664   T 020 7486 0746
E info@suzannwade.com
W www.suzannwade.com

WALK TALL MANAGEMENT
Contact: By e-mail. Accepts Showreels. 35 Performers
Britannia House, Lower Road
Ebbsfleet, Kent DA11 9BL   T/F 01474 561200
E annduke@lineone.net

WALMSLEY Peter ASSOCIATES
No Representation. Do Not Write
37A Crimsworth Road, London SW8 4RJ
M 07778 347312   T 020 7787 6419
E associates@peterwalmsley.net

WARING & McKENNA
PMA Member
11-12 Dover Street, Mayfair, London W1S 4LJ
F 020 7629 6466   T 020 7629 6444
E dj@waringandmckenna.com
W www.waringandmckenna.com

WELCH Janet PERSONAL MANAGEMENT
Contact: By Post
Old Orchard, The Street
Ubley, Bristol BS40 6PJ   T/F 01761 463238
E info@janetwelchpm.co.uk

WEST CENTRAL MANAGEMENT
CPMA Member. Co-operative of 21 Performers
Contact: By Post/e-mail
Room 4, East Block
Panther House, 38 Mount Pleasant
London WC1X 0AN   T/F 020 7833 8134
E mail@westcentralmanagement.co.uk
W www.westcentralmanagement.co.uk

WEST END MANAGEMENT
Contact: Maureen Cairns, Allan Jones
2nd Floor, 34 Argyle Arcade Chambers
Buchanan Street, Glasgow G2 8BD   T 0141 222 2333
E info@west-endmgt.com
W www.west-endmgt.com

WHATEVER ARTISTS MANAGEMENT LTD
F24 Argo House
Kilburn Park Road, London NW6 5LF
F 020 7372 5111   T 020 7372 4777
E info@wamshow.biz
W www.wamshow.biz

WHITEHALL ARTISTS
10 Lower Common South
London SW15 1BP
F 020 8788 2340   T 020 8785 3737
E mwhitehall@msn.com

WHITTINGHAM Ian Zachary AGENTS
77 Brick Lane, Liverpool Street
London E1 6QL   T 020 3246 0088
E zachwhittingham@ymail.com

WILKINSON David ASSOCIATES
PMA Member
Existing Clients only
115 Hazlebury Road, London SW6 2LX
F 020 7371 5161   T 020 7371 5188
E info@dwassociates.net

WILLIAMS BULLDOG MANAGEMENT LTD
Suite 238, 241-251 Ferndale Road
London SW9 8BJ   T 020 7733 3823
E info@williamsbulldog.co.uk
W www.williamsbulldog.co.uk

www.Legend-Photography.com
Sussex studio 01424 430055

WILLIAMSON & HOLMES
51 St Martin's Lane, London WC2N 4EA
F 020 7240 0408   T 020 7240 0407
E info@williamsonandholmes.co.uk

WILLOW PERSONAL MANAGEMENT
Specialist Agency for Short Actors (5 feet & under) & Tall
Actors (7 feet & over)
151 Main Street, Yaxley
Peterborough, Cambs PE7 3LD   T 01733 240392
E office@willowmanagement.co.uk
W www.willowmanagement.co.uk

WILLS Newton MANAGEMENT
Personal Manager
Contact: By Post/e-mail
Accepts Showreels/Voicereels
3 Agents represent 52 Performers
Commercials. Dancers. Films. Singers. Stage. Television
The Studio, 29 Springvale Avenue
Brentford, Middlesex TW8 9QH
F 00 33 468 218685   M 07989 398381
E newtoncttg@aol.com
W www.newtonwills.com

WINSLETT Dave ASSOCIATES
4 Zig Zag Road, Kenley, Surrey CR8 5EL
F 020 8668 9216   T 020 8668 0531
E info@davewinslett.com
W www.davewinslett.com

WINTERSON Niki
See GLOBAL ARTISTS

WIS CELTIC MANAGEMENT
Welsh, Irish, Scottish Performers
86 Elphinstone Road, Walthamstow, London E17 5EX
F 020 8523 4523   T 020 8523 4234

WISE BUDDAH TALENT
Contact: Chris North
74 Great Titchfield Street, London W1W 7QP
F 020 7307 1601   T 020 7307 1600
E chris.north@wisebuddah.com
W www.wisebuddah.com

WMG MANAGEMENT EUROPE LTD
Sports Management Company
5th Floor, 33 Soho Square, London W1D 3QU
F 020 3230 1053   T 020 7009 6000
W www.wmglk.com

WYMAN Edward AGENCY
Contact: Edward Wyman, Audrey Williams, Judith Gay
By Post. Accepts Showreels/Voicereels. 3 Agents. English &
Welsh Language. Commercials. Corporate. Television
Voice Overs. Walk-on & Supporting Artists
67 Llanon Road, Llanishen, Cardiff CF14 5AH
F 029 2075 2444   T 029 2075 2351
E edward.wyman@btconnect.com
W www.wymancasting.co.uk

XL MANAGEMENT
Edmund House, Rugby Road
Leamington Spa, Warwickshire CV32 6EL
F 01926 811420   T 01926 810449
E office@xlmanagement.co.uk
W www.xlmanagement.co.uk

YAT MANAGEMENT
(Young Actors Theatre Management)
70-72 Barnsbury Road, London N1 0ES
F 020 7833 9467   T 020 7278 2101
E agent@yati.org.uk
W www.yati.org.uk

YELLOW BALLOON PRODUCTIONS LTD
Contact: Mike Smith
Freshwater House, Outdowns, Effingham, Surrey KT24 5QR
F 01483 281501   T 01483 281500
E yellowbal@aol.com

ZWICKLER Marlene & ASSOCIATES
1 Belgrave Crescent Lane
Edinburgh EH4 3AG   T/F 0131 343 3030
E info@mza-artists.com
W www.mza-artists.com

Artist Management
adults children

Byron's Management
Tel: 020 7242 8096
byronsmanagement@aol.com
www.byronsmanagement.co.uk

A & J MANAGEMENT
242A The Ridgeway, Botany Bay
Enfield EN2 8AP   T 020 8342 0542
E info@ajmanagement.co.uk
W www.ajmanagement.co.uk

ABACUS AGENCY
The Studio, 4 Bailey Road,
Westcott, Dorking, Surrey RH4 3QS
F 01306 877813   T 01306 877144
E admin@abacusagency.co.uk
W www.abacusagency.co.uk

ACT OUT AGENCY
Children, Teenagers & New Graduates
22 Greek Street, Stockport
Cheshire SK3 8AB   T/F 0161 429 7413
E ab22actout@aol.com

ALL THE ARTS CHILDREN'S CASTING AGENCY
PO Box 61687, London SE9 9BP
M 07908 618083   T 020 8850 2384
E jillian@alltheartsagency.co.uk
W www.alltheartsagency.co.uk

ALLSORTS AGENCY
Suite 3 Marlborough Business Centre
96 George Lane, London E18 1AD
F 020 8989 5600   T 020 8989 0500
E bookings@allsortsagency.com
W www.allsortsagency.com

ALLSORTS DRAMA FOR CHILDREN
In Association with Sasha Leslie Management
34 Crediton Road, London NW10 3DU
F 020 8969 3196   T/F 020 8969 3249
E sasha@allsortsdrama.com

infopage

How can my child become an actor?

If your child is interested in becoming an actor, they should try to get as much practical experience as possible. For example, joining the drama club at school, taking theatre studies as an option, reading as many plays as they can, and going to the theatre on a regular basis. They could also attend local youth theatres or drama groups. Some theatres offer evening or Saturday classes. However, as any agency or school will tell you, the entertainment industry is highly competitive and for every success story there are many children who will never be hired for paid acting work. Child artists and their parents should think very carefully before getting involved in the industry and be prepared for disappointments along the way.

What is the difference between stage schools and agencies?

Stage schools provide specialised training in acting, singing and dancing for the under 18's. They offer a variety of full and part-time courses. Please see the 'Drama Training, Schools and Coaches' section for listings. Children's and Teenagers' agencies specialise in the representation of child artists, promoting them to casting opportunities and negotiating contracts on their behalf. In return they will take commission, usually ranging from 10-15%. Some larger stage schools also have agencies attached to them. A number of agents are listed in the following pages.

Why does my child need an agent?

While many parents feel they want to retain control over their child's career, they will not have the contacts and authority a good agent will have in the industry. Casting directors are more likely to look to an agent they know and trust to provide the most suitable children for a job than an independent, unrepresented child. This does not mean to say that a child will never get work without an agent to put them forward for work, but it will certainly be more difficult.

How should these listings be used?

The following pages list up-to-date contact details for agencies specialising in the representation of children and teenagers. Every company listed is done so by written request to us. Always research agencies carefully before approaching them to make sure they are suitable for your child. Many have websites you can visit, or ask around for personal recommendations. You should make a short-list of the ones you think are most appropriate rather than sending a standard letter to hundreds of agencies. Please see the main 'Agents and Personal Managers' advice section for further guidance on choosing and approaching agents.

Who can I contact for general advice?

Your local education authority should be able to help with most queries regarding your child's education, working hours, chaperones and general welfare if they are aged 16 or under. Unfortunately Spotlight is not able to advise performers on specific agents, nor is it in a position to handle any financial or contractual queries or complaints. For agent-related queries we suggest you contact The Agents Association www.agents-uk.com or The Personal Managers' Association (PMA) www.thepma.com, or you could try one of the independent advisors on our website www.spotlight.com/artists/advice/independent For legal guidance please see the 'Accountants, Insurance & Law' section for listings.

Should I pay an agent to represent my child? Or sign a contract?

Equity does not recommend that you pay an agent an upfront fee to place your child on their client list. Before signing a contract, you should be very clear about the terms and commitments involved. For advice on both of these issues, or if you experience any problems with a current agent, we recommend that you contact Equity www.equity.org.uk

Why do child actors need licences?

Strict regulations apply to children working in the entertainment industry. These cover areas including the maximum number of performance hours per day/week, rest times, meal times and tutoring requirements. When any child under 16 performs in a professional capacity, the production company must obtain a Child Performance Licence from the child's local education authority.

Who are chaperones?

Child artists must also be accompanied by a chaperone at all times when they are working. Registered chaperones are generally used instead of parents as they have a better understanding of the employment regulations involved, and they have professional experience of dealing with production companies. Registered chaperones have been police checked and approved by their local education authority to act in loco parentis. Always contact your local education authority if you have any questions or concerns.

What is the Spotlight Children and Young Performers directory?

Children who are currently represented by an agent or attend a stage school can appear in the Spotlight Children and Young Performers directory used to source child artists for TV, film, stage or commercial work. Each child pays an annual membership fee to have their photo featured in the printed directory as well as receiving their own individual online CV on the Spotlight website, searchable by casting professionals. For further information visit www.spotlight.com/join or speak to your child's stage school or agency.

Jackie Michael became a theatrical agent in the early eighties and formed A&J Management in 1985. Many of the company's clients have gone on to become national and international stars.

It all started when Charlie Chaplin introduced a 10-year-old Jackie Coogan to a mutual chorus of sighs and tears in his classic film, *The Kid*. Then two more followed: Shirley Temple – all curls and cuteness – tip-tapping her way to stardom; and Judy Garland, a stunning young talent with an electrifying voice that would captivate audiences throughout the world for over five decades.

These were the actors who were to set the precedent for aspiring child actors for many years to come, and the demand for young talent remains just as prolific and intense now as it was during those evolutionary days of cinema.

While children's agents play an integral role in discovering and nurturing possible stars of the future, they also have a responsibility and duty that partners this remit. For parents looking for representation for their child, they must ensure they make a carefully considered choice. Talk to other parents who have children with agencies. The initial move to securing an agency with the right credentials is vitally important: look for one that is highly respected within the business with an impeccable reputation for honesty and reliability. Joining any reputable agency in this country is free, and registration fees should NOT be paid under any circumstances.

Quite often the nature of the business will require frequent contact, and under these circumstances it is essential that a strong rapport exists between parent and agent. The agent assumes the role of a surrogate parent and because of this position a mutual trust needs to be established and sustained.

Throughout their 25-year existence A&J Management has remained a 'boutique' agency, whose client base ranges from the very young to a couple of octogenarians. With around 200 requests for representation each month, it would be easy to break this mould by taking on new clients indiscriminately. We audition many of those who apply on a monthly basis, but only offer places to those we feel would stand a chance in what has become a ruthlessly competitive marketplace. Understandably there are many parents out there who feel their own children have a real and very special talent. Sometimes when put to the test and through several failed auditions they become disillusioned. Patience and determination are twin virtues during this early period, as it often takes considerable time before finally breaking through. Overnight stardom is a myth.

There are also other parents who see things differently. Does it really matter whether their boy or girl has any talent? They want to put them into the acting arena just for the pure enjoyment and fun they'll get out of it. This is fine, but these parents need to look in a different direction and should send their children to drama or dance schools instead. Without the required commitment and dedication, they would be wasting their time looking for representation.

First and foremost, a complimentary set of photographs is *de rigueur*, so it is essential to find a good photographer. A few years ago, agents would produce annual directories which would 'sell' clients based purely on a CV and picture. Today the internet has changed the entire face and perspective of casting and 'selling' clients. Our website and Spotlight's website now allow casting directors et al to access a range of photographs as well as clips from selective film and television roles, and voice clips for any potential radio or voice-over work. This makes it all substantially easier for casting directors to reach a decision.

If you are a child or teenager reading this and are selected to audition for a film or television production, ensure you know and understand (a) the character you've been selected to audition for, (b) the theme and storyline and (c) most importantly, ensure you familiarise yourself with any script sent to you. Finally, it is always advantageous to swat up on the director and their film resume. This never fails to impress.

At the end of the day, once you have decided this is the business you are determined to break into; once you understand that there will sometimes be more tears than laughter; once you have accepted that you will almost certainly experience unbearably lengthy periods of silence from an agent equally desperate to fill your dance card; and once you realise that the industry you have chosen to be a part of has around 90% unemployment at any given time, yet you are still happy and content to hang around until that big break emerges, then unquestionably through your patience, determination, tenacity and sheer doggedness you deserve all the success and fame that could be heading your way. *Bonne chance!*

Please visit www.ajmanagement.co.uk for further information.

ALLSTARS CASTING
66 Hope Street, Liverpool L1 9BZ
M 07739 359737 T/F 0151 707 2100
E sylvie@allstarscasting.co.uk
W www.allstarscasting.co.uk

ALPHABET KIDZ ACTING & VOICE-OVER AGENCY
Nice Business Park
19-35 Sylvan Grove, London SE15 1PD
F 020 7252 4341 T 020 7252 4343
E lisa@alphabetkidz.co.uk
W www.alphabetkidz.co.uk

ANNA'S MANAGEMENT
Formerly of Aladdin's Cave
Children. Teenagers. Young Adults
25 Tintagel Drive, Stanmore, Middlesex HA7 4SR
F 020 8238 2899 T 020 8958 7636
E annasmanage@aol.com
W www.annasmanagement.com

ARAENA/COLLECTIVE
10 Bramshaw Gardens, South Oxhey
Herts WD19 6XP T/F 020 8428 0037
E info@collectivedance.co.uk

A.R.K. AGENCY (ALL ROUND KIDS)
54 Oaklands, Curdworth, Sutton Coldfield B76 9HD
M 07976 755434 T 01675 475026
E allroundkids@hotmail.co.uk
W www.allroundkids.co.uk

ARNOULD KIDZ
1 Brook Gardens, Kingston-upon-Thames, Surrey KT2 7ET
M 07720 427828 T 020 8942 1879
E info@arnouldkidz.co.uk
W www.arnouldkidz.co.uk

ARTS ACADEMY (T.A.A.) THE
15 Lexham Mews, London W8 6JW
F 020 7376 2416 T 020 7376 0267
E jill@galloways.ltd.uk

ASHCROFT ACADEMY OF DRAMATIC ART & AGENCY
Malcolm Primary School, Malcolm Road
Penge, London SE20 8RH
M 07799 791586 T/F 0844 8005328
E geraldi.gillma@btconnect.com
W www.ashcroftacademy.com

ASPARATIONS
Arabesque School of Performing Arts
Quarry Lane, Chichester PO19 8NY
M 07825 239391 T 01243 531144
E asparations2006@aol.com

AWA - ANDREA WILDER AGENCY
23 Cambrian Drive
Colwyn Bay, Conwy LL28 4SL
F 07092 249314 M 07919 202401
E andreawilder@fastmail.fm
W www.awagency.co.uk

BABY BODENS
Bodens Studios & Agency, 99 East Barnet Road
New Barnet, Herts EN4 8RF
F 020 8449 5212 T 020 8447 0909
E info@bodensagency.com
W www.bodensagency.com

BABYSHAK AGENCY
Bizzy Studios, First Floor Hall
10-12 Pickford Lane
Bexleyheath, Kent DA7 4QW
F 0845 5200401 T 0845 5200400
E clients@babyshak.com
W www.babyshak.com

BANANAFISH MANAGEMENT
The Arts Village, 20-26 Henry Street, Liverpool L1 5BS
M 07974 206622 T 0151 708 5509
E info@bananafish.co.uk
W www.bananafish.co.uk

BIG ACT MANAGEMENT
90 Chapel Way, Epsom, Surrey KT18 5SY
M 07816 524066 T 01737 211541
E lucy@bigacttheatre.co.uk
W www.bigacttheatre.co.uk

BIZZYKIDZ
Bizzy Studios, First Floor Hall
10-12 Pickford Lane, Bexleyheath, Kent DA7 4QW
F 0845 5200401 T 0845 5200400
E bookings@bizzykidz.com
W www.bizzykidz.com

BODENS AGENCY
99 East Barnet Road, New Barnet
Herts EN4 8RF T 020 8447 0909
E info@bodensagency.com
W www.bodensagency.com

BONNIE AND BETTY LTD
County House, 221-241 Beckenham Road
Beckenham, Kent BR3 4UF T 020 8676 6294
E agency@bonnieandbetty.com
W www.bonnieandbetty.com

BOURNE Michelle MULTICULTURAL ACADEMY & AGENCY
Studio 1, 22 Dorman Walk
Garden Way, London NW10 0PF M 07852 932473
E info@michellebourneacademy.co.uk
W www.michellebourneacademy.co.uk

BRUCE & BROWN
203 Canalot Studios, 222 Kensal Road, London W10 5BN
F 020 8964 0457 T 020 8968 5585
E info@bruceandbrown.com
W www.bruceandbrown.com

BRUNO KELLY LTD
4th Floor, Albany House, 324-326 Regent St, London W1B 3HH
F 020 7183 7332 T 020 7183 7331
E info@brunokelly.com
W www.brunokelly.com

BUBBLEGUM
Pinewood Studios, Pinewood Road
Iver Heath, Bucks SL0 0NH T 01753 642673
E info@bubblegummodels.com
W www.bubblegummodels.com

BYRON'S MANAGEMENT
Children & Adults
180 Drury Lane, London WC2B 5QF T 020 7242 8096
E byronsmanagement@aol.com
W www.byronsmanagement.co.uk

CAROUSEL KIDZ
1 Dukes Court, 250 Croydon Road
Beckenham, Kent BR3 4DA T/F 020 8249 3597
E info@carouselkidz.co.uk
W www.carouselkidz.co.uk

CARR Norrie AGENCY
Babies, Children & Adults
Holborn Studios, 49-50 Eagle Wharf Road, London N1 7ED
F 020 7253 1772 T 020 7253 1771
E info@norriecarr.com
W www.norriecarr.com

CAVAT SCHOOL OF THEATRE ARTS & AGENCY
16A Hook Hill, South Croydon
Surrey CR2 0LA T 020 8651 1099
E enquiries@cavattheatrearts.co.uk
W www.cavattheatrearts.co.uk

CHADWICK Jacqueline ACADEMY THE
Oakdene Studios
Brewery Lane, Leigh WN7 2RJ   M 07918 685296
E chadwickacademy@yahoo.com
W www.jacquelinechadwickacademy.co.uk

CHILDSPLAY MODELS LLP
114 Avenue Road, Beckenham, Kent BR3 4SA
F 020 8778 2672   T 020 8659 9860
E info@childsplaymodels.co.uk
W www.childsplaymodels.co.uk

CHILLI KIDS
Talisman House
47-49 Bath Street, Walsall WS1 3BX
F 0333 666 2469   T 0333 666 2468
E info@chillikids.co.uk
W www.chillikids.co.uk

CHRYSTEL ARTS AGENCY
6 Eunice Grove, Chesham, Bucks HP5 1RL
M 07799 605489   T 01494 773336
E chrystelarts@waitrose.com

CIRCUS MANIACS AGENCY
Circus, Theatre, Dance, Extreme Sports
Unit 62, Basepoint Business Centre
Oakfield Close, Tewkesbury Business Park, Tewkesbury
Gloucestershire GL20 8SD
M 07977 247287   T 01684 854412
E agency@circusmaniacs.com
W www.circusmaniacs.com

CONTI Italia AGENCY LTD
Italia Conti House, 23 Goswell Road, London EC1M 7AJ
F 020 7253 1430   T 020 7608 7500
E agency@italiaconti.co.uk

CORONA MANAGEMENT
3 Thameside Centre, Kew Bridge Road
Brentford, Middlesex TW8 0HF   T 020 8758 2553
E info@coronatheatreschool.com
W www.coronatheatreschool.com

CPA AGENCY
The Studios, 219B North Street, Romford, Essex RM1 4QA
F 01708 766077   T 01708 766444
E info@cpaagency.co.uk
W www.cpastudios.co.uk

CREATIVE KIDZ & CO
Incorporating NeighbourHood Productions
9 Weavers Terrace, Fulham
London SW6 1QE   M 07958 377595
E info@creativekidzandco.co.uk

CS MANAGEMENT
Children & Young Adults
The Croft, 7 Cannon Road, Southgate, London N14 7HE
F 020 8886 7555   T 020 8886 4264
E carole@csmanagementuk.com
W www.csmanagementuk.com

D & B MANAGEMENT & THEATRE SCHOOL
470 Bromley Road, Bromley, Kent BR1 4PN
F 020 8697 8100   T 020 8698 8880
E bonnie@dandbmanagement.com
W www.dandbperformingarts.co.uk

DD'S CHILDREN'S AGENCY
6 Acle Close, Hainault, Essex IG6 2GQ
M 07957 398501   T 020 8502 6866
E ddsagency@yahoo.co.uk
W www.ddtst.com

DRAGON DRAMA
Improvisational Drama for Children
1B Station Road, Hampton Wick KT1 4HG   T 020 8617 3141
E askus@dragondrama.co.uk
W www.dragondrama.co.uk

DRAMA STUDIO EDINBURGH THE
19 Belmont Road, Edinburgh EH14 5DZ   T 0131 453 3284
E info@thedramastudio.com
W www.thedramastudio.com

DREAMS THEATRE
Unit 2 Gracious Farm, High Street
Southill, Bedfordshire SG18 9JB   T 01462 81040
E dreams-theatre@hotmail.com
W www.dreamstheatre.co.uk

EARACHE KIDS (VOICE-OVERS)
177 Wardour Street, London W1F 8WX
F 020 7287 2288   T 020 7287 2211
E julie@earachevoices.com
W www.earachevoices.com

EARNSHAW Susi MANAGEMENT
The Bull Theatre, 68 High Street, Barnet, Herts EN5 5SJ
F 020 8364 9618   T 020 8441 5010
E casting@susiearnshaw.co.uk
W www.susiearnshawmanagement.com

EDUCATION IN STAGE & THEATRE ARTS (E.S.T.A.)
16 British Grove, Chiswick, London W4 2NL
F 020 8746 3219   T 020 8741 2843
E esta@clara.co.uk
W www.estatheatreschool.com

ELITE ACADEMY OF PERFORMING ARTS
City Studios, 4 Sandford Street, Lichfield, Staffs WS13 6QA
M 07976 971178
E elitedancing@hotmail.com

ENGLISH Doreen '95
Contact: Gerry Kinner
4 Selsey Avenue, Aldwick
Bognor Regis, West Sussex PO21 2QZ   T/F 01243 825968

EUROKIDS CASTING & MODEL AGENCY
The Warehouse Studios, Glaziers Lane
Culcheth, Warrington, Cheshire WA3 4AQ
F 01925 767563   T 01925 761088
E castings@eka-agency.com
W www.eka-agency.com

EXPRESSIONS CASTING AGENCY
3 Newgate Lane, Mansfield, Nottingham NG18 2LB
F 01623 647337   T 01623 424334
E expressions-uk@btconnect.com
W www.expressionsperformingarts.co.uk

FBI AGENCY
PO Box 250, Leeds LS1 2AZ
M 07515 567309   T/F 07050 222747
E casting@fbi-agency.co.uk
W www.fbi-agency.co.uk

FEA MANAGEMENT (Ferris Entertainment)
London. Belfast. Cardiff
Number 8, 132 Charing Cross Road
London WC2H 0LA   T 0845 4724725
E info@ferrisentertainment.com
W www.ferrisentertainment.com

FILM CAST CORNWALL & SW
c/o 3 Church Walk, Truro TR1 1JH   T 01326 311419
E enquiries@filmcastcornwall.co.uk
W www.filmcastcornwall.co.uk

FIORENTINI Anna AGENCY
Islington Business Design Centre, Unit 101
52 Upper Street, London N1 0QH
M 07904 962779   T/F 020 7682 3677
E rhiannon@annafiorentini.co.uk
W www.annafiorentini.co.uk

tuesdaychild
Established for over 35 years
The agency for adults and children

Babies, Children and Adults (0-80+)   North and South UK

Tel: 01625 501765 • info@tuesdaychildagency.co.uk • www.tuesdaychildagency.co.uk

FOOTSTEPS THEATRE SCHOOL CASTING AGENCY
55 Pullan Avenue, Eccleshill, Bradford BD2 3RP
T/F 01274 637429   T 01274 636036
E helen@footsteps.fslife.co.uk

FOX Julie ASSOCIATES YOUNG PERFORMERS
47 Furze Platt Road, Maidenhead
Berks SL6 7NF   T 01628 777853
E agent@juliefoxassociates.co.uk

GENESIS THEATRE SCHOOL & AGENCY
88 Hempland Close, Great Oakley
Corby, Northants NN18 8LT   T 01536 460928
E info@saracharles.com

GLOBAL7
PO Box 56232, London N4 4XP
M 07956 956652   T/F 020 7281 7679
E global7castings@gmail.com
W www.global7casting.com

GLYNNE Frances THEATRE STUDENTS & MANAGEMENT
Flat 9, Elmwood, 6 The Avenue
Hatch End, Middlesex HA5 4EP   M 07950 918355
E franandmo@gmail.com

GO FOR IT CHILDREN'S AGENCY
Children & Teenagers
Green Gables, 47 North Lane
Teddington, Middlesex TW11 0HU
M 07956 646412   T 020 8943 1120
E agency@goforitcentre.com
W www.goforitcentre.com

GOBSTOPPERS MANAGEMENT
37 St Nicholas Mount, Hemel Hempstead, Herts HP1 2BB
M 07961 372319   T 01442 269543
E chrisgobstoppers@btinternet.com

GP ASSOCIATES
4 Gallus Close
Winchmore Hill, London N21 1JR
F 020 8882 9189   T 020 8886 2263
E info@gpassociates.co.uk
W www.greasepaintanonymous.co.uk

HARLEQUIN STUDIOS AGENCY FOR CHILDREN
122A Phyllis Avenue, Peacehaven
East Sussex BN10 7RQ   T 01273 581742

HARRIS AGENCY LTD
71 The Avenue, Watford, Herts WD17 4NU
F 01923 211666   T 01923 211644
E theharrisagency@btconnect.com

HOBSONS KIDS
62 Chiswick High Road, London W4 1SY
F 020 8996 5350   T 020 8995 3628
E kids@hobsons-international.com
W www.hobsons-international.com

HOWE Janet CASTING AGENCY
58A High Street
Newcastle Under Lyme
Staffordshire ST5 1QE   T 01782 661777
E info@janethowe.com
W www.janethowecasting.co.uk

The Pie Factory, 101 Broadway
Salford Quays, Manchester M50 2EQ
M 07801 942178   T/F 0161 660 1104

HOXTON STREET CASTING
Hoxton Hall, 130 Hoxton Street
London N1 6SH   T 020 7503 5131
E lucy@hoxtonstreetcasting.co.uk
W www.hoxtonstreetcasting.co.uk

STOMP! MANAGEMENT *Representing:*
- CHILDREN & TEENAGERS 6-19 yrs
- CONFIDENT, TRAINED, NATURAL. MANY BOY ACTORS.
- COMPLIMENTARY CASTING FACILITIES.

T: 020 8446 9898

www.stompmanagement.com

HSD KIDS AGENCY
10 Iona Way, Wickford SS12 9QX
M 07858 535860   T 01268 561572
E hsd.kidsagency@googlemail.com
W www.hsdkidsagency.co.uk

INTER-CITY KIDS
27 Wigan Lane, Wigan
Greater Manchester WN1 1XR   T/F 01942 321969
E intercitycasting@btconnect.com

JABBERWOCKY AGENCY
Children & Teenagers
Glassenbury Hill Farm, Glassenbury Road
Cranbrook, Kent TN17 2QF
F 01580 714346   T 01580 714306
E info@jabberwockyagency.com
W www.jabberwockyagency.com

JAM THEATRE COMPANY
21 Beechtree Avenue, Marlow
Buckinghamshire SL7 3NH   T 01628 487773
E office@jamtheatre.co.uk
W www.jamtheatre.co.uk

JERMIN Mark MANAGEMENT
8 Heathfield, Swansea SA1 6EJ
F 01792 458844   T 01792 458855
E info@markjermin.co.uk
W www.markjermin.co.uk

JIGSAW ARTS MANAGEMENT
*Representing Children & Young People
from Jigsaw Performing Arts Schools*
64-66 High Street, Barnet, Herts EN5 5SJ   T 020 8447 4530
E admin@jigsaw-arts.co.uk
W www.jigsaw-arts.co.uk

JOHNSTON & MATHERS ASSOCIATES LTD
PO Box 3167, Barnet, Herts EN5 2WA   T/F 020 8449 4968
E johnstonmathers@aol.com
W www.johnstonandmathers.com

JUNIOR MODEL MANAGEMENT
PO Box 61667, London SE9 9AT
F 0845 8388987   T 0845 8388985
E donia@juniormm.com
W www.juniormm.com

KELLY MANAGEMENT
10 White Horse Street,
Mayfair, London W1J 7LJ
F 020 7499 9388   T 020 7499 8402
E office@kelly-management.com
W www.kelly-management.com

KIDS LONDON
67 Dulwich Road, London SE24 0NJ
F 020 8671 5910   T 020 7924 9595
E info@kidslondonltd.com
W www.kidslondonltd.com

KIDS PLUS
Malcolm House, Malcolm Primary School
Malcolm Road, Penge, London SE20 8RH
M 07799 791586   T 0844 8005328
E geraldi.gillma@btconnect.com
W www.kidsplusagency.co.uk

KIDSHAK AGENCY
Suite 3, 90 Frobisher Road
Erith, Kent DA8 2PQ   T 0845 4600623
E agency@kidshak.com
W www.kidshak.com

KIDZ LTD
348 Moorside Road, Swinton
Manchester M27 9PW
F 0871 2180843   T 0871 2180884
E info@kidzltd.com
W www.kidzltd.com

KIDZ ON THE HILL PERFORMING ARTS SCHOOL
PO Box 56951, Muswell Hill
London N10 2AS   M 07881 553480
E kidzonthehill@gmail.com
W www.kidzonthehill.co.uk

KRACKERS KIDS THEATRICAL AGENCY
6-7 Electric Parade, Seven Kings Road
Ilford, Essex IG3 8BY   T/F 01708 502046
E krackerskids@hotmail.com
W www.krackerskids.co.uk

KYT AGENCY
Mulberry Croft, Mulberry Hill, Chilham CT4 8AJ
M 07967 580213   T/F 01227 730177
E richard@kyt.org.uk
W www.kentyouththeatre.co.uk

LAMONT CASTING AGENCY
2 Harewood Avenue, Ainsdale
Merseyside PR8 2PH   M 07736 387543
E diane@lamontcasting.co.uk
W www.lamontcasting.co.uk

LESLIE Sasha MANAGEMENT
In Association with Allsorts Drama for Children
34 Crediton Road
London NW10 3DU   T/F 020 8969 3249
E sasha@allsortsdrama.com

LIFE AND SOUL THEATRE AGENCY
Boxmoor Hall, St Johns Road
Hemel Hempstead, Herts HP1 1JR   T/F 01442 233050
E lifeandsoulta@hotmail.com
W www.lifeandsoultheatreacademy.co.uk

Mark Jermin
★ ★ ★ Management

8 Heathfield, Swansea SA1 6EJ
Phone: 01792 458855
Fax: 01792 458844
Email: info@markjermin.co.uk
www.markjermin.co.uk

* Children and young adults from all over the UK.
* Audition workshops and classes in London, Manchester, Bristol and Wales.
* Children with open performance licences, guaranteed to be licensed for any production and at very short notice.

LIL DEVILS AGENCY
1st Floor, 76 School Road
Tilehurst, Reading, Berks RG31 5AW
F 0118 941 7273   T 0118 943 3057
E kids@lildevils.co.uk
W www.lildevils.co.uk

LINTON MANAGEMENT
3 The Rock, Bury BL9 0JP
F 0161 761 1999   T 0161 761 2020
E carol@linton.tv

LITTLE ADULTS ACADEMY & MODELLING AGENCY LTD
Studio 1, Essex House, 375-377 High Street
Stratford, London E15 4QZ   T 020 8519 9755
E info@littleadults.demon.co.uk
W www.littleadultsagency.co.uk

LIVE & LOUD AGENCY
Contact: Maureen Cairns, Allan Jones
2nd Floor, 34 Argyle Arcade Chambers
Buchanan Street, Glasgow G2 8BD   T 0141 222 2333
E info@liveandloudagency.com

McDONAGH Melanie MANAGEMENT (ACADEMY OF PERFORMING ARTS & CASTING AGENCY)
14 Apple Tree Way, Oswaldtwistle
Accrington, Lancashire BB5 0FB
M 07909 831409   T 01254 392560
E mcdonaghmgt@aol.com
W www.mcdonaghmanagement.co.uk

MELODY'S THEATRICAL AGENCY
Melody House, Gillotts Corner
Henley-on-Thames, Oxon RG9 1QU
F 01491 411533   T 01491 572000
E info@jgdance.co.uk   W www.jgdance.co.uk

MONDI ASSOCIATES LTD
Contact: Michelle Sykes
Unit 3 0, Cooper House
2 Michael Road
London SW6 2AD   M 07817 133349
E info@mondiassociates.com
W www.mondiassociates.com

MOOSE MANAGEMENT
44 Quarry Road, Winchester
Hampshire SO23 0JS   M 07969 976408
E moosemanagement@rocketmail.com

MRS WORTHINGTON'S
6-16 Years
16 Ouseley Road, London SW12 8EF   T/F 020 8767 6944

NFD - THE FILM AND TV AGENCY
PO Box 76
Leeds LS25 9AG   T/F 01977 681949
E info@film-tv-agency.com
W www.film-tv-agency.com

O'FARRELL STAGE & THEATRE SCHOOL
Babies, Children, Teenagers & Young Adults
36 Shirley Street, Canning Town
London E16 1HU   M 07956 941497
E linda@ofarrells.wanadoo.co.uk

ORR MANAGEMENT AGENCY
Children, Teenagers & Adults
1st Floor, 147-149 Market Street
Farnworth
Greater Manchester BL4 8EX
M 07773 227784   T 01204 579842
E barbara@orrmanagement.co.uk
W www.orrmanagement.co.uk

PALMER Jackie AGENCY
30 Daws Hill Lane, High Wycombe, Bucks HP11 1PW
F 01494 510479   T 01494 520978
E jackie.palmer@btinternet.com
W www.jackiepalmer.co.uk

PAUL'S THEATRE AGENCY
Ardleigh House, 42 Ardleigh Green Road
Hornchurch, Essex RM11 2LG   T 01708 447123
E info@paulstheatreschool.com
W www.paulstheatreschool.com

PC THEATRICAL, MODEL & CASTING AGENCY
10 Strathmore Gardens, Edgware, Middlesex HA8 5HJ
F 020 8933 3418   T 020 8381 2229
E twinagy@aol.com
W www.twinagency.com

PERFORMERS AGENCY LTD
Southend Road, Corringham, Essex SS17 8JT
F 01375 672353   T 01375 665716
E office@performersagency.biz
W www.performersagency.biz

PHA YOUTH
Tanzaro House, Ardwick Green North, Manchester M12 6FZ
F 0161 273 4567   T 0161 273 4444
E youth@pha-agency.co.uk
W www.pha-agency.co.uk

PLATFORM TALENT MANAGEMENT LTD
16 Shalbourne Rise, Camberley
Surrey GU15 2EJ   T 01276 23256
E castings@kidsagency.tv
W www.kidsagency.tv

POLLYANNA MANAGEMENT LTD
1 Knighten Street, Wapping
London E1W 1PH   T/F 020 8530 6722
E aliceharwood@talktalk.net
W www.pollyannatheatre.org

POWER MODEL MANAGEMENT CASTING AGENCY
PO Box 1198, Salhouse, Norwich NR13 6WD   T 01603 777190
E info@powermodel.co.uk
W www.powermodel.co.uk

PWASSOCIATES
7 Catherine Cottages, Calvert Road
Middle Claydon, Bucks MK18 2HA   T 01296 733258
E emma@pwacademy.com
W www.pwacademy.com

RAMA YOUNG ACTORS
Huntingdon House, 278-290 Huntingdon Street
Nottingham NG1 3LY
F 0115 948 3696   T 0845 0540255
E martin@rama-global.co.uk
W www.ramayoungactors.co.uk

RASCALS MODEL AGENCY
13 Jubilee Parade, Snakes Lane East
Woodford Green, Essex IG8 7QG
F 020 8559 1035   T 020 8504 1111
E kids@rascals.co.uk
W www.rascals.co.uk

RAVENSCOURT MANAGEMENT
See CORONA MANAGEMENT

RDDC MANAGEMENT AGENCY
52 Bridleway, Waterfoot, Rossendale, Lancashire BB4 9DS
M 07900 840758   T 01706 211161
E info@rddc.co.uk   W www.rddc.co.uk

**REBEL SCHOOL OF THEATRE ARTS &
CASTING AGENCY LTD**
Based in Leeds & Huddersfield
PO Box 169, Huddersfield HD8 1BE   M 07808 803637
E suerebeltheatre@aol.com
W www.rebelschool.co.uk

REDROOFS THEATRE SCHOOL AGENCY
26 Bath Road, Maidenhead, Berks SL6 4JT
T 01628 822982 (Holiday Times)   T 01628 674092
E sam@redroofs.co.uk
W www.redroofs.co.uk

REFLECTIONS AGENCY
34 Knowle Avenue, Bexleyheath, Kent DA7 5LX
M 07958 617976   T/F 01322 410003
E c.johnson717@ntlworld.com
W www.riverside-reflections.webs.com

RHODES AGENCY
5 Dymoke Road, Hornchurch, Essex RM11 1AA
F 01708 730431   T 01708 747013
E rhodesarts@hotmail.com

RIDGEWAY MANAGEMENT
Fairley House, Andrews Lane, Cheshunt, Herts EN7 6LB
F 01992 633844   T 01992 633775
E info@ridgewaystudios.co.uk
W www.ridgewaystudios.co.uk

RISING STARS AGENCY
6 Gibsons Place, High Street, Eynsford, Kent DA4 0AA
M 07958 617976   M 07709 429354
E risingstars_agency@yahoo.co.uk
W www.risingstarsmusicaltheatre.webs.com

RISING STARS AGENCY
16 Llwyn Yr Eos Grove, Penyard, Merthyr Tydfil
Mid Glamorgan, Wales CF47 0GD
M 07894 164104   M 07947 345434
E risingstarsagency@yahoo.co.uk
W www.risingstarsagency.co.uk

ROSS David ACTING ACADEMY
8 Farrier Close, Sale, Cheshire M33 2ZL   M 07957 862317
E info@davidrossacting.com
W www.davidrossacting.com

SCALA KIDS CASTING
42 Rufford Avenue, Yeadon, Leeds LS19 7QR
F 0113 250 8806   T 0113 250 6823
E office@scalakids.com
W www.scalakids.com

SCALLYWAGS AGENCY LTD
12-18 Hoxton Street, London N1 6NG
F 020 7739 5753   T 020 7739 8820
E info@scallywags.co.uk
W www.scallywags.co.uk

SCHOOL CASTING
Liddiard Theatre, Polam Hall, Grange Road
Darlington, Durham DL1 5PA
F 01325 383539   T 01325 463383
E steve@schoolcasting.co.uk
W www.schoolcasting.co.uk

SCREAM MANAGEMENT
The Pie Factory, 101 Broadway
Media City, Manchester M50 2EQ   T 0161 660 3652
E info@screammanagement.com
W www.screammanagement.com

SELECT MANAGEMENT
PO Box 748, London NW4 1TT
F 020 8203 2007   M 07956 131494
E mail@selectmanagement.info
W www.selectmanagement.info

SEQUINS THEATRICAL AGENCY
8 Bideford Gardens, Bush Hill Park
Enfield, Middlesex EN1 2RP   T 020 8360 6601

SHINE MANAGEMENT
Flat 10, Valentine House
Church Road
Guildford, Surrey GU1 4NG   T 020 8133 1827
E info@shine-management.com
W www.shine-management.com

SINGER Sandra ASSOCIATES
21 Cotswold Road, Westcliff-on-Sea
Essex SS0 8AA   T 01702 331616
E sandrasingeruk@aol.com
W www.sandrasinger.com

SMARTYPANTS AGENCY
San-Marie Studios, Southend Road, Billericay CM11 2PZ
F 01277 633998   T 01277 633772
E office@smartypantsagency.co.uk
W www.smartypantsagency.co.uk

SMITH Elisabeth LTD
8 Dawes Lane, Sarratt
Rickmansworth, Herts WD3 6BB   T 0845 8721331
E models@elisabethsmith.co.uk
W www.elisabethsmith.co.uk

SPEAKE Barbara AGENCY
East Acton Lane, London W3 7EG   T 020 8743 6096
E speakekids2@aol.com

SRA AGENCY
Lockhart Road, Cobham, Surrey KT11 2AX   T 01932 863194
E agency@susanrobertsacademy.co.uk

STAGE 84 YORKSHIRE SCHOOL OF PERFORMING ARTS
Old Bell Chapel, Town Lane, Idle, Bradford
West Yorks BD10 8PR
M 07785 244984   T 01274 569197
E valeriejackson@stage84.com

STAGE CENTRAL CASTING AGENCY
14 Gilsforth Lane, Whixley YO26 8BF
M 07940 014448   T 01423 331478
E stagecentral@gmail.com
W www.stagecentral.co.uk

STAGE KIDS AGENCY
Children, Teenagers & Adults
1 Greenfield, Welwyn Garden City
Herts AL8 7HW   T 01707 328359
E stagekds@aol.com
W www.stagekids.co.uk

STAGECOACH AGENCY UK & IRELAND
PO Box 127, Ross-on-Wye HR9 6WZ
F 0845 4082464   T 0845 4082468
E tarquin@stagecoachagency.co.uk
W www.stagecoachagency.co.uk

STAGEWORKS PERFORMING ARTS SCHOOL
The Stablehouse Barn, Remenham Hill
Henley on Thames, Oxon RG9 3HN   M 07775 795354
E emma_taylor@sky.com
W www.stageworks.org.uk

STARDOM CASTING AGENCY & THEATRE SCHOOL
16 Pinebury Drive, Queensbury, Bradford BD13 2TA
M 07740 091019   T/F 01274 818051
E liz.stardom@btinternet.com

STARMAKER
17 Kendal Avenue, Shinfield, Reading, Berks RG2 9AR
F 0118 988 8708   T 0118 988 7959
E dave@starmakeruk.org
W www.starmakeruk.org

STARSTRUCK MANAGEMENT
85 Hewson Road, Lincoln
Lincolnshire LN1 1RZ   T 01522 887894
E starstruckacademy@hotmail.com

STOMP! MANAGEMENT
c/o Suite 2, Fiboard House, 5 Oakleigh Gardens
London N20 9AB   T 020 8446 9898
E stompmanagement@aol.com
W www.stompmanagement.com

TAKE2 CASTING AGENCY & TALENT MANAGEMENT
28 Beech Park Road
Foxrock, Dublin 18   T 00 353 872563403
E pamela@take2.ie
W www.take2.ie

TALENTED KIDS PERFORMING ARTS SCHOOL & AGENCY
23 Burrow Manor, Calverstown
Kilcullen, Co. Kildare, Ireland
M 00 353 872480348   T/F 00 353 45485464
E talentedkids@hotmail.com
W www.talentedkidsireland.com

TANWOOD
72 Nyland Road, Nythe
Swindon, Wilts SN3 3RJ   M 07774 517469
E tanwood.agency2@ntlworld.com
W www.tanwood.co.uk

TELEVISION WORKSHOP THE
Nottingham Group
30 Main Street, Calverton
Notts NG14 6FQ   T 0115 845 0764
E ian@thetelevisionworkshop.co.uk

THAMES VALLEY THEATRICAL AGENCY
Dorchester House, Wimblestraw Road, Berinsfield
Oxfordshire OX10 7LZ
M 07956 256189   T 01865 340333
E donna@childactors.tv

TICKLEDOM AGENCY
31 Rectory Gardens, London N8 7PJ   T 020 8341 7044
E agency@tickledomtheatreschool.com
W www.tickledomtheatreschool.com

TK MANAGEMENT
Spires Meade, 4 Bridleways
Wendover, Bucks HP22 6DN
F 01296 623969   M 07985 510038
E tkpamanagement@aol.com

TOMORROW'S TALENT AGENCY
Contact: By e-mail only. Based in Chelmsford, Essex
T 01202 526667
E agents@tomorrowstalent.co.uk
W www.tomorrowstalent.co.uk

TOP TALENT AGENCY LTD
*Representing Child Actors & Models
from Babies to Teenagers*
c/o Top Hat Stage & Screen School, PO Box 860
St Albans, Herts AL1 9BR
F 01727 812666   T 01727 855903
E admin@toptalentagency.co.uk
W www.toptalentagency.co.uk

TRULY SCRUMPTIOUS LTD
66 Bidwell Gardens
London N11 2AU
F 020 8888 4584   T 020 8888 4204
E bookings@trulyscrumptious.co.uk
W www.trulyscrumptious.co.uk

TUESDAYS CHILD
Children, Teenagers & Adults
Oakfield House, Springwood Way
Macclesfield SK10 2XA   T/F 01625 501765
E info@tuesdayschildagency.co.uk
W www.tuesdayschildagency.co.uk

TURNSTONE CASTING & ENTERTAINMENT
Hilton Hall, Hilton Lane, Essington WV11 2BQ
M 07866 211647   T 0845 5570927
E mark_turner85@hotmail.com

TWINS
See PC THEATRICAL, MODEL & CASTING AGENCY

URBAN ANGELS
PO Box 45453, London SE26 6UZ
F 0845 8387774   T 0845 8387773
E south@urbanangelsagency.com

URBAN ANGELS NORTH
Contact: Sarah Heeler
Portland House, Belmont Business Park
Belmont, Durham DH1 1TW
F 0191 375 5701   T 0191 375 5704
E sarah@urbanangelsagency.com
W www.urbanangelsagency.com

VALLÉ ACADEMY THEATRICAL AGENCY
The Vallé Academy Studios, Wilton House
Delamare Road, Cheshunt, Herts EN8 9SG
F 01992 622868   T 01992 622861
E agency@valleacademy.co.uk   W www.valleacademy.co.uk

W-A-P-A AGENCY
6-8 Akroyd Place, Halifax, West Yorkshire HX1 1YH
F 01422 360958   T 01422 351958
E enquiries@w-a-p-a.co.uk   W www.w-a-p-a.co.uk

WHITEHALL PERFORMING ARTS CENTRE
Rayleigh Road, Leigh-on-Sea
Essex SS9 5UU   T/F 01702 529290
W www.whitehallcollege.co.uk

WILLIAMSON & HOLMES
51 St Martin's Lane, London WC2N 4EA
F 020 7240 0408   T 020 7240 0407
E info@williamsonandholmes.co.uk

WINGS AGENCY
29 Portsmouth Road, Godalming, Surrey GU7 2JU
F 01483 424522   T 01483 428998
E admin@wingsagency.co.uk
W www.angelstheatreschool.co.uk

WYSE AGENCY
Hill House, 1 Hill Farm Road
Whittlesford, Cambs CB22 4NB   T 01223 832288
E frances.wyse@btinternet.com

YAT MANAGEMENT (Young Actors Theatre)
70-72 Barnsbury Road, London N1 0ES
F 020 7833 9467   T 020 7278 2101
E agent@yati.org.uk   W www.yati.org.uk

YOUNG Sylvia AGENCY
Sylvia Young Theatre School
1 Nutford Place, London W1H 5YZ
M 07779 145732   T 020 7723 0037
E info@sylviayoungagency.com

YOUNG ACTORS COMPANY LTD THE
3 Marshall Road, Cambridge CB1 7TY
F 01223 416511   T 01223 416474
E info@theyoungactorscompany.com
W www.theyoungactorscompany.com

YOUNG ACTORS FILE THE
31 Nursery Road, Angmering
West Sussex BN16 4GQ
M 07789 888575   T 01903 782354
E young.actorsfile@btinternet.com

YOUNGBLOOD THEATRE COMPANY
c/o The BWH Agency Ltd
117 Shaftesbury Avenue, London WC2H 8AD
F 020 7240 2287   T 020 7240 5299
E info@thebwhagency.co.uk   W www.thebwhagency.co.uk

YOUNGSTARS
Contact: Coralyn Canfor-Dumas
4 Haydon Dell, Bushey, Herts WD23 1DD
F 020 8950 5701   M 07966 176756
E youngstarsagency@gmail.com

ZADEK NOWELL MANAGEMENT
66 Twyford Avenue, London N2 9NL   T 020 7240 5931
E zadeknowell@gmail.com   W www.zadeknowell.com

ACORN ENTERTAINMENTS LTD
PO Box 64, Cirencester, Glos GL7 5YD
F 01285 642291   T 01285 644622
E info@acornents.co.uk
W www.acornents.co.uk

ARTIST PROMOTION MANAGEMENT
Concert Promotion
13-14 Margaret Street, London W1W 8RN
F 020 7224 0111   T 020 7224 1992
E mail@harveygoldsmith.com
W www.harveygoldsmith.com

ASKONAS HOLT LTD
Classical Music
Lincoln House, 300 High Holborn, London WC1V 7JH
F 020 7400 1799   T 020 7400 1700
E info@askonasholt.co.uk
W www.askonasholt.co.uk

AVALON PROMOTIONS LTD
4A Exmoor Street, London W10 6BD
F 020 7598 7334   T 020 7598 7333
E enquiries@avalonuk.com

BARRUCCI LEISURE ENTERPRISES LTD
Promoters
45-47 Cheval Place, London SW7 1EW
F 020 7581 2509   T 020 7225 2255
E barrucci@barrucci.com

BLOCK Derek ARTISTES AGENCY
70-76 Bell Street, Marylebone, London NW1 6SP
F 020 7724 2102   T 020 7724 2101
E derekblock@derekblock.co.uk

FLYING MUSIC
FM House, 110 Clarendon Road, London W11 2HR
F 020 7221 5016   T 020 7221 7799
E info@flyingmusic.co.uk
W www.flyingmusic.com

GUBBAY Raymond LTD
Dickens House
15 Tooks Court, London EC4A 1LB
F 020 7025 3751   T 020 7025 3750
E info@raymondgubbay.co.uk
W www.raymondgubbay.co.uk

HOBBS Liz GROUP LTD
65 London Road, Newark
Nottinghamshire NG24 1RZ
F 01636 703343   T 0870 0702702
E info@lizhobbsgroup.com
W www.lizhobbsgroup.com

HOCHHAUSER Victor
4 Oak Hill Way, London NW3 7LR
F 020 7431 2531   T 020 7794 0987
E admin@victorhochhauser.co.uk

IMG ARTS & ENTERTAINMENT
McCormack House
Burlington Lane, London W4 2TH
F 020 8233 5301   T 020 8233 5300

McINTYRE Phil ENTERTAINMENT
85 Newman Street, London W1T 3EU   T 020 7291 9000
E info@mcintyre-ents.com

MEADOW Jeremy LTD
73 Great Titchfield Street, London W1W 6RD
F 0870 7627882   T 020 7436 2244
E info@jeremymeadow.com
W www.jeremymeadow.com

RBM
Comedy
3rd Floor, 168 Victoria Street
London SW1E 5LB
F 020 7630 6549   T 020 7630 7733
E info@rbmcomedy.com
W www.rbmcomedy.com

ACCELERATE LTD
374 Ley Street, Ilford IG1 4AE
M 07956 104086   M 07782 199181
E info@accelerate-productions.co.uk
W www.accelerate-productions.co.uk

BODYWORK AGENCY
17-19 Brookside, Cambridge CB2 1JE
F 01223 568231   T 01223 309990
E agency@bodyworkds.co.uk

CREATIVE KIDZ & CO
Incorporating NeighbourHood Productions
9 Weavers Terrace, Fulham
London SW6 1QE   M 07958 377595
E info@creativekidzandco.co.uk

DANCERS
1 Charlotte Street, London W1T 1RD
F 020 7636 1657   T 020 7636 1473
E info@features.co.uk
W www.features.co.uk

DANCERS@BBA
First Floor, 23 Tavistock Street
Covent Garden, London WC2E 7NX
F 020 7379 5560   T 020 7395 1405
E dancers@buchanan-associates.co.uk
W www.dancersatbba.co.uk

DANCERS INC. INTERNATIONAL COLLECTIVE
9-13 Grape Street, Covent Garden
London WC2H 8ED
F 020 7557 6656   T 020 7557 6650
E miranda@internationalcollective.com
W www.dancersinc.co.uk

ELLITE MANAGEMENT
'The Dancer', 8 Peterson Road
Wakefield WF1 4EB
M 07957 631510   T 0845 6525361
E enquiries@ellitemanagement.co.uk
W www.elliteproductions.co.uk

EVENT MODEL MANAGEMENT
Dancers. Models
Suite 230, 405 Kings Road
Chelsea, London SW10 0BB   M 07581 223738
E info@eventmodel.co.uk
W www.eventmodelmanagement.co.uk

FEATURES
1 Charlotte Street, London W1T 1RD
F 020 7636 1657   T 020 7637 1487
E info@features.co.uk
W www.features.co.uk

HEADNOD TALENT AGENCY
63 Redchurch Street, London E2 7DJ   T/F 020 7502 9478
E info@headnodagency.com
W www.headnodagency.com

JK DANCE PRODUCTIONS
South Manchester Film & Television Studios
Battersea Road
Stockport SK4 3EA   T 0161 432 5222
E info@jkdance.co.uk
W www.jkdance.co.uk

K TALENT
24-25 Macklin Street, Covent Garden
London WC2B 5NN
T 0844 5672470   T 020 7691 8930
E mail@ktalent.co.uk
W www.ktalent.co.uk

KEW PERSONAL MANAGEMENT
PO Box 679, RH1 9BT   T 020 8871 3697
E info@kewpersonalmanagement.com
W www.kewpersonalmanagement.com

KMC AGENCIES
Garden Studios
11-15 Betterton Street, London WC2H 9BP
F 0870 4421780   T 0845 6602459
E london@kmcagencies.co.uk

PO Box 122, 48 Great Ancoats Street
Manchester M4 5AB
F 0161 237 9812   T 0161 237 3009
E casting@kmcagencies.co.uk

LONGRUN ARTISTES
Contact: Gina Long, Irene Wernli
Marylebone Dance Studios
12 Lisson Grove, London NW1 6TS
F 0871 5227926   T 020 8316 6662
E gina@longrunartistes.co.uk
W www.longrunartistes.co.uk

MARLOWES DANCERS & MUSICAL THEATRE AGENCY
HMS President, Victoria Embankment
Blackfriars, London EC4Y 0HJ   T 020 7193 4484
E mitch@marlowes.eu
W www.marlowes.eu

MITCHELL MAAS McLENNAN
MD2000 Offices, 29 Thomas Street
Woolwich, London SE18 6HU
M 07540 995802   T/F 020 8301 8745
E agency@mmm2000.co.uk
W www.mmm2000.co.uk

PINEAPPLE AGENCY
Montgomery House
159-161 Balls Pond Road, Islington, London N1 4BG
F 020 7241 3006   T 020 7241 6601
E pineapple.agency@btconnect.com
W www.pineappleagency.com

RAZZAMATAZZ MANAGEMENT
204 Holtye Road, East Grinstead RH19 3ES
M 07836 268292   T/F 01342 301617
E razzamatazzmanagement@btconnect.com

REANIMATOR
The Old Cinema, 1st Floor, 59-61 The Broadway
Haywards Heath, West Sussex RH16 3AS
F 01444 447030   T 01444 447020
E management@reanimator.co.uk
W www.reanimator.co.uk

info**page**

Why do I need a dance agent?

As with any other agent, a dance agent will submit their clients for jobs, negotiate contracts, handle paperwork and offer advice. In return for these services they will charge commission ranging from 10-15%. The agents listed on the following pages specialise in representing and promoting dancers. They will possess the relevant contacts in the industry that you need to get auditions and jobs.

How should I use these listings?

If you are a dancer getting started in the industry, looking to change your existing agent, or wishing to take on an additional agent that represents you for dance alongside your main acting agent, the following pages will supply you with up-to-date contact details for dance agencies. Every company listed is done so by written request to us. Please see the main 'Agents and Personal Managers' advice section for further guidance on choosing and approaching agents.

Should I pay an agent to join their books? Or sign a contract?

Equity (the actors' trade union) does not recommend that artists pay an agent to join their client list. Before signing a contract, you should be very clear about the terms and commitments involved. For advice on both of these issues, or if you experience any problems with a current agent, we recommend that you contact Equity www.equity.org.uk. They also produce the booklet *You and your Agent* which is free to all Equity members and available from their website's members' area.

What is Spotlight Dancers?

Spotlight Dancers is a specialist casting directory published annually by Spotlight. Members receive a page in the directory containing a headshot and body shot, agency contact details and selected credits as well as an online CV on the Spotlight website. These are used by dance employers throughout the UK to locate dancers and send out casting or audition information. Dancers who attend CDET (Council for Dance Education and Training) accredited schools receive a discount when applying in their graduating year. Dancers wishing to promote themselves for job opportunities in commercial theatre, musicals, opera, film, television, live music and video, corporate events and many other areas of the industry should consider joining: for more information visit www.spotlight.com/artists/dancers.

Should I join Spotlight's Actors/Actresses directory or the Dancers directory?

Depending on your skills, training and experience, you may be eligible for both directories if you are interested in promoting yourself both as an actor and as a dancer. If you join both, you would receive an entry into each directory and two separate online CVs. You would also qualify for a 25% discount off the Dancers membership fee. If you only want to join one or the other, then you will need to consider which area of the industry you want to focus on in your career. Musical theatre experience can qualify you for either directory, depending on whether your training/roles involved mainly dancing or acting. This is something you will need to think about, and something you should discuss with your agent if you sign with one.

Where can I find more information?

Please refer to the guest article on the next page and the info pages preceding the 'Dance Companies' listings for further information about the dance industry.

Mitchell Maas McLennan (a.k.a. MMM) was originally started to represent the graduates of Millennium Performing Arts Theatre School. The highly trained graduates achieved success very quickly and, in consequence, the agency's name rapidly became known to the profession and to other performers.

Compared to some agencies our client list is small. It is our intention to keep the group manageable and personal. Our books are always open as we continuously look to fill age gaps, character types, ethnicities and nationalities. This applies across the board for all areas of theatre and musical theatre. Everyone, including MPA graduates, must audition for the agency. We audition every two to three months.

What do we look for? We rate performance quality at the top with technique a very close second. This goes for all disciplines. We divide musical theatre into two categories - those who can dance or not! Everyone is expected to sing and act. There is always an actor/director present for acting auditions.

The job of an agent is not dissimilar to that of a good teacher when preparing young dancers and musical theatre performers for a successful career. Mental attitude and common sense are the tools that guide a successful career of longevity. Support, advice and encouragement - without creating dependency - are the tools that a good agent employs in the client/agent relationship. An effective agent should be able to make a young performer understand that a good career should have a campaign strategy.

We are very fortunate at Mitchell Maas McLennan because the careers of the three directors/agents were in the field of dance and musical theatre. Our assessments are based on years of experience. Taken as given that performance quality and sound technique are in place, the character traits we look for are determination, positive attitude and a realistic understanding of the business. Body language is also very important. Dancers should be bursting with vibrant energy; anyone who needs the *barre* as a continuous prop or who stretches languidly in a chair during the interview doesn't engender a lot of confidence.

The agency considers membership of Spotlight a priority; this is a prerequisite to joining MMM. We consider commercials a healthy source of income for resting and working artists alike and we pursue them with fervour!

At Mitchell Maas McLennan we pride ourselves on offering continuing professional development to our clients. We believe that honing skills keeps them sharp. We arrange workshops and private tuition for those interested. A recent workshop offered was an 'audition day' with Tim Sheader, Director of the Regents Park Open Air Theatre and Mary King, the world renowned singing coach. Our clients had the opportunity to present monologues and songs to the panel.

Too many dancers fail to realise that on graduation their job begins. Too many fail to make the connection - unless they are members of dance companies - that they are akin to athletes and that training never stops. Too many fail to realise that to reach the top and maintain status one must strive continuously to seek elusive 'perfection'.

The young dancer often imagines that they will take the West End by storm because they have been very successful in their college. They do not appreciate the full impact of what the West End entails until they go to their first big audition and stand next to the 'war horses' that have been in the business for years. Only a small percentage of graduates can cope. Often the best route for the newcomer is to go abroad or take regional work to gain the polish that only continuous performing gives before engaging on the West End assault.

Wishing you all the best from Ikky Maas, Donald McLennan and me... Jacki Mitchell.

Please send any enquiries to agency@mmm2000.co.uk, or visit www.mmm2000.co.uk for more information.

RED & BLACK
E info@red-black.co.uk
M 07722 887277
W www.red-black.co.uk

RUDEYE DANCE AGENCY
73 St John Street
London EC1M 4NJ
T 020 7014 3023
E info@rudeye.com
W www.rudeye.com

SCRIMGEOUR Donald ARTISTS AGENT
49 Springcroft Avenue
London N2 9JH
F 020 8883 9751
T 020 8444 6248
E vwest@dircon.co.uk

SHOW TEAM PRODUCTIONS THE
Dancers & Choreographers
9 Church Street
Brighton BN1 1US
T 0845 4671010
E info@theshowteam.co.uk
W www.theshowteam.co.uk

SINGER Sandra ASSOCIATES
Dancers & Choreographers
21 Cotswold Road
Westcliff-on-Sea
Essex SS0 8AA
T 01702 331616
E sandrasingeruk@aol.com
W www.sandrasinger.com

S.O.S.
85 Bannerman House
Lawn Lane, London SW8 1UA
M 07740 359770
T 020 7735 5133
E info@sportsofseb.com
W www.sportsofseb.com

SUCCESS
Room 236, 2nd Floor, Linen Hall
162-168 Regent Street, London W1B 5TB
F 020 7494 3787
T 020 7734 3356
E ee@successagency.co.uk
W www.successagency.co.uk

SUMMERS Mark MANAGEMENT
1 Beaumont Avenue, West Kensington
London W14 9LP
T 020 7229 8413
E info@marksummers.com
W www.marksummers.com

T W MANAGEMENT AGENCY
66-74 The Promenade, Blackpool
Lancashire FY1 1HB
T 01253 749332
E marie.cavney@twmanagementagency.co.uk
W www.twmanagementagency.co.uk

TWITCH EVENT CHOREOGRAPHY
5 Breakspears Mews, Brockley SE4 1PY
M 07932 656358
M 07747 770816
E info@twitch.uk.com
W www.twitch.uk.com

UNITED PRODUCTIONS
Choreographers, Dancers, Stylists
6 Shaftesbury Mews, Clapham
London SW4 9BP
T/F 020 7498 6563
E info@unitedproductions.biz
W www.unitedproductions.biz

W ATHLETIC
The Hub, Fowler Avenue
IQ Farnborough Business Park GU14 7JF
T 01252 302255
E wathletic@me.com
W www.wathletic.com

SAMUEL FRENCH LTD

Publishers of Plays • Agents for the Collection of Royalties
Specialist Booksellers
52 Fitzroy Street London W1T 5JR
Tel 020 7255 4300 (Bookshop) 020 7387 9373 (Enquiries)
Fax 020 7387 2161 www.samuelfrench-london.co.uk
e-mail: theatre@samuelfrench-london.co.uk

A & B PERSONAL MANAGEMENT LTD
PMA Member
PO Box 64671, London NW3 9LH — T 020 7434 4262
E billellis@aandb.co.uk

ABNER STEIN
10 Roland Gardens, London SW7 3PH
F 020 7370 6316 — T 020 7373 0456
E abner@abnerstein.co.uk

AGENCY (LONDON) LTD THE
PMA Member
24 Pottery Lane, Holland Park
London W11 4LZ
F 020 7727 9037 — T 020 7727 1346
E info@theagency.co.uk
W www.theagency.co.uk

A R G (ARTISTS RIGHTS GROUP LTD)
PMA Member
4 Great Portland Street
London W1W 8PA
F 020 7436 6700 — T 020 7436 6400
E argall@argtalent.com

ASPER Pauline MANAGEMENT
PMA Member
Jacobs Cottage, Reservoir Lane
Sedlescombe, East Sussex TN33 0PJ — T/F 01424 870412
E pauline.asper@virgin.net

BERLIN ASSOCIATES
PMA Member
7 Tyers Gate, London SE1 3HX
F 020 7632 5296 — T 020 7836 1112
E agents@berlinassociates.com
W www.berlinassociates.com

BLAKE FRIEDMANN
Novels, Non-Fiction & TV/Film Scripts
122 Arlington Road, London NW1 7HP
F 020 7284 0442 — T 020 7284 0408
E info@blakefriedmann.co.uk
W www.blakefriedmann.co.uk

BRITTEN Nigel MANAGEMENT
Riverbank House
1 Putney Bridge Approach
London SW6 3JD
F 020 7384 3862 — T 020 7384 3842
E office@nbmanagement.com

BRODIE Alan REPRESENTATION LTD
PMA Member
Paddock Suite, The Courtyard
55 Charterhouse Street, London EC1M 6HA
F 020 7253 6226 — T 020 7079 7990
E info@alanbrodie.com
W www.alanbrodie.com

CANN Alexandra REPRESENTATION
52 Beauchamp Place
London SW3 1NY — T 020 7584 9047
E alex@alexandracann.co.uk

CASAROTTO RAMSAY & ASSOCIATES LTD
PMA Member
Waverley House, 7-12 Noel Street
London W1F 8GQ
F 020 7287 9128 — T 020 7287 4450
E info@casarotto.co.uk
W www.casarotto.co.uk

CLOWES Jonathan LTD
PMA Member
10 Iron Bridge House
Bridge Approach
London NW1 8BD
F 020 7722 7677 — T 020 7722 7674
E admin@jonathanclowes.co.uk

COCHRANE Elspeth PERSONAL MANAGEMENT
Existing Clients only
No New Applicants
See ASQUITH & HORNER page 26

CULVERHOUSE & JAMES LTD
Office 3-4, Orchard House
Halsall Business Park
17 Summerwood Lane
Halsall L39 8TH
F 01704 840410 — T 01704 841320
E enquiries@culverhousejames.co.uk
W www.culverhousejames.co.uk

West Farm, Southerndown
Vale of Glamorgan CF32 0PY — T 01656 881068

CURTIS BROWN GROUP LTD
PMA Member
5th Floor, Haymarket House
28-29 Haymarket, London SW1Y 4SP
F 020 7393 4403 — T 020 7393 4400
E cb@curtisbrown.co.uk
W www.curtisbrown.co.uk

DAISH Judy ASSOCIATES LTD
PMA Member
2 St Charles Place, London W10 6EG
F 020 8964 8966 — T 020 8964 8811
E judy@judydaish.com
W www.judydaish.com

DENCH ARNOLD AGENCY THE
PMA Member
10 Newburgh Street
London W1F 7RN
F 020 7439 1355 — T 020 7437 4551
E contact@denseharnold.com
W www.denseharnold.com

de WOLFE Felix
PMA Member
Kingsway House, 103 Kingsway
London WC2B 6QX
F 020 7242 8119 — T 020 7242 5066
E info@felixdewolfe.com
W www.felixdewolfe.com

DREW Bryan LTD
31 Oakley House, 103 Sloane Street
London SW1X 9PP   T 020 7823 2346
E bryan@bryandrewltd.com

FARNES Norma MANAGEMENT
9 Orme Court, London W2 4RL
F 020 7792 2110   T 020 7727 1544

FILLINGHAM Janet ASSOCIATES
PMA Member
52 Lowther Road, London SW13 9NU
F 020 8748 7374   T 020 8748 5594
E info@jfillassoc.co.uk
W www.janetfillingham.com

FILM RIGHTS LTD
Suite 306, Belsize Business Centre
258 Belsize Road, London NW6 4BT
F 020 7624 3629   T 020 7316 1837
E information@filmrights.ltd.uk
W www.filmrights.ltd.uk

FITCH Laurence LTD
Suite 306, Belsize Business Centre
258 Belsize Road, London NW6 4BT
F 020 7624 3629   T 020 7316 1837

FRENCH Samuel LTD
PMA Member
52 Fitzroy Street, Fitzrovia
London W1T 5JR
F 020 7387 2161   T 020 7387 9373
E theatre@samuelfrench-london.co.uk
W www.samuelfrench-london.co.uk

FUTERMAN, ROSE & ASSOCIATES
PMA Member. TV/Film, Showbiz & Music Biographies
91 St Leonards Road, London SW14 7BL
F 020 8286 4860   T 020 8255 7755
E guy@futermanrose.co.uk
W www.futermanrose.co.uk

GILLIS Pamela MANAGEMENT
46 Sheldon Avenue, London N6 4JR
F 020 8341 5564   T 020 8340 7868

GLASS Eric LTD
25 Ladbroke Crescent, Notting Hill
London W11 1PS
F 020 7229 6220   T 020 7229 9500
E eglassltd@aol.com

HALL Rod AGENCY LTD THE
PMA Member
7 Mallow Street, London EC1Y 8RQ   F 0845 6384094
E office@rodhallagency.com
W www.rodhallagency.com

HANCOCK Roger LTD
PMA Member
7 Broadbent Close, Highgate Village
London N6 5JW
F 020 8348 4087   T 020 8341 7243
E tim@rogerhancock.com

HIGHAM David ASSOCIATES LTD
PMA Member
5-8 Lower John Street, Golden Square
London W1F 9HA
F 020 7437 1072   T 020 7434 5900
E dha@davidhigham.co.uk
W www.davidhigham.co.uk

HOSKINS Valerie ASSOCIATES LTD
PMA Member
20 Charlotte Street, London W1T 2NA
F 020 7637 4493   T 020 7637 4490
E vha@vhassociates.co.uk

INDEPENDENT TALENT GROUP LTD
PMA Member. Formerly ICM, London
Oxford House, 76 Oxford Street
London W1D 1BS
F 020 7323 0101   T 020 7636 6565
W www.independenttalent.com

JFL (Jill Foster Ltd)
PMA Member
1 Lyric Square, London W6 0NB   T 020 7602 1263
E agents@jflagency.com
W www.jflagency.com

KASS Michelle ASSOCIATES
PMA Member
85 Charing Cross Road
London WC2H 0AA
F 020 7734 3394   T 020 7439 1624
E office@michellekass.co.uk

KENIS Steve & Co
PMA Member
Royalty House, 72-74 Dean Street
London W1D 3SG
F 020 7287 6328   T 020 7434 9055
E sk@sknco.com

MACFARLANE CHARD ASSOCIATES LTD
PMA Member
33 Percy Street, London W1T 2DF
F 020 7636 7751   T 020 7636 7750
E enquiries@macfarlane-chard.co.uk
W www.macfarlane-chard.co.uk

MACNAUGHTON LORD REPRESENTATION
PMA Member
Unit 10, The Broomhouse Studios
50 Sulivan Road, London SW6 3DX
F 020 7371 7563   T 020 7384 9517
E info@mlrep.com
W www.mlrep.com

MANN Andrew LTD
1 Old Compton Street, London W1D 5JA
F 020 3441 0988   T 020 7734 4751
E info@andrewmann.co.uk
W www.andrewmann.co.uk

MANS Johnny PRODUCTIONS LTD
PO Box 196, Hoddesdon
Herts EN10 7WG
F 01992 470516   T 01992 470907
E johnnymansagent@aol.com
W www.johnnymansproductions.co.uk

MARJACQ SCRIPTS LTD
Prose. Screenplays. No Stage Plays or Musicals
34 Devonshire Place, London W1G 6JW
F 020 7935 9115   T 020 7935 9499
E enquiries@marjacq.com
W www.marjacq.com

MARVIN Blanche
21A St Johns Wood High Street
London NW8 7NG   T/F 020 7722 2313
E blanchemarvin17@hotmail.com

Culverhouse **and** James **limited** Literary Agents

- Halsall Business Park, Orchard House, 17 Summerwood Lane, Halsall L39 8TH
- West Farm, Southerndown, Vale of Glamorgan CF32 0PY
- T: 01704 841320   e: enquiries@culverhousejames.co.uk   www.culverhousejames.co.uk

---

M.B.A. LITERARY AGENTS LTD
PMA Member
62 Grafton Way, London W1T 5DW
F 020 7387 2042   T 020 7387 2076
E intern@mbalit.co.uk
W www.mbalit.co.uk

McLEAN Bill PERSONAL MANAGEMENT
23B Deodar Road, London SW15 2NP   T 020 8789 8191

MLR
See MACNAUGHTON LORD REPRESENTATION

MORRIS William ENDEAVOR ENTERTAINMENT
PMA Member
Centre Point, 103 New Oxford Street
London WC1A 1DD
F 020 7534 6900   T 020 7534 6800

NARROW ROAD COMPANY THE
PMA Member
182 Brighton Road, Coulsdon
Surrey CR5 2NF
F 020 8763 2558   T 020 8763 9895
E richardireson@narrowroad.co.uk

PFD
PMA Member
Drury House, 34-43 Russell Street
London WC2B 5HA
F 020 7836 9539   T 020 7344 1000
E info@pfd.co.uk
W www.pfd.co.uk

POLLINGER LTD
9 Staple Inn, Holborn
London WC1V 7QH
F 020 7242 5737   T 020 7404 0342
E info@pollingerltd.com
W www.pollingerltd.com

ROSICA COLIN LTD
1 Clareville Grove Mews, London SW7 5AH
F 020 7244 6441   T 020 7370 1080

SAYLE SCREEN LTD
PMA Member. Screenwriters & Directors for Film, Stage &
Television
11 Jubilee Place, London SW3 3TD
F 020 7823 3363   T 020 7823 3883

SEIFERT Linda MANAGEMENT LTD
PMA Member
91 Berwick Street, London W1F ONE
F 020 7292 7391   T 020 7292 7390
E contact@lindaseifert.com
W www.lindaseifert.com

SHARLAND ORGANISATION LTD
PMA Member
The Manor House, Manor Street
Raunds, Northants NN9 6JW   T 01933 626600
E tso@btconnect.com

SHEIL LAND ASSOCIATES LTD
PMA Member. Literary, Film & Stage
52 Doughty Street
London WC1N 2LS
F 020 7831 2127   T 020 7405 9351
E info@sheilland.co.uk

STEEL Elaine
PMA Member. Writers' Agent
110 Gloucester Avenue
London NW1 8HX
F 01273 772400   T 01273 739022
E ecmsteel@aol.com

STEINBERG Micheline ASSOCIATES
PMA Member
104 Great Portland Street
London W1W 6PE   T 020 7631 1310
E info@steinplays.com
W www.steinplays.com

STEVENS Rochelle & Co
PMA Member
2 Terretts Place, Upper Street
London N1 1QZ
F 020 7354 5729   T 020 7359 3900
E info@rochellestevens.com

TENNYSON AGENCY THE
10 Cleveland Avenue
Merton Park
London SW20 9EW   T 020 8543 5939
E submissions@tenagy.co.uk

TYRRELL Julia MANAGEMENT
PMA Member
57 Greenham Road, London N10 1LN
F 020 8374 5580   T 020 8374 0575
E julia@jtmanagement.co.uk
W www.jtmanagement.co.uk

WARE Cecily LITERARY AGENTS
PMA Member
19C John Spencer Square
London N1 2LZ
F 020 7226 9828   T 020 7359 3787
E info@cecilyware.com
W www.cecilyware.com

WEINBERGER Josef LTD
PMA Member
12-14 Mortimer Street, London W1T 3JJ
F 020 7436 9616   T 020 7580 2827
E general.info@jwmail.co.uk
W www.josef-weinberger.com

WESSON Penny
PMA Member
26 King Henry's Road, London NW3 3RP
F 020 7483 2890   T 020 7722 6607
E penny@pennywesson.demon.co.uk

ALLEN Debi ASSOCIATES
The Heals Building, 22 Torrington Place
London WC1E 7HP
F 020 7255 6128   T 020 7255 6123
E info@debiallenassociates.com
W www.debiallenassociates.com

APM ASSOCIATES
Contact: Linda French
Pinewood Studios, Pinewood Road
Iver Heath, Bucks SL0 0NH
F 01753 639205   T 01753 639204
E apm@apmassociates.net
W www.apmassociates.net

ARLINGTON ENTERPRISES LTD
1-3 Charlotte Street, London W1T 1RD
F 020 7580 4994   T 020 7580 0702
E info@arlington-enterprises.co.uk
W www.arlingtonenterprises.co.uk

BARR Becca MANAGEMENT
174 New Bond Street, London W1S 4RG   T 020 3137 2980
E becca@beccabarrmanagement.co.uk
W www.beccabarrmanagement.co.uk

BLACKBURN SACHS ASSOCIATES
Argyll House, All Saints Passage
London SW18 1EP   T 020 7292 7555
E presenters@blackburnsachsassociates.com
W www.blackburnsachsassociates.com

CAMERON Sara MANAGEMENT
See TAKE THREE MANAGEMENT

CHASE PERSONAL MANAGEMENT
2nd Floor, 3 Kew Road
Richmond, Surrey TW9 2NQ
M 07775 683955   T 020 8940 7198
E sue@chasemanagement.co.uk
W www.chasepersonalmanagement.co.uk

CHP ARTIST MANAGEMENT
Meadowcroft Barn, Crowbrook Road
Askett, Princes Risborough
Buckinghamshire HP27 9LS   T 01844 345630
E contact@chproductions.org.uk
W www.chproductions.org.uk

CINEL GABRAN MANAGEMENT
PO Box 101, Newholm, Whitby
North Yorkshire YO21 3WT
F 0845 0666601   T 0845 0666605
E mail@cinelgabran.co.uk
W www.cinelgabran.co.uk

PO Box 5163, Cardiff CF5 9BJ
E info@cinelgabran.co.uk   T 029 2066 6600

CRAWFORDS
PO Box 56662, London W13 3BH   T 020 8947 9999
E cr@wfords.com
W www.crawfords.tv

CURTIS BROWN GROUP LTD
Haymarket House
28-29 Haymarket, London SW1Y 4SP
F 020 7393 4403   T 020 7393 4460
E presenters@curtisbrown.co.uk
W www.curtisbrown.co.uk

DAVID ANTHONY PROMOTIONS
PO Box 286, Warrington, Cheshire WA2 8GA
M 07836 752195   T 01925 632496
E dave@davewarwick.co.uk
W www.davewarwick.co.uk

DOWNES PRESENTERS AGENCY
96 Broadway, Bexleyheath
Kent DA6 7DE   T 020 8304 0541
E downes@presentersagency.com
W www.presentersagency.com

EVANS Jacque MANAGEMENT LTD
Top Floor Suite, 14 Holmesley Road, London SE23 1PJ
F 020 8699 5192   T 020 8699 1202
E jacque@jacqueevans.com

EXCELLENT
118-120 Great Titchfield Street, London W1W 6SS
F 020 7637 4091   T 0845 2100111
E marie-claire@excellenttalent.com
W www.excellenttalent.com

EXPERTS MANAGEMENT SERVICES LTD
T/A Jane Hughes Management
PO Box 200, Stockport, Cheshire SK12 1GW
M 07766 130604   T 01625 858556
E gill@jhm.co.uk

FBI AGENCY THE
PO Box 250, Leeds LS1 2AZ
M 07515 567309   T 07050 222747
E casting@fbi-agency.co.uk
W www.fbi-agency.co.uk

FLETCHER ASSOCIATES
Broadcast & Media
25 Parkway, London N20 0XN
F 020 8361 8866   T 020 8361 8061
W www.fletcherassociates.net

**FORD-CRUSH June PERSONAL MANAGEMENT
& REPRESENTATION**
PO Box 57948, London W4 2UJ
M 07711 764160   T/F 020 8742 7724
E june@junefordcrush.com
W www.junefordcrush.com

GAY Noel
19 Denmark Street, London WC2H 8NA
F 020 7287 1816   T 020 7836 3941
E info@noelgay.com
W www.noelgay.com

GLOBAL7
PO Box 56232, London N4 4XP
M 07956 956652   T/F 020 7281 7679
E global7castings@gmail.com
W www.global7casting.com

GLORIOUS MANAGEMENT
Lower Ground Floor, 79 Noel Road
London N1 8HE   T 020 7704 6555
E lisa@glorioustalent.co.uk
W www.gloriousmanagement.com

GRANT James MEDIA
94 Strand On The Green, Chiswick, London W4 3NN
F 020 8742 4951   T 020 8742 4950
E enquiries@jamesgrant.co.uk
W www.jamesgrant.co.uk

GURNETT J. PERSONAL MANAGEMENT LTD
12 Newburgh Street, London W1F 7RP
F 020 7287 9642   T 020 7440 1850
E info@jgpm.co.uk
W www.jgpm.co.uk

HICKS Jeremy ASSOCIATES LTD
3 Richmond Buildings, London W1D 3HE
F 020 7734 6302   T 020 7734 7957
E info@jeremyhicks.com
W www.jeremyhicks.com

INTERNATIONAL ARTISTES LTD
4th Floor, Holborn Hall
193-197 High Holborn, London WC1V 7BD
F 020 7404 9865   T 020 7025 0600
E reception@internationalartistes.com
W www.internationalartistes.com

JLA (Jeremy Lee Associates Ltd)
Supplies celebrities and after dinner speakers
80 Great Portland Street, London W1W 7NW
F 020 7907 2801   T 020 7907 2800
E talk@jla.co.uk

JOYCE Michael MANAGEMENT
4th Floor, 14-18 Heddon Street
London W1B 4DA
F 020 7745 6275   T 020 7745 6274
E info@michaeljoycemanagement.com
W www.michaeljoycemanagement.com

KBJ MANAGEMENT LTD
TV Presenters
5 Soho Square, London W1D 3QA
F 020 7287 1191   T 020 7434 6767
E general@kbjmgt.co.uk
W www.kbjmgt.co.uk

KNIGHT AYTON MANAGEMENT
35 Great James Street, London WC1N 3HB
F 020 7831 4455   T 020 7831 4400
E info@knightayton.co.uk
W www.knightayton.co.uk

KNIGHT Hilary MANAGEMENT LTD
Grange Farm, Church Lane
Old, Northamptonshire NN6 9QZ   T 01604 781818
E hilary@hkmanagement.co.uk
W www.hkmanagement.co.uk

LEIGH Mike ASSOCIATES
37 Marylebone Lane, London W1U 2NW
F 020 7486 5886   T 020 7935 5500
W www.mikeleighassoc.com

LYTE Seamus MANAGEMENT LTD
Apt 5, Oswald Building
Chelsea Bridge Wharf
374 Queenstown Road, London SW8 4NU   M 07930 391401
E seamus@seamuslyte.com

MACFARLANE CHARD ASSOCIATES LTD
33 Percy Street, London W1T 2DF
F 020 7636 7751   T 020 7636 7750
E enquiries@macfarlane-chard.co.uk
W www.macfarlane-chard.co.uk

MARKS PRODUCTIONS LTD
2 Gloucester Gate Mews, London NW1 4AD   T 020 7486 2001

MARSH Billy ASSOCIATES LTD
76A Grove End Road, St John's Wood
London NW8 9ND
F 020 7449 6933   T 020 7449 6930
E talent@billymarsh.co.uk
W www.billymarsh.co.uk

McKENNA Deborah LTD
Celebrity Chefs & Lifestyle Presenters only
64-66 Glentham Road, London SW13 9JJ
F 020 8846 0967   T 020 8846 0966
E info@deborahmckenna.com
W www.deborahmckenna.com

MEDIA PEOPLE (The Celebrity Group)
12 Archery Close, Connaught Square
London W2 2BE   T 0871 2501234
E info@celebrity.co.uk
W www.celebrity.co.uk

MILES John ORGANISATION
Cadbury Camp Lane, Clapton-in-Gordano
Bristol BS20 7SB
F 01275 810186   T 01275 854675
E john@johnmiles.org.uk
W www.johnmilesorganisation.org.uk

MONDI ASSOCIATES LTD
Contact: Michelle Sykes
Unit 3 O, Cooper House, 2 Michael Road
London SW6 2AD   M 07817 133349
E info@mondiassociates.com
W www.mondiassociates.com

MPC ENTERTAINMENT
MPC House, 15-16 Maple Mews, London NW6 5UZ
F 020 7624 4220   T 020 7624 1184
E info@mpce.com
W www.mpce.com

MTC (UK) LTD
20 York Street, London W1U 6PU
F 020 7935 8066   T 020 7935 8000
E geraldine@mtc-uk.com
W www.mtc-uk.com

NOEL John MANAGEMENT
Block B, Imperial Works
Perren Street, London NW5 3ED
F 020 7428 8401   T 020 7428 8400
E john@johnnoel.com
W www.johnnoel.com

infopage

How do I become a presenter?

There is no easy answer to this question. Some presenters start out as actors and move into presenting work, others may be 'experts' such as chefs, designers or sports people who are taken on in a presenting capacity. Others may have a background in stand-up comedy. All newsreaders are professional journalists with specialist training and experience. Often presenters work their way up through the production side of broadcasting, starting by working as a runner or researcher and then moving to appear in front of the camera. To get this kind of production work you could contact Film and TV Production companies, many of whom are listed in this book. A number of Performing Arts Schools, Colleges and Academies also offer useful part-time training courses for presenters. See the 'Drama Training, Schools and Coaches' section of this book for college/school listings.

Why do I need a presenting agent?

As with any other agent, a presenting agent will promote their clients to job opportunities, negotiate contracts on their behalf, handle paperwork and offer advice. In return for these services they take commission ranging from 10-15%. The following pages contain contact details for the UK's leading presenter agencies. They will possess the relevant contacts in the industry that you need to get auditions and jobs.

How should I use these listings?

Before you approach any agency looking for representation, do some research into their current client list and the areas in which they specialise. Many have websites you can visit. Once you have made a short-list of the ones you think are most appropriate, you should send them your CV with a covering letter and a good quality, recent photograph which is a genuine likeness of you. Showreels can also be a good way of showcasing your talents, but only send these if you have checked with the agency first. Enclosing a stamped-addressed envelope with sufficient postage (SAE) will also give you a better chance of a reply. Please see the main 'Agents and Personal Managers' advice section for further guidance on choosing and approaching agents.

Should I pay a presenter's agent to join their books? Or sign a contract?

As with other types of agencies, Equity (the actors' trade union) does not recommend that artists pay an agent to join their client list. Before signing any contract, you should be very clear about the terms and commitments involved. For advice on both of these issues, or if you experience any problems with a current agent, we recommend that you contact Equity www.equity.org.uk. They also produce the booklet *You and your Agent* which is free to all Equity members and available from their website's members' area.

What is Spotlight Presenters?

Spotlight Presenters is a specialist casting directory published annually. It contains photographs and contact details for over seven hundred professional TV and radio presenters and is a great way of promoting yourself for work. It is used by production companies, casting directors, TV and radio stations, advertising agencies and publicists to browse and locate talent for future productions. Membership is available to any presenter with proven professional broadcast experience. Just starting out in your presenting career? New presenters with limited broadcast experience or training can join the Spotlight Presenters directory in the 'Emerging Talent' pages. Please see www.spotlight.com/artists/presenters to join or for more information.

Should I join the Spotlight Actors/Actresses directory or the Presenters directory?

Depending on your skills, training and experience, you may be eligible for both directories if you are interested in promoting yourself as an actor and as a presenter. You would receive an entry into each directory and two separate online CVs. You would also qualify for a 25% discount off the Presenters membership fee. You will however have to prove that you already have professional experience and/or relevant training.

Miranda Loy has experience within TV, radio and the internet. Companies she has worked with include QVC, LGR Radio, WebActors, Inside Success and many more. She is also a member of Spotlight Presenters, having started off in the new Emerging Talent section. She is currently working on various projects and should be hosting her own radio show very soon!

When you mention the word "presenting" it can sound like a very easy and amazing job. However, as great and exciting as it can be, I can safely say that it involves a lot of hard work and dedication. It is important to remember that when you first start out it can take a while before you get your foot on the ladder, so you must be patient!

I originally started out in commercial modelling and after having a great time in that field I decided that I wanted to pursue a career within presenting. While it really helped that I was used to being in front of bright lights and cameras and had gained a lot of confidence, I quickly learned that being a good presenter isn't just about having the right looks and great presentation skills – it is about this and a whole lot more!

I didn't have a huge budget when I started out, but I decided to put together a showreel myself so I could showcase what I was all about as a presenter. I did heaps of research, watched hundreds of showreels to get some ideas, and then I got a friend to film me in action.

Next I sent out my reel to various production companies and agents. It wasn't until I had a few knock-backs and received a lot of constructive criticism that I realized it was important to know the industry inside out and essential to offer something different. At the end of the day there are hundreds of presenters like me trying to get their foot through the door, so what makes me different? What can I bring to a company?

Of course, you always hear people saying that in this industry it's all about being in the right place at the right time and that luck always plays a part in getting your next break, but in reality this may only be the case for 1 in 20 of us. It is still highly important to make sure you always put in 110%. You have to work hard, you network, you keep pushing and, from my experience, it'll pay off providing you do the right research and work strategically.

Sometimes you may have to work for little pay or you may not be paid at all. With everything you do you are constantly building up your experience, and don't forget you can always use the footage for your showreel. Having said that, remember to always think wisely about how your career will benefit long-term. If you are serious about being a great presenter then money shouldn't be an object to begin with.

My first day in my first presenting job was nerve-racking and my adrenaline was pumping all day! I quickly realised that the most important thing was to remain calm and be myself. We all make mistakes but we learn from them, and at the end of the day we're all human. Luckily for me everything went well and it turned out to be a successful job.

One thing I have learned along the way is that it is essential to watch myself back, no matter what type of footage it is. It is important to be your own critic – this will help you improve and better your skills, even if it makes you cringe. Trust me, it really helps!

All the work I initially found was through my own blood, sweat and tears, and then eventually along my presenting journey and through my contacts I landed myself an agent. This didn't stop me from working hard; it just means that there are now two of us working on my behalf to further my career.

I am a firm believer that you only get out what you put in, and as delighted as I am to finally have an agent, it does not mean that I will not carry on putting in my all. At the end of the day, having an agent still doesn't guarantee me work.

I am now working within TV and radio. However, I will continue turning up to the right castings, networking, making those phone calls and sending out those e-mails. A wise friend once told me: "As quick as something comes, as quickly it can go." You must always be ready and prepared because sometimes an opportunity could come up quicker than you expect – the key thing to remember is to be ready when it does!

Please visit www.mirandaloy.com for further information on Miranda Loy and to view her showreel.

OFF THE KERB PRODUCTIONS
Comedy Presenters & Comedians
3rd Floor, Hammer House
113-117 Wardour Street
London W1F 0UN
F 020 7437 0647　　　　　　　　T 020 7437 0607
E westend@offthekerb.co.uk
W www.offthekerb.co.uk

PANMEDIA UK LTD
18 Montrose Crescent, London N12 0ED　　T 020 8446 9662
E enquiries@panmediauk.co.uk
W www.panmediauk.co.uk

PEOPLEMATTER.TV
Contact: Tony Fitzpatrick
40 Bowling Green Lane
Clerkenwell, London EC1R 0NE
F 020 7415 7074　　　　　　　　T 020 7415 7070
E tony@peoplematter.tv
W www.peoplematter.tv

P F D
Presenters. Public Speakers
Drury House, 34-43 Russell Street
London WC2B 5HA
F 020 7836 9539　　　　　　　　T 020 8744 1000
E info@pfd.co.uk
W www.pfd.co.uk

PVA MANAGEMENT LTD
County House, St Mary's Street
Worcester WR1 1HB
F 01905 610709　　　　　　　　T 01905 616100
E post@pva.co.uk
W www.pva.co.uk

RARE TALENT ACTORS MANAGEMENT
Tanzaro House
Ardwick Green North
Manchester M12 6FZ
F 0161 273 4567　　　　　　　　T 0161 273 4444
E info@raretalentactors.com
W www.raretalentactors.com

RAZLAND
34 Corrour Road, Newton Mearns
Glasgow G77 6EU　　　　　　　　M 07765 422561
E kandi_razan@hotmail.com
W www.razland.com

RAZZAMATAZZ MANAGEMENT
204 Holtye Road
East Grinstead
West Sussex RH19 3ES
M 07836 268292　　　　　　　　T 01342 301617
E razzamatazzmanagement@btconnect.com

RED 24 MANAGEMENT
3rd Floor, 10 Carlisle Street
London W1D 3BR　　　　　　　　T 020 7559 3611
E info@red24management.com
W www.red24management.com

RED CANYON MANAGEMENT
M 07939 365578　　　　　　　　M 07931 381696
E info@redcanyon.co.uk
W www.redcanyon.co.uk

RPM2
Studio House
Delamare Road
Cheshunt, Hertfordshire EN8 9SH　　T 0845 3625456
E rhino-rpm2@hotmail.com
W www.rhino2-rpm.com

SINGER Sandra ASSOCIATES
21 Cotswold Road
Westcliff-on-Sea
Essex SS0 8AA　　　　　　　　T 01702 331616
E sandrasingeruk@aol.com
W www.sandrasinger.com

SOMETHIN' ELSE
20-26 Brunswick Place, London N1 6DZ
F 020 7250 0937　　　　　　　　T 020 7250 5500
E info@somethinelse.com
W www.somethinelse.com

SPEAK-EASY LTD
PO Box 648, Draughton
Northampton NN6 9XT　　　　　　T 01604 686100
E kate@speak-easy.co.uk
W www.speak-easy.co.uk

STAR MANAGEMENT LTD
16A Winton Drive
Glasgow G12 0QA　　　　　　　　T 0844 8002292
E star@starmanagement.co.uk
W www.starmanagement.co.uk

TAKE THREE MANAGEMENT
110 Gloucester Avenue, Primrose Hill
London NW1 8HX
F 020 7209 3770　　　　　　　　T 020 7209 3777
E info@take3management.com
W www.take3management.co.uk

TALENT4 MEDIA LTD
Studio LG16, Shepherds Building Central
Charecroft Way, London W14 0EH
F 020 7183 4331　　　　　　　　T 020 7183 4330
E enquiries@talent4media.com
W www.talent4media.com

TRIPLE A MEDIA
30 Great Portland Street
London W1W 8QU　　　　　　　　T 020 3370 4988
E gina@tripleamedia.com
W www.tripleamedia.com

TROIKA
3rd Floor, 74 Clerkenwell Road
London EC1M 5QA
F 020 7490 7642　　　　　　　　T 020 7336 7868
E info@troikatalent.com
W www.troikatalent.com

WANDER Jo MANAGEMENT
110 Gloucester Avenue, Primrose Hill
London NW1 8HX　　　　　　　　T 020 7209 3777
E jo@jowandermanagement.com
W www.jowandermanagement.com

WILLCOCKS John MEDIA AGENCY LTD
34 Carisbrook Close, Enfield
Middlesex EN1 3NB　　　　　　　T 020 8364 4556
E john.willcocks@blueyonder.co.uk

WISE BUDDAH TALENT
74 Great Titchfield Street
London W1W 7QP
F 020 7307 1601　　　　　　　　T 020 7307 1600
E talent@wisebuddah.com
W www.wisebuddah.com

ZWICKLER Marlene & ASSOCIATES
1 Belgrave Crescent Lane
Edinburgh EH4 3AG　　　　　　　T 0131 343 3030
E info@mza-artists.com
W www.mza-artists.com

ACCENT BANK
420 Falcon Wharf
34 Lombard Road
London SW11 3RF T 020 7223 5160
E info@accentbank.co.uk
W www.accentbank.co.uk

AD VOICE
Oxford House, 76 Oxford Street
London W1D 1BS
F 020 7323 0101 T 020 7323 2345
E info@advoice.co.uk
W www.advoice.co.uk

ALPHABET KIDZ ACTING & VOICE-OVER AGENCY
Nice Business Park
19-35 Sylvan Grove
London SE15 1PD
F 020 7252 4341 T 020 7252 4343
E lisa@alphabetkidz.co.uk
W www.alphabetkidz.co.uk

AMERICAN AGENCY VOICES THE
14 Bonny Street, London NW1 9PG
F 020 7482 4666 T 020 7485 8883
E americanagency@btconnect.com
W www.americanagency.tv

ANOTHER TONGUE VOICES LTD
The Basement
10-11 D'Arblay Street
London W1F 8DS
F 020 7494 7080 T 020 7494 0300
E john@anothertongue.com
W www.anothertongue.com

ASQUITH & HORNER
Contact: By Post (SAE)
The Studio, 14 College Road
Bromley, Kent BR1 3NS T 020 8466 5580

BRAIDMAN Michelle ASSOCIATES LTD
2 Futura House
169 Grange Road
London SE1 3BN
F 020 7231 4634 T 020 7237 3523
E info@braidman.com

CALYPSO VOICES
25-26 Poland Street, London W1F 8QN
F 020 7437 0410 T 020 7734 6415
E calypso@calypsovoices.com
W www.calypsovoices.com

CASTAWAY
Suite 3, 15 Broad Court
London WC2B 5QN
F 020 7240 2772 T 020 7240 2345
E info@castaway.org.uk
W www.castaway.org.uk

CINEL GABRAN MANAGEMENT
PO Box 5163, Cardiff CF5 9BJ
F 0845 0666601 T 029 2066 6600
E info@cinelgabran.co.uk
W www.cinelgabran.co.uk

PO Box 101
Newholm, Whitby
North Yorkshire YO21 3WT
F 0845 0666601 T 0845 0666605

infopage

How do I become a voice-over artist?

The voice-over business has opened up a lot more to newcomers in recent years; you don't have to be a celebrity already to be booked for a job. However, it is a competitive industry, and it is important to bear in mind that only a select few are able to earn a living from voice-over work. It is more likely that voice-over work could become a supplement to your regular income.

In order to get work you must have a great voice and be able to put it to good use. Being able to act does not necessarily mean that you will also be able to do voice-overs. Whether your particular voice will get you the job or not will ultimately depend on the client's personal choice, so your technical ability to do voice-over work initially comes second in this industry. Once the client has chosen you, however, then you must be able to consistently demonstrate that you can take direction well, you don't need numerous takes to get the job finished, you have a positive attitude and you don't complain if recording goes a little over schedule.

Before you get to this stage, however, you will need a professional-sounding voicereel and, in the majority of cases, an agent.

How do I produce a voicereel?

Please see the 'Promotional Services' section for advice on creating your voicereel.

Why do I need a voice-over agent?

As with any other agent, a voice-over agent will promote their clients to job opportunities, negotiate contracts on their behalf, handle paperwork and offer advice. In return for these services they take commission ranging from 10-15%. The agents listed on the following pages specialise in representing and promoting voice-over artists, mostly in the commercial and corporate sectors, but also areas such as radio and animation. They will possess the relevant contacts in the industry that you need to get auditions and jobs. In this industry in particular, time is money, and clients are often more likely to trust that an agent can provide someone who can get the job done in the least amount of takes but still sounds good in every project, rather than taking on an unknown newcomer.

How do I find work in radio?

Please see the 'Radio' section of Contacts for further information on this specific area of voice work.

How should I use these listings?

Whether you are completely new to the industry, looking to change your existing agent, or wishing to take on an additional agent to represent you for voice-overs alongside your main acting or presenting agent, the following pages will supply you with up-to-date contact details for voice-over agencies. Every company listed is done so by written request to us. Please see the main 'Agents and Personal Managers' advice section for further guidance on choosing and approaching agents.

Should I pay an agent to join their books? Or sign a contract?

Equity (the actors' trade union) does not recommend that artists pay an agent to join their client list. Before signing a contract, you should be very clear about the terms and commitments involved. For advice on both of these issues, or if you experience any problems with a current agent, we recommend that you contact Equity www.equity.org.uk. They also produce the booklet *You and your Agent* which is free to all Equity members and available from their website's members' area.

info**page**

Alex Mactavish joined Lip Service in 2004 as a junior agent. She became senior agent in 2006, a director of the company in 2009 and Managing Director in 2010. Her love of voice-overs began whilst working as a runner for Zoo, Jungle and Marmalade Studios (The Jungle Group) in Soho and as a PA for the Radio Agency, Radioville. Lip Service was established in 1987 and is one of the most experienced voice-over agencies in the UK, offering not only a superb roster and excellent casting but an incredibly friendly service.

Actors' Voice-over Helpline:

AGONY AUNT:	Good morning! Actors' voice-over helpline, how can I help you?
CALLER:	Hello, I'm a first time caller and I want to get into voice-overs.
AGONY AUNT:	Why is that?
CALLER:	Why? Well, easy money of course!
AGONY AUNT:	Really? To be honest, I don't think that's quite how it works!
CALLER:	Yeah, it is. You just turn up to some "poncey" studio in Soho, order breakfast or lunch, use their phone, hop into the sound booth, put on a sexy voice for something or other, then shoot off and meet a few pals for a glass of wine in one of those private members clubs... *kerching!*
AGONY AUNT:	And who told you that, exactly?
CALLER:	An actor mate of mine.
AGONY AUNT:	And does this actor friend of yours do a lot of voice-overs?
CALLER:	Well, not so many now. But he used to do tons.
AGONY AUNT:	Hmm, can't think why...

Voice-over work can be rewarding, but it's very competitive and hard to do well, especially in today's saturated market. Most TV and radio advertising scripts are not written with a particular actor in mind and decisions on casting are both subjective and financial. Agencies and production companies like to work with people who understand the world of advertising: you can make a huge difference with the right attitude and good representation.

If you really want to get voice-over work, do your homework and put together a showreel which really demonstrates what you're about. Make sure your natural accent is clearly demonstrated and for goodness sake, if you say you can do every accent and character under the sun put it on your reel. Nearly all voice-over castings come about from reels and it's your biggest tool to obtain work. Creatives in agencies love to hear 'sound bites' from your acting or stage work too.

Another thing to remember is that when you do a voice-over session there is often no director to guide you; clients frequently rely on the recording engineer to fulfil this role. On arrival, always work out who you should listen to and don't be afraid to make suggestions to improve the script – without being too presumptuous, of course. If you're good enough to get a job, try to be confident and relaxed (clients want to feel reassured), friendly (most people want to work with actors they get along with) and, whatever you do, *make sure you get to the studio in good time.*

When you record a voice-over think of yourself as invisible. The listener has to be able to see you through your voice. You create the scene and scenario through the use of your voice; there are no props, costumes or sets to help you. So remember your voice is as naked as the day you were born.

Good luck out there.

Please visit **www.lipservice.co.uk** for further information.

International Centre for Voice

Based at the Central School of Speech & Drama   Patrons: Cicely Berry CBE and Barbara Houseman

The ICV exists to serve the needs of professional users of voice and speech, including actors, singers, directors, voice coaches, musicians and teachers. We host workshops with world-renowned practitioners and enable members to develop their practical skills as part of a supportive network of people who are passionate about voice.

For further details please visit www.icvoice.co.uk or email icv@cssd.ac.uk

---

CONWAY VAN GELDER GRANT LTD
3rd Floor, 8-12 Broadwick Street
London W1F 8HW
F 020 7287 1940   T 020 7287 1070
E kate@conwayvg.co.uk
W www.conwayvangeldergrant.com

CREATIVE KIDZ & Co
Incorporating NeighbourHood Productions
9 Weavers Terrace, Fulham
London SW6 1QE   M 07958 377595
E info@creativekidzandco.co.uk

CUT GLASS VOICES
169-175 Queens Crescent
Camden, London NW5 4DS   T 020 7267 2339
E info@cutglassproductions.com
W www.cutglassproductions.com

DAMN GOOD VOICES
25B Eastlake Road, London SE5 9QJ   M 07702 228185
E damngoodvoices@me.com
W www.damngoodvoices.com

DIAMOND MANAGEMENT
31 Percy Street, London W1T 2DD
F 020 7631 0500   T 020 7631 0400
E hj@diman.co.uk

DREW Bryan LTD
31 Oakley House, 103 Sloane Street
London SW1X 9PP   T 020 7823 2346
E bryan@bryandrewltd.com

EARACHE VOICES
177 Wardour Street, London W1F 8WX
F 020 7287 2288   T 020 7287 2291
E alex@earachevoices.com
W www.earachevoices.com

EVANS O'BRIEN
2 Lampmead Road, London SE12 8QL   T 020 8318 9058
E info@evansobrien.co.uk
W www.evansobrien.co.uk

EXCELLENT
118-120 Great Titchfield Street, London W1W 6SS
F 020 7637 4091   T 0845 2100111
E info@excellenttalent.com
W www.excellenttalent.com

FERRIS ENTERTAINMENT VOICES
London. Belfast. Cardiff
Number 8, 132 Charing Cross Road
London WC2H 0LA   T 0845 4724725
E info@ferrisentertainment.com
W www.ferrisentertainment.com

FIRST VOICE AGENCY
Foxgrove House, School Lane
Seer Green HP9 2QJ
F 01494 730166   T 01494 678277
E jenny@firstvoiceagency.com
W www.firstvoiceagency.com

FOREIGN LEGION
1 Kendal Road, London NW10 1JH   T 020 8450 4451
E voices@foreignlegion.co.uk
W www.foreignlegion.co.uk

FOREIGN VERSIONS LTD
Translation
                                   T 0333 123 2001
E info@foreignversions.co.uk
W www.foreignversions.com

GAY Noel VOICES
19 Denmark Street, London WC2H 8NA
F 020 7287 1816   T 020 7836 3941
E info@noelgay.com
W www.noelgay.com

GLOBAL7
PO Box 56232, London N4 4XP
M 07956 956652   T/F 020 7281 7679
E global7castings@gmail.com
W www.global7casting.com

GORDON & FRENCH
Contact: By Post
12-13 Poland Street, London W1F 8QB
F 020 7734 4832   T 020 7734 4818
E voices@gordonandfrench.net
W www.gordonandfrench.co.uk

GREAT BRITISH VOICE COMPANY THE
339 Norristhorpe Lane
Liversedge
West Yorkshire WF15 7AZ   T 0845 8622202
E info@greatbritishvoice.co.uk
W www.greatbritishvoice.co.uk

HAMILTON HODELL LTD
Contact: Louise Donald
5th Floor, 66-68 Margaret Street
London W1W 8SR
F 020 7636 1226   T 020 7636 1221
E louise@hamiltonhodell.co.uk
W www.hamiltonhodell.co.uk

HARVEY VOICES
No unsolicited correspondence
58 Woodlands Road, London N9 8RT   T 020 7952 4361
E info@harveyvoices.co.uk
W www.harveyvoices.co.uk

HOBSONS SINGERS
62 Chiswick High Road, London W4 1SY
F 020 8996 5350   T 020 8995 3628
E singers@hobsons-international.com
W www.hobsons-international.com

HOBSONS VOICES
62 Chiswick High Road
London W4 1SY
F 020 8996 5350   T 020 8995 3628
E voices@hobsons-international.com
W www.hobsons-international.com

Would you like to invest your money in a voiceover demo that actually stands you a chance of getting work?

Consistently produce demos of the highest Standard
David Hodge - Hobson's Voices

Definitely the best showreels
Leigh Matty - The Just Voices Agency

Professional and high quality demos
Penny Brown - Voicecall

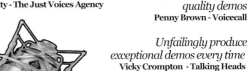

Professional, sharp, well presented quality demos
Ben Romer Lee – Vocal Point

Unfailingly produce exceptional demos every time
Vicky Crompton - Talking Heads

Excellent demos. I've always been impressed
Sheila Britten - Castaway Voice Agency

Outstanding quality reels
Alex Lynch White - Earache Voice Agency

The best produced audio reels we receive
Victoria Braverman -Voicebookers.com

Professional and unique showreels, 2 very important aspects for a top quality demo
Jennifer & Clair - Shining Management Ltd

Learn the skills needed on our one day voiceover workshop

Learn the "insider" secrets to starting a career in this lucrative industry.

Everyday we get calls and emails from people who want to know how to get started and they come from all walks of life not just from the "acting" side. In fact we've taught news readers, after dinner speakers, sales reps, teachers, actors, DJs, dentists, presenters, vets, lawyers, painters, bio-chemists and even "Brian" a Concord pilot (seriously) and have come to understand that just because people "tell" you, you've got a good sounding voice doesn't mean you should drop everything and make a demo.

A comprehensive, fun and interactive workshop.

Packed with insider information and loads of "tricks and techniques" on how to succeed in today's industry, this workshop gives you the opportunity to learn the skills and techniques used by working professionals. Small class sizes allow you plenty of time behind the "mic" and the chance to experience what it's really like to be in a commercial recording situation while being directed by one of London's most experienced Voice Producers, JP Orr.

This "heads up" will give you the headstart you need to move your voice career forward.

We know it's not possible to teach you everything there is to know about voiceovers in a single workshop, but we guarantee that having attended this session you will, with our help, be able to make an educated decision about whether voiceovers are for you.

If it is, then we will help you move forward. If it's not, then we will be honest and tell you that you would be wasting your time pursuing this line of work.

We also know that you can't get practical "hands-on" information in any one book, on the internet or at the end of a telephone. We've seen and pretty much heard it all and are willing to share our knowledge with you to help you get started. After all, you only get one chance to "get it right".

It's a serious decision you are about to make. We suggest you at least learn the basics before you spend your hard-earned money on a Voice Showreel you may end up not using.

22 years working with London's top agents and the best voices in the business.

Our Logo goes on every demo we produce. A badge we've earned by not "just turning out" voice demos that have no chance of getting our clients work. That's why the top London agents choose us to produce their client's voice demos.

But don't just take our word for it. Call them and ask them. Most will send you to us to "cut" your reel. Why? Because they know we offer a proven process for all our clients. A voiceover plan that works!

* *Learn the skills to get started*
* *Put those skills into practice.*
* *Record your Showreel.*
* *Learn how to market your voice.*

One Day Voiceover Workshop: Special Offer Just £99.00

Our next workshop dates are now online at www.theshowreel.com.

Please also feel free to call one of our "voice team" if you have any other questions on **020 7043 8660**

theShowreel.com
Get Heard Get Hired Get Paid

tel: 020 7043 8660   email: info@theshowreel.com

voiceover agency
www.damngoodvoices.com
+44 (0)7702 228185

CRYING OUT LOUD PRODUCTIONS

voiceover demo production company
www.cryingoutloud.co.uk
+44 (0)7809 549887

HOPE Sally ASSOCIATES
108 Leonard Street, London EC2A 4XS
F 020 7613 4848   T 020 7613 5353
E casting@sallyhope.biz
W www.sallyhope.biz

HOWARD Amanda ASSOCIATES
See JONESES THE

ICAN TALK LTD
Palm Tree Mews
39 Tymecrosse Gardens
Market Harborough, Leicestershire LE16 7US
F 01858 455445   T 01858 466749
E hello@icantalk.co.uk
W www.icantalk.co.uk

J H A VOICE
3 Richmond Buildings, London W1D 3HE
F 020 7734 7597   T 020 7734 6302
E info@jeremyhicks.com
W www.jeremyhicks.com

JONESES THE
21 Berwick Street, London W1F 0PZ
F 020 7287 7785   T 020 7287 9666
E mail@meetthejoneses.co.uk
W www.meetthejoneses.co.uk

JUST VOICES AGENCY THE
140 Buckingham Palace Road
London SW1W 9SA
F 020 7881 2569   T 020 7881 2567
E info@justvoicesagency.com
W www.justvoicesagency.com

KIDZTALK LTD
Young Voices, Children, Teenagers, Twenties
F 01737 352456   T 01737 350808
E studio@kidztalk.com
W www.kidztalk.com

LIP SERVICE CASTING LTD
60-66 Wardour Street, London W1F 0TA
F 020 7734 3373   T 020 7734 3393
E bookings@lipservice.co.uk
W www.lipservice.co.uk

MARCUS & McCRIMMON VOICES
1 Heathgate Place, 75 Agincourt Road
Hampstead, London NW3 2NU
F 020 3012 3478   T 020 3012 3477
E voices@marcusandmccrimmon.com
W www.marcusandmccrimmon.com

MARKHAM, FROGGATT & IRWIN
4 Windmill Street, London W1T 2HZ
F 020 7637 5233   T 020 7636 4412
E tig@markhamfroggattirwin.com
W www.markhamfroggattirwin.com

McREDDIE Ken ASSOCIATES LTD
Contact: Jan Thornton
11 Connaught Place, London W2 2ET
F 020 7734 6530   T 020 7439 1456
E jan@kenmcreddie.com

PEMBERTON VOICES
193 Wardour Street, London W1F 8ZF
F 020 7734 2522   T 020 7734 4144
E rosemary@pembertonassociates.com
W www.pembertonvoices.com

Express Networks, 1 George Leigh Street
Manchester M4 5DL
F 0161 235 8442   T 0161 235 8440

QVOICE
4th Floor, Holborn Hall
193-197 High Holborn, London WC1V 7BD
F 020 7025 0659   T 020 7025 0660
E info@qvoice.co.uk
W www.qvoice.co.uk

RABBIT VOCAL MANAGEMENT LTD
2nd Floor
18 Broadwick Street
London W1F 8HS
F 020 7287 6566   T 020 7287 6466
E info@rabbitvocalmanagement.co.uk
W www.rabbitvocalmanagement.co.uk

RED 24 VOICES
3rd Floor, 10 Carlisle Street
London W1D 3BR   T 020 7559 3611
E paul@red24voices.com
W www.red24voices.com

RED CANYON MANAGEMENT
M 07931 381696   M 07939 365578
E info@redcanyon.co.uk
W www.redcanyon.co.uk

RHUBARB VOICES
1st Floor
1A Devonshire Road, London W4 2EU
F 020 8742 8693   T 020 8742 8683
E enquiries@rhubarbvoices.co.uk
W www.rhubarbvoices.co.uk

RPM2
Studio House, Delamare Road
Cheshunt, Hertfordshire EN8 9SH
T 0845 3625456   T/F 0845 2415585
E rhino-rpm2@hotmail.com
W www.rhino2-rpm.com

SHINING MANAGEMENT LTD
12 D'Arblay Street, London W1F 8DU   T 020 7734 1981
E info@shiningvoices.com
W www.shiningvoices.com

SPEAK-EASY LTD
PO Box 648, Draughton
Northampton NN6 9XT   T 01604 686100
E enquiries@speak-easy.co.uk
W www.speak-easy.co.uk

SVMK LTD
Studio 1A, 151 Tower Bridge Road
London SE1 3LW
F 020 7407 9661   T 020 7407 9660
E info@svmk.co.uk
W www.svmk.co.uk

TALKING HEADS
Argyll House, All Saints Passage
London SW18 1EP   T 020 7292 7575
E voices@talkingheadsvoices.com
W www.talkingheadsvoices.com

TERRY Sue VOICES LTD
3rd Floor, 18 Broadwick Street
London W1F 8HS
F 020 7434 2042   T 020 7434 2040
E sue@sueterryvoices.co.uk
W www.sueterryvoices.co.uk

TONGUE & GROOVE
4th Floor, Manchester House
84-86 Princess Street, Manchester M1 6NG
F 0161 237 1809   T 0161 228 2469
E info@tongueandgroove.co.uk
W www.tongueandgroove.co.uk

VOCAL POINT
131 Great Titchfield Street, London W1W 5BB   T 020 7419 0700
E enquiries@vocalpoint.net
W www.vocalpoint.net

VOICE BANK LTD
1st Floor, 100 Talbot Road
Old Trafford, Manchester M16 0PG
F 0161 888 2242   T 0161 874 5741
E elinors@voicebankltd.co.uk
W www.voicebankltd.co.uk

VOICE MASTER
Creators of the only Voiceover Technique in the World
88 Erskine Hill, London NW11 6HR   T 020 8455 2211
E stevehudson@voicemaster.co.uk
W www.voicemaster.co.uk

VOICE SHOP
First Floor, Thomas Place
1A Devonshire Road
London W4 2EU
F 020 8742 7011   T 020 8742 7077
E info@voice-shop.co.uk
W www.voice-shop.co.uk

VOICE SQUAD
1 Kendal Road, London NW10 1JH   T 020 8450 4451
E voices@voicesquad.com
W www.voicesquad.com

VOICEBANK, THE IRISH VOICE-OVER AGENCY
The Barracks
76 Irishtown Road
Dublin 4, Ireland
F 00 353 1 6607850   T 00 353 1 6687234
E voicebank@voicebank.ie
W www.voicebank.ie

VOICECALL
67A Gondar Gardens, London NW6 1EP   T 020 7209 1064
E voices@voicecall-online.co.uk
W www.voicecall-online.co.uk

VOICEOVER GALLERY THE
The Cobalt Building
19-20 Noel Street
London W1F 8GW T 020 7987 0951
E london@thevoiceovergallery.co.uk
W www.thevoiceovergallery.co.uk

Manchester M16 0LN T 0161 881 8844
E manchester@thevoiceovergallery.co.uk

VOICEOVERS.CO.UK
PO Box 326, Plymouth
Devon PL4 9YQ T 020 7099 2264
E info@voiceovers.co.uk
W www.voiceovers.co.uk

VSI - VOICE & SCRIPT INTERNATIONAL
Foreign Language Specialists
132 Cleveland Street
London W1T 6AB
F 020 7692 7711 T 020 7692 7700
E info@vsi.tv
W www.vsi.tv

WAM VOICES
The Voice Agency of Waring & McKenna
11-12 Dover Street
Mayfair
London W1S 4LJ
F 020 7629 6466 T 020 7495 6665
E info@wamvoices.com
W www.wamvoices.com

WOOTTON Suzy VOICES
72 Towcester Road, Far Cotton
Northampton NN4 8LQ
F 0870 7659668 T 0870 7659660
E suzy@suzywoottonvoices.com
W www.suzywoottonvoices.com

YAKETY YAK
7A Bloomsbury Square
London WC1A 2LP
F 020 7404 6109 T 020 7430 2600
E info@yaketyyak.co.uk
W www.yaketyyak.co.uk

2020 CASTING LTD
2020 Hopgood Street, London W12 7JU
F 020 8735 2727
T 020 8746 2020
E info@2020casting.com
W www.2020casting.com

AGENCY OAKROYD
Oakroyd, 89 Wheatley Lane
Ben Rhydding, Ilkley, Yorkshire LS29 8PP
F 01943 600820
M 07840 784337
E paula@agencyoakroyd.com
W www.agencyoakroyd.com

ALLSORTS AGENCY
Modelling
Suite 3, Marlborough Business Centre
96 George Lane, London E18 1AD
F 020 8989 5600
T 020 8989 0500
E bookings@allsortsagency.com
W www.allsortsagency.com

ARTIST MANAGEMENT UK LTD
PO Box 96, Liverpool L9 8WY
T 0151 523 6222
E chris@artistmanagementuk.com
W www.artistmanagementuk.com

AVENUE ARTISTES LTD
PO Box 1573, Southampton SO16 3XS
T 023 8076 0930
E info@avenueartistes.com
W www.avenueartistes.com

AWA - ANDREA WILDER AGENCY
23 Cambrian Drive, Colwyn Bay
Conwy LL28 4SL
F 07092 249314
M 07919 202401
E casting@awagency.co.uk
W www.awagency.co.uk

BENNETTON - CMP
Raines Business Centre
Raines House, Denby Dale Road
Wakefield, West Yorkshire WF1 1HR
M 07540 693657
T 01924 882414
E enquiries@bennetton-cmp.co.uk
W www.bennetton-cmp.co.uk

BODENS ADVANCED
Bodens Studios & Agency
99 East Barnet Road
New Barnet, Herts EN4 8RF
M 07545 696888
T 020 8447 0909
E info@bodensagency.com
W www.bodensagency.com

BONNIE AND BETTY LTD
County House
221-241 Beckenham Road
Beckenham, Kent BR3 4UF
T 020 8676 6294
E agency@bonnieandbetty.com
W www.bonnieandbetty.com

BROADCASTING AGENCY
3rd Floor, Block A, Morelands
5-23 Old Street, London EC1V 9HL
T 020 7490 4225
E info@broadcastingagency.co.uk
W www.broadcastingagency.co.uk

BROOK Dolly CASTING AGENCY
PO Box 5436, Dunmow CM6 1WW
F 01371 875996
T 01371 875767
E dollybrookcasting@btinternet.com

CAIRNS AGENCY THE
Contact: Maureen Cairns, Allan Jones
2nd Floor
34 Argyle Arcade Chambers
Buchanan Street, Glasgow G2 8BD
T 0141 222 2333
E info@thecairnsagency.com

CAMCAST
Laragain, Upper Banavie
Fort William
Inverness-shire PH33 7PB
T 01397 772523
E anne@camcast.co.uk
W www.camcast.co.uk

CAST YOU
20 Berkeley Square
Mayfair, London W1J 6HF
F 0870 2853250
T 0844 2572327
E info@castyou.co.uk
W www.castyou.co.uk

CASTING COLLECTIVE LTD THE
Olympic House
317-321 Latimer Road
London W10 6RA
F 020 8962 0333
T 020 8962 0099
E enquiries@castingcollective.co.uk
W www.castingcollective.co.uk

CASTING NETWORK LTD THE
4 Vidler Close, Chessington
Surrey KT9 2GL
F 020 8391 5119
T 020 8391 2979
E info@thecastingnetwork.co.uk
W www.thecastingnetwork.co.uk

infopage

Who are Walk-on and Supporting Artists?

Sometimes known as 'Extras', walk-on and supporting artists appear in the background of TV and film scenes in order to add a sense of realism, character or atmosphere. They do not have individual speaking roles, unless required to make background/ambient noise. Working as a walk-on or supporting artist does not require any specific 'look', training or experience as such; however it does involve more effort than people think. Artists are often required to start very early in the morning (6am is not uncommon), and days can be long with lots of waiting around, sometimes in tough conditions on location. It is certainly not glamorous, nor is it a way to become a TV or film star! Artists must be reliable and available at very short notice, which can make it difficult to juggle with other work or family commitments. Requirements vary from production to production and, as with mainstream acting work, there are no guarantees that you will get regular work, let alone be able to earn a living as a walk-on.

How should I use these listings?

If you are serious about working as a walk-on artist, you will need to register with an agency in order to be put forward for jobs. In return for finding you work, you can expect an agency to take between 10-15% in commission. The following pages contain contact details of many walk-on and supporting artist agencies. Some will specialise in certain areas, so make sure you research the different companies carefully to see if they are appropriate for you. Many have websites you can visit. It is also worth asking questions about how long an agency has existed, and about their recent production credits. When approaching an agency for representation, you should send them your CV with a covering letter and a recent photograph which is a genuine, natural likeness of you. Enclosing a stamped-addressed envelope with sufficient postage (SAE) will give you a better chance of a reply.

Should I pay a Walk-on Agent to join their books? Or sign a contract?

As with other types of agencies, Equity does not generally recommend that artists pay an agent to join their client list. Before signing any contract, you should be clear about the terms and commitments involved. Always speak to Equity www.equity.org.uk or BECTU www.bectu.org.uk if you have any concerns or queries. Equity also produces the booklet *You and your Agent* which is free to all Equity members and available from their website's members' area.

Where can I find more information?

You may find it useful to contact the Film Artists Association, part of BECTU www.bectu.org.uk, or the National Association of Supporting Artistes Agents www.nasaa.org.uk

Ray Knight Casting Ltd was founded in 1988 and is an agency specialising in the supply of walk-on and supporting artistes for film, television and commercials. They have a main workforce of approximately 2600 artistes on their books. Ray Knight offers the following advice to budding supporting artistes:

Supporting artiste work is not for everybody. You need to have endless patience, a very compliant and tolerant attitude, and the ability to get on with other people in close and often awkward circumstances. The vast majority of employment is handled by agencies specialising in this field of work. I have been such an agent since 1988 and like to think I have done a good job for both artiste and client, building a reputation for fairness and reliability.

When seeking an agent to represent you, please bear the following useful pointers in mind. There are unfortunately some real cowboys in the field. Do not part with any money in advance of receiving any viable work, whatever the explanation you are given. Be it for registration, photographs, advertising or promotional material or for any other reason, do not pay anything 'up-front'. Honest agencies will make a nominal charge for promotional material they produce on behalf of their artistes, but this will always be taken from fees earned from work supplied. It will be a one-off annual charge and, by law, only based on an estimate of cost basis.

A good agent will want to see you before he or she will offer to put you forward for employment – be keen to make an appointment. This will give you an opportunity to check that the agent has proper premises and is operating in a viable fashion. Get to know as much as you can about your agent, both before and after you join. Check to see if they are members of the trade association NASAA at www.nasaa.org.uk. Owing to the curse of 'photoshop', agents will prefer to take your photographs themselves, and this should be done without charge.

Supporting artiste work does not lead to stardom. If you want to be an actor, go to drama school. It is essentially a part-time occupation for those who have a good level of availability, often at short notice, and find it both rewarding and interesting. Much depends on types and age groups. Over the years it has been my perception that 60% of work goes to men and 40% to women, with the greatest demand being for men aged between 25 and 45, and women between 20 and 40. This does not mean that there is no work for those outside those rough parameters, just that it is likely to be more erratic than for those in the categories for which there is a concentration of demand. It also helps to be of average size and measurements.

Please remember that leading artistes are carrying the burden of scripted lines and close-up action, and will be focusing on their work. They may not welcome chatting to the supporting artistes, even though at other times they would be very approachable. Do not bother them unless they invite you to socialise with them, give them space and respect their need for concentration.

The best supporting artistes are the ones who turn up on time, wearing the right clothes where appropriate, only need telling once, are quick to re-position, and are amenable to all they work with be it fellow artiste or crew. Do not adopt a high profile – people who try to get noticed are only seen as irritating. There is enough ego and stress on a film set already, it is not a good idea for supporting artistes to add to it.

Having said all of this, supporting artistes can have an interesting, rewarding and enjoyable time with the right attitude and approach. I have been fortunate to represent some lovely people whom I have very much enjoyed having on my books. I hope they have thought as well of me as I of them.

Please visit www.rayknight.co.uk for further information.

SÉVA
DHALIVAAL
07956 553879

CELEX CASTING LTD
Adults & Children available
PO Box 7317, Derby DE1 0GS
F 01332 232115   T 01332 232445
E anne@celex.co.uk

CENTRAL CASTING LTD
See also KNIGHT Ray CASTING
21A Lambolle Place, Belsize Park
London NW3 4PG
F 020 7722 2322   T 020 7722 1551
E casting@rayknight.co.uk
W www.rayknight.co.uk

CREATIVE KIDZ & CO
9 Weavers Terrace, Fulham
London SW6 1QE   M 07958 377595
E info@creativekidzandco.co.uk

DAVID AGENCY THE
26-28 Hammersmith Grove
London W6 7BA   T 020 8834 1615
E casting@davidagency.co.uk
W www.davidagency.co.uk

DOE John ASSOCIATES
123 Hanover Road, London NW10 3DN
M 07957 114175   T 020 8960 2848
E casting@johndoemgt.com
W www.johndoemgt.com

ELLIOTT AGENCY LTD THE
10 High Street
Shoreham-by-Sea BN43 5DA   T 01273 454111
E elliottagency@btconnect.com
W www.elliottagency.co.uk

ETHNIKA CASTING
14 Bowmont Gardens
Glasgow G12 9LR
M 07778 296002   T 0845 6031266
E ethnikacasting@yahoo.co.uk
W www.ethnikacasting.co.uk

EUROKIDS & EKA CASTING AGENCIES
The Warehouse Studios
Glaziers Lane
Culcheth, Warrington
Cheshire WA3 4AQ
F 01925 767563   T 01925 761088
E castings@eka-agency.com
W www.eka-agency.com

EXTRA-PEOPLE LTD
42 Old Compton Street, Soho
London W1D 4TX
F 020 7287 2855   T 020 7734 7606
E contact@extra-people.com
W www.extra-people.com

EXTRASPECIAL LTD
The Price Building, 110 York Road
Battersea, London SW11 3RD
F 020 7240 4879   T 020 7240 9240
E info@extraspecialartists.com

FACE MUSIC
Musician's Agency
Lambourne Farm, TR16 5HA   T 01209 820796
E facemusic@btinternet.com

FBI AGENCY
PO Box 250, Leeds LS1 2AZ
M 07515 567309   M 07050 222747
E casting@fbi-agency.co.uk
W www.fbi-agency.co.uk

FEATURED & BACKGROUND CASTING LTD
Contact: Lois Ward, Suzanne Johns
Audley Cottage, High Street
Cookham, Berkshire SL6 9SF
M 07899 898286   T 01628 531475
E info@fabcastingagency.com
W www.fabcastingagency.com

FILM CAST CORNWALL & SW
c/o 3 Church Walk
Truro TR1 1JH   T 01326 311419
E enquiries@filmcastcornwall.co.uk
W www.filmcastcornwall.co.uk

FRESH AGENTS LTD
Actors. Extras. Modelling. Promotional
Suite 5, Saks House
19 Ship Street, Brighton BN1 1AD
T 0845 4080998   T 01273 711777
E info@freshagents.co.uk
W www.freshagents.co.uk

FROOTFUL TALENT
Cams Hall, Cams Hill
Fareham, Hampshire PO16 8AB
M 07818 492680   M 07866 211647
E mark_turner85@hotmail.com
W www.frootfultalent.com

FTS CASTING AGENCY
55 Pullan Avenue, Eccleshill
Bradford BD2 3RP
F 01274 637429   T 01274 636036
E helen@footsteps.fslife.co.uk

GADBURY CASTING
5 Bolton Road, Atherton
Manchester M46 9JQ
M 07791 737306   T 01942 635556
E vicky@gadbury-casting.co.uk
W www.gadburycasting.co.uk

GOLD-CAST AGENCY
PO Box 30, Treharris
Mid Glamorgan CF46 9AN   M 07970 187801
E enquiries@gold-castagency.co.uk
W www.gold-castagency.co.uk

GUYS & DOLLS CASTING
Trafalgar House
Grenville Place
Mill Hill, London NW7 3SA
M 07890 774454
E info@guysanddollscasting.com
W www.guysanddollscasting.com
T 020 8906 4144

HERRON Alana PERSONAL MANAGEMENT
51 Medrox Gardens
Glasgow G67 4AL
M 07877 984636
E alana@alanaherron.com
W www.alanaherron.com

HOWE Janet CASTING AGENCY
The Pie Factory
101 Broadway
Salford Quays, Manchester M50 2EQ
M 07801 942178
E info@janethowe.com
W www.janethowecasting.co.uk
T/F 0161 660 1104

58A High Street
Newcastle-under-Lyme
Staffordshire ST5 1QE
T 01782 661777

INDUSTRY CASTING
332 Royal Exchange
Manchester M2 7BR
F 0161 839 1661
E mark@industrypeople.co.uk
W www.industrycasting.co.uk
T 0161 839 1551

IPM TALENT
The Studios
102 Kirkstall Road
Leeds, West Yorkshire LS3 1JA
E dean@ipmcasting.com
W www.ipmtalent.com
T 0113 244 3222

JACLYN AGENCY
52 Bessemer Road, Norwich
Norfolk NR4 6DQ
E info@jaclynagency.co.uk
W www.jaclynagency.co.uk
T 01603 622027

JPM EXTRAS
A Division of Janet Plater Management Ltd
D Floor, Milburn House
Dean Street
Newcastle upon Tyne NE1 1LF
E extras@tynebridge.demon.co.uk
W www.janetplatermanagement.co.uk
T 0191 221 2491

KNIGHT Ray CASTING
21A Lambolle Place, Belsize Park
London NW3 4PG
F 020 7722 2322
E casting@rayknight.co.uk
W www.rayknight.co.uk
T 020 7722 4111

Any artist, Any where, Any time

uni★VERSAL EXTRAS
www.universalextrascasting.co.uk
0845 3700 884

KREATE PROMOTIONS
Unit 232, 30 Great Guildford Street
London SE1 0HS
F 020 7401 3003
E enquiries@kreatepromotions.co.uk
W www.kreate.co.uk
T 020 7401 9007

LEMON CASTING LTD
The Pie Factory, 101 Broadway
Salford Quays, Manchester M50 2EQ
M 07723 317489
E lemon.tv@btconnect.com
T 0161 876 0088

LINTON MANAGEMENT
3 The Rock, Bury BL9 0JP
F 0161 761 1999
E mail@linton.tv
T 0161 761 2020

MAD DOG CASTING LTD
2nd Floor, Holborn Hall
193-197 High Holborn
London WC1V 7BD
F 020 7831 7267
E info@maddogcasting.com
T 020 7269 7910

**McDONAGH Melanie MANAGEMENT (ACADEMY OF
PERFORMING ARTS & CASTING AGENCY)**
14 Apple Tree Way
Oswaldtwistle
Accrington, Lancashire BB5 0FB
M 07909 831409
E mcdonaghmgt@aol.com
W www.mcdonaghmanagement.co.uk
T 01254 392560

NEMESIS AGENCY LTD
Nemesis House
1 Oxford Court
Bishopsgate, Manchester M2 3WQ
F 0161 228 6727
E julie@nmsmanagement.co.uk
W www.nemesisagency.co.uk
T 0161 228 6404

Bennetton-cmp

Bennetton casting, modelling and promotions (cmp) has been involved in the media for 2 decades providing hands on experience, to both clients and associates, which is second to none.

Our assignments are many fold with television work, film & cinema, advertising, modelling and promotions. Our work also extends into magazine & editorial assignments, exhibition and events.

Bennetton is renowned for building an excellent rapport with each individual on our books. We pride ourselves on first class dedication to our client's specification, to ensure we make the right choice for all assignments delivering high quality services.

Contact us at:
Bennetton-cmp, Raines Business Centre, Raines House, Denby Dale Road, WAKEFIELD, West Yorkshire, WF1 1HR.
T: 01924 882414   **T:** 07540 693657   **Fax:** 01924 291008
E: enquiries@bennetton-cmp.co.uk www.bennetton-cmp.co.uk

NIDGES CASTING AGENCY
Fourways House
57 Hilton Street, Manchester M1 2EJ
F 0161 236 1237
E cath@nidgescasting.co.uk
T 0161 237 0101

NORTHERN PROFESSIONALS CASTING COMPANY
21 Cresswell Avenue
North Shields
Tyne & Wear NE29 9BQ
E bill@northernprocasting.co.uk
W www.northernprocasting.co.uk
T 0191 257 8635

ORIENTAL CASTING AGENCY LTD (Peggy Sirr)
22 Wontford Road
Purley, Surrey CR8 4BL
F 020 8674 9303
E peggy.sirr@btconnect.com
W www.orientalcasting.com
T 020 8660 0101

PAN ARTISTS AGENCY LTD
Cornerways, 34 Woodhouse Lane
Sale, Cheshire M33 4JX
M 07890 715115
E panartists@btconnect.com
W www.panartists.co.uk
T 0800 6349147

PC THEATRICAL MODEL & CASTING AGENCY
10 Strathmore Gardens
Edgware, Middlesex HA8 5HJ
F 020 8933 3418
E twinagy@aol.com
W www.twinagency.com
T 020 8381 2229

PERFORMERS LEAGUE AGENCY LTD THE
55 Openshaw Road
Abbeywood, London SE2 0TB
M 07538 800083
E info@tpla.co.uk
W www.tpla.co.uk
T 020 8854 4576

PHA CASTING
Tanzaro House
Ardwick Green North, Manchester M12 6FZ
F 0161 273 4567
E info@pha-agency.co.uk
W www.pha-agency.co.uk
T 0161 273 4444

PHOENIX CASTING AGENCY
PO Box 387, Bristol BS99 3JZ
F 0117 973 4160
E info@phoenixagency.biz
W www.phoenixagency.biz
T 0117 973 1100

POLEASE
1 Noake Road, Hucclecote
Gloucester GL3 3PE
M 07811 504079
E info@polease.co.uk
W www.polease.co.uk
T 05600 650524

POWER MODEL MANAGEMENT CASTING AGENCY
PO Box 1198, Salhouse
Norwich NR13 6WD
E info@powermodel.co.uk
W www.powermodel.co.uk
T 01603 777190

RAPID TALENT LTD
5 Vancouver Road
Eastbourne
East Sussex BN23 5BF
M 07980 899156
E enquiries@rapidtalent.co.uk
W www.rapidtalent.co.uk
T 020 7734 5775

RAY'S NORTHERN CASTING AGENCY
7 Wince Close
Alkrington
Middleton, Manchester M24 1UJ
E rayscasting@yahoo.co.uk
T/F 0161 643 6745

REGENCY AGENCY
25 Carr Road, Calverley
Pudsey, West Yorks LS28 5NE
T 0113 255 8980

REVOLUTION TALENT MANAGEMENT
Central Chambers
93 Hope Street, Glasgow G2 6LD
F 0141 221 8622
E enquiries@revolutiontalentmanagement.com
W www.revolutiontalentmanagement.com
T 0141 221 2258

REYNOLDS Sandra AGENCY
Bacon House
35 St Georges Street
Norwich NR3 1DA
F 01603 219825
E info@sandrareynolds.co.uk
W www.sandrareynolds.co.uk
T 01603 623842

Shakespeare House
168 Lavender Hill
London SW11 5TF
F 020 7387 5848
T 020 7387 5858

RHODES AGENCY
5 Dymoke Road, Hornchurch
Essex RM11 1AA
F 01708 730431
E rhodesarts@hotmail.com
T 01708 747013

SA19 - THE UNIFORMED ARTISTE AGENCY
2020 Hopgood Street
Shepherds Bush
London W12 7JU
F 020 8735 2727
E info@sa19.co.uk
W www.sa19.co.uk
T 020 8746 2523

SAPPHIRES MODEL MANAGEMENT
The Makers Dozen
Studio 11
8 Wulfruna Street
Wolverhampton WV1 1LW
F 0870 9127563
E contact@sapphiresmodel.com
W www.sapphiresmodel.com
T 0844 8845404

SCREAM MANAGEMENT
The Pie Factory
101 Broadway
Media City, Manchester M50 2EQ
F 01253 309069   T 0161 660 3653
E info@screammanagement.com
W www.screammanagement.com

SCREENLITE AGENCY
Shepperton Studios
Studios Road
Shepperton, Middlesex TW17 0QD
T 01932 592271   T 01932 561388
E enquiries@screenliteagency.co.uk
W www.screenliteagency.co.uk

SHARMAN Alan AGENCY
28-29 Tenby Street
Birmingham B1 3EE   T 0121 212 0090
E info@alansharmanagency.com
W www.alansharmanagency.com

SNODE Chris PROMOTIONS LTD
56 Church Road
Crystal Palace, London SE19 2EZ
F 020 8771 4704   T 020 8771 4700
E agent@sportspromotions.co.uk
W www.sportspromotions.co.uk

SOLOMON ARTISTES
30 Clarence Street
Southend-on-Sea
Essex SS1 1BD
T 01702 437118   T 020 7748 4409
E info@solomon-artistes.co.uk
W www.solomon-artistes.co.uk

SPIRIT MODEL MANAGEMENT
Alternative & Character Agency
98 Woodside Road, Ketley
Telford, Shropshire TF1 5WT   M 07896 978972
E enquiries@spiritmodelmanagement.com
W www.spiritmodelmanagement.com

SUMMERS Mark MANAGEMENT
Formerly Extras Unlimited
1 Beaumont Avenue
West Kensington, London W14 9LP   T 020 7229 8413
E info@marksummers.com
W www.marksummers.com

TUESDAYS CHILD LTD
Children & Adults
Oakfield House
Springwood Way, Macclesfield SK10 2XA   T/F 01625 501765
E info@tuesdayschildagency.co.uk
W www.tuesdayschildagency.co.uk

TURNSTONE CASTING AGENCY
Suite 8, Hilton Hall, Hilton Lane, Essington WV11 2BQ
M 07866 211647   T 0845 5570927
E mark_turner85@hotmail.com

UNI-VERSAL EXTRAS
Pinewood Studios, Pinewood Road, Iver Heath
Buckinghamshire SL0 0NH   T 0845 0090344
E info@universalextras.co.uk
W www.universalextrascasting.co.uk

WARD CASTING
Studio 5
155 Commercial Street, London E1 6BJ   T 020 8886 5676
E casting@wardcasting.com
W www.wardcasting.com

A1 ANIMALS
Farm, Domestic & Exotic Animals
Wattel Hill Farm, Dunstew
Ledwell, Oxon OX7 7AN   T 01608 683954
E a1animals@btinternet.com
W www.a1animals.co.uk

A-Z ANIMALS LTD
The Bell House, Bell Lane
Fetcham, Surrey KT22 9ND   T 01372 377111
E info@a-zanimals.com
W www.a-zanimals.com

ACTION STUNT DOGS & ANIMALS
3 The Chestnuts, Clifton
Deddington, Oxon OX15 0PE   T 01869 338546
E gill@stuntdogs.net

ALTERNATIVE ANIMALS
Contact: Trevor Smith. Animatronics. Taxidermy
19 Greaves Road, High Wycombe, Bucks HP13 7JU
F 01494 441385   M 07956 564715
E animalswork1@yahoo.co.uk
W www.animalswork.co.uk

ANIMAL ACTING
Animals. Horse-drawn Vehicles. Props. Stunts
7 Dovedale Court, Windermere Road
Middleton, Manchester M24 5QT
M 07831 800567   T 0161 655 3700
E information@animalacting.com
W www.animalacting.com

ANIMAL ACTORS
Animals. Birds. Reptiles
95 Ditchling Road, Brighton
Sussex BN1 4ST   T 020 8654 0450

ANIMAL AMBASSADORS
Old Forest, Hampstead Norreys Road
Hermitage, Berks RG18 9SA
M 07831 558594   T 01635 200900
E kayweston@tiscali.co.uk
W www.animalambassadors.co.uk

ANIMAL CASTING
119 Magdalen Road, London SW18 3ES
M 07956 246450   T 020 8874 9530
E silcresta@aol.com

ANIMAL WELFARE FILMING FEDERATION
Free Consultancy Service
28 Greaves Road, High Wycombe, Bucks HP13 7JU
F 01494 441385   M 07770 666088
E animalswork1@yahoo.co.uk
W www.animalworld.org.uk

ANIMALS GALORE LTD
208 Smallfield Road, Horley
Surrey RH6 9LS   T 01342 842400
W www.animals-galore.co.uk

ANIMALS O KAY
16 Queen Street, Chipperfield
Kings Langley, Herts WD4 9BT   T 01923 291277
E kayraven@btinternet.com
W www.animalsokay.com

ANIMALS WORK WITH TREVOR SMITH
Contact: Trevor Smith
28 Greaves Road
High Wycombe, Bucks HP13 7JU
M 07770 666088   M 07956 564715
E animalswork1@yahoo.co.uk
W www.animalswork.co.uk

CELEBRITY REPTILES
11 Tramway Close
London SE20 7DF   T 020 8659 0877
E info@celebrityreptiles.co.uk
W www.celebrityreptiles.co.uk

CHEESEMAN Virginia
21 Willow Close, Flackwell Heath
High Wycombe, Bucks HP10 9LH
M 07971 838724   T 01628 522632
E virginia@virginiacheeseman.co.uk
W www.virginiacheeseman.co.uk

COTSWOLD FARM PARK
Rare Breed Farm Animals
Guiting Power, Cheltenham
Gloucestershire GL54 5UG
F 01451 850423   T 01451 850307
E info@cotswoldfarmpark.co.uk

CREATURE FEATURE
Animal Agent
Gubhill Farm, Ae, Dumfries, Scotland DG1 1RL
M 07770 774866   T 01387 860648
E david@creaturefeature.co.uk
W www.creaturefeature.co.uk

DOG EXTRAS
11 Colster Way, Colsterworth, Grantham, Lincs NG33 5JT
M 07956 369890   T 01476 862028
E info@dog-extras.co.uk
W www.dog-extras.co.uk

DOLBADARN FILM HORSES
Dolbadarn Hotel, High Street, Llanberis
Gwynedd, North Wales LL55 4SU
M 07710 461341   T 01286 870277
E info@filmhorses.co.uk
W www.filmhorses.co.uk

DUDLEY Yvonne LRPS ARAD FISTD
Glamour Dogs & Stories for Films
55 Cambridge Park, Wanstead
London E11 2PR   T 020 8989 1528

FILM & TV HORSES
Patterdale Farm, Blackbird Cottage, Drift Road, Hawthorn Hill
Nr Maidenhead, Berkshire SL6 3SX
M 07831 629662   T 01628 675105
E filmhorses@yahoo.co.uk
W www.filmhorses.com

GET STUFFED
Taxidermy
105 Essex Road, London N1 2SL
M 07831 260062   T 020 7226 1364
E taxidermy@thegetstuffed.co.uk
W www.thegetstuffed.co.uk

GRAY Robin COMMENTARIES
Equestrian Equipment. Horse Race Commentaries.
Voice Overs
Comptons, Isington
Alton, Hants GU34 4PL
M 07831 828424   T 01420 23347
E gray@isington.fsnet.co.uk

HILTON HORSES
Contact: Samantha Jones
478 London Road, Ashford
Middlesex TW15 3AD   M 07958 292222
E samantha@hilton-horses.com
W www.hilton-horses.com

KNIGHTS OF ARKLEY THE
Glyn Sylen Farm, Five Roads
Llanelli SA15 5BJ   T 01269 861001
E penny@knightsofarkley.fsnet.co.uk
W www.knightsofarkley.com

KNIGHTS OF MIDDLE ENGLAND THE
Horses & Riders for Film, Opera & TV
Warwick International School of Riding, Guys Cliffe
Coventry Road
Warwick CV34 5YD   T 01926 400401
E info@knightsofmiddleengland.co.uk
W www.knightsofmiddleengland.co.uk

MILLENNIUM BUGS
Live Insects
28 Greaves Road
High Wycombe, Bucks HP13 7JU
F 01494 441385   T 01494 442750
E animalswork1@yahoo.co.uk
W www.animalworld.org.uk

MINI PONY HIRE
18 South View, Cambois
Blyth, Northumberland NE24 1RX   M 07777 678687
E miniponyhire@hotmail.co.uk
W www.miniponyhire.com

MORTON Geoff
Shire Horse & Equipment
Hasholme Carr Farm, Holme on Spalding Moor
York YO43 4BD   T 01430 860393

NOLTON STABLES
Nolton, Nr Newgale
Haverfordwest
Pembrokeshire SA62 3NW
F 01437 710967   T 01437 710360
E noltonstables@aol.com
W www.noltonstables.com

OTTERS
Contact: Daphne & Martin Neville. Tame Otters
Baker's Mill, Frampton Mansell
Stroud, Glos GL6 8JH   T 01285 760234
E martin_neville_bakers_mill@yahoo.co.uk

PROP FARM LTD
Contact: Pat Ward
Grange Farm, Elmton
Nr Creswell, North Derbyshire S80 4LX
F 01909 721465   T 01909 723100
E les@propfarm.co.uk

ROCKWOOD ANIMALS ON FILM
Lewis Terrace
Llanbradach, Caerphilly CF83 3JZ
M 07973 930983   T 029 2088 5420
E martin@rockwoodanimals.com
W www.rockwoodanimals.com

SCHOOL OF NATIONAL EQUITATION LTD
Contact: Sam Humphrey
Bunny Hill Top, Costock
Loughborough, Leicestershire LE12 6XN
M 07977 930083   T 01509 852366
E sam@bunnyhill.co.uk
W www.bunnyhill.co.uk

WHITE DOVES COMPANY LTD THE
Provision of up to 150 Doves for Release
Suite 210 Sterling House
Langston Road
Loughton, Essex IG10 3TS
F 020 8502 2461   T 020 8508 1414
E thewhitedovecompany@yahoo.co.uk
W www.thewhitedovecompany.co.uk

WOLF SPECIALISTS THE
The UK Wolf Conservation Trust, UK Wolf Centre
Butlers Farm, Beenham, Berks RG7 5NT   T 0118 971 3330
E ukwct@ukwolf.org
W www.ukwolf.org

WOODS Sue
Animal Promotions. Specialising in Dogs, Domestic Cats,
Rodents, Poultry & Farm Stock
White Rocks Farm, Underriver
Sevenoaks, Kent TN15 0SL
F 01732 763767   T 01732 761888
E sue.woods@animalpromotions.co.uk
W www.animalpromotions.co.uk

YORKSHIRE TERRIER
Based in Central London
17 Gardnor Road, London NW3 1HA   M 07963 818845
E woodlandcreature10@hotmail.com

ALDERSHOT
West End Centre
Queens Road
Aldershot, Hants GU11 3JD
BO 01252 330040 T 01252 408040
E westendcentre@hants.gov.uk
W www.westendcentre.co.uk

BILLERICAY
Billericay Arts Association
The Fold, 72 Laindon Road
Billericay, Essex CM12 9LD T 01277 659286
E baathefold@yahoo.co.uk
W www.baathefold.org.uk

BINGLEY
Bingley Arts Centre, Main Street
Bingley, West Yorkshire BD16 2LZ T 01274 431576
E community-halls@bradford.gov.uk

BIRMINGHAM
The Custard Factory
Gibb Street, Digbeth
Birmingham B9 4AA
F 0121 604 8888 T 0121 693 7777
E info@custardfactory.co.uk
W www.custardfactory.co.uk

BOSTON
Blackfriars Arts Centre
Contact: Mike Raymond
Spain Lane
Boston, Lincolnshire PE21 6HP
F 01205 358855 T 01205 363108
E director@blackfriarsartscentre.co.uk
W www.blackfriarsartscentre.co.uk

BRACKNELL
South Hill Park Arts Centre
Contact: Ron McAllister (Chief Executive)
Ringmead, Bracknell, Berkshire RG12 7PA
F 01344 411427
BO 01344 484123 T 01344 484858
E admin@southhillpark.org.uk
W www.southhillpark.org.uk

BRADFORD
Theatre in The Mill
University of Bradford
Shearbridge Road, Bradford, West Yorkshire BD7 1DP
BO 01274 233200 T 01274 233185
E theatre@bradford.ac.uk
W www.bradford.ac.uk/theatre

BRENTFORD
Watermans Arts Centre
40 High Street
Brentford TW8 0DS
F 020 8232 1030
BO 020 8232 1010 T 020 8232 1020
E info@watermans.org.uk
W www.watermans.org.uk

BRIDGWATER
Bridgwater Arts Centre
11-13 Castle Street
Bridgwater, Somerset TA6 3DD T 01278 422700
E info@bridgwaterartscentre.co.uk
W www.bridgwaterartscentre.co.uk

BRISTOL
Arnolfini
16 Narrow Quay, Bristol BS1 4QA
F 0117 917 2303 T 0117 917 2300
E boxoffice@arnolfini.org.uk

BUILTH WELLS
Wyeside Arts Centre
Castle Street
Builth Wells, Powys LD2 3BN T 01982 553668
E marketing@wyeside.co.uk
W www.wyeside.co.uk

BURY
The Met
Contact: David Agnew (Director)
Market Street, Bury, Lancs BL9 0BW
F 0870 0520297
BO 0161 761 2216 T 0161 761 7107
E post@themet.biz
W www.themet.biz

CANNOCK
Prince of Wales Centre
Contact: Richard Kay (General Manager)
Church Sreet
Cannock, Staffs WS11 1DE
F 01543 574439
BO 01543 578762 T 01543 466453
E princeofwales@cannockchasedc.gov.uk

CARDIFF
Chapter Arts Centre
Market Road
Canton, Cardiff CF5 1QE
BO 029 2030 4400 T 029 2031 1050
W www.chapter.org

CHIPPING NORTON
The Theatre
Contact: John Terry (Director), Ambereene Hitchcox (Head of Operations)
2 Spring Street
Chipping Norton, Oxon OX7 5NL
F 01608 642324
BO 01608 642350 T 01608 642349
E admin@chippingnortontheatre.com
W www.chippingnortontheatre.com

CHRISTCHURCH
The Regent Centre
Contact: Eliot Walker (Manager)
51 High Street
Christchurch, Dorset BH23 1AS BO 01202 499199
E info@regentcentre.co.uk
W www.regentcentre.co.uk

CIRENCESTER
New Brewery Arts, Brewery Court
Cirencester, Glos GL7 1JH
F 01285 644060 T 01285 657181
E admin@newbreweryarts.org.uk
W www.newbreweryarts.org.uk

COLCHESTER
Colchester Arts Centre
Contact: Anthony Roberts (Director)
Church Street
Colchester, Essex CO1 1NF T 01206 500900
E info@colchesterartscentre.com
W www.colchesterartscentre.com

COVENTRY
Warwick Arts Centre
Contact: Alan Rivett (Director)
University of Warwick
Coventry CV4 7AL
BO 024 7652 4524 T 024 7652 3734
E arts.centre@warwick.ac.uk
W www.warwickartscentre.co.uk

CUMBERNAULD
Cumbernauld Theatre
Kildrum
Cumbernauld G67 2BN
F 01236 738408
BO 01236 732887   T 01236 737235
E info@cumbernauldtheatre.co.uk
W www.cumbernauldtheatre.co.uk

DARLINGTON
Darlington Arts Centre
Vane Terrace
Darlington, County Durham DL3 7AX
BO 01325 486555   T 01325 348843
W www.darlingtonarts.co.uk

EDINBURGH
Scottish Storytelling Centre
Contact: Dr Donald Smith (Director)
43-45 High Street
Edinburgh EH1 1SR   T 0131 556 9579
E reception@scottishstorytellingcentre.com
W www.scottishstorytellingcentre.co.uk

EDINBURGH
Theatre Workshop
Contact: Robert Rae (Director)
34 Hamilton Place
Edinburgh EH3 5AX
F 0131 220 0112   T 0131 225 7942
W www.theatre-workshop.com

EPSOM
Playhouse
Contact: Trevor Mitchell (General Manager/Artistic Director)
Ashley Avenue
Epsom, Surrey KT18 5AL
F 01372 726228
BO 01372 742555   T 01372 742226
E tmitchell@epsom-ewell.gov.uk
W www.epsomplayhouse.co.uk

EXETER
Exeter Phoenix
Contact: Patrick Cunningham (Director)
Bradninch Place, Gandy Street
Exeter, Devon EX4 3LS
F 01392 667599
BO 01392 667080   T 01392 667060
E admin@exeterphoenix.org.uk
W www.exeterphoenix.org.uk

FAREHAM
Ashcroft Arts Centre
Contact: Annabel Cook (Director/Programmer)
Osborn Road, Fareham, Hants PO16 7DX
F 01329 825661
BO 01329 223100   T 01329 235161
E info@ashcroft.org.uk
W www.ashcroft.org.uk

FROME
Merlin Theatre
Bath Road
Frome, Somerset BA11 2HG
BO 01373 465949   T 01373 461360
E admin@merlintheatre.co.uk
W www.merlintheatre.co.uk

GAINSBOROUGH
Trinity Arts Centre
Trinity Street
Gainsborough
Lincolnshire DN21 2AL   T 01427 676655 (BO/Admin)
W www.trinityarts.co.uk

GREAT TORRINGTON
The Plough Arts Centre
9-11 Fore Street, Great Torrington, Devon EX38 8HQ
BO 01805 624624   T 01805 622552
E mail@theploughartscentre.org.uk
W www.theploughartscentre.org.uk

HARLECH
Theatr Harlech
Harlech, Gwynedd LL46 2PU   BO 01766 780667
E sara@theatrharlech.com

HAVANT
Spring Arts & Heritage Centre
Contact: Amanda O'Reilly (Director)
East Street
Havant, Hants PO9 1BS   BO 023 9247 2700
E info@thespring.co.uk
W www.thespring.co.uk

HELMSLEY
Helmsley Arts Centre
Contact: Claire Lishman (Marketing & Theatre Manager)
Meeting House Court, Helmsley, York YO62 5DW
BO 01439 771700   T 01439 772112
E theatrehelmsleyarts@yahoo.co.uk
W www.helmsleyarts.co.uk

HEMEL HEMPSTEAD
Old Town Hall Theatre
Contact: Sara Railson (Art & Entertainment Manager)
High Street, Hemel Hempstead, Herts HP1 3AE
BO 01442 228091   T 01442 228095
E othadmin@dacorum.gov.uk
W www.oldtownhall.co.uk

HEXHAM
Queens Hall Arts
Contact: Geof Keys (Artistic Director)
Beaumont Street, Hexham, Northumberland NE46 3LS
F 01434 652478
BO 01434 652477   T 01434 652476
E boxoffice@queenshall.co.uk
W www.queenshall.co.uk

HORSHAM
The Capitol
North Street, Horsham, West Sussex RH12 1RG
F 01403 756092   T 01403 756080
W www.thecapitolhorsham.com

HUDDERSFIELD
Kirklees Culture & Leisure Services
Kirklees. Various Venues
The Stadium Business & Leisure Complex
Stadium Way, Huddersfield HD1 6PG
BO 01484 223200   T 01484 234000
W www.kirklees.gov.uk

INVERNESS
Eden Court
Contact: Colin Marr (Director)
Bishop's Road, Inverness IV3 5SA
BO 01463 234234   T 01463 239841
E admin@eden-court.co.uk
W www.eden-court.co.uk

JERSEY
Jersey Arts Centre
Contact: Daniel Austin (Director)
Phillips Street, St Helier, Jersey JE2 4SW
F 01534 700401
BO 01534 700444   T 01534 700400
E enquiries@artscentre.je
W www.artscentre.je

KENDAL
Brewery Arts Centre
Contact: Richard Foster (Chief Executive)
Highgate
Kendal, Cumbria LA9 4HE
BO 01539 725133   T 01539 722833
E admin@breweryarts.co.uk
W www.breweryarts.co.uk

KING'S LYNN
King's Lynn Arts Centre
29 King Street
King's Lynn, Norfolk PE30 1HA
F 01553 762141
BO 01553 764864   T 01553 765565
W www.kingslynnarts.co.uk

LEICESTER
Phoenix Square
Midland Street
Leicester LE1 1TG
BO 0116 242 2800   T 0116 242 2803
W www.phoenix.org.uk

LICHFIELD
Lichfield District Arts Association
Contact: Brian Pretty (Director)
Donegal House
Bore Street, Lichfield WS13 6LU
F 01543 308211   T 01543 262223
E info@lichfieldarts.org.uk
W www.lichfieldarts.org.uk

LISKEARD
Sterts Theatre & Arts Centre
Upton Cross, Liskeard, Cornwall PL14 5AZ
T 01579 362382   T 01579 362962
W www.sterts.co.uk

LONDON
The Albany
Douglas Way, Deptford, London SE8 4AG
F 020 8469 2253   T 020 8692 4446
E albany@thealbany.org.uk
W www.thealbany.org.uk

LONDON
Artsdepot
5 Nether Street, Tally Ho Corner
North Finchley, London N12 0GA   BO 020 8369 5454
E info@artsdepot.co.uk
W www.artsdepot.co.uk

LONDON
BAC
Lavender Hill, Battersea, London SW11 5TN
F 020 7978 5207
BO 020 7223 2223   T 020 7223 6557
E mailbox@bac.org.uk
W www.bac.org.uk

LONDON
Beyond
21 Stonehouse, 199 Eade Road, London N4 1DN
M 07886 984526   T 020 8809 6946
E amy@beyond-centre.com
W www.beyond-centre.com

LONDON
Chats Palace
Contact: Sarah Wickens (Centre Director)
42-44 Brooksby's Walk
Hackney, London E9 6DF   T 020 8533 0227 (BO/Admin)
E info@chatspalace.com
W www.chatspalace.com

LONDON
Cockpit Theatre
Gateforth Street, London NW8 8EH
F 020 7258 2921
BO 020 7258 2925   T 020 7258 2920
E dave.wybrow@cwc.ac.uk
W www.cockpittheatre.org.uk

LONDON
The Drill Hall
16 Chenies Street, London WC1E 7EX
F 020 7307 5062
BO 020 7307 5060   T 020 7307 5061
E box.office@drillhall.co.uk
W www.drillhall.co.uk

LONDON
The Hangar Arts Trust
Contact: Alex Frith (Space Manager/Trust Chairman)
7A Melish House
Harrington Way, London SE18 5NR   T 020 8317 8401
E alex@aircraftcircus.com
W www.hangaruk.com

LONDON
Hoxton Hall Arts Centre
Contact: Jane Caley (Operations Manager)
130 Hoxton Street
London N1 6SH
F 020 7729 3815   T 020 7684 0060
E info@hoxtonhall.co.uk
W www.hoxtonhall.co.uk

LONDON
Institute of Contemporary Arts
Contact: Jamie Eastman (Head of Live Performance)
No in-house productions or castings
The Mall
London SW1Y 5AH
F 020 7306 0122
BO 020 7930 3647   T 020 7930 0493
W www.ica.org.uk

LONDON
Islington Arts Factory
2 Parkhurst Road, London N7 0SF
F 020 7700 7229   T 020 7607 0561
E info@islingtonartsfactory.org
W www.islingtonartsfactory.org

LONDON
Jacksons Lane
269A Archway Road, London N6 5AA
F 020 8348 2424
BO 020 8341 4421   T 020 8340 5226
E reception@jacksonslane.org.uk
W www.jacksonslane.org.uk

LONDON
Menier Chocolate Factory
Contact: David Babani (Artistic Director)
53 Southwark Street, London SE1 1RU
F 020 7378 1713
BO 020 7907 7060   T 020 7378 1712
E office@menierchocolatefactory.com
W www.menierchocolatefactory.com

LONDON
The Nettlefold
Contact: Joanne Johnson, Mark Sheehan (Centre Development Officers)
West Norwood Library Centre
1 Norwood High Street
London SE27 9JX   T 020 7926 8070 (BO/Admin)

LONDON
October Gallery
Contact: Jo Walsh
24 Old Gloucester Street
London WC1N 3AL
F 020 7405 1851   T 020 7831 1618
E rentals@octobergallery.co.uk
W www.octobergallery.co.uk

LONDON
Oval House Theatre
Contact: Ben Evans (Programmer), Deborah Bestwick
(Director)
52-54 Kennington Oval
London SE11 5SW   T 020 7582 0080
E info@ovalhouse.com
W www.ovalhouse.com

LONDON
Polish Social & Cultural Association
238-246 King Street
London W6 0RF   T 020 8741 1940

LONDON
Riverside Studios
Crisp Road, Hammersmith, London W6 9RL
F 020 8237 1001
BO 020 8237 1111   T 020 8237 1000
E admin@riversidestudios.co.uk
W www.riversidestudios.co.uk

LONDON
The Stables Gallery & Arts Centre
Gladstone Park
Dollis Hill Lane, London NW2 6HT   T 020 8452 8655
E stablesgallery@msn.com
W www.brentarts.org.uk

MAIDENHEAD
Norden Farm Centre For The Arts
Contact: Jane Corry (Director)
Altwood Road
Maidenhead SL6 4PF
F 01628 682525
BO 01628 788997   T 01628 682555
E admin@nordenfarm.org
W www.nordenfarm.org

MAIDSTONE
Hazlitt Arts Centre
Contact: Mandy Hare (Theatre & Events Manager)
Earl Street
Maidstone, Kent ME14 1PL
F 01622 750530
BO 01622 758611   T 01622 753922
E theatreandevents@maidstone.gov.uk

MANCHESTER
Greenroom
Contact: Garfield Allen (Artistic Director)
54-56 Whitworth Street West
Manchester M1 5WW
F 0161 615 0516
BO 0161 615 0500   T 0161 615 0515
E info@greenroomarts.org
W www.greenroomarts.org

MANCHESTER
The Lowry
Contact: Steve Cowton (Theatre Production Bookings)
Pier 8
Salford Quays M50 3AZ
F 0161 876 2021   BO 0843 2086000
E info@thelowry.com
W www.thelowry.com

MILFORD HAVEN
Torch Theatre
Contact: Peter Doran (Artistic Director)
St Peter's Road
Milford Haven
Pembrokeshire SA73 2BU
F 01646 698919
BO 01646 695267   T 01646 694192
E info@torchtheatre.co.uk
W www.torchtheatre.co.uk

NEWPORT (Isle of Wight)
Quay Arts
Sea Street
Newport Harbour
Isle of Wight PO30 5BD
F 01983 526606   T 01983 822490
E info@quayarts.org
W www.quayarts.org

NORTH SHIELDS
North Tyneside Arts
Saville Exchange
Howard Street
North Shields NE30 1SE   T 0191 643 7093
E saville-arts@northtyneside.gov.uk

NORWICH
Norwich Arts Centre
St Benedicts Street
Norwich, Norfolk NR2 4PG
BO 01603 660352   T 01603 660387
E stuart@norwichartscentre.co.uk
W www.norwichartscentre.co.uk

NUNEATON
Abbey Theatre & Arts Centre
Contact: Tony Deeming (Chairman)
Pool Bank Street
Nuneaton, Warks CV11 5DB
BO 024 7635 4090   T 024 7632 7359
E admin@abbeytheatre.co.uk
W www.abbeytheatre.co.uk

PLYMOUTH
Plymouth Arts Centre
Contact: Ian Hutchinson (Director)
38 Looe Street
Plymouth, Devon PL4 0EB
F 01752 206118   T 01752 206114
E info@plymouthartscentre.org
W www.plymouthartscentre.org

POOLE
Lighthouse Poole Centre for The Arts
Kingland Road
Poole, Dorset BH15 1UG   T 0844 4068666 (BO/Admin)
W www.lighthousepoole.co.uk

RADLETT
The Radlett Centre
1 Aldenham Avenue
Radlett, Herts WD7 8HL
F 01923 857592   T 01923 857546
E admin@radlettcentre.com
W www.radlettcentre.co.uk

ROTHERHAM
Rotherham Civic Theatre
Contact: Mark Scott (Theatre Manager)
Catherine Street
Rotherham
South Yorkshire S65 1EB
BO 01709 823621   T 01709 823641
W www.rotherham.gov.uk/theatres

SALISBURY
Salisbury Arts Centre
Bedwin Street, Salisbury, Wiltshire SP1 3UT
F 01722 343030
BO 01722 321744   T 01722 343020
E info@salisburyarts.co.uk
W www.salisburyartscentre.co.uk

SHREWSBURY
Shrewsbury & District Arts Association
The Gateway, Chester Street
Shrewsbury, Shropshire SY1 1NB   T 01743 355159
E gateway.centre@shropshire-cc.gov.uk
W www.shropshirecouncil.gov.uk

SOUTHPORT
Southport Arts Centre
Lord Street, Southport
Merseyside PR8 1DB
BO 01704 540011   T 0151 934 2131
E artsops@seftonarts.co.uk
W www.seftonarts.co.uk

STAMFORD
Stamford Arts Centre
Contact: Graham Burley (General Manager)
27 St Mary's Street, Stamford, Lincolnshire PE9 2DL
F 01780 766690
BO 01780 763203   T 01780 480846
E boxoffice@stamfordartscentre.com
W www.stamfordartscentre.co.uk

STIRLING
MacRobert Arts Centre
University of Stirling, Stirling FK9 4LA
BO 01786 466666   T 01786 467155
E info@macrobert.org
W www.macrobert.org

SWANSEA
Taliesin Arts Centre
Contact: Sybil Crouch (Head of Cultural Services)
Swansea University
Singleton Park, Swansea SA2 8PZ   T 01792 295238
E s.e.crouch@swansea.ac.uk
W www.taliesinartscentre.co.uk

SWINDON
Wyvern Theatre
Theatre Square, Swindon, Wiltshire SN1 1QN
BO 01793 524481   T 01793 535534

TAUNTON
Brewhouse Theatre & Arts Centre
Contact: Robert Miles (Director)
Coal Orchard, Taunton
Somerset TA1 1JL
BO 01823 283244   T 01823 274608
E info@thebrewhouse.net
W www.thebrewhouse.net

TOTNES
The Arts at Dartington
The Barn, Dartington Hall
Totnes, Devon TQ9 6DE
BO 01803 847070   T 01803 847074
E arts@dartington.org
W www.dartington.org/arts

TUNBRIDGE WELLS
Trinity Theatre
Church Road
Tunbridge Wells, Kent TN1 1JP
BO 01892 678678   T 01892 678670
E enquiries@trinitytheatre.net

ULEY
Prema
Contact: Gordon Scott (Director)
South Street
Uley, Nr Dursley, Glos GL11 5SS   T 01453 860703
E info@prema.demon.co.uk
W www.prema.demon.co.uk

VALE OF GLAMORGAN
St Donats Arts Centre
Contact: Sharon Stone (General Manager)
St Donats Castle
The Vale of Glamorgan CF61 1WF
F 01446 799101
BO 01446 799100   T 01446 799095
E admin@stdonats.com

WAKEFIELD
Wakefield Arts Centre
Wakefield College
Thornes Park Centre
Thornes Park, Horbury Road
Wakefield WF2 8QZ
BO 01924 211311   T 01924 215531
W www.theatreroyalwakefield.co.uk

WASHINGTON
The Arts Centre Washington
Biddick Lane, Fatfield
Washington, Tyne & Wear NE38 8AB
F 0191 219 3458   T 0191 219 3455
E matthew.blyth@sunderland.gov.uk

WELLINGBOROUGH
The Castle
Contact: Gail Arnott (Executive Director), Nik Ashton (Artistic Director)
Castle Way
Wellingborough, Northants NN8 1XA
F 01933 229888   T 01933 229022
E info@thecastle.org.uk
W www.thecastle.org.uk

WIMBORNE
Layard Theatre
Contact: Chris Thomas (Director of Drama), Christine Haynes (Administrator)
Canford School
Canford Magna, Wimborne
Dorset BH21 3AD
T/F 01202 847525 (BO)   T 01202 847529
E layardtheatre@canford.com

WINCHESTER
The Tower @ Kings
Contact: Ben Ward (Tower Co-ordinator)
Romsey Road
Winchester, Hampshire SO22 5PW   T 01962 867986
W www.towerarts.co.uk

WINDSOR
The Firestation
The Old Court
St Leonards Road
Windsor, Berks SL4 3BL   T 01753 866865
E info@firestationartscentre.com
W www.firestationartscentre.com

WREXHAM
Oriel Wrecsam/Wrexham Arts Centre
Rhosddu Road
Wrexham LL11 1AU
F 01978 292611   T 01978 292093
E oriel.wrecsam@wrexham.gov.uk

ARTS COUNCIL ENGLAND, EAST
Norfolk, Suffolk, Bedfordshire, Cambridgeshire, Essex,
Hertfordshire & the unitary authorities of Luton,
Peterborough, Southend-on-Sea & Thurrock
Eden House
48-49 Bateman Street
Cambridge CB2 1LR
F 0870 2421271   T 0845 3006200
W www.artscouncil.org.uk

ARTS COUNCIL ENGLAND, EAST MIDLANDS
Derbyshire, Leicestershire, Lincolnshire excluding North &
North East Lincolnshire, Northamptonshire, Nottinghamshire
& the unitary authorities of Derby, Leicester, Nottingham &
Rutland
St Nicholas Court
25-27 Castle Gate
Nottingham NG1 7AR
F 0115 950 2467   T 0845 3006200
W www.artscouncil.org.uk

ARTS COUNCIL ENGLAND, LONDON
Greater London
14 Great Peter Street
London SW1P 3NQ
F 020 7608 4100   T 0845 3006200
W www.artscouncil.org.uk

ARTS COUNCIL ENGLAND, NORTH EAST
Durham, Northumberland, metropolitan authorities of
Gateshead, Newcastle upon Tyne, North Tyneside, South
Tyneside, Sunderland & the unitary authorities of Darlington,
Hartlepool, Middlesborough, Red Car & Cleveland,
Stockton-on-Tees
Central Square
Forth Street
Newcastle upon Tyne NE1 3PJ
F 0191 230 1020   T 0845 3006200
W www.artscouncil.org.uk

ARTS COUNCIL ENGLAND, NORTH WEST
Lancashire, Cheshire, Cumbria & the metropolitan authorities
of Bolton, Bury, Knowsley, Liverpool, Manchester, Oldham,
Rochdale, St Helens, Salford, Sefton, Stockport, Tameside,
Trafford, Wigan, Wirral & the unitary authorities of Blackburn
with Darwen, Blackpool, Halton & Warrington
The Hive
49 Lever Street
Manchester M1 1FN
F 0161 834 6969   T 0845 3006200
W www.artscouncil.org.uk

ARTS COUNCIL ENGLAND, SOUTH EAST
Buckinghamshire, East Sussex, Hampshire, Isle of Wight, Kent,
Oxfordshire, Surrey, West Sussex & the unitary authorities of
Bracknell Forest. Brighton & Hove, Medway Towns,
Milton Keynes, Portsmouth
Sovereign House
Church Street
Brighton BN1 1RA
F 0870 2421257   T 0845 3006200
W www.artscouncil.org.uk

ARTS COUNCIL ENGLAND, SOUTH WEST
Cornwall, Devon, Dorset, Gloucestershire, Somerset
& Wiltshire & the unitary authorities of Bristol, Bath,
Bournemouth, Plymouth, Poole, Torbay & Swindon
Senate Court
Southernhay Gardens
Exeter, Devon EX1 1UG   T 0845 3006200
E enquiries@artscouncil.org.uk
W www.artscouncil.org.uk

ARTS COUNCIL ENGLAND, WEST MIDLANDS
Herefordshire, Worcestershire, Staffordshire, Warwickshire
& Shropshire, Stoke-on-Trent, Telford & Wrekin & districts of
Birmingham, Coventry, Dudley, Sandwell, Solihull,
Walsall & Wolverhampton
82 Granville Street
Birmingham B1 2LH
F 0121 643 7239   T 0845 3006200
W www.artscouncil.org.uk

ARTS COUNCIL ENGLAND, YORKSHIRE
North Yorkshire, metropolitan authorities of Barnsley,
Bradford, Calderdale, Doncaster, Kirklees, Leeds, Rotherham,
Sheffield, Wakefield & the unitary authorities of East Riding
of Yorkshire, Kingston upon Hull, North Lincolnshire,
North East Lincolnshire
21 Bond Street
Dewsbury
West Yorkshire WF13 1AX
F 01924 466522   T 0845 3006200
W www.artscouncil.org.uk

ARTS COUNCIL OF WALES, MID & WEST WALES OFFICE
Ceredigion, Carmarthenshire, Pembrokeshire, Powys,
Swansea, Neath & Port Talbot
6 Gardd Llydaw
Jacksons Lane
Carmarthen SA31 1QD
F 01267 233084   T 01267 234248
W www.artswales.org

ARTS COUNCIL OF WALES, NORTH WALES OFFICE
Isle of Anglesey, Gwynedd, Conwy, Denbighshire,
Flintshire, Wrexham
36 Prince's Drive
Colwyn Bay
Conwy LL29 8LA
F 01492 533677   T 01492 533440
E north@artswales.org.uk
W www.artswales.org.uk

ARTS COUNCIL OF WALES, SOUTH WALES & CENTRAL OFFICE
Vale of Glamorgan, Cardiff, Newport, Monmouthshire,
Torfaen, Blaenau Gwent, Caerphilly, Merthyr Tydfil,
Rhonda Cynon Taff, Bridgend
Bute Place
Cardiff CF10 5AL
F 029 2041 1400   T 0845 8734900
E info@artswales.org.uk
W www.artswales.org.uk

C

Casting Directors

For information regarding membership of the Casting Directors' Guild (CDG) please see www.thecdg.co.uk

Consultants
Costumes, Wigs & Make-up
Critics

1066 PRODUCTIONS
8 Blackstone House, Off Bowen Drive
West Dulwich, London SE21 8NY
E loischada@1066productions.com
W www.1066productions.com
T 020 7193 6156

A C A CASTING
Contact: Catherine Arton
32A Edenvale Street, London SW6 2SF
E catherine@acacasting.com
T/F 020 7384 2635

ADAMSON-PARKER Jo
Northern Spirit Creative (Casting)
Studio 81, Kirkstall Road, Leeds LS3 1LH
M 07787 311270
E jo@northernspiritcreative.co.uk
W www.northernspiritcreative.co.uk
T 0113 219 2896

AILION Pippa
CDG Member
3 Towton Road, London SE27 9EE
E enquiries@pippaailioncasting.co.uk
T/F 020 8670 4816

ALL DIRECTIONS OF LONDON
Contact: By Post only
7 Rupert Court, Off Wardour Street
London W1D 6EB
T 020 7437 5879

ANDERSON Jane
CDG Member
E casting@janeandersononline.com

ANDREW Dorothy CASTING
CDG Member
Campus Manor
Childwall Abbey Road
Childwall, Liverpool L16 0JP
F 0151 737 4006
T 0151 737 4042

ASHTON HINKINSON CASTING
1 Charlotte Street, London W1T 1RD
F 020 7637 0328
E casting@ahcasting.com
W www.ashtonhinkinson.com
T 020 7580 6101

BAIG Shaheen CASTING
c/o The Bureau, 2nd Floor
18 Phipp Street, London EC2A 4NU
E shaheenbaigcasting@me.com
T 020 7613 3173

BARNES Derek
CDG Member
BBC DRAMA SERIES CASTING
BBC Elstree, Room N221
Neptune House, Clarendon Road
Borehamwood, Herts WD6 1JF
F 020 8228 8311
T 020 8228 7096

BEACH CASTING LTD
Contact: Brendan McNamara
1st Floor, 21 Whiston Road
London E2 8EX
M 07903 630964
E brendan@beach-casting.com
W www.beach-casting.com
T 0844 5679595

BEASTALL AND NORTH LTD
Contact: Lesley Beastall
41E Elgin Crescent, London W11 2JD
M 07956 516603
E lesley@beastallnorth.co.uk
T 020 7727 6496

Contact: Sophie North
M 07956 516606
E sophie@beastallnorth.com
T 020 8450 6474

Valerie Colgan

- For professional actors who need a voice production "MOT"
- Private individual classes
- Valerie Colgan and a consortium of tutors as appropriate on audition technique

Ex Head of Drama at the City Lit • 5 Drama Schools • The Actors Centre

Tel: 020 7267 2153 The Green, 17 Herbert Street, London NW5 4HA

BEATTIE Victoria
Contact: By e-mail. Accepts Showreels
Feature Films. Television Drama
Flat 1, Kenmare Mansions
Gondar Gardens, London NW6 1ET
E victoria@victoriabeattie.com

BEAUCHAMP Lauren CASTING
34A Brightside, Billericay CM12 0LJ
F 01277 656147   M 07961 982198
E laurenbeauchamp@talktalk.net

BECKLEY Rowland
BBC DRAMA SERIES CASTING
BBC Elstree, Room N222
Neptune House
Clarendon Road
Borehamwood, Herts WD6 1JF   F 020 8228 7130

BERTRAND Leila CASTING
53 Hormead Road, London W9 3NQ   T/F 020 8964 0683
E leilabcasting@aol.com

BEVAN Lucy
CDG Member
2nd Floor, 138 Portobello Road
London W11 2DZ   T 020 7727 5572

BEWICK Maureen CASTING
104A Dartmouth Road
London NW2 4HB   T 020 8450 1604

BEXFIELD DEITCH ASSOCIATES
80-81 St Martin's Lane, London WC2N 4AA   T 020 7395 7525
E casting@bexfielddeitch.co.uk

BIRD Sarah
CDG Member
PO Box 32658, London W14 0XA   T 020 7371 3248

BIRKETT Hannah CASTING
123 Hanover Road, London NW10 3DN
M 07957 114175   T 020 8960 2848
E hannah@hbcasting.com

BLIGH Nicky
CDG Member. Comedy. Entertainment
BBC Television Centre, Wood Lane, Room 4018
London W12 7RJ   T 020 8225 8488
E nicky.bligh@bbc.co.uk

BRACKE Siobhan
CDG Member. Contact: By Post
Basement Flat, 22A The Barons
St Margaret's TW1 2AP   T 020 8891 5686

BROADCASTING AGENCY
Contact: Ilisa Richter
3rd Floor, Block A, Morelands
5-23 Old Street, London EC1V 9HL
F 020 7250 1357   T 020 7490 4225
E ilisa@broadcastingagency.co.uk
W www.broadcastingagency.co.uk

BUCKINGHAM Jo
Comedy. Entertainment
BBC Television Centre, Wood Lane
London W12 7RJ   T 020 8225 7585
E jo.buckingham@bbc.co.uk

CANDID CASTING
1st Floor, 32 Great Sutton Street
London EC1V 0NB
F 020 7490 8966   T 020 7490 8882
E mail@candidcasting.co.uk
W www.candidcasting.co.uk

CANNON John
CDG Member
BBC DRAMA SERIES CASTING
BBC Elstree, Room N223, Neptune House
Clarendon Road, Borehamwood, Herts WD6 1JF
F 020 8228 8311   T 020 8228 7322
E john.cannon@bbc.co.uk

CANNON DUDLEY & ASSOCIATES
Contact: Carol Dudley (CDG Member). By Post
Film. Stage. Television
43A Belsize Square, London NW3 4HN
F 020 7813 2048   T 020 7433 3393
E cdacasting@blueyonder.co.uk

CARLING Di CASTING
CDG Member
1st Floor, 49 Frith Street
London W1D 4SG
F 020 7287 6844   T 020 7287 6446

CARROLL Anji
CDG Member. Contact: By e-mail (Small Attachments only)
Film. Stage. Television
PO Box 47, High Peak SK23 9WS
M 07957 253769   T 0560 2514485
E anji@anjicarroll.tv

CASTING COMPANY (UK) THE
Contact: Michelle Guish
PO Box 66013, London W3 3BX
E casting@michguish.com

infopage

Who are casting directors?

Casting directors are employed by directors/production companies to source the best available actors for roles across TV, film, radio, theatre and commercials. They do the groundwork and present a shortlist of artists to the director, who often makes the final selection. Many casting directors work on a freelance basis, others are employed permanently by larger organisations such as the BBC or the National Theatre. Discovering new and emerging talent also plays an important part in their job.

Why should I approach them?

If you are an actor looking for work, you can promote yourself directly to casting directors by sending them your photo and CV. They keep actors' details on file and may consider you for future productions. Bear in mind that you will not be guaranteed a response as casting directors are physically unable to reply to every one of the vast numbers of letters they receive from actors, but it is worth your while to explore this opportunity to find work.

How should I approach them?

Many of the following casting directors have indicated the method in which they prefer actors to contact them for the first time. This tends to be by post but some accept or prefer e-mails. Some are happy to receive telephone calls, but be aware that casting directors are very busy and you should not continually call them with questions or updates once you have sent your CV. If they have not specified whether they prefer postal or e-mail contact, you should send them your CV, a headshot and a covering letter by post only, as this is the traditional method of contacting casting professionals. You should **always** include a stamped-addressed envelope (SAE) big enough to contain your 10 x 8 photo and with sufficient postage. This will increase your chances of getting a reply. Write your name and telephone number on the back of your headshot in case it gets separated from your CV.

Should I send a casting director my showreel and/or voicereel?

Some casting directors have also indicated that they are happy for actors to send showreels and/or voicereels along with their CVs and headshots, but if this is not indicated, we would recommend that you leave these out of your correspondence but indicate in your covering letter that they are available. If a casting director is interested in you, they can contact you later for these items, but they usually prefer not to sift through hundreds of unsolicited showreels until they have first established an interest in an actor.

How do I target my search?

It is not advisable to send a generic CV to every casting director listed in the following pages. Research the following names and companies and then target your letters accordingly. Find out what areas of the industry each one usually casts for (some specify this in their listing) and what productions they have previously cast. Keep an eye on TV, film and theatre credits so you become familiar with the casting directors used for different productions. Some of these casting directors have their own websites. If a casting director has 'CDG Member' after their name, it means they are a member of the Casting Directors' Guild, the professional organisation of casting directors working in the UK (see www.thecdg.co.uk for more information and their article on the following page).

How do I write an effective CV and covering letter?

Once you have made a short-list of suitable casting directors you should send them your CV, your headshot, and an individually tailored covering letter. The covering letter should demonstrate that you have researched the casting director, and ideally you will have a particular reason for contacting them at this time: perhaps you can tell them about your next showcase, or where they can see you currently appearing on stage. Your CV should be no longer than one page, up-to-date and spell-checked. Please see the 'Promotional Services' section of Contacts for further advice on writing CVs and covering letters.

How do I prepare for a casting/audition?

Make sure you are fully prepared with accurate information about the audition time, venue, format and the people you will be meeting. Unless it's a last minute casting, you should always read the script in advance and try to have some opinions on it. If you are asked in advance to prepare a piece, always stick to the brief with something suitable and relevant. On the day, allow plenty of time to get there so you are not flustered when you arrive. Try to be positive and enjoy yourself. Remember, the casting director doesn't want to spend several days auditioning - they want you to get the job! Never criticise previous productions you have worked on. And at the end of the casting, remember to take your script away unless you are asked to leave it, otherwise it can look as if you're not interested. Please see 'Rehearsal Rooms and Casting Suites' for more detailed advice on preparing for and attending auditions.

Should I attend a casting in a house or flat?

Professional auditions are rarely held anywhere other than an official casting studio or venue. Be very wary if you are asked to go elsewhere. Trust your instincts. If something doesn't seem right to you, it probably isn't. Always take someone with you if you are in any doubt.

How do I become a casting director?

The best way to gain experience in this field is to work as a casting assistant. Vacancies are sometimes advertised in The Stage www.thestage.co.uk or PCR www.pcrnewsletter.com. Alternatively you could try sending your CV to casting directors asking for an internship or work experience. Just as we advise actors, remember to research any casting director you are considering approaching to make sure they actually work in the area you are interested in. Work experience is likely to be unpaid, but the experience and contacts you gain will be invaluable. You may find it helpful to refer to Equity's advice leaflet *Low Pay/No Pay* which is available at http://www.equity.org.uk/Documents/Public/low%20pay%20no%20pay%202010.pdf

infopage

When you read CDG after a Casting Director's name, you know he/she is a member of The Casting Directors' Guild and will therefore have a minimum of five years' experience. The current CDG Committee has prepared the following advice for actors.

Casting directors are there to help actors and not to hinder them. We want you to do your best as that reflects back on us, and you should realise that we are only as good as the actors we submit for each role.

Much of our work consists of creating a shortlist of potential actors and reducing it to a suitably sized group to present for audition. We also spend a great deal of time watching you work. Members of the CDG endeavour to cover as many performances as possible on film, television and in the theatre. There is no substitute to seeing you act.

When asked to attend an interview or audition, an actor should feel confident in asking his/her agent any relevant questions about the role and the project. If this is not forthcoming, arrive early and seek information from the casting director or, better still, contact him/her the day before. If it is only possible to speak to the casting director on the day, preferably do so before entering the audition room, rather than in front of the director or producer. The casting director will be happy to help.

Sometimes you will only receive pages for a role, but a casting director will always endeavour to give you as much information about a character as is available. When possible, read the entire play/screenplay rather than just the scenes your 'character' appears in, and ideally be able to talk about the script as a whole during the interview. Take your time when reading; preparation is worth a lot but don't be fazed if you get lost over their script. If you feel that a scene is going terribly it's ok to start again.

For most non-theatre jobs these days you will find that your meeting will be recorded on video tape. These tapes are then shown to the various producers involved, and this is when the process can slow down. It takes time to build a company and for final casting choices to be made.

Casting is a matter of interpretation. As well as character information derived from the script, the vision of the producer, director, casting director and indeed the actor all come into play. There are many reasons why one actor will be chosen over another, and even the best audition might not necessarily secure a part. Every aspect of the actor comes into play. Is he/she too young or too mature? Do they work as a family? Could they be mother and son? Does the chemistry work? There is also the frustrating problem of scripts, and parts, being re-written. A character may have an entirely different physical description in a later draft. Sadly we do not have control over this.

When it comes to contacting casting directors, most are happy to receive letters, updated photos and CVs. The best correspondence for casting directors to receive is performance information. Letters should be brief and to the point, with the production name, director, venue and/or TV channel clearly stated. If you are enquiring about work be as specific as possible, e.g. "I would like to be seen for the part of ... in ... because ..." or something similar. Dear Sir or Madam letters just don't work.

CVs should be well laid out. List most recent work first and use your spell checker. 6x4 photos are fine to send but include an SAE if you want them returned. Casting directors rarely like unsolicited DVDs and showreels: you must be aware that we do get inundated. Also bear in mind that not receiving a response to your letter does not mean it hasn't been read and filed: it is virtually impossible to reply to the volume of mail received from actors.

In our greener world it's great that Spotlight and other web media now have the facility for us to view CVs, photos and showreels online. Use the technology: it's very easy to keep your CV up-to-date online and you can change your photo at any time of year without having to do a huge mail out to let people know.

Actors are a fundamental tool of this industry: CDG members are aware of this and aim to put actors at their ease. Audition nerves are a given but you should feel secure that the reason you are in the room is because someone wants you to get that role and not because they want to see you fail.

Please visit www.thecdg.co.uk for further information.

CASTING CONNECTION THE
Contact: Michael Syers
Dalrossie House, 16 Victoria Grove
Stockport, Cheshire SK4 5BU   T 0161 432 4122

CASTING COUCH THE
Contact: Moira Townsend
213 Trowbridge Road
Bradford on Avon
Wiltshire BA15 1EU   M 07932 785807
E moira@everymansland.com

CATLIFF Suzy
CDG Member
PO Box 39492, London N10 3YX   T 020 8442 0749
E soosecat@mac.com

CHAND Urvashi
CDG Member
Cinecraft, 69 Teignmouth Road
London NW2 4EA   T 020 8208 3861
E urvashi@cinecraft.biz

CHARD Alison
CDG Member
23 Groveside Court
4 Lombard Road
Battersea, London SW11 3RQ   T 020 7223 9125
E chardcasting@btinternet.com

CHARKHAM CASTING
Contact: Beth Charkham
Suite 361
14 Tottenham Court Road
London W1T 1JY   M 07956 456630
E charkhamcasting@btconnect.com

CLARK Andrea
Contact: By Post. Accepts Showreels
Children & Adults. Commercials. Film. Stage. Television
PO Box 28895
London SW13 0WG   T 020 8876 6869
E andrea@aclarkcasting.com
W www.aclarkcasting.com

CLAYPOLE Sam
Live Stream Casting
PO Box 123, Darlington
Durham DL3 7WA   T 0845 6501777
E info@claypolemanagement.co.uk
W www.claypolemanagement.co.uk

CLAYTON Rosalie
CDG Member
E rosalie@rosalieclayton.com   T/F 020 7242 8109

COGAN Ben
BBC DRAMA SERIES CASTING
BBC Elstree, Room N221
Neptune House, Clarendon Road
Borehamwood, Herts WD6 1JF
F 020 8228 8311   T 020 8228 7516

COLLINS Jayne CASTING
CDG Member
4th Floor, 20 Bedford Street
London WC2E 9HP
F 020 7240 5323   T 020 7836 9792
E info@jaynecollinscasting.com
W www.jaynecollinscasting.com

CORDORAY Lin
66 Cardross Street, London W6 0DR

COTTON Irene
CDG Member
25 Druce Road, Dulwich Village
London SE21 7DW
T/F 020 8299 2787   T 020 8299 1595
E irenecotton@btinternet.com

CRAMPSIE Julia
Casting Executive
BBC DRAMA SERIES CASTING
BBC Elstree, Room N224
Neptune House, Clarendon Road
Borehamwood, Herts WD6 1JF
F 020 8228 8311   T 020 8228 7170

CRANE Carole CASTING
E crane.shot@virgin.net   M 07976 869442

CRAWFORD Kahleen CASTING
Film City Glasgow, Govan Town Hall
401 Govan Road, Glasgow G51 2QJ
M 07950 414164   T 0141 425 1725
E casting@kahleencrawford.com
W www.kahleencrawford.com

CROCODILE CASTING COMPANY THE
Contact: Claire Toeman, Tracie Saban. By e-mail only
E croccast@aol.com   T 020 8203 7009
W www.crocodilecasting.com

CROSS Louise
CDG Member
128A North View Road, London N8 7LP   T 020 8341 2200

CROWE Sarah CASTING
75 Amberley Road, London W9 2JL
F 020 7286 5030   T 020 7286 5080
E sarah@sarahcrowecasting.co.uk

CROWLEY Suzanne
CDG Member. See CROWLEY POOLE CASTING

CROWLEY POOLE CASTING
Contact: Suzanne Crowley (CDG Member)
Gilly Poole (CDG Member)
11 Goodwins Court, London WC2N 4LL
F 020 7379 5971   T 020 7379 5965

DAVIES Jane CASTING
Contact: Jane Davies (CDG Member)
John Connor (CDG Member)
PO Box 680, Sutton
Surrey SM1 3ZG
F 020 8644 9746   T 020 8715 1036
E info@janedaviescasting.co.uk

DAVIS Leo (Miss)
Just Casting
20th Century Theatre
291 Westbourne Grove
London W11 2QA
F 020 7792 2143   T 020 7229 3471

DAVY Gary
CDG Member
Film. Television
T 020 7437 0880
E casting@garydavy.com

DAWES Gabrielle
CDG Member
PO Box 52493, London NW3 9DZ   T 020 7435 3645
E gdawescasting@tiscali.co.uk

DAWES Stephanie
CDG Member
13 Nevern Square
London SW5 9NW   M 07802 566642
E stephaniedawes5@gmail.com

DAY Kate
CDG Member
Pound Cottage
27 The Green South
Warborough, Oxon OX10 7DR   T/F 01865 858709

DE FREITAS Paul
CDG Member
E info@pauldefreitas.com

DICKENS Laura
CDG Member
197 Malpas Road
London SE4 1BH   M 07958 665468
E dickenscasting@aol.com

DOWD Kate
74 Wells Street, London W1T 3QG
F 020 7580 6688   T 020 7580 8866

DOWLING ERDELY CASTING
2 Eleanor Road
London N11 2QS
M 07970 071605   M 07958 391198
E info@dowlingerdely.com
W www.dowlingerdely.com

DRURY Malcolm
CDG Member
34 Tabor Road, London W6 0BW   T 020 8748 9232

DUDLEY Carol
CDG Member. See CANNON DUDLEY & ASSOCIATES

DUFF Julia
CDG Member
PO Box 67506, London EC1P 1PH
T 020 7689 2074   T 020 7503 8650

DUFF Maureen
CDG Member
PO Box 47340, London NW3 4TY
F 020 7681 7172   T 020 7586 0532
E belgrove@dircon.co.uk

EARNSHAW Rob
35 Bishops Hill, Hexham
Northumberland NE46 4NH   M 07707 083674
E robertearnshaw@btinternet.com
W www.robertearnshawcasting.co.uk
117 Park Lane, London W1K 7AH   M 07707 083674

EAST Irene CASTING
CDG Member. Contact: By Post. Film. Stage
40 Brookwood Avenue, Barnes
London SW13 0LR   T 020 8876 5686
E irneast@aol.com

EH7 CASTING
9 Claremont Bank
Edinburgh EH7 4DR   T 0131 556 9339
E contact@eh7casting.com
W www.eh7casting.com

EJ CASTING
PO Box 63617, London SW9 1AN
M 07891 632946   T 020 7564 2688
E info@ejcasting.com

EMMERSON Chloe
46 Bassein Park Road
London W12 9RZ   T 020 8740 0982
E c@chloeemmerson.com

EPMC TALENT
Contact: Aldo Arcilla. By e-mail. Accepts Showreels/Voicereels
18 Soho Square, London W1D 3QL
F 0871 6619916   T 020 7193 4230
E casting@epmctalent.com
W www.epmctalent.com

EVANS Camilla CASTING
CDG Member
2 Dalberg Road
London SW2 1AN   M 07768 977050
E camilla@camillaevans.com
W www.thecdg.co.uk

EVANS Richard
CDG Member
10 Shirley Road
London W4 1DD   T 020 8994 6304
E contact@evanscasting.co.uk
W www.evanscasting.co.uk

EYE CASTING THE
First Floor, 92 Commercial Street (Entrance Puma Court)
London E1 6LZ
F 05602 059199   T 020 7377 2700
E jody@theeyecasting.com
W www.theeyecasting.com

FEARNLEY Ali CASTING
3rd Floor, 58-60 Rivington Street
London EC2A 3AU   M 07764 945614
E cast@alifearnley.com

FIGGIS Susie
19 Spencer Rise, London NW5 1AR   T 020 7482 2200

FILDES Bunny CASTING
CDG Member
56 Wigmore Street, London W1   T 020 7935 1254

FOX Celestia
23 Leppoc Road, London SW4 9LS   T 020 7720 6143
E celestiafox@me.com

FOX CASTING
Contact: By e-mail only
T 01628 771084   E lefoxcasting@gmail.com

FRAZER Janie
CDG Member
E janiefrazercasting@gmail.com

FRECK Rachel
CDG Member
T 020 8673 2455
E casting@rachelfreck.com

FREND Amanda
87 Swindon Road, Horsham
West Sussex RH12 2HF
E amandafrendcasting@hotmail.co.uk

FRISBY Jane CASTING
Contact: By Post. Accepts Showreels/Voicereels only on request. Commercials. Film. Stage
51 Ridge Road, London N8 9LJ T 020 8341 4747
E janefrisby@hotmail.co.uk

FUNNELL Caroline
CDG Member
25 Rattray Road, London SW2 1AZ T 020 7326 4417

GALLAGHER Juliet CASTING
E julietgallagher@hotmail.com
W www.julietgallagher.com

GANE CASTING
Contact: Natasha Gane
52 Woodhouse Road, London N12 0RJ
M 07970 535911 T 020 8446 2551
E natasha@ganecasting.com

GILLHAM Tracey
CDG Member. Comedy. Entertainment
BBC Television Centre, Room 4018
Wood Lane, London W12 7RJ T 020 8225 8648

GILLON Tamara CASTING
26 Carson Road, London SE21 8HU
F 020 8265 6330 T 020 8766 0099
E tamaragillon@yahoo.co.uk

GING Thyrza CASTING
E thyrzaging@gmail.com
W www.castingireland.ie

GLOBAL7
PO Box 56232, London N4 4XP
M 07956 956652 T/F 020 7281 7679
E global7castings@gmail.com
W www.global7casting.com

GOLD Nina
CDG Member
117 Chevening Road, London NW6 6DU
F 020 8968 6777 T 020 8960 6099
E info@ninagold.co.uk

GOOCH Miranda CASTING
Contact: By Post/e-mail. Accepts Showreels/Voicereels Film. Stage. Television
102 Leighton Gardens, London NW10 3PR
F 020 8962 9579 T 020 8962 9578
E mirandagooch@gmail.com

GREEN Jill CASTING
CDG Member
PO Box 56927, London N10 3UR T 020 8815 1825

GREENE Francesca CASTING
37 Keyes Road, London NW2 3XB T 020 8450 5577
E francesca@francescagreene.co.uk
W www.francescagreenecasting.com

GROSVENOR Angela
CDG Member
27 Rowena Crescent
London SW11 2ST T 020 7738 0449

GUISH Michelle
See CASTING COMPANY (UK) THE

HALL David CASTING
E davidhallcasting@btinternet.com M 07513 294360

HALL Janet
3 Shore Road, Littleborough
Oldham OL15 9LG
M 07956 822773 T 01706 377900
E janethall1@yahoo.co.uk

HALL Pippa
Children. Teenagers
E pippa@pippahallcasting.com

HAMMOND Louis
97 Mortimer Street
London W1W 7SU T 020 7927 8392
E louis.hammond@virgin.net

HAMPSON Janet CASTING
Vision & Media
100 Broadway, Salford M50 2UW
M 07931 513223 T 0161 408 2037
E janet@janethampson.co.uk
W www.janethampson.co.uk

HANCOCK Gemma
CDG Member. Contact: By e-mail
E gemma@hancockstevenson.com

HARKIN Julie
CDG Member
22 Clonbrock Road
London N16 8RR T 020 7241 0728
E julieharkincasting@gmail.com

HARRIS Lisa
290 Coulsdon Road, Old Coulsdon
Surrey CR5 1EB M 07956 561247
E londonlis@hotmail.com

HAWES Jo
Children's Casting for Film, Stage & Television
21 Westfield Road, Maidenhead
Berkshire SL6 5AU
M 07824 337222 T 01628 773048
E jo.hawes@virgin.net

HAWSER Gillian CASTING
CDG Member
Contact: Gillian Hawser
24 Cloncurry Street
London SW6 6DS
F 020 7731 0738 T 020 7731 5988
E gillianhawser@btinternet.com

HAYNES Clair CASTING
20 Hawcliffe Road, Mountsorrel
Leicester LE12 7AA T 01509 828365
E clairhaynes@gmail.com
W www.clairhaynescasting.co.uk

HILL Serena
Sydney Theatre Company
Pier 4, Hickson Road
Walsh Bay, NSW 2000, Australia T 00 612 925 01727
E shill@sydneytheatre.com.au

HOOTKINS Polly
CDG Member
PO Box 52480, London NW3 9DH   T 020 7692 1184
E phootkins@clara.net

HORAN Julia
CDG Member
26 Falkland Road, London NW5 2PX   T 020 7267 5261

HUBBARD CASTING
*Contact: Dan Hubbard (CDG Member), Amy Hubbard
Ros Hubbard, John Hubbard. No Showreels*
14 Rathbone Place, London W1T 1HT
F 020 7636 7117   T 020 7631 4944
E info@hubbardcasting.com

HUGHES Sarah
CDG Member
T 020 8291 0304
E mail@sarahhughescasting.co.uk

HUGHES Sylvia
Casting Suite, The Deanwater
Wilmslow Road, Woodford, Cheshire SK7 1RJ
M 07770 520007   T/F 01625 560000
E sylviahughes@hotmail.co.uk

JACKSON Sue
CDG Member
53 Moseley Wood Walk
Leeds LS16 7HQ   T 0113 267 0819

JAFFA Janis CASTING
CDG Member
Contact: By Post. Accepts Showreels
67 Starfield Road, London W12 9SN   T 020 7565 2877
E janis@janisjaffacasting.co.uk

JAFFREY Jennifer
Contact: By Post
Room 11, Heath Farm
Pinewood Studios, Pinewood Road
Iver Heath, Bucks SL0 0NH
F 01753 785163   T 01753 785162
E jaffreyproductions@btconnect.com

JAY Jina CASTING
CDG Member
Office 2, Sound Centre
Twickenham Film Studios, The Barons, St Margarets
Twickenham, Middlesex TW1 2AW
F 020 8607 8982   T 020 8607 8888

JELOWICKI Ilenka
Mad Dog Casting Ltd. Contact: By Post/e-mail. Accepts Showreels/Voicereels. Children. Real People. Street Casting
2nd Floor, Holborn Hall
193-197 High Holborn
London WC1V 7BD
F 020 7831 7267 T 020 7269 7910
E ilenka@maddogcasting.com

JENKINS Lucy
CDG Member. Contact: By Post/e-mail. Accepts Showreels/Voicereels. Commercials. Film. Stage. Television
74 High Street, Hampton Wick
Kingston on Thames KT1 4DQ T 020 8943 5328
E lucy.jenkins@blueyonder.co.uk

JENKINS Victor
CDG Member. See VALENTINE HENDRY & JENKINS

JN PRODUCTION
16-24 Underwood Street
London N1 7JQ
F 020 7780 7470 T 020 7278 8800
E james@jnproduction.net

JOHN Priscilla
CDG Member
PO Box 22477, London W6 0GT
F 020 8741 4005 T 020 8741 4212

JOHNSON Alex CASTING
15 McGregor Road, London W11 1DE T 020 7229 8779
E alex@alexjohnsoncasting.com

JOHNSON Marilyn
CDG Member
1st Floor, 11 Goodwins Court
London WC2N 4LL
F 020 7497 5530 T 020 7497 5552
E casting@marilynjohnsoncasting.com

JONES Doreen
CDG Member
PO Box 22478, London W6 0WJ
F 020 8748 8533 T 020 8746 3782
E artists@dorcast.demon.co.uk

JONES Lenka
Coach House, Pinewood Road
Iver Heath, Buckinghamshire SL0 0NH M 07921 182055
E lenki13@yahoo.co.uk

JONES Sue
CDG Member
E info@suejones.net

KATE & LOU CASTING
The Basement, Museum House
25 Museum Street, London WC1A 1JT
M 07976 252531 M 07885 763429
E cast@kateandloucasting.com
W www.kateandloucasting.com

KENNEDY Anna CASTING
8 Rydal Road, London SW16 1QN T 020 8677 6710
E anna@kennedycasting.com

KEOGH Beverley CASTING LTD
29 Ardwick Green North
Ardwick Green
Manchester M12 6DL
F 0161 273 4401 T 0161 273 4400
E drama@beverleykeogh.tv

KESTER Gaby
Room B1.14
Ancillary Block
Elstree Film Studios
Shenley Road, Borehamwood
Herts WD6 1JG T 020 8324 2571
E casting@gabykester.com

KIBBEY Leoni CASTING
M 07855 313552 T 01727 375166
E casting@leonikibbey.com
W www.leonikibbey.com

KLIMEK Nana CASTING
63 Redchurch Street
London E2 7DJ T 020 7502 9478
E casting@nanaklimek.com
W www.nanaklimek.com

KNIGHT-SMITH Jerry
CDG Member
Royal Exchange Theatre Company
St Ann's Square
Manchester M2 7DH
F 0161 615 6691 T 0161 615 6761

KOREL Suzy
CDG Member
E suzy@korel.org T 020 7586 9611

KRUGER Beatrice
FBI Casting S.r.l.
46 via della Pelliccia
00153 Roma, Italy
F 00 39 06 23328203 T 00 39 06 58332747
E beatrice.kruger@fbicasting.it
W www.fbicasting.com

KYLE CASTING
Contact: Greg Kyle
71B North Worple Way, Mortlake
London SW14 8PR T 020 8876 6763
E kylecasting@btinternet.com

LARCA LTD
Welsh Language/English. Commercials. Film. Stage. Television
Ynyslas Uchaf Farm, Blackmill
Bridgend CF35 6DW
F 01656 841815 M 07779 321954
W www.leigh-annregancasting.co.uk

SPOTLIGHT

Casting from start to finish

Spotlight Database

- Browse over 35,000 actors, actresses, presenters, stunt artists, children and dancers

- View performer CVs, photos, showreels, portfolios and contact details

- Know that every Spotlight performer has professional training or experience

Spotlight Website

- Email casting calls calls to hundreds of UK agents and performers and receive responses in minutes

- Find exactly the right performer for the part with our award-winning search engine

Spotlight Rooms & Studios

- Six meeting rooms and three state-of-the-art casting studios

- Hold your auditions in the heart of central London

- Post DVD quality audition clips online in minutes

www.spotlight.com   020 7437 7631   casting@spotlight.com

LAYTON Claudie CASTING
Unit 308, Canalot Studios
222 Kensal Road, London W10 5BN
F 020 8968 1330   M 07956 450755
E casting@claudielayton.com

LEVENE Jon
M 07977 570899   T 020 7792 8501
E jonlevene@mac.com
W www.jonlevenecasting.com

LEVINSON Sharon
30 Stratford Villas, London NW1 9SG   T 020 7485 2057
E levinson.sharon@gmail.com

LIHUK CASTING
28 Meir Yaari, Tel Aviv 69371   T +972 77 7675006
E info@lihuk.co.il
W www.lihuk.co.il

LINDSAY-STEWART Karen
CDG Member
PO Box 2301, London W1A 1PT   T 020 7439 0544

LIP SERVICE CASTING LTD
Contact: By Post. Accepts Voicereels. Voice Overs only
60-66 Wardour Street, London W1F 0TA
F 020 7734 3373   T 020 7734 3393
E bookings@lipservice.co.uk
W www.lipservice.co.uk

LUNN Maggie
CDG Member
Unit HG14, Aberdeen Centre, 22-24 Highbury Grove
London N5 2EA   T 020 7226 7502
E maggie@maggielunn.co.uk

MAGSON Kay
CDG Member. Contact: By e-mail. Stage
PO Box 175, Pudsey
Leeds LS28 7WY   T 0113 236 0251
E kay.magson@btinternet.com

MANN Andrew
Studio 125, 77 Beak Street
London W1F 9DB
T 020 7993 5165   T 020 7993 6042
E andrew.mann@castinguk.com
W www.andrewmanncasting.co.uk

MANNING John
4 Holmbury Gardens, Hayes
Middlesex UB3 2LU   T 020 8573 5463

MARCH Heather CASTING
*Contact: By e-mail. Commercials. Idents
Photographic. Pop Promos*
14 Albany Works, Gunmakers Lane
London E3 5SB   T 020 8981 4184
E hm@heathermarchcasting.com
W www.heathermarchcasting.com

McCANN Joan
CDG Member
26 Hereford Road, London W3 9JW
F 020 8992 8715   T 020 8993 1747

McLEOD Carolyn CASTING
Contact: By e-mail. Commercials. Film. Television
2nd Floor, 189 Wardour Street
London W1F 8ZD   M 07946 476425
E info@cmcasting.co.uk
W www.cmcasting.co.uk

McLEOD Thea
M 07941 541314   T 020 8888 8993
E mcleodcasting@hotmail.com

McMURRICH Chrissie
Contact: By Post. Accepts Showreels
16 Spring Vale Avenue
Brentford, Middlesex TW8 9QH   T 020 8568 0137

McSHANE Sooki
CDG Member
8A Piermont Road, East Dulwich
London SE22 0LN   T 020 8693 7411

McWILLIAMS Debbie
48 Vestry Road, Camberwell
London SE5 8NX
M 07785 575805   T 020 7564 8860
E debbie@debbiemcwilliamscasting.com

MEULENBERG Thea
Keizersgracht 116, 1015 CW
Amsterdam, The Netherlands
F 00 31 20 622 9894   T 00 31 20 626 5846
E info@theameulenberg.com
W www.theameulenberg.com

MILLER Hannah
CDG Member. See ROYAL SHAKESPEARE COMPANY

MOISELLE Frank
7 Corrig Avenue, Dun Laoghaire
Co. Dublin, Ireland
F 00 353 1 2803277   T 00 353 1 2802857

MOISELLE Nuala
7 Corrig Avenue, Dun Laoghaire
Co. Dublin, Ireland
F 00 353 1 2803277   T 00 353 1 2802857

MOORE Stephen
BBC DRAMA SERIES CASTING
BBC Elstree, Room N222
Neptune House, Clarendon Road
Borehamwood, Herts WD6 1JF
F 020 8228 8311   T 020 8228 7109

MORGAN Andy CASTING
CDG Member
Coach House, 114 Palace Road
London SW2 3JZ   T 020 8674 5375

MORRISON Melika
Contact: By Post. Accepts Showreels. Film. Radio. Television
12A Rosebank, Holyport Road
London SW6 6LG   T/F 020 7381 1571

MUGSHOTS
Contact: Becky Kidd
E becky@mugshots.co.uk   M 07880 896911

MURDER MY DARLINGS
London W6 8DT   T 020 7386 0560
E office@murdermydarlings.com

MURPHY CHARPENTIER CASTING
22 Gledhow Gardens
London SW5 0AZ   M 07976 931264
E casting@murphycharpentiercasting.com

NAPIER-BELL CASTING
179 Wardour Street, London W1F 8WY   M 07702 748078
E fiona@napier-bell.tv
W www.napier-bell.tv

NATIONAL THEATRE CASTING DEPARTMENT
Contact: Wendy Spon, Head of Casting (CDG Member)
Alastair Coomer, Deputy Head of Casting (CDG Member)
Juliet Horsley, Casting Assistant. By Post
Upper Ground, South Bank
London SE1 9PX
F 020 7452 3340   T 020 7452 3336
W www.nationaltheatre.org.uk

NEEDLEMAN Sue
CDG Member
19 Stanhope Gardens, London NW7 2JD
F 020 8959 0225   T 020 8959 1550

NORCLIFFE Belinda
Contact: Belinda Norcliffe, Matt Selby
23 Brougham Road, London W3 6JD
F 020 8992 8643   T 020 8992 1333
E belinda@bncasting.co.uk

O'BRIEN Debbie
72 High Street, Ashwell
Nr Baldock, Herts SG7 5NS
F 01462 743110   T 01462 742919

O'CONNOR Orla
The Out of The Blue Drill Hall
36 Dalmeny Street
Edinburgh EH6 8RG   T 0131 553 0559
E orlaoconnor@live.co.uk

O'DONNELL Rory
178A Adelaide Avenue, London SE4 1JN
F 020 8690 8005   M 07940 073165
E tyrconnellpictures@hotmail.com

ORANGE James CASTING
CDG Member
PO Box 51130
London SE13 7ZW   T 020 8297 0524
E casting@jamesorange.com

PALMER Helena
CDG Member. See ROYAL SHAKESPEARE COMPANY

PARLOUR CASTING
Contact: Rose Wicksteed, Amelia Hashemi
Based in London
F 020 3318 3090   T 020 3318 3010
E info@parlourcasting.com
W www.parlourcasting.com

PARRISS Susie CASTING
CDG Member
PO Box 40, Morden SM4 4WJ
F 020 8543 3327   T 020 8543 3326

PETTS Tree CASTING
125 Hendon Way, London NW2 2NA   T 020 8458 8898
E casting@treepetts.co.uk

PLANTIN Kate
4 Riverside, Lower Hampton Road
Sunbury on Thames TW16 5PW
F 01932 783235   T 01932 782350
E kateplantin@hotmail.com

POLENTARUTTI Tania CASTING
CDG Member. Contact: By e-mail
M 07720 299635   T 020 8555 3163
E tania@filmtvcasting.com

POOLE Gilly
CDG Member. See CROWLEY POOLE CASTING

POWELLCASTING
Contact: Annelie Powell
W www.powellcasting.com

PROCTOR Carl
CDG Member
15B Bury Place, London WC1A 2JB
M 07956 283340   T 020 7681 0034
E carlproctor@btconnect.com
W www.carlproctor.com

PRYOR Andy
CDG Member
Suite 3, 15 Broad Court
London WC2B 5QN
F 020 7836 8299   T 020 7836 8298

PURO CASTING
F 07006 056678   T 020 7193 8799
E office@purocasting.com
W www.purocasting.com

REICH Liora
25 Manor Park Road
London N2 0SN   T 020 8444 1686

REYNOLDS Gillian CASTING
E gillianreynoldscasting@gmail.com   T 00 353 87 2619718
W www.gillianreynoldscasting.com

REYNOLDS Simone
CDG Member
60 Hebdon Road
London SW17 7NN   T 020 8672 5443

RHODES JAMES Kate
CDG Member. CSA Member
PO Box 444, Teddington TW11 1AU
E office@krjcasting.com

RIPLEY Jane
E jane@janeripleycasting.co.uk   T 020 8342 8216

ROBERTSON Sasha CASTING LTD
Contact: Sasha Robertson (CDG Member)
Maddy Hinton (Associate)
19 Wendell Road
London W12 9RS
F 020 8740 1396   T 020 8740 0817
E casting@sasharobertson.com

ROFFE Danielle
CDG Member
E danielle@danielleroffe.com

RONANE Jessica CASTING
CDG Member
26 Aybrook Street, London W1U 4AN   T 020 7534 9750
E jessica@jessicaronane.com

ROSE Dionne
78 York Street
London W1H 1DP   T 0118 941 5465
E casting@drbentertainment.co.uk

ROWAN Amy CASTING
CDG Member
PO Box 10247, Blackrock
Co. Dublin, Ireland
F 00 353 1 2802005   T 00 353 1 2140514

ROWE Annie CASTING
98 St Albans Avenue
London W4 5JR   T 020 8354 2699
E annie@annierowe-casting.com
W www.annierowe-casting.com

ROYAL SHAKESPEARE COMPANY
Contact: Hannah Miller, Head of Casting (CDG Member)
Helena Palmer (CDG Member), Janine Snape (CDG Member)
Jim Arnold
Casting Department, 1 Earlham Street
London WC2H 9LL
F 020 7845 0505   T 020 7845 0530
W www.rsc.org.uk

RYCROFT CASTING
Contact: Amy Rycroft
20B Turners Road, London E3 4LE   M 07958 540815
E amy@rycroftcasting.co.uk
W www.rycroftcasting.co.uk

SALBERG Jane
86 Stade Street, Hythe, Kent CT21 6DY
M 07931 932103   T 01303 239277
E janesalberg@aol.com

SCHILLER Ginny
CDG Member
53 Clapton Common
London E5 9AA   T 020 8806 5383
E ginny.schiller@virgin.net

SCHOFIELD Gilly
CDG Member
E gillyschofield1@btinternet.com

SCHWARTZ Marie Claude
13 Av de Fouilleuse, Saint Cloud
92210, France   T 00 33 146 02 99 09
E mc.schwartz@assorda.com
W www.assorda.com

SCOTT Laura
CDG Member
56 Rowena Crescent, London SW11 2PT
F 020 7924 1907   T 020 7978 6336
E laurascottcasting@mac.com
W www.thecdg.co.uk

SEARCHERS THE
70 Sylvia Court, Cavendish Street
London N1 7PG
F 020 7684 5763   M 07958 922829
E waynesearcher@mac.com

SEECOOMAR Nadira
PO Box 167
Twickenham TW1 2UP   T 020 8892 8478

SELECT CASTING LTD
PO Box 748, London NW4 1TT
F 020 8203 2007   M 07956 131494
E info@selectcasting.co.uk
W www.selectcasting.co.uk

SHAW David
See KEOGH Beverley CASTING LTD

SHAW Phil
Suite 476, 2 Old Brompton Road
South Kensington, London SW7 3DQ   T 020 8715 8943
E shawcastlond@aol.com

SHEPHERD Debbie CASTING
Suite 16, 63 St Martin's Lane
London WC2N 4JS
E casting@debbieshepherd.com
T 020 7240 0400

SID PRODUCTIONS
110 Sandringham Flats
Charing Cross Road, London WC2H 0BP
E casting@sidproductions.co.uk
W www.sidproductions.co.uk
T 01932 863194

SIMPSON Georgia
88 Ashley Drive, Bangor, Co Down
Northern Ireland BT20 5RD
E georgia@georgiasimpson.com
W www.georgiasimpson.com
T 028 9147 0800

SINGER Sandra ASSOCIATES
Contact: By e-mail
21 Cotswold Road
Westcliff-on-Sea, Essex SS0 8AA
E sandrasingeruk@aol.com
W www.sandrasinger.com
T 01702 331616

SMITH Michelle CASTING LTD
CDG Member. Contact: Michelle Smith. By Post
Accepts Showreels/Voicereels
Animation. Commercials Corporate. Film. Television
220 Church Lane
Stockport SK7 1PQ
F 0161 439 0622
E michelle.smith18@btinternet.com
T 0161 439 6825

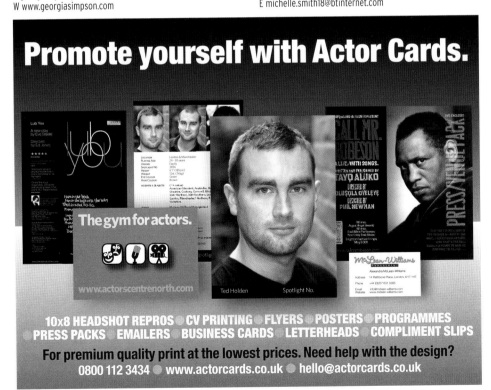

SMITH Suzanne
CDG Member
33 Fitzroy Street, London W1T 6DU
E zan@dircon.co.uk
T 020 7436 9255

SNAPE Janine
CDG Member. See ROYAL SHAKESPEARE COMPANY

SOLOMON Alison
Birmingham Repertory Theatre
Centenary Square
Broad Street, Birmingham B1 2EP
T 0121 245 2023

SPORTSCASTINGS.COM
Contact: Penny Burrows
3 Thornlow Road
London SE27 0SH
M 07973 863263
E info@sportsmodels.com
W www.sportsmodels.com

STAFFORD Emma CASTING
T 020 7866 5424 (London)   T 0161 833 4263 (Manchester)
E info@emmastafford.tv
W www.emmastafford.tv

STAFFORD Helen
14 Park Avenue
Enfield, Middlesex EN1 2HP
F 020 8372 0611
T 020 8360 6329
E helen.stafford@blueyonder.co.uk

STARK CASTING
M 07956 150689
T 020 8800 0060
E stark.casting@virgin.net

STEVENS Gail CASTING
CDG Member
Greenhill House
90-93 Cowcross Street
London EC1M 6BF
F 020 7253 6574
T 020 7253 6532
E office@gailstevenscasting.com

STEVENS MILLEFIORINI Danny
Via Sillaro 14
Cerveteri, Rome, Italy 00052
T 0039 389 435 22 00
E dannystevens62@gmail.com

STEVENSON Sam
CDG Member
E sam@hancockstevenson.com

STEWART Amanda CASTING
Apartment 1
35 Fortess Road
London NW5 1AD
T 020 7485 7973

STOLL Liz
BBC DRAMA SERIES CASTING
BBC Elstree, Room N223
Neptune House, Clarendon Road
Borehamwood, Herts WD6 1JF
F 020 8228 8311
T 020 8228 8285

STUFFED ANIMALS MEDIA LTD
Contact: Adam Morley
The Lodge, Wentworth Hall
The Ridgeway
Mill Hill, London NW7 1RJ
E adam.e.morley@gmail.com
M 07855 133836

STYLE Emma
CDG Member
1 Overton Cottages
Kings Lane, Cookham
Maidenhead SL6 9BA
T 01628 483740

SUMMERS Mark CASTING
Formerly Casting Unlimited
1 Beaumont Avenue
West Kensington, London W14 9LP
E mark@marksummers.com
W www.marksummers.com
T 020 7229 8413

SYERS Michael
See CASTING CONNECTION THE

SYSON GRAINGER CASTING
Contact: Lucinda Syson (CDG Member)
Elaine Grainger (CDG Member)
1st Floor, 33 Old Compton Street
London W1D 5JT
F 020 7287 3629
T 020 7287 5327
E office@sysongraingercasting.com

TABAK Amanda
CDG Member. See CANDID CASTING

TEECE Shirley CASTING
Contact: By e-mail
106 North View Road, London N8 7LP   T 020 8347 9241
E shirlteece@btinternet.com

TOPPING Nicci
The Media Centre
7 Northumberland Street
West Yorkshire HD1 1RL
M 07802 684256   T 01484 511988
E general@toppscasting.co.uk
W www.toppscasting.co.uk

TREVELLICK Jill
CDG Member
92 Priory Road, London N8 7EY   T 020 8340 2734
E jill@jilltrevellick.com

TREVIS Sarah
CDG Member
F 020 7602 8110   T 020 7602 5552
E info@sarahtrevis.com

VALENTINE HENDRY Kelly
CDG Member. See VALENTINE HENDRY & JENKINS

VALENTINE HENDRY & JENKINS
22 Torrington Place
London WC1 7HP   T 020 7255 6146
E kelly@vhjcasting.com
W www.vhjcasting.com

VAUGHAN Sally
CDG Member. Theatre
2 Kennington Park Place
London SE11 4AS   T 020 7735 6539
E svaughan12@btinternet.com

VOSSER Anne CASTING
PO Box 408, Aldershot GU11 9DS
M 07968 868712   T 01252 404716
E anne@vosser-casting.co.uk
W www.vosser-casting.co.uk

WAUDBY Melissa
E mail@vital-productions.co.uk   M 07957 284709

WEIR Fiona
CDG Member
2nd Floor, 138 Portobello Road
London W11 2DZ   T 020 7727 5600

WEST June
CDG Member
Granada Television, Quay Street
Manchester M60 9EA
F 0161 827 2853   T 0161 952 1000

WESTERN Matt CASTING
Contact: By Post/e-mail. Accepts Showreels
Children. Commercials. Film. Television
150 Blythe Road
London W14 0HD   T 020 7602 6646
E matt@mattwestern.co.uk
W www.mattwestern.co.uk

WHALE Toby
CDG Member
80 Shakespeare Road
London W3 6SN
F 020 8993 8096   T 020 8993 2821
E toby@whalecasting.com
W www.whalecasting.com

WHITTINGHAM Ian Zachary CASTING
77A Brick Lane, Liverpool Street
London E1 6QL
F 020 3246 0081   T 020 3246 0088
E zach@manictv.co.uk
W www.manictv.co.uk

WILDMANHALL CASTING
Contact: Vicky Wildman, Buffy Hall
1 Child's Place, London SW5 9RX   T 020 7373 2036
E wildmanhall@mac.com

WILLIS Catherine
Contact: By e-mail
The Heals Building
22 Torrington Place
London WC1E 7HP   T 020 7255 6130
E catherine@cwcasting.co.uk

YOUNGSTAR CASTING
Children & Teenagers only
5 Union Castle House
Canute Road SO14 3FJ   T 023 8047 7717
E info@youngstar.tv
W www.youngstar.tv

ZIMMERMANN Jeremy CASTING
36 Marshall Street
London W1F 7EY
F 020 7437 4747   T 020 7478 5161

ACADEMY OF PERSONAL TRAINING LTD (APT LTD)
West Acre, Hurst Lane
Egham, Surrey TW20 8QJ   M 07776 304511
E alan@academypt.org

ACE FEATURE FILM
Contact: Margaret Cooper (Executive Producer). Sourcing
Investors, Product Placement, Cast & Crew
6 Ollerton Road, London N11 2LA   M 07765 927008
E acefilm1@yahoo.com
W www.acefeaturefilm.ning.com

ACTING BUDDY
E info@actingbuddy.com   T 020 7558 8020
W www.actingbuddy.com

ACTOR'S ONE-STOP SHOP THE
Showreels for Performing Artists
First Floor, Above The Gate Pub
Station Road, London N22 7SS   T 020 8888 7006
E info@actorsonestopshop.com
W www.actorsonestopshop.com

AGENTFILE
Software for Agents
E admin@agentfile.com   M 07050 683662
W www.agentfile.com

AKA
Advertising. Design. Digital. Marketing. Promotions
Sales & Ticketing
1st Floor, 115 Shaftesbury Avenue
Cambridge Circus, London WC2H 8AF
F 020 7836 8787   T 020 7836 4747
E aka@akauk.com
W www.akauk.com

ARIAS Enrique
Subtitles. Translations. Voice-overs
E enriqueag@gmail.com   M 07956 261568
W www.nwlondon.com/eag

ARTS VA THE
Contact: Bronwyn Robertson (Experienced PA)
Admin Support
M 07815 192135   T 01789 552559
E bronwyn@theartsva.com
W www.theartsva.com

AUDIO DESCRIPTION (THEATRE DESCRIPTION)
West End & on Tour
E info@theatredescription.com   M 07747 655215

BARTERCARD
Lakeside House, 1 Furzeground Way
Stockley Park East, Uxbridge UB11 1BD   T 0845 2197000
E info@bartercard.co.uk
W www.bartercard.co.uk

BIG PICTURE
Casual Work in IT Field Marketing
13 Netherwood Road, London W14 0BL   T 020 7371 4455
E info@ebigpicture.co.uk
W www.ebigpicture.co.uk

BOARDMAN Emma
Creative Events. Entertainment. Media Expert
143 Talgarth Road, Barons Court
London W14 9DA   M 07976 294604
E ideas@emmaboardman.net
W www.emmaboardman.net

BRITISH ASSOCIATION OF DRAMATHERAPISTS
Waverley, Battledown Approach
Cheltenham, Glos GL52 6RE   T/F 01242 235515
E enquiries@badth.org.uk
W www.badth.org.uk

BUTCHER Litz
Psychic Medium
Cromer Mansions
Cheam Road, Sutton SM1 2SR   T 020 8401 6234
E litz@litzbutcher.co.uk

BYFORD Simon PRODUCTION MANAGEMENT SERVICES
Production & Event Management
22 Freshfield Place, Brighton
East Sussex BN2 0BN
F 01273 606402   T 01273 623972
E simon@simonbyfordpms.com

BYRNE John
One-to-one Advice from The Stage's Career Advisor
E johnbyrnecontact@gmail.com   M 07535 142728
W www.showbusiness-success.com

CAP PRODUCTION SOLUTIONS LTD
Technical Production Services
116 Wigmore Road, Carshalton
Surrey SM5 1RQ
F 07970 763480   M 07973 432576
E leigh@leighporter.com

CASTLE MAGICAL SERVICES
Contact: Michael Shepherd. Magical Effect Consultants
Broompark
131 Tadcaster Road
Dringhouses, York YO24 1QJ   T/F 01904 709500
E info@castlemagicalservices.co.uk

CAULKETT Robin Dip SM MIIRSM
Abseiling. Rope Work
3 Churchill Way, Mitchell Dean
Glos GL17 0AZ   M 07970 442003

CELEBRITIES WORLDWIDE LTD
Celebrity Contacts & Booking
39-41 New Oxford Street
London WC1A 1BN
F 020 7240 7717   T 020 7836 7702
E info@celebritiesworldwide.com
W www.celebritiesworldwide.com

CHAPERONE AGENCY THE
E chaperoneagency@hotmail.co.uk   M 07960 075928
W www.chaperoneagency.com

CHAPERONES & TUTORS
141 Main Road
Nottingham
Nottinghamshire NG16 5GQ   M 07896 651552
E arlenedecruz@hotmail.co.uk
W www.chaperonesandtutors.co.uk

CHILD CHAPERONE - DENISE SMITH
Stage, Television & Film Industry
E denisesmith916@btinternet.com   M 07956 427442
W www.childchaperone.co.uk

CHRISALYS CIRCUS
Circus Casting. Consultancy Service. Training. London
E chrisbab@hotmail.com
W www.chrisalys-circus.com

CIRCUS MANIACS
Choreography. Circus. Dance. Extreme Sports. Theatre
Unit 62
Basepoint Business Centre
Oakfield Close
Tewkesbury Business Park
Tewkesbury, Gloucestershire GL20 8SD
M 07977 247287   T 01684 854412
E agency@circusmaniacs.com
W www.circusmaniacs.com

Magus Lynius Shadeè
'King of all Witches'

Psychic ~ International ~ Occult Investigator & Consultant
Specialist in
*Psychic Research • Paranormal Phenomena • Practical Ritual Workings • Hauntings
Physical Mediumship • Materialisations • Direct Voice Communications • Exorcisms
• Transcendental Magic • Witchcraft • White & Black Magic • The Occult*

Suite 362   10 Great Russell Street   London WC1B 3BC   Tel: 020 8378 6844   Mob: 07740 043156
email: maguslyniusshadee@hotmail.com   www.occultcentre.com   www.lifeafterdeath.net

102 Rue de Normandy   53250   Neuilly Le Vendin   France
Tel: (00) (33) 2430395   www.barackobama4u.com   www.infantjesus.com

---

CLASS - CARLINE LUNDON ASSOCIATES
25 Falkner Square, Liverpool L8 7NZ   M 07853 248957
E carline.lundon@ukonline.co.uk

COBO MEDIA LTD
Performing Arts, Entertainment & Leisure Marketing
43A Garthorne Road, London SE23 1EP
F 020 8291 4969   T 020 8291 7079
E admin@cobomedia.com
W www.cobomedia.com

COLCLOUGH John
Practical Independent Guidance for Actors and Actresses
E john@johncolclough.org.uk   T 020 8873 1763
W www.johncolclough.co.uk

COMBAT INTERNATIONAL
27 High Street, Kincardine
Alloa FK10 4RJ   T 01259 731010
E info@clanronald.org
W www.clanronald.org

CREATIVE CULTURE
21E Heathmans Road, London SW6 4TJ   T 020 7193 3076
E m.chevalier@creativecultureint.com
W www.creativecultureint.com

CREATIVE INDUSTRIES DEVELOPMENT AGENCY (CIDA)
*Professional Development & Business Support for Artists &
Creative Businesses*
Media Centre, Huddersfield
West Yorkshire HD1 1RL
F 01484 483150   T 01484 483140
E info@cida.org
W www.cida.org

CREATIVE MAGIC DIRECTOR (TONY MIDDLETON)
67 De Tany Court, St Albans, Herts AL1 1TX
M 07738 971077   T 01727 838656
E tony@force10magic.co.uk
W www.consultantmagician.com

CROFTS Andrew
Book Writing Services
Westlands Grange, West Grinstead
Horsham, West Sussex RH13 8LZ   T/F 01403 864518
E croftsa@aol.com
W www.andrewcrofts.com

CS SPORTS PROMOTIONS LTD
Production Advisors. Safety. Sport. Stunts
56 Church Road, Crystal Palace, London SE19 2EZ
F 020 8771 4704   T 020 8771 4700
E agent@sportspromotions.co.uk
W www.sportspromotions.co.uk

EARLE Kenneth PERSONAL MANAGEMENT
214 Brixton Road, London SW9 6AP
F 020 7274 9529   T 020 7274 1219
E kennethearle@agents-uk.com

EQUIP
11 Balmoral Road, Gidea Park
Romford, Essex RM2 5XD   T 01708 479898
E sales@equip-u.com
W www.equip-u.com

ES GROUP LTD
Bell Lane, North Woolwich Road, London E16 2AB
F 020 7055 7201   T 020 7055 7200
E info@esgroup-uk.com
W www.esgroup-uk.com

FACADE
Creation & Production of Musicals
43A Garthorne Road, London SE23 1EP
F 020 8291 4969   T 020 8291 7079
E facade@cobomedia.com

FERRIS ENTERTAINMENT MUSIC
Music for Film & Television. London. Cardiff. Belfast
Number 8, 132 Charing Cross Road
London WC2H 0LA   T 0845 4724725
E info@ferrisentertainment.com
W www.ferrisentertainment.com

FIGHT CHOREOGRAPHER & ACTION DIRECTOR
*Contact: Nic Main (Professional Actor, Film Fighting
Choreographer). South East*
E nicmain@nicmain.com   M 07739 184418
W www.nicmain.com

FISHER Judy Associates
Recruitment Consultants
7 Swallow Street, London W1B 4DE
F 020 7434 2696   T 020 7437 2277
E margaret@judyfisher.co.uk
W www.judyfisher.co.uk

FLAMES MARTIAL ARTS ACADEMY
Contact: Adam Richards
Unit 2, 128 Milton Road Business Park
Gravesend, Kent DA12 2PG   M 07950 396389
E stunts@adamrichardsstunts.co.uk
W www.kuentao.com

FOUR SEASONS RECRUITMENT
Recruitment Company
Landmark House, Hammersmith Bridge Road, London W6 9EJ
F 020 8237 8999   T 020 8237 8900
E lizi@fsrl.co.uk
W www.fsrl.co.uk

FRANCO THE MAGICIAN
Flat 1, 79 Brent Street, London NW4 2EA   T/F 020 8202 4940
E franco@francomagic.co.uk
W www.francomagic.co.uk

GHOSTWRITER/AUTHOR
Contact: John Parker
Dove Cottage, The Street, Ickham CT3 1QP   T 01227 721071
E parkerwrite@aol.com
W www.ghostwriteruk.info

GILMOUR Rev/Prof/Dr Glenn MscD SHsc.D NFH BCMA.Reg
Fully Qualified/International Medium. Clairvoyant, Healer
& Holistic Therapist. Consultant Paranormal/Metaphysics/
Occult for Radio/Television
E drglenngilmour@yahoo.com   T 0114 231 6500
W www.drglenngilmour.com

GOLDIELLE PROMOTIONS
Event Management & Entertainment
68 Lynton Drive, Hillside, Southport, Merseyside PR8 4QQ
M 07977 936826   T 01704 566604
E goldielle@yahoo.co.uk
W www.goldiellepromotions.com

GREGOR Katherine
Guidelines for Actors. Independent Advisory Service
for Actors
E kgassocs@yahoo.com   M 07968 899223
W www.katherinegregorassociates.webs.com

HANDS UP PUPPETS
Contact: Marcus Clarke
7 Cavendish Vale, Nottingham NG5 4DS   M 07909 824630
E enquiries@handsuppuppets.com
W www.handsuppuppets.com

HARLEY PRODUCTIONS
68 New Cavendish Street, London W1G 8TE
F 020 8202 8863   T 020 7580 3247
E harleyprods@aol.com

HAYES Susan
Choreographer
46 Warrington Crescent, London W9 1EP   M 07721 927714
E susan22@btconnect.com

HERITAGE RAILWAY ASSOCIATION
10 Hurdeswell, Long Hanborough
Witney, Oxfordshire OX29 8DH   T 01993 883384
W www.heritagerailways.com

IMAGE DIGGERS
Slide/Stills/Audio/Video Library. Theme Research
618B Finchley Road, London NW11 7RR   T 020 8455 4564
E lambhorn@gmail.com
W www.imagediggers.netfirms.com

IMPACT AGENCY THE
Public Relations
3 Bloomsbury Place, London WC1A 2QL
F 020 7580 7200   T 020 7580 1770
E mail@impactagency.co.uk
W www.theimpactagency.com

I R A - INDEPENDENT REVIEWS ARTS SERVICES
Stories from the Art World
E critic@independentradioarts.com   M 07956 212916

JACKSON Kim
Forum Theatre Practitioner
Transforum, Studio B402
LCB Depot, 31 Rutland Street
Leicester LE1 1RW   T 0116 253 3429
E kim@transforum.co.uk

JENKINS Andrew LTD
Accountancy. General Management
63 Kidbrooke Park Road, London SE3 0EE
F 020 8856 7106   T 020 8319 3657
E info@andrewjenkinsltd.com
W www.andrewjenkinsltd.com

JFL SEARCH & SELECTION
Recruitment Consultants
27 Beak Street, London W1F 9RU
F 020 7734 6501   T 020 7009 3500
W www.jflrecruit.com

JOHNSON Gareth LTD
Plas Hafren, Eglwyswrw
Crymych, Pembrokeshire SA41 3UL
M 07770 225227   T 01239 891368
E gjltd@mac.com

JORDAN Richard PRODUCTIONS LTD
Festivals. General Management. Production Consultancy
UK & International Productions
Mews Studios
16 Vernon Yard, London W11 2DX
F 020 7313 9667   T 020 7243 9001
E richard.jordan@virgin.net

KEAN LANYON LTD
Contact: Sharon Kean, Iain Lanyon. PR & Web/Graphic
Consultants
Rose Cottage, Aberdeen Centre
22 Highbury Grove, London N5 2EA
F 020 7359 0199   T 020 7354 3362
E sharon@keanlanyon.com
W www.keanlanyon.com

KELLER Don
Marketing Consultancy. Project Management
65 Glenwood Road, Harringay
London N15 3JS   T 020 8800 4882
E info@dakam.org.uk

KIEVE Paul
Magical Effects for Film & Stage
2 St Philip's Road, London E8 3BP   T/F 020 7502 2213
E mail@stageillusion.com
W www.stageillusion.com

LAMBOLLE Robert
Script Evaluation/Editing
618B Finchley Road, London NW11 7RR   T 020 8455 4564
E lambhorn@gmail.com
W www.readingandrighting.netfirms.com

LAWINSPORT.COM
Contact: Sean Cottrell, Alfonso Valero (Co-editors)
Free Sports law resource providing news, articles of legal
opinion, book reviews & events
E sean@lawinsport.com   T 020 7193 1877
W www.lawinsport.com

LAWSON LEAN David
Chaperone Service for Children in Entertainment
72 Shaw Drive, Walton-on-Thames
Surrey KT12 2LS   T 01932 230273
E dlawsonlean@aol.com
W www.davidlawsonlean.com

LEEP MARKETING & PR
Marketing. Press. Publicity
5 Nassau House
122 Shaftesbury Avenue, London W1D 5ER
F 020 7439 8833   T 020 7439 9777
E philip@leep.biz

LEO MEDIA & ENTERTAINMENT GROUP THE
Executive Production. Film, Television & Literary Consultancy Legal Work
PO Box 19909, London NW3 3FF
F 07006 057893   T 020 7183 3177
E info@leomediagroup.com
W www.leomediagroup.com

LICENSED CHAPERONE
Orchard Cottage, 31 Whitecroft Way
Beckenham, Kent BR3 3AQ   T/F 020 8650 8997
E elaineboyle@msn.com

LOCATION TUTORS NATIONWIDE
Fully Qualified/Experienced Teachers working with Children on Film Sets & Covering all Key Stages of National Curriculum
16 Poplar Walk, Herne Hill, London SE24 0BU
F 020 7207 8794   T 020 7978 8898
E locationtutorsnationwide@googlemail.com
W www.locationtutors.co.uk

LOVE Billie HISTORICAL PHOTOGRAPHS
Picture Research. Formerly 'Amanda' Theatrical Portraiture
3 Winton Street, Ryde, Isle of Wight PO33 2BX
F 01983 616565   T 01983 812572

LUXFACTOR GROUP (UK) THE
Fleet Place, 12 Nelson Drive, Petersfield, Hampshire GU31 4SJ
F 0845 3700588   T 0845 3700589
E info@luxfactor.co.uk
W www.luxfactor.co.uk

MAGICIANS.CO.UK
Entertainers. Magic Consultants
Regent House, 291 Kirkdale, London SE26 4QD
F 0845 0062443   T 0845 0062442
E mail@magicians.co.uk

MAIN Nic
Experienced Stage, Television & Film Action/ Fight Director/Actor
62 Kingsway, Blackwater
Camberley, Surrey GU17 0JB   M 07739 184418
E nicmain@nicmain.com
W www.nicmain.com

MATT-LX LTD
Event Lighting. Technical Production
Gunnery House, 9 Gunnery Terrace, London SE18 6SW
F 020 8301 8149   T 020 8301 8692
E intray@mattlx.com
W www.mattlx.com

MATT-LX HEALTH & SAFETY TRAINING
Gunnery House, 9 Gunnery Terrace
London SE18 6SW   T 020 8301 8692
E safetyshop@mattlx.com   W www.mattlx.com/training_64

MAYS Lorraine
Children's Licensed Chaperone
Park View, Stanley Avenue, Chesham, Bucks HP5 2JF
M 07778 106552   T 01494 771029
E lorrainebmays@aol.com

McKENNA Deborah LTD
Celebrity Chefs & Lifestyle Presenters only
64-66 Glentham Road, London SW13 9JJ
F 020 8846 0967   T 020 8846 0966
E info@deborahmckenna.com
W www.deborahmckenna.com

MEDIA LEGAL
Education Services. Jurisconsults
Town House, 5 Mill Pond Close
Sevenoaks, Kent TN14 5AW   T 01732 460592

MILDENBERG Vanessa
Choreographer. Director. Movement Director
Flat 6, Cameford Court
New Park Road, London SW2 4LH   M 07796 264828
E vanessamildenberg@me.com
W http://web.me.com/vanessamildenberg

MILITARY ADVISORY & INSTRUCTION SPECIALISTS
Contact: John Sessions. Advice on Weapons, Drill, Period to Present. Ex-Army Instructors. Health & Safety. IOSH. Military Bugler & Drummer
38 Knapton Close, Strensall, York YO32 5ZF   T 01904 491198
E johnmusic1@hotmail.com

MINIMAL RISK
Security Consultancy
3rd Floor, 111 Buckingham Palace Road
London SW1W 0SR   T 01432 360643
E london@minimalrisk.co.uk
W www.minimalrisk.co.uk

MINISTRY OF FUN THE
Entertainment. Promotions. PR Marketing Campaigns
Unit 1, Suffolk Studios
127-129 Great Suffolk Street, London SE1 1PP
F 020 7407 5763   T 020 7407 6077
E james@ministryoffun.net
W www.ministryoffun.net

MORGAN Jane ASSOCIATES (JMA)
Marketing. Media
8 Heathville Road, London N19 3AJ
F 020 7263 9877   T 020 7263 9867
E jma@janemorganassociates.com

MUSIC SOLUTIONS LTD
Garden Studios, 11-15 Betterton Street
London WC2H 9BP   T 020 7866 8160
E mail@musicsolutions.ltd.uk

NEATE Rodger PRODUCTION MANAGEMENT
15 Southcote Road, London N19 5BJ   T 020 7609 9538
E rneate@dircon.co.uk

NEXTSTOPLAX
Relocation of Entertainment Industry Professionals
1210 Poinsettia Drive, West Hollywood, CA 90046
T (323) 798 5102   T (323) 798 5103
E info@nextstoplax.com
W www.nextstoplax.com

ORANGE TREE STUDIO LTD & MUSIC SERVICES
*Original Music/Composition & Production. Saxophonist &
Brass Section For Hire. Live or in Studio*
31A New Road, Croxley Green
Herts WD3 3EJ   M 07768 146200
E richard@orangetreestudio.com
W www.redhornz.co.uk

PB PRODUCTIVE
*Photographers' Agent. Shoot, Production & Event
Management*
Ubbeston Lodge, Ubbeston
Halesworth, Suffolk IP19 0EY   M 07957 424776
E info@pbproductive.com
W www.pbproductive.com

PENROSE Scott
Magic for Film, Stage & Television
17 Berkeley Drive, Billericay
Essex CM12 0YP   M 07767 336882
E mail@stagemagician.com
W www.stagemagician.com

PINEWOOD NET
Networking Group
86 Hurst Farm Road, East Grinstead
West Sussex RH19 4DH   M 07882 794583
E katy@pinewoodnet.net
W www.pinewoodnet.net

PRE-PRODUCTION COMPANY
Riverside Studios, Crisp Road
London W6 9RL   T 020 8237 1080
E info@associatedstudios.co.uk
W www.associatedstudios.co.uk

PSYCHOLOGY GROUP THE
*Assessments. Counselling. Expert Opinion. Presentation
Psychotherapy*
F 0845 2805243   T 0870 6092445
E info@psychologygroup.co.uk
W www.psychologygroup.co.uk

PUKKA PRESENTING
Training in Television Presenting & Presentation Techniques
Appletree Cottage, 51 Erskine Hill
London NW11 6EY   T 020 8455 1385
E kathryn@pukkapresenting.co.uk
W www.pukkapresenting.co.uk

PUPPET CENTRE TRUST
*Development & Advocacy Agency for Puppetry & Related
Animated Theatre*
BAC, Lavender Hill, London SW11 5TN   T 020 7228 5335
E pct@puppetcentre.org.uk   W www.puppetcentre.org.uk

RAINBOW BIGBOTTOM & CO LTD
Children's Warm-up Artists for Stage & Television
Park View, Stanley Avenue
Chesham, Bucks HP5 2JF   T 01494 771029
E lorrainebmays@aol.com   W www.mrpanda.co.uk

RED HOT ID - THE BRANDING SERVICE FOR ACTORS
Unit 6, Farriers Mews, London SE15 3XP   T 020 7635 8988
E id@redhotentertainment.biz
W www.redhotentertainment.biz

RICHARDS Adam
Fight Director
Unit 2
128 Milton Road Business Park
Gravesend, Kent DA12 2PG   M 07950 396389
E stunts@adamrichardsstunts.co.uk
W www.kuentao.com

RIPLEY-DUGGAN PARTNERSHIP THE
Tour Booking
26 Goodge Street, London W1T 2QG   T 020 7436 1392
E info@ripleyduggan.com

SHADEE' Magus Lynius
Psychic. Occult Investigator & Consultant
Suite 362, 10 Great Russell Street
London WC1B 3BC
M 07740 043156   T 020 8378 6844
E maguslyniusshadee@hotmail.com
W www.occultcentre.com

SHAW Jennifer EVENTS
Event Management & Promotions
15 Ladyhouse Lane, Milnrow OL16 4EH   T 0845 1309517
E jennifer@jennifershawevents.co.uk
W www.jennifershawevents.co.uk

SHOWBIZ FRIENDS
Community Website for all Showbiz People
W www.showbizfriends.com

SINCLAIR Andy
Mime
E andynebular@hotmail.com   M 07831 196675
W www.andyjsinclair.co.uk

SOUTHAM FERRARI Maggie
6 Oak Tree Court
Meadway
Midhurst, West Sussex GU29 9SE
M 07986 045724   T 01730 814177
E margaret.ferrari@virgin.net
W www.deadendkids.co.uk

SPENCER Ivor SCHOOL FOR BUTLERS THE
12 Little Bornes, Dulwich
London SE21 8SE   T 020 8670 5585
E ivor@ivorspencer.com
W www.ivorspencer.com

STAGE CRICKET CLUB
Cricketers & Cricket Grounds
39-41 Hanover Steps, St George's Fields
Albion Street, London W2 2YG
F 020 7262 5736   T 020 7402 7543
E brianjfilm@aol.com
W www.stagecc.co.uk

STUNT ACTION SPECIALISTS (S.A.S.)
Corporate & Television Stunt Work
110 Trafalgar Road
Portslade, East Sussex BN41 1GS
F 01273 708699   T 01273 230214
E wayne@stuntactionspecialists.co.uk
W www.stuntactionspecialists.co.uk

STYLES John - MAGICAL MART
Magic, Ventriloquism & Punch & Judy Consultant
42 Christchurch Road, Sidcup
Kent DA15 7HQ   T/F 020 8300 3579
W www.johnstylesentertainer.co.uk

TALENT SCOUT THE
Referral Service. Agents & Managers
19 Edge Road, Thornhill
Dewsbury, West Yorkshire WF12 0QA   T 01924 464049
E connect@thetalentscout.org

TAY ASSOCIATES LTD
Media Recruitment Agency Specialising in Support Staff for Arts, Film, Stage & Television
10 Throgmorton Avenue, London EC2N 2DL   T 020 7065 6700
E dib@tayassociates.co.uk
W www.tayassociates.com

THEATRE PROJECTS CONSULTANTS
4 Apollo Studios, Charlton Kings Road, London NW5 2SW
F 020 7284 0636   T 020 7482 4224
E info@theatreprojects.com
W www.theatreprojects.com

THERAPEDIA LONDON BRIGHTON
93 Gloucester Place, London W1U 6JQ   M 07941 300871
E info@gregmadison.net
W www.gregmadison.net

TODD Carole
Choreographer. Director
c/o Chris Davis Management Ltd
Tenbury House, 36 Teme Street
Tenbury Wells, Worcs WR15 8AA
F 01584 819076   T 01584 819005
E cdavis@cdm-ltd.com

TWINS THE
Magical Special Effects for Film, Stage & Television Productions
30 Westmill Crescent, Wareham, Dorset BH20 4BW
M 07971 589186   T 0845 0523683
E info@thetwins.co.uk
W www.thetwinsfx.com

UK THEATRE AVAILABILITY
Bookings Service for Theatre Producers
1 Hogarth Hill, London NW11 6AY   T 020 8455 3278
E info@uktheatreavailability.co.uk
W www.uktheatreavailability.co.uk

UNITED KINGDOM COPYRIGHT BUREAU
Script Services
110 Trafalgar Road, Portslade
East Sussex BN41 1GS   T 01273 277333
E info@copyrightbureau.co.uk
W www.copyrightbureau.co.uk

VERNON Doremy
Archivist. Author 'Tiller Girls'. Dance Routines Tiller Girl Style
16 Ouseley Road, London SW12 8EF   T/F 020 8767 6944

VOCALEYES
Audio Description "Describing The Arts"
1st Floor, 54 Commercial Street
London E1 0LT   T 020 7375 1043
E enquiries@vocaleyes.co.uk
W www.vocaleyes.co.uk

VOICEATWORK
Voice Coach
5 Anhalt Road, London SW11 4NZ   M 07973 871479
E kateterris@voiceatwork.co.uk
W www.voiceatwork.co.uk

WELBOURNE Jacqueline
Choreographer. Circus Trainer. Consultant
c/o Circus Maniacs
Unit 62
Basepoint Business Centre
Oakfield Close
Tewkesbury Business Park
Tewkesbury, Gloucestershire GL20 8SD
M 07977 247287   T 01684 854412
E jackie@circusmaniacs.com
W www.circusmaniacs.com

WEST END WORKSHOPS
Arts Workshops. Audition Coaching
E info@westendworkshops.co.uk   T 01202 526667
W www.westendworkshops.co.uk

WHITE Leonard
Stage & Television Credits
Highlands
40 Hill Crest Road
Newhaven, Brighton
East Sussex BN9 9EG   T 01273 514473
E leoguy.white@virgin.net

WILKINSON Gavin
Children's Director
E enquiries@tomorrowstalent.co.uk   T 01202 526667
W www.tomorrowstalent.co.uk

WISE MONKEY FINANCIAL COACHING
Contact: Simonne Gnessen
14 Eastern Terrace Mews
Brighton BN2 1EP   T 0845 6346713
E simonne@financial-coaching.co.uk
W www.financial-coaching.co.uk

WWW.EYENNCEE.COM
Professional Networking Site
I.N.C. Space
9-13 Grape Street
Covent Garden, London WC2H 8ED
F 020 7557 6656   T 020 7557 6650
E chris@inc-space.com
W www.eyenncee.com

YOUNGBLOOD
Fight Direction
E info@youngblood.co.uk   T 020 7193 3207
W www.youngblood.co.uk

Samaurai Warrior, photo shoot

Rosemarie Swinfield
m a k e - u p d e s i g n e r
Rosie's Make-up Box
m: 07976-965520
e: rosiesmake-up@uw.club.net
www.rosiesmake-up.co.uk
Author of:
- Stage Make-Up Step By Step
- Period Make-Up For The Stage
- Hair And Wigs For The Stage
Also
Courses, Workshops & Seminars

Richard Walters - Burton

ACADEMY COSTUMES
50 Rushworth Street
London SE1 0RB
F 020 7928 6287   T 020 7620 0771
E info@academycostumes.com
W www.academycostumes.com

AJ COSTUMES LTD
Theatrical Costume Hire, Design & Making
Sullom Lodge
Sullom Side Lane
Barnacre, Garstang PR3 1GH
F 01253 407715   T 0871 2003343
E info@trendsgroup.co.uk
W www.trendsgroup.co.uk

ALL-SEWN-UP
Mechanics Institute
7 Church Street
Heptonstall
West Yorks HX7 7NS   T/F 01422 843407
E nwheeler_allsewnup@hotmail.com
W www.allsewnup.org.uk

AND SEW TO DANCE
Unit 11, Cornwallis House
Howard Chase
Basildon, Essex SS14 3BB   T 01268 285050
E andsewtodance@blueyonder.co.uk

ANELLO & DAVIDE
Handmade Shoes
15 St Albans Grove
London W8 5BP   T 020 7938 2255
W www.handmadeshoes.co.uk

ANGELS
Fancy Dress. Revue
119 Shaftesbury Avenue, London WC2H 8AE
F 020 7240 9527   T 020 7836 5678
E party@fancydress.com
W www.fancydress.com

ANGELS THE COSTUMIERS
1 Garrick Road, London NW9 6AA
F 020 8202 1820   T 020 8202 2244
E angels@angels.uk.com
W www.angels.uk.com

ANGELS WIGS
Facial Hair Suppliers. Wig Hire/Makers
1 Garrick Road
London NW9 6AA
F 020 8202 1820   T 020 8202 2244
E wigs@angels.uk.com
W www.angels.uk.com

ANTOINETTE COSTUME HIRE
Fancy Dress. Film. Stage
High Street Buildings, 134 Kirkdale
London SE26 4BB   T 020 8699 1913
E antoinettehire@aol.com
W www.costumehirelondon.com

ARMS & ARCHERY
Armour. Banners. Chainmail. Medieval Tents
Warrior Costumes. Weaponry
Thrift Lane, off London Road
Ware, Herts SG12 9QS   T 01920 460335
E armsandarchery@btconnect.com

ATTLE COSTUMIERS LTD
Contact: Jamie Attle. Designs, Makes & Hires Costumes
4 Toynbee Road, Wimbledon
London SW20 8SS   T/F 020 8540 3044
E aalexiscolby@aol.com

BAHADLY R.
Hair & Make-up Artist, incl. Bald Caps, Ageing & Casualty
47 Ploughmans Way, Macclesfield
Cheshire SK10 2UN
M 07973 553073   T 01625 615878
E rosienico@hotmail.co.uk

BERTRAND Henry
London Stockhouse for Silk
52 Holmes Road, London NW5 3AB
F 020 7424 7001   T 020 7424 7000
E sales@henrybertrand.co.uk
W www.henrybertrand.co.uk

BIRMINGHAM COSTUME HIRE
Suites 209-210, Jubilee Centre
130 Pershore Street, Birmingham B5 6ND
F 0121 622 2758   T 0121 622 3158
E info@birminghamcostumehire.co.uk

BISHOP Kerry
Hair & Make-up Artist
Flat 4, 49 Upper Rock Gardens
Brighton, East Sussex BN2 1QF   M 07759 704394
E kerrybishop@email.com

BRIGGS Ron DESIGN
Costume Design, Embroidery & Making
1 Bedford Mews, London N2 9DF   T 020 8444 8801
E costumes@ronbriggs.com

BRODY Shirley
14 Jenner House
London WC1N 1BL   M 07717 855684
E s.brody@blueyonder.co.uk

BURLINGTONS
Hairdressers
14 John Princes Street
London W1G 0JS   T 0844 8008884
E ccm@newidstudios.co.uk
W www.newidstudios.co.uk

CALICO FABRICS
Suppliers of Unbleached Calico & other Fabrics for Stage,
Costumes, Backdrops etc
3 Ram Passage, High Street
Kingston-upon-Thames
Surrey KT1 1HH
F 020 8546 7755   T 020 8541 5274
E sales@calicofabrics.co.uk
W www.calicofabrics.co.uk

CAPEZIO
Dance Products
95 Whiffler Road, Norwich, Norfolk NR3 2AW
F 0870 3500074   T 0870 3500073
E eusales@balletmakers.com
W www.capeziodance.com

CHRISANNE LTD
Specialist Fabrics & Accessories for Dance & Stage
Chrisanne House
110-112 Morden Road
Mitcham, Surrey CR4 4XB
F 020 8640 2106   T 020 8640 5921
E sales@chrisanne.com
W www.chrisanne.com

CLANRANALD COSTUME
27 High Street, Kincardine, Alloa FK10 4RJ   T 01259 731010
E info@clanranald.org
W www.clanranald.org

COLTMAN Mike
See COSTUME CONSTRUCTION

COOK Sheila TEXTILES
Vintage Textiles, Costumes & Accessories for Sale/Hire
26 Addison Place, London W11 4RJ   T 020 7603 3003
E sheilacook@sheilacook.co.uk
W www.sheilacook.co.uk

COSPROP LTD
Accessories. Costumes
469-475 Holloway Road, London N7 6LE
F 020 7561 7310   T 020 7561 7300
E enquiries@cosprop.com
W www.cosprop.com

COSTUME BOUTIQUE
Costume Hire for Events & Parties
38 Great Western Studios
65 Alfred Road
London W2 5EU
M 07973 794450   T 020 8968 4606
E costumeboutique@me.com
W www.costumeboutique.co.uk

COSTUME CONSTRUCTION
Costumes. Masks. Props. Puppets
Studio 1, Croft Street
Cheltenham GL53 0EE   T 01242 581847
E mike@costumeconstruction.co.uk
W www.costumeconstruction.co.uk

COSTUME CREATIONS
10 Olinthus Avenue
Wolverhampton WV11 3DE   T 01902 738282
E yourcostume@googlemail.com
W www.costumecreations.co.uk

COSTUME GUIDE THE
Products & Suppliers Directory
E tp@tessap.plus.com   T 020 7602 2857

COSTUME SOLUTIONS
43 Rowan Road, London W6 7DT   T 020 7603 9035
E karen@costumesolutions.co.uk
W www.costumesolutions.co.uk

COSTUME STORE LTD THE
Costume Accessories
16 Station Street, Lewes
East Sussex BN7 2DB
F 01273 477191   T 01273 479727
E enquiries@thecostumestore.co.uk
W www.thecostumestore.co.uk

COSTUME STUDIO LTD
Costumes. Wigs
Montgomery House
159-161 Balls Pond Road, London N1 4BG
T/F 020 7923 9065   T 020 7275 9614
E costume.studio@btconnect.com
W www.costumestudio.co.uk

COSTUMIA
Unit 9, Hockley Goods Yard
Pitsford Street, Hockley
Birmingham B18 6PT   T 0121 551 2710
E info@costumia.co.uk
W www.costumia.co.uk

COUTURE BEADING & EMBELLISHMENT
6 Milton Road, London E17 4SR   M 07985 076729
E enquiries@couturebeading.com
W www.couturebeading.com

CRAZY CLOTHES CONNECTION
1920's-1980's for Sale or Hire
134 Lancaster Road, Ladbroke Grove
London W11 1QU   T 020 7221 3989
E info@crazy-clothes.co.uk
W www.crazy-clothes.co.uk

DANCIA INTERNATIONAL
168 Drury Lane, London WC2B 5QA   T 020 7831 9483
E dancialondon@btconnect.com
W www.dancia.co.uk/london

DAVIES Bryan Philip COSTUMES
Lavish Pantomime. Musical Shows. Opera
68 Court Road, Lewes, East Sussex BN7 2SA
M 07931 249097   T/F 01273 481004
E bryan@bpdcostumes.co.uk
W www.bpdcostumes.co.uk

DELAMAR ACADEMY
Make-up Training
Ealing Studios, Building D, 2nd Floor
Ealing Green, London W5 5EP   T/F 020 8579 9511
E info@delamaracademy.co.uk
W www.delamaracademy.co.uk

DESIGNER ALTERATIONS
Restyling & Remodelling of Clothes & Costumes
220A Queenstown Road, Battersea
London SW8 4LP
F 020 7622 4148   T 020 7498 4360
E info@designeralterations.com
W www.designeralterations.com

DR. BOO
22 North Cross Road, East Dulwich
London SE22 9EU   T 020 8693 4823
E info.boo@virgin.net
W www.drboo.co.uk

EASTON Derek
Wigs For Film, Stage & Television
1 Dorothy Avenue, Peacehaven
East Sussex BN10 8LP
M 07768 166733   T/F 01273 588262
E wigs@derekeastonwigs.co.uk
W www.derekeastonwigs.co.uk

EIA MILLINERY DESIGN
1620 W. Nelson Street, Chicago
Illinois 60657   T 001 773 975 5959
E info@eiahatart.com

EVOLUTION SETS & COSTUMES LTD
Set & Costume Hire
Langdon Abbey, West Langdon
Dover, Kent CT15 5HJ
F 01304 615353   T 01304 615333
E emily@evolution-productions.co.uk

FOX Charles H. LTD
The Professional Make-up Centre
22 Tavistock Street
London WC2E 7PY
F 020 7379 3410   T 020 7240 3111
E makeup@charlesfox.co.uk
W www.charlesfox.co.uk

FOXTROT PRODUCTIONS LTD
Armoury Services. Costume & Prop Hire. Firearms
3B Brassie Avenue, East Acton
London W3 7DE   T 020 8964 3555
E mail@foxtrot-productions.co.uk
W www.foxtrot-productions.co.uk

FREED OF LONDON
Dance Shoes. Dancewear
94 St Martin's Lane, London WC2N 4AT
F 020 7240 3061   T 020 7240 0432
E shop@freed.co.uk
W www.freedoflondon.com

FUNN LTD
Silk, Cotton & Wool Stockings. Opaque Opera Tights
40's Rayon Stockings
PO Box 102, Steyning
West Sussex BN44 3EB
F 0870 8794450   T 0870 8743866
E funn.biz@lycos.com

GAMBA THEATRICAL
See THEATRICAL FOOTWEAR COMPANY LTD THE

GAV NICOLA THEATRICAL SHOES
M 07961 974278
E gavnicola@yahoo.com
W www.theatricalshoes.com

GILLHAM Felicite
Wig Makers for Film, Opera & Stage
Gallis Ash, Kilmersdon
Near Bath, Somerset BA3 5SZ
M 07802 955908   T 01761 437142
E felicite@gillywigs.co.uk

GREASEPAINT SCHOOL OF MAKE-UP & HAIR
143 Northfield Avenue, Ealing, London W13 9QT
F 020 8840 3983   T 020 8840 6000
E info@greasepaint.co.uk
W www.greasepaint.co.uk

GROVE Sue DESIGNS
Costume Designers & Makers. Historical Specialist
12 Ampthill Road, Shirley
Southampton, Hants SO15 8LP   T 023 8078 6849
E sue.grove1@tiscali.co.uk

HAIRAISERS
Hair Extensions. Wigs
9-11 Sunbeam Road, Park Royal
London NW10 6JP
F 020 8963 1600   T 020 8965 2500
E info@hairaisers.com
W www.hairaisers.com

HAND & LOCK
Embroidery for Costumes & Interiors
86 Margaret Street, London W1W 8TE
F 020 7580 7499   T 020 7580 7488
E enquiries@handembroidery.com
W www.handembroidery.com

HARVEYS OF HOVE
Military Specialists. Theatrical Costumes
110 Trafalgar Road, Portslade
Sussex BN41 1GS
F 01273 708699   T 01273 430323
E harveys.costume@ntlworld.com
W www.harveysofhove.co.uk

HENRY Lewis LTD
Dress Makers
111-113 Great Portland Street
London W1W 6QQ   T 020 7636 6683

HIREARCHY
Classic & Contemporary Costume
45-47 Palmerston Road, Boscombe
Bournemouth, Dorset BH1 4HW   T 01202 394465
E hirearchy1@aol.com
W www.hirearchy.co.uk

HODIN Annabel
Costume Designer/Stylist
12 Eton Avenue, London NW3 3EH
M 07836 754079   T 020 7431 8761
E annabelhodin@aol.com

HOPKINS Trisha
6 Willow Grove, Formby L37 3NX
M 07957 368598   T 01704 873055
E trisha_hopkins@hotmail.co.uk

INTERNATIONAL DANCE SUPPLIES/GRISHKO UK LTD
Importer & Distributor of Dance Shoes & Dancewear
9 Ballard Close, Milton
Cambridge CB24 6DW
F 01223 280388   T 01223 861425
E info@grishko.co.uk
W www.grishko.co.uk

JULIETTE DESIGNS
Diamante Jewellery Manufacturers
90 Yerbury Road, London N19 4RS
F 020 7281 7326   T 020 7263 7878
E juliettedesigns@hotmail.com
W www.stagejewellery.com

KATIE'S WIGS
Wig Supplier & Maker
15 Birchwood Gardens, Idle Park
Bradford BD10 9EW   T 07900 250853
E katie.hunt@katieswigs.com

KIDD Ella J.
Bespoke Millinery, Wigs & Head-dresses for Film,
Stage & Television
T 020 8539 2786
W www.ellajkidd.co.uk

LARGER THAN LIFE STAGEWEAR
Theatrical Costumes for Hire
2 Sundridge Parade
Bromley, Kent BR1 4DT   T/F 020 8466 9010
E info@largerthanlifestagewear.co.uk
W www.largerthanlifestagewear.co.uk

LOCK Josie MAKEUP ARTIST
Flat 2, Liwood House, 217 Kennington Lane
Kennington, London SE11 5QT   M 07722 358425
E hello@josielock.co.uk
W www.josielockmakeup.co.uk

MADDERMARKET THEATRE COSTUME HIRE
Costume Hire & Wig Hire. Period Clothing
St John's Alley, Norwich NR2 1DR
F 01603 661357   T 01603 626292
E mmtheatre@btconnect.com
W www.maddermarket.co.uk

MAKE-UP ON THE MOVE
17 Henley Road, Wolverhampton
West Midlands WV10 6UY   M 07949 943688
E info@makeuponthemove.co.uk

MAKEUP 4 DANCERS
82 Recreation Way, Kemsley
Sittingbourne, Kent ME10 2TG   T 01795 556003
E jill@makeup4dancers.co.uk
W www.makeup4dancers.co.uk

MARSDEN Chloe COSTUMES & MILLINERY
1st Floor, 61-63 Coldharbour Lane
London SE5 9NS   M 07786 427386
E mail@chloemarsden.co.uk
W www.chloemarsden.co.uk

MASK Kim
Costume & Make-up Protection Masks
E info@kimmask.com   T 0845 0568482
W www.kimmask.com

MASTER CLEANERS THE
Dry Cleaning of Theatrical Costumes & Antique Garments
189 Haverstock Hill, London NW3 4QG   T 020 7431 3725
E info@themastercleaners.com
W www.themastercleaners.com

MEANANDGREEN.COM
87 Darlington Street
Wolverhampton WV1 4EX   T 0845 8991133
E custserv@meanandgreen.com
W www.meanandgreen.com

MORRIS Heather
Wigs
c/o The Hair Clinic at JBC
50-54 Wigmore Street
London W1U 2AU   T 020 7935 9200
E heather.morris@btconnect.com
W www.fortysevenhair.co.uk

NATIONAL THEATRE
Costume, Furniture & Props Hire
Chichester House
Kennington Park Estate
1-3 Brixton Road, London SW9 6DE
T 020 7735 4774 (Costume)   T 020 7820 1358 (Props)
E costume_hire@nationaltheatre.org.uk

NEW ID
Makeover & Photographic Studios
2 Lacemaker Court, London Road
Old Amersham HP7 0HS   T 0870 8701299
E bookings@newidstudios.co.uk
W www.newidstudios.co.uk

NORMAN Sam
Hair. Make-up
E sam@samnorman.co.uk   M 07932 397465
W www.samnorman.co.uk

ORIGINAL KNITWEAR
Contact: Gina Pinnick. Inc. Fake Fur
Avalon, Tregoney Hill
Mevagissey, Cornwall PL26 6RG
M 07957 376855   T 01726 844807
E okgina@btinternet.com
W www.originalknitwear.co.uk

PACE Terri MAKE-UP DESIGN
E info@terripace.com   M 07939 698999
W www.terripace.com

PALMER Johnny
Wardrobe Master & Supplier. Glasgow
M 07786 101360
E jonboyjohnny@yahoo.co.uk

PATEY (LONDON) LTD
Unit 1, 9 Gowlett Road, London SE15 4HX
F 020 7732 9538   T 020 7635 0030
E trevor@pateyhats.com
W www.pateyhats.com

PEARCE Kate
Costume Maker
Thistledown, Wellfield Road
Marshfield, Near Newport CF3 2UB   M 07749 283802
E kpearce55@hotmail.com

PINK POINTES DANCEWEAR
1A Suttons Lane, Hornchurch
Essex RM12 6RD   T/F 01708 438584
E pink.pointes@btconnect.com

POLAND DENTAL STUDIO
Film/Stage Dentistry
1 Devonshire Place, London W1G 6HH
F 020 7486 3952 T 020 7935 6919
E robpoland@btconnect.com

PORSELLI
4 Frensham Road, Sweet Briar Industrial Estate
Norwich NR3 2BT
F 01603 406676 T 0845 0170817
E porselliuk@aol.com
W www.dancewear.co.uk

PROBLOOD
11 Mount Pleasant, Framlingham
Suffolk IP13 9HQ T/F 01728 723865

QUATTROCIOCCHI Adele
Make-up Artist
98 Otter Close, Newham
London E15 2PX M 07551 422358
E adeleq@alice.it

RAINBOW PRODUCTIONS LTD
Manufacture & Handling of Costume Characters
Unit 3, Green Lea Park, Prince George's Road
London SW19 2JD
F 020 8254 5306 T 020 8254 5300
E info@rainbowproductions.co.uk
W www.rainbowproductions.co.uk

REPLICA WAREHOUSE
Costumiers. Props
200 Main Road, Goostrey
Cheshire CW4 8PD T/F 01477 534075
E lesleyedwards@replicawarehouse.co.uk
W www.replicawarehouse.co.uk

ROBBINS Sheila
Wig Hire
Broombarn, 7 Ivy Cottages
Hinksey Hill, Oxford OX1 5BQ T/F 01865 735524

ROLANDI Gianluca
Hair. Make-up
83 Deroy Lodge, Wicklow Street
London WC1X 9LF M 07990 637299
E gluca@gluca.co.uk
W www.glmakeup.com

ROSE Eda MILLINERY
Ladies' Hats. Design & Manufacture
Lalique, Mongewell, Wallingford, Oxon OX10 8BP
F 01491 835909 T 01491 837174
E edarose.lawson@btconnect.com

ROUSSINOV Sarah
20 Isabella Place
Kingston Upon Thames KT2 5PB M 07747 777493
E sarahroussinov@aol.com
W www.sarahroussinov.co.uk

ROYAL EXCHANGE THEATRE COSTUME HIRE
Period Costumes & Accessories
47-53 Swan Street, Manchester M4 5JY T/F 0161 819 6660
E costume.hire@royalexchange.co.uk
W www.royalexchange.co.uk

ROYER Hugo INTERNATIONAL LTD
Hair & Wig Materials
10 Lakeside Business Park, Swan Lane
Sandhurst, Berkshire GU47 9DN
F 01252 878852 T 01252 878811
E enquiries@royer.co.uk
W www.hugoroyer.com

RSC COSTUME HIRE
28 Timothy's Bridge Road
Stratford Enterprise Park
Stratford-upon-Avon
Warwickshire CV37 9UY T 01789 205920
E costume.hire@rsc.org.uk

RUMBLE Jane
Masks, Millinery & Helmets Made to Order
121 Elmstead Avenue, Wembley
Middlesex HA9 8NT T 020 8904 6462

SAGUARO Jen
35 Southey Street, Bristol BS2 9RE M 07773 385703
E jrsaguaro@googlemail.com

SERENDIPITY STUDIO LTD
77 High Street, Egham, Surrey TW20 9HY   T 01784 558281
E chrissie@serendipitystudio.co.uk
W www.serendipitystudio. co.uk

SEXTON Sally Ann
Hair & Make-up Designer
c/o The Harris Agency Ltd
71 The Avenue
Watford, Herts WD17 4NU
M 07973 802842   T 01923 211644
E theharrisagency@btconnect.com

SILVESTER Michaela
Chantry, Chapel Lane
Pirbright, Surrey GU24 0JY   M 07595 725047
E kaylasilvester@hotmail.co.uk

SINGER Sandra ASSOCIATES
Fashion Stylists for Stage & Television, Costume/Designer
21 Cotswold Road, Westcliff-on-Sea
Essex SS0 8AA   T 01702 331616
E sandrasingeruk@aol.com
W www.sandrasinger.com

SLEIMAN Hilary
Specialist & Period Knitwear
72 Godwin Road, London E7 0LG
M 07940 555663   T 020 8555 6176
E hilary.sleiman@ntlworld.com

SOFT PROPS
Costume & Model Makers
92 Fentiman Road, London SW8 1LA
F 020 7207 0062   T 020 7587 1116
E jackie@softprops.co.uk

SOLAK Shenay
51 Drury House, London SW8 4JL   M 07771 921931
E shenays@yahoo.de

STAGEWORKS WORLDWIDE PRODUCTIONS
Largest Costume Wardrobe in North
525 Ocean Boulevard, Blackpool FY4 1EZ
F 01253 342702   T 01253 342426
E simone.bolajuzon@stageworkswwp.com
W www.stageworkswwp.com

STRIBLING Joan
*BAFTA Member. Film & Television Make-up, Prosthetics &
Hair Designer. BAFTA Craft, Design & Art Director's Awards
London/Southwest Based*
M 07791 758480   T 0845 4266169
E joanstribling@hotmail.com
W www.joanstribling.com

SWINFIELD Rosemarie
Rosie's Make-up Box. Make-up Design & Training
E rosiesmake-up@uw.club.net   M 07976 965520
W www.rosiesmake-up.co.uk

TALK TO THE HAND PUPPETS
Custom Puppets for Film, Stage & Television
Studio 277, Wimbledon Art Studios, Riverside Yard
Earlsfield, London SW17 0BB
M 07813 682293   M 07855 421454
E info@talktothehandpuppets.com
W www.talktothehandpuppets.com

THEATREKNITS
102C Belgravia Workshops
157-163 Marlborough Road
London N19 4NF   T/F 020 7561 0044
E theatreknits@yahoo.co.uk

THEATRICAL FOOTWEAR COMPANY LTD THE
Trading as GAMBA Theatrical
Unit 14, Chingford Industrial Centre
Hall Lane, Chingford, London E4 8DJ
F 020 8529 7995   T 020 8529 9195
E gambatheatrical1@btconnect.com

THEATRICAL SHOEMAKERS LTD
Footwear
Unit 7A, Thames Road Industrial Estate
Thames Road, Silvertown, London E16 2EZ
F 020 7476 5220   T 020 7474 0500
E ts@shoemaking.co.uk
W www.shoemaking.co.uk

THORNE Sarah Kate
Based in Berkshire
T 07776 196733
E sarah@sarahkatethorne.co.uk
W www.sarahkatethorne.co.uk

TRYFONOS Mary MASKS
Designer & Maker of Masks & Costume Properties
59 Shaftesbury Road, London N19 4QW
M 07764 587433   T 020 7561 9880
E marytryfonos@aol.com

TUTU-TOPIA
Lincoln LN1   M 07999 553021
E sales@tutu-topia.co.uk
W www.tutu-topia.co.uk

VINTAGE SHIRT COMPANY THE
2 Mount Place, Lewes
East Sussex BN7 1YH   T/F 01273 477699
E info@vintageshirt.co.uk
W www.vintageshirt.co.uk

WEST YORKSHIRE FABRICS LTD
*Barathea. Crepe. Linen. Stretch Fabrics. Suiting. Venetian
Cut Lengths*
Unit 5 Milestone Court
Stanningley, Leeds LS28 6HE   T 0113 225 6550
E neil@wyfabrics.com

WIG EXPECTATIONS
3 Northernhay Walk, Morden
Surrey SM4 4BS   T 020 8540 5667
E wigexpectations@aol.com
W www.wigexpectations.com

WIG ROOM THE
22 Coronation Road, Basingstoke
Hants RG21 4HA   T 01256 415737
E darren@wigroom.co.uk

WIG SPECIALITIES LTD
Hand Made Wigs & Facial Hair, Hair Extensions etc
First Floor Mezzanine
67-69 George Street
London W1U 8LT
F 020 7935 2137   T 020 7935 2826
E wigspecialities@btconnect.com
W www.wigspecialities.co.uk

WIGS & MAKE-UP SPECIALIST
7A Cassey Bottom Lane, Bristol
Avon BS5 8BX   M 07887 683555
E rachellisajones@hotmail.co.uk

WILLIAMS Emma
Costume Designer & Stylist. Film, Stage & Television
E emmacoz@dsl.pipex.com   M 07710 130345

DAILY EXPRESS
Contact: Caroline Jowett (Theatre, Films, Dance, Opera), Matt
Baylis (Television)
Northern Shell Building
10 Lower Thames Street
London EC3R 6EN   T 020 8612 7000
E arts.editor@express.co.uk

DAILY MAIL
Contact: Quentin Letts (Theatre), Chris Tookey (Films)
Northcliffe House
2 Derry Street
Kensington, London W8 5TT   T 020 7938 6000

DAILY STAR
Contact: Alan Frank (Films & Video), Nigel Pauley, Amy Watts,
Charli Morgan (Television & Show Business)
Northern Shell Building
10 Lower Thames Street
London EC3R 6EN   T 0871 4341010

DAILY TELEGRAPH
Contact: Charles Spencer, Dominic Cavendish (Theatre),
Sukhdev Sandhu, Tim Robey (Films), Gillian Reynolds (Radio),
Richard Dorment (Art), Sarah Crompton, Mark Monahan
(Dance), Geoffrey Norris, Ivan Hewitt (Music)
111 Buckingham Palace Road
London SW1W 0DT   T 020 7931 2000

FINANCIAL TIMES
Contact: Sarah Hemmings, Ian Shuttleworth (Theatre), Nigel
Andrews, Karl French (Films), Martin Hoyle, John Lloyd
(Television)
1 Southwark Bridge
London SE1 9HL   T 020 7873 3000

GUARDIAN
Contact: Michael Billington (Theatre), Nancy Banks-Smith
(Television)
King's Place
90 York Way
London N1 9GU   T 020 3353 2000

INDEPENDENT
Contact: Gerard Gilbert (Television)
2 Derry Street, London W8 5HF   T 020 7005 2000

LONDON EVENING STANDARD
Contact: Henry Hitchings, Fiona Mountford, Kieron Quirke
(Theatre), Derek Malcolm (Films), Jane Shilling (Television),
Barry Millington (Classical Music & Opera)
Northcliffe House
2 Derry Street
Kensington, London W8 5EE   T 020 3367 7000
W www.thisislondon.co.uk

MAIL ON SUNDAY
Contact: Georgina Brown (Theatre), Jason Solomons,
Matthew Bond (Films), Simon Garfield (Radio)
(Review Section)
Northcliffe House
2 Derry Street, London W8 5TS   T 020 7938 6000

MIRROR
Contact: Dave Edwards (Films), James Simon, Jim Shelley
(Television)
Mirror Group Newspapers Ltd
1 Canada Square
Canary Wharf
London E14 5AP   T 020 7510 3000

MORNING STAR
Contact: Katie Lambert (Theatre & Films)
William Rust House
52 Beachy Road
London E3 2NS   T 020 8510 0815

NEWS OF THE WORLD
Contact: Robbie Collin (Films), Dan Wootton (Show Business)
News International Plc
1 Virginia Street
London E98 1NW   T 020 7782 4000

OBSERVER
Contact: Susannah Clapp (Theatre), Philip French (Films),
Sarah Donaldson (Films & Television), Miranda Sawyer
(Radio), Luke Jennings (Dance), Fiona Maddocks (Opera)
King's Place
90 York Way
London N1 9GU   T 020 3353 2000

PEOPLE
Contact: Conor Nolan (Films), John Wise (Television & Radio),
Caroline Waterson (Features), Katie Hind (Show Business)
1 Canada Square
Canary Wharf
London E14 5AP   T 020 7293 3000

SPORT
Contact: Neil Goodwin (Features & Showbusiness)
Sport Newspapers Ltd
19 Great Ancoats Street
Manchester M60 4BT   T 0161 236 4466

SUN
Contact: Grant Rollings (Films), Ally Ross (Television)
News International Plc
1 Virginia Street
Wapping, London E98 1SN   T 020 7782 4000

SUNDAY EXPRESS
Contact: Mark Shenton (Theatre), Henry Fitzherbert (Films),
David Stephenson (Television), Clare Heal (Radio & Arts)
Northern Shell Building
10 Lower Thames Street
London EC3R 6EN   T 0871 4341010

SUNDAY MIRROR
Contact: Kevin O'Sullivan (Theatre & Television), Mark Adams
(Films), Dean Piper (Show Business)
Mirror Group, 1 Canada Square
Canary Wharf
London E14 5AP   T 020 7510 3000

SUNDAY TELEGRAPH
Contact: Tim Walker (Theatre), Jenny McCartney (Films),
John Preston (Television)
111 Buckingham Palace Road
London SW1W 0DT   T 020 7931 2000

SUNDAY TIMES
Contact: Christopher Hart (Theatre), Cosmo Landesman
(Films), A. A. Gill (Television), Paul Donovan (Radio)
News International Plc, 1 Pennington Street
London E98 1ST   T 020 7782 5000

TIMES
Contact: Libby Purves (Theatre), Kate Muir (Films), James
Jackson (Television), Ed Potton (Music)
News International Plc, 1 Pennington Street
London E98 1TT   T 020 7782 5000

D

Dance Companies & Organisations
Dance Training & Professional Classes
Drama Schools (Conference of)
Drama Training, Schools & Coaches

[CONTACTS 2011]

AKADEMI SOUTH ASIAN DANCE UK
213 Haverstock Hill
Hampstead Town Hall
Haverstock Hill, London NW3 4QP
F 020 7691 3211   T 020 7691 3210
E info@akademi.co.uk
W www.akademi.co.uk

ANJALI DANCE COMPANY
The Mill Arts Centre
Spiceball Park
Banbury, Oxford OX16 5QE   T 01295 251909
E info@anjali.co.uk
W www.anjali.co.uk

BALLETBOYZ
Sadler's Wells
Rosebery Avenue
Islington, London EC1R 4TN
F 020 7278 5684   T 020 7278 5508
E dance@balletboyz.com
W www.balletboyz.com

BALLROOM, LONDON THEATRE OF
Contact: Paul Harris® (Artistic Director)
24 Montana Gardens
Sutton, Surrey SM1 4FP
M 07958 784462   T/F 020 8722 8798
E office@londontheatreofballroom.com
W www.londontheatreofballroom.com

BIRMINGHAM ROYAL BALLET
Thorp Street, Birmingham B5 4AU
F 0121 245 3570   T 0121 245 3500
E administrator@brb.org.uk
W www.brb.org.uk

BOLLYWOOD GROOVES DANCE COMPANY
Contact: Minila Shah
6 Vesta Court, London SE1 3BP   M 07875 023744
E info@bollywoodgrooves.com
W www.bollywoodgrooves.com

CANDOCO DANCE COMPANY
2T Leroy House
436 Essex Road, London N1 3QP
F 020 7704 1645   T 020 7704 6845
E info@candoco.co.uk
W www.candoco.co.uk

CHOLMONDELEYS & FEATHERSTONEHAUGHS THE
LF1.1 Lafone House
The Leathermarket
11-13 Leathermarket Street
London SE1 3HN
F 020 7378 8810   T 020 7378 8800
E admin@thecholmondeleys.org
W www.thecholmondeleys.org

COMPANY OF CRANKS
1st Floor, 62 Northfield House
London SE15 6TN   M 07963 617981
E mimetic16@yahoo.com
W www.mimeworks.com

DANCE SOUTH WEST
PO Box 5457
Bournemouth, Dorset BH1 1WU   T 01202 554131
E info@dancesouthwest.org.uk
W www.dancesouthwest.org.uk

DAVIES Siobhan DANCE
85 St George's Road, London SE1 6ER
F 020 7091 9669   T 020 7091 9650
E info@siobhandavies.com
W www.siobhandavies.com

DV8 PHYSICAL THEATRE
Arts Admin, Toynbee Studios
28 Commercial Street, London E1 6AB
F 020 7247 5103   T 020 7655 0977
E dv8@artsadmin.co.uk
W www.dv8.co.uk

ENGLISH NATIONAL BALLET LTD
Markova House, 39 Jay Mews
London SW7 2ES
F 020 7225 0827   T 020 7581 1245
E comments@ballet.org.uk
W www.ballet.org.uk

ENGLISH YOUTH BALLET
Appledowne, The Hillside
Orpington, Kent BR6 7SD
M 07732 383600   T 01689 856747
E misslewis@englishyouthballet.co.uk
W www.englishyouthballet.co.uk

FRANCOIS' Ryan SWING X-TREME
Orchard View, Love Lane
Iver, Bucks SL0 9QT   M 07590 695361
E ryan@swingextreme.co.uk
W www.swingextreme.co.uk

GREEN CANDLE DANCE COMPANY
Oxford House, Derbyshire Street
Bethnal Green, London E2 6HG
F 020 7739 7731   T 020 7739 7722
E info@greencandledance.com
W www.greencandledance.com

IJAD DANCE COMPANY
22 Allison Road, London N8 0AT   M 07930 378639
E info@ijad.freeserve.co.uk
W www.ijad.freeserve.co.uk

INDEPENDENT BALLET WALES
30 Glasllwch Crescent
Newport
South Wales NP20 3SE
F 01633 221690   T 01633 253985
E dariusjames@welshballet.co.uk
W www.welshballet.co.uk

JEYASINGH Shobana DANCE COMPANY
Moving Arts Base
134 Liverpool Road
Islington, London N1 1LA   T 020 7697 4444
E admin@shobanajeyasingh.co.uk
W www.shobanajeyasingh.co.uk

KHAN Akram COMPANY
Unit 232A, 35A Britannia Row, London N1 8QH
F 020 7354 5554   T 020 7354 4333
E office@akramkhancompany.net
W www.akramkhancompany.net

KOSH THE
Physical Theatre
59 Stapleton Hall Road
London N4 3QF   T/F 020 8374 0407
E info@thekosh.com

LUDUS DANCE
Assembly Rooms
King Street, Lancaster LA1 1RE
F 01524 847744   T 01524 35936
E info@ludusdance.org
W www.ludusdance.org

NEIGHBOURHOOD PRODUCTIONS
9 Weavers Terrace
Fulham
London SW6 1QE   M 07958 377595
E info@creativekidzandco.co.uk

NEW ADVENTURES
Sadler's Wells
Rosebery Avenue
London EC1R 4TN   T 020 7713 6766
E info@new-adventures.net
W www.new-adventures.net

NORTHERN BALLET
Quarry Hill, Leeds L52 7PA
F 0113 220 8001   T 0113 220 8000
E info@northernballet.com

PHOENIX DANCE THEATRE
3 St Peter's Buildings
St Peter's Square, Leeds LS9 8AH
F 0113 244 4736   T 0113 242 3486
E info@phoenixdancetheatre.co.uk
W www.phoenixdancetheatre.co.uk

PLACE THE
Robin Howard Dance Theatre
17 Duke's Road, London WC1H 9PY
F 020 7121 1142   T 020 7121 1000
E info@theplace.org.uk
W www.theplace.org.uk

PMB PRESENTATIONS LTD
Vicarage House
58-60 Kensington Church Street
London W8 4DB
F 020 7368 3338   T 020 7368 3337
E p@triciamurraybett.com
W www.pmbpresentations.co.uk

RAMBERT DANCE COMPANY
94 Chiswick High Road, London W4 1SH
F 020 8747 8323   T 020 8630 0600
E rdc@rambert.org.uk
W www.rambert.org.uk

info**page**

How do I become a professional dancer?

Full-time vocational training can start from as young as ten years old. A good starting point for researching the different schools and courses available is CDET (Council for Dance Education & Training) www.cdet.org.uk. There are over nineteen dance colleges offering professional training accredited by CDET, and nearly three hundred university courses which include some form of dance training. It is estimated that over one thousand dancers graduate from vocational training schools or university courses every year, so it is a highly competitive career. Therefore anyone wanting to be a professional dancer must obtain as many years of training and experience as possible, plus go to see plenty of performances spanning different types and genres of dance. If you require further information on vocational dance schools, applying to accredited dance courses, auditions and funding, contact CDET's information line 'Answers for Dancers' on 020-7240 5703 or see their article on the following pages.

What are dance companies?

There are more than two hundred dance companies in the UK, spanning a variety of dance styles including ballet, contemporary, hip hop and African. A dance company will either be resident in a venue, be a touring company, or a combination of both. Many have websites which you can visit for full information. Most dance companies employ ensemble dancers on short to medium contracts, who may then work on a number of different productions for the same company over a number of months. In addition, the company will also employ principal/leading dancers on a role-by-role basis.

What are dance organisations?

There are numerous organisations which exist to support professional dancers, covering important areas including health and safety, career development, networking and legal and financial aspects. Other organisations (e.g. Regional/National Dance Agencies) exist to promote dance within the wider community.

I have already trained to be a dancer. Why do I need further training?

Dance training should not cease as soon as you get your first job or complete a course. Throughout your career you should continuously strive to maintain your fitness levels, enhance and develop your existing skills and keep learning new ones in order to retain a competitive edge. You must also be prepared to continuously learn new dance styles and routines for specific roles. Ongoing training and classes can help you stay fit and active, and if you go through a period of unemployment you can keep your mind and body occupied, ready to take on your next job.

How should I use these listings?

The following pages will supply you with up-to-date contact details for a wide range of dance companies and organisations, followed by listings for dance training and professional classes. Always research schools and classes thoroughly, obtaining copies of prospectuses where available. Most vocational schools offer two and three year full-time training programmes, many also offer excellent degree programmes. Foundation Courses offer a sound introduction to the profession, but they can never replace a full-time vocational course. Many schools, organisations and studios also offer part-time/evening classes which offer a general understanding of dance and complementary technique or the opportunity to refresh specific dance skills; they will not, however, enable a student to become a professional dancer.

How else can I find work as a dancer?

Dance also plays a role in commercial theatre, musicals, opera, film, television, live music and video, corporate events and many other industries. Dancers may also want to be represented by an agent. Agents have many more contacts within the industry than an individual dancer can have, and can offer advice and negotiate contracts on your behalf as well as submit you for jobs. A number of specialist dance agencies are listed in the 'Agents - Dance' section towards the front of this book.

infopage

What is Spotlight Dancers?

Dancers wishing to promote themselves to these types of job opportunities should consider joining Spotlight's specialist casting directory for dancers. This is a central directory of dancers published annually which is used by dance employers throughout the UK to locate dancers and send out casting or audition information. Members receive a page in the directory containing a headshot and body shot, agency contact details and selected credits as well as an online CV. Dancers who attend CDET accredited schools receive a discount when applying in their graduating year. Please see www.spotlight.com/artists/dancers for more information.

What other careers are available in dance?

Opportunities also exist to work as a teacher, choreographer, technician or manager. Dance UK www.danceuk.org is a valuable source of information for anyone considering this type of work.

What should I do to avoid injury?

An injury is more likely to occur if you are inflexible and unprepared for sudden physical exertion. The last thing you want to do is to pick up an injury, however minor, and be prevented from working, so continuous training during both employment and unemployment will help you to minimise the risk of an injury during a performance or rehearsal. If you do sustain an injury you will want to make sure it does not get any worse by getting treatment with a specialist. The British Association for Performing Arts Medicine (BAPAM) provides specialist health support for performers, free health assessment clinics and a directory of performing arts health practitioners and specialists. Visit their website www.bapam.org.uk for more information. You may also find the advice preceding the 'Health & Wellbeing' section of Contacts useful.

I'm not a professional dancer but I enjoy dancing. Why should I use these listings?

People don't just dance to perform, teach or advise within the industry. Dance can be pursued for fun, recreation, social reasons and for health. Training and professional advice should still be pursued to ensure that you do not injure yourself while dancing and prevent yourself from working. You can also use the 'Dance Training & Professional Classes' listings to find suitable dance lessons in your area, which you could attend to make friends, keep fit and stay occupied.

Where can I find more information?

For further advice about the dance industry, you could try contacting CDET (www.cdet.org.uk) for training information, Dance UK (www.danceuk.org) regarding the importance and needs of dance and dancers, or BAPAM (www.bapam.org.uk) for health issues. You may want to get involved with Move It - the UK's biggest dance exhibition which takes place every year in March. Visit www.moveitdance.co.uk for more information. If you are looking for a dance agent to promote you to job opportunities, please see the 'Agents - Dance' section of Contacts.

infopage

The Council for Dance Education and Training (CDET) is the accrediting body of the dance and musical theatre industry. It is the first point of contact for students wishing to work professionally in dance and musical theatre, students wanting to take dance or dance teaching qualifications and those who want to dance simply because it's there.

CDET runs a free information service – *Answers for Dancers (AfD)* – on all aspects of dance and musical theatre education and publishes the annual *UK Handbook of Accredited Courses in Dance and Musical Theatre*. The *Handbook*, sponsored by Spotlight, is the country's most comprehensive dance and musical theatre guide and is available free of charge from **www.samuelfrench-london.co.uk.** *Answers for Dancers* information sheets can be found on the CDET website and personal advice is also available by telephone. AfD addresses thousands of enquiries a year from students, parents, dancers and musical theatre artists. Here are some *Answers for Dancers*...

How do I become a professional dancer, dance teacher or musical theatre artist?
Whether you want to dance for leisure or professionally it is vitally important you get teaching of the highest quality in studios properly equipped to ensure you are safe and secure. Injury is an occupational hazard of the dancer and it is essential you are taught by professionals who understand the effect of hard, physical work on the body, that you dance on floors designed to minimise the risk of stress and strain and that you work in a space big enough to let you move freely and safely. Whether you dance professionally or as a serious hobby, injury means you have to stop until you have recovered. For professionals it might mean losing the next job.

Where can I find professional teachers who work to standards approved by the industry?
At a CDET accredited vocational dance or musical theatre school or college and at a CDET accredited Dance Awarding Organisation.

What makes CDET accredited education and training so special?
Every CDET accredited institution has been inspected by trained panels of dance and musical theatre professionals to ensure it meets the needs of both the industry and the student. Council inspection reports are used by the government, Ofsted, charitable foundations and trusts when making funding decisions. If a school or college fails to maintain its standards, it can lose its accreditation.

What is a CDET accredited vocational dance or musical theatre school?
A CDET accredited vocational school is a school or college offering performance or teaching courses for students over the age of 16 (Further Education) or 18 (Higher Education).

What is a CDET accredited Dance Awarding Organisation?
A CDET accredited Dance Awarding Organisation (and Dance Teaching Society) offers qualifications by means of examinations and other forms of assessment.

What are the CDET *Recognised Awards*?
The Council's Recognised Awards are three industry recognised awards available to dance and musical theatre schools, teachers and instructors meeting the standards of professional practice of CDET. The Awards are provided by CDET in association with Dancing Times and The Stage. More information about the Awards can be found on the CDET website www.cdet.org.uk.

Students applying to a vocational dance or musical theatre school, taking the qualifications of a Dance Awarding Organisation or attending a pre- or non-vocational dance or musical theatre school are **strongly advised to ensure it holds CDET approval.**

Competition for places at CDET accredited dance and musical theatre schools and colleges is fierce and you may be considering an offer from a vocational school not accredited by the Council. If so, make sure you are confident you will receive the quality of training you expect, that studio facilities and medical resources are suitable for the teaching of dance or musical theatre and that you request a written explanation as to why the school does not hold CDET accreditation.

Whatever your query regarding dance or musical theatre education and training visit the Council website at www.cdet.org.uk or telephone the Council on 020 7240 5703.

Joce Giles is Head of Learning & Participation at Rambert Dance Company. Rambert is the UK's national company for contemporary dance. The Company performs a diverse repertoire by many leading choreographers from both Britain and abroad, and in 2010 was awarded the Olivier Award for Outstanding Achievement in Dance. The following advice is tailored towards applications for Rambert, but much of it will also be relevant when approaching other dance companies.

Rambert employs 22 dancers - some of the finest and most versatile in the world - on full-time contracts. They are required to be strong in both classical and contemporary technique, and able to meet the challenge of performing a range of styles with precision and flair.

Rambert recruits its dancers either by invitation to join a Company class, where dancers may be asked to perform a short solo or a section of repertoire prepared in advance, or through a formal audition process. Aspiring dancers will need to send in a CV along with a covering letter and photographs. You must research the Company and invest time to make your application relevant to the skills and experience required of a Rambert dancer.

As Rambert dancers have to be extremely versatile, it is not always the case that every new dancer has the complete range of required experience when they join. For this reason the information included in the covering letter is extremely important and can be used to address any gaps in your CV. It also gives you a chance to highlight any relevant information or experience that might not stand out in your CV. For example, a dancer in a classical company should mention why they are looking to make the transition to a contemporary dance company. It would also be beneficial to give examples of any relevant contemporary experience either in training or performance. Male dancers should also give details of their experience in partnering work.

Rambert's dancers train in both classical and contemporary techniques; however not all dancers auditioning have extensive experience in both. A strong technique in one of these disciplines is a good starting point if the artistic team can see potential, and through the specialised training that is a core part of the dancers' working week, the contemporary or classical technique can be developed.

Rambert currently runs an apprentice dancers' scheme for recent graduates or young professional dancers with less experience of working in a full-time company. If you are applying to this scheme it is always beneficial to give detailed information about your training, including names of teachers and in which techniques you have trained.

It is important to be organised and plan ahead as the opportunity to join a Company class or take part in an audition is always by invitation only. If you are living abroad or outside of London and request to join class the following week, it will probably not be possible. It is also a good idea to check Rambert's website as the Company could be on tour on your preferred date.

Photographs are another important tool which can influence the outcome of the initial application process. Rambert's artistic team - the Artistic Director and Rehearsal Directors - look at all applications and need to be able to clearly see the dancer's line in at least one of the photographs (ideally this should not be a purely classical ballet position). Two relevant photos are sufficient and better than five less appropriate ones such as headshots or dancing in traditional classical ballet productions.

It can be useful to send in film footage on a DVD, especially for more experienced dancers, but this should be a good quality film where line and movement are easily visible and should be no longer than a maximum of five minutes.

At an audition, remember that the way you present yourself is important. You should wear suitable clothing that allows whoever is watching you to see how your body moves, so no baggy or untidy dance wear. It is not solely your dancing ability that is being looked at but also how you interact with others, so while it is always good to be confident it is also important to be courteous and polite.

Although Rambert might not be looking for new dancers at a particular time, the artistic team may still be interested to see who is available. If they are interested in you and feel you have potential they will look to build a relationship with you and give feedback - for instance, if you need to strengthen certain areas of technique or gain more performance experience. When a contract does become available, you will then be in a strong position provided you have acted on the feedback received.

Please visit www.rambert.org.uk for further information.

ROTIE Marie-Gabrielle PRODUCTIONS
7 Trinity Rise
London SW2 2QP
E rotiemanager@aol.com
W www.rotieproductions.com
M 07840 936268

ROYAL BALLET THE
Royal Opera House
Covent Garden, London WC2E 9DD
F 020 7212 9121
E balletcompany@roh.org.uk
T 020 7240 1200 Ext 712

RUSS Claire ENSEMBLE
Choreography. Commercial. Contemporary. Corporate
4 Heatham Park
Twickenham TW2 7SF
E info@clairerussensemble.com
W www.clairerussensemble.com
M 07932 680224

SCOTTISH BALLET
Tramway, 25 Albert Drive
Glasgow G41 2PE
W www.scottishballet.co.uk
T 0141 331 2931

SCOTTISH DANCE THEATRE
Dundee Repertory Theatre
Tay Square
Dundee DD1 1PB
F 01382 228609
E achinn@dundeereptheatre.co.uk
W www.scottishdancetheatre.com
T 01382 342600

SKY BLUE PINK
M 07779 866439
E info@skybluepinkproductions.com
W www.skybluepinkproductions.com
T 020 8715 5007

SLOVAK DANCE THEATRE
Holicska 50
811 05 Bratislava, Slovakia
E sdt@sdt.sk
W www.sdt.sk
T 00 42 12 54 64 58 11

SPLITZ THEATRE ARTZ
5 Cow Lane, Fulbourn
Cambridge CB21 5HB
E splitz-ta@btopenworld.com
W www.splitz-ta.co.uk
T 01223 880389

SPRINGS DANCE COMPANY
99 Tressillian Road
London SE4 1XZ
M 07775 628442
E info@springsdancecompany.org.uk
W www.springsdancecompany.org.uk
T 01634 817523

TRANSITIONS DANCE COMPANY
Creekside, London SE8 3DZ
E transitions@laban.org
T 020 8469 9471

TWITCH EVENT CHOREOGRAPHY
5 Breakspears Mews, Brockley
London SE4 1PY
M 07932 656358
E info@twitch.uk.com
W www.twitch.uk.com
M 07747 770816

UNION DANCE
Top Floor, 6 Charing Cross Road
London WC2H 0HG
F 020 7836 7847
E info@uniondance.co.uk
W www.uniondance.co.uk
T 020 7836 7837

ACCELERATE PRODUCTIONS LTD
374 Ley Street, Ilford IG1 4AE M 07782 199181
E info@accelerate-productions.co.uk
W www.accelerate-productions.co.uk

AKADEMI SOUTH ASIAN DANCE UK
Hampstead Town Hall
213 Haverstock Hill, London NW3 4QP
F 020 7691 3211 T 020 7691 3210
E info@akademi.co.uk
W www.akademi.co.uk

ALLIED DANCING ASSOCIATION
137 Greenhill Road, Mossley Hill
Liverpool L18 7HQ T 0151 724 1829

ASSOCIATION OF DANCE OF THE AFRICAN DIASPORA
Urdang, The Old Finsbury Town Hall
Rosebery Avenue, London EC1R 4QT
F 020 7833 2363 T 020 7841 7357
E info@adad.org.uk
W www.adad.org.uk

BENESH INSTITUTE THE
36 Battersea Square
London SW11 3RA
T 020 7326 8031 T 020 7326 8035
E beneshinstitute@rad.org.uk
W www.benesh.org

BLUE EYED SOUL DANCE COMPANY
The Lantern, Meadow Farm Drive
Shrewsbury SY1 4NG T 01743 210830
E admin@blueeyedsouldance.com
W www.blueeyedsouldance.com

BRITISH ARTS THE
12 Deveron Way
Rise Park
Romford RM1 4UL T 01708 756263
W www.britisharts.org

BRITISH ASSOCIATION OF TEACHERS OF DANCING
Pavilion, 8 Upper Level
Watermark Business Park
315 Govan Road
Glasgow G51 2SE T 0141 427 3699
E enquiries@batd.co.uk
W www.batd.co.uk

BRITISH BALLET ORGANISATION
Dance Examining Society. Teacher Training
Woolborough House
39 Lonsdale Road
Barnes, London SW13 9JP T 020 8748 1241
E info@bbo.org.uk
W www.bbo.org.uk

BRITISH THEATRE DANCE ASSOCIATION
Garden Street, Leicester LE1 3UA
F 0845 1662189 T 0845 1662179
E info@btda.org.uk
W www.btda.org.uk

CHISENHALE DANCE SPACE
64-84 Chisenhale Road
Bow, London E3 5QZ
F 020 8980 9323 T 020 8981 6617
E mail@chisenhaledancespace.co.uk
W www.chisenhaledancespace.co.uk

COUNCIL FOR DANCE EDUCATION & TRAINING

The Council for Dance Education and Training (CDET)

- accredits professional training programmes in vocational dance and musical theatre schools
- validates the qualifications of Dance Awarding Organisations
- awards three marks of recognition, *Recognised Schools, Recognised Qualified Teachers* and *Registered Instructors* to dance and musical theatre schools and teachers working with students under the age of sixteen.

CDET also

- offers a comprehensive and free information service, *Answers for Dancers* to students, parents, teachers, dance artists and employers on all aspects of dance education and training
- holds the CDET searchable database containing the details of all *Recognised schools, teachers* and *instructors*

For more information on CDET please contact:

Council for Dance Education and Training
Old Brewer's Yard, 17-19 Neal Street, Covent Garden, London, WC2H 9UY
Tel 020 7240 5703, **Email** info@cdet.org.uk, **Website** www.cdet.org.uk

COUNCIL FOR DANCE EDUCATION & TRAINING
Old Brewer's Yard, 17-19 Neal Street
Covent Garden, London WC2H 9UY
F 020 7240 2547   T 020 7240 5703
E info@cdet.org.uk
W www.cdet.org.uk

DANCE4
3-9 Hockley, Nottingham NG1 1FH
F 0115 941 0776   T 0115 941 0773
E info@dance4.co.uk
W www.dance4.co.uk

DANCE BASE NATIONAL CENTRE FOR DANCE
14-16 Grassmarket
Edinburgh EH1 2JU
F 0131 225 5234   T 0131 225 5525
E dance@dancebase.co.uk
W www.dancebase.co.uk

DANCE CITY
National Dance Agency
Temple Street
Newcastle-upon-Tyne NE1 4BR   T 0191 261 0505
E info@dancecity.co.uk
W www.dancecity.co.uk

DANCE DIGITAL
2 Bond Street, Chelmsford
Essex CM1 1GH   T 01245 346036
E admin@dancedigital.org.uk
W www.dancedigital.org.uk

DANCE EAST
Jerwood Dance House
Foundry Lane, Ipswich IP4 3DJ   T 01473 295230
E info@danceeast.co.uk
W www.danceeast.co.uk

DANCE HOUSE
20 St Andrew's Street, Glasgow G1 5PD   T 0141 552 2442
E info@dancehouse.org
W www.dancehouse.org

DANCE IN DEVON
County Dance Development Agency
Exeter Phoenix, Bradnich Place
Gandy Street, Exeter EX4 3LS   T 01392 667050
E info@danceindevon.org.uk
W www.danceindevon.org.uk

DANCE INITIATIVE GREATER MANCHESTER
Zion Arts Centre, Stretford Road
Hulme, Manchester M15 5ZA
F 0161 232 7483   T 0161 232 7179
E info@digm.org.uk
W www.digm.org

DANCE SOUTH WEST
PO Box 5457, Bournemouth
Dorset BH1 1WU   T 01202 554131
E info@dancesouthwest.org.uk
W www.dancesouthwest.org.uk

DANCE UK
Including the Healthier Dancer Programme
The Old Finsbury Town Hall
Rosebery Avenue, London EC1R 4QT
F 020 7833 2363   T 020 7713 0730
E info@danceuk.org
W www.danceuk.org

DANCE UMBRELLA
1 Brewery Square, London SE1 2LF
F 020 8741 7902   T 020 8741 4040
E mail@danceumbrella.co.uk
W www.danceumbrella.co.uk

DANCERS' CAREER DEVELOPMENT
Plouviez House, 19-20 Hatton Place
London EC1N 8RU
F 020 7242 1462   T 020 7831 1449
E admin@thedcd.org.uk
W www.thedcd.org.uk

DANCEXCHANGE
National Dance Agency
Birmingham Hippodrome, Thorp Street
Birmingham B5 4TB   T 0121 689 3170
E info@dancexchange.org.uk
W www.dancexchange.org.uk

DANCING IN THE UK
82 Recreation Way, Kemsley
Sittingbourne, Kent ME10 2TG   T 01795 556003
E andy@dancingintheuk.co.uk
W www.dancingintheuk.co.uk

DAVIES Siobhan DANCE
Professional Development for Dance Artists & Education
85 St George's Road, London SE1 6ER
F 020 7091 9669   T 020 7091 9650
E info@siobhandavies.com
W www.siobhandavies.com

EAST LONDON DANCE
Stratford Circus
Theatre Square, London E15 1BX
F 020 8279 1054   T 020 8279 1050
E office@eastlondondance.org
W www.eastlondondance.org

FOUNDATION FOR COMMUNITY DANCE
LCB Depot, 31 Rutland Street, Leicester LE1 1RE
F 0116 261 6801   T 0116 253 3453
E info@communitydance.org.uk
W www.communitydance.org.uk

GREENWICH DANCE
The Borough Hall, Royal Hill
London SE10 8RE   T 020 8293 9741
E info@greenwichdance.org.uk
W www.greenwichdance.org.uk

IDTA (INTERNATIONAL DANCE TEACHERS' ASSOCIATION)
International House, 76 Bennett Road
Brighton, East Sussex BN2 5JL
F 01273 674388   T 01273 685652
E info@idta.co.uk
W www.idta.co.uk

LANGUAGE OF DANCE CENTRE
Oxford House, Derbyshire Street
London E2 6HG   T 020 7749 1131
E info@lodc.org
W www.lodc.org

LONDON CONTEMPORARY DANCE SCHOOL
16 Flaxman Terrace, London WC1H 9AT
F 020 7121 1145   T 020 7121 1111
E lcds@theplace.org.uk
W www.lcds.ac.uk

LUDUS DANCE
The Assembly Rooms, King Street, Lancaster LA1 1RE
F 01524 847744   T 01524 35936
E info@ludusdance.org
W www.ludusdance.org

MERSEYSIDE DANCE INITIATIVE
National Dance Agency
24 Hope Street, Liverpool L1 9BX   T 0151 708 8810
E info@mdi.org.uk
W www.mdi.org.uk

MIDLAND INTERNATIONAL DANCE ARTS ASSOCIATION
29A Sycamore Road
Birmingham B23 5QP
F 0121 694 0013   T 0121 694 0012
E midaa.hq@hotmail.com
W www.midaa.co.uk

NATIONAL RESOURCE CENTRE FOR DANCE
University of Surrey, Guildford GU2 7XH
F 01483 689500   T 01483 689316
E nrcd@surrey.ac.uk
W www.surrey.ac.uk/nrcd

PLACE THE
National Dance Agency
Robin Howard Dance Theatre
17 Duke's Road, London WC1H 9BY
F 020 7121 1142   T 020 7121 1000
E info@theplace.org.uk
W www.theplace.org.uk

PROFESSIONAL TEACHERS OF DANCING
Contact: Mellissa Harrop
Quay West Business Centre, Quay Lane
Gosport, Hants PO12 4LJ   T 023 9260 4285
E ptdenquiries@msn.com
W www.ptdance.com

SOUTH EAST DANCE
National Dance Agency
28 Kensington Street, Brighton BN1 4AJ
F 01273 697212   T 01273 696844
E info@southeastdance.org.uk
W www.southeastdance.org.uk

SWINDON DANCE
National Dance Agency
Town Hall Studios, Regent Circus
Swindon SN1 1QF   T 01793 601700
E info@swindondance.org.uk
W www.swindondance.org.uk

TWITCH EVENT CHOREOGRAPHY
5 Breakspears Mews, Brockley, London SE4 1PY
M 07932 656358   M 07747 770816
E info@twitch.uk.com
W www.twitch.uk.com

WELSH INDEPENDENT DANCE
Chapter, Market Road
Canton, Cardiff CF5 1QE   T 029 2038 7314
E info@welshindance.co.uk
W www.welshindance.co.uk

YORKSHIRE DANCE
National Dance Agency
3 St Peters Buildings, St Peters Square, Leeds LS9 8AH
F 0113 259 5700   T 0113 243 9867
E admin@yorkshiredance.com
W www.yorkshiredance.com

ACADEMY FOR THEATRE ARTS THE
1 Vale View, Porthill
Newcastle under Lyme
Staffordshire ST5 0AF
F 01782 610363   T 01782 631895
E no1theacademy@aol.com

AIRCRAFT CIRCUS LTD
Unit 7A, Mellish House
Harrington Way, London SE18 5NR   T 020 8317 8401
E moira@aircraftcircus.com
W www.aircraftcircus.com

ARTS EDUCATIONAL SCHOOLS, LONDON
Cone Ripman House, 14 Bath Road
Chiswick, London W4 1LY   T 020 8987 6666
E receptionist@artsed.co.uk
W www.artsed.co.uk

AVIV DANCE STUDIOS
Watford Boys Grammar School
Rickmansworth Road
Watford WD18 7JF   T/F 01923 250000
E info@avivdance.com
W www.avivdance.com

BALLROOM, LONDON THEATRE OF
Artistic Director: Paul Harris® (Mentor "Faking It")
24 Montana Gardens, Sutton
Surrey SM1 4FP
M 07958 784462   T 020 8722 8798
E office@londontheatreofballroom.com
W www.londontheatreofballroom.com

BHAVAN CENTRE
4A Castletown Road, London W14 9HE   T 020 7381 3086
E info@bhavan.net
W www.bhavan.net

BIRD COLLEGE DANCE MUSIC & THEATRE PERFORMANCE
Dance & Theatre Performance HE & FE Programmes
The Centre, 27 Station Road
Sidcup, Kent DA15 7EB
F 020 8308 1370   T 020 8300 6004
E admin@birdcollege.co.uk
W www.birdcollege.co.uk

BODENS STUDIOS
Performing Arts Classes
Bodens Studios & Agency
99 East Barnet Road
New Barnet, Herts EN4 8RF
M 07545 696888   T 020 8447 0909
E info@bodenstudios.com
W www.bodenstudios.com

BRIGHTON DANCE DIVERSION
93 Sea Lane, Rustington
West Sussex BN16 2RS   T 01903 770304
E info@brightondancediversion.com
W www.brightondancediversion.com

CAMBRIDGE PERFORMING ARTS AT BODYWORK
Bodywork Company Dance Studios
25-29 Glisson Road
Cambridge CB1 2HA   T 01223 314461
E admin@bodyworkds.co.uk
W www.bodywork-dance.co.uk

CANDOCO DANCE COMPANY
2T Leroy House, 436 Essex Road
London N1 3QP   T 020 7704 6845
E info@candoco.co.uk
W www.candoco.co.uk

CENTRAL SCHOOL OF BALLET
Full Time Vocational Training
Open Classes Beginner/Professional Level
10 Herbal Hill, Clerkenwell Road
London EC1R 5EG
F 020 7833 5571   T 020 7837 6332
E info@csbschool.co.uk
W www.centralschoolofballet.co.uk

CENTRE - PERFORMING ARTS COLLEGE THE
Building 62, Level 4
37 Bowater Road, Charlton
London SE18 5TF
F 020 8855 6662   T 020 8855 6661
E dance@thecentrepac.com
W www.thecentrepac.com

COLLECTIVE DANCE & DRAMA
The Studio, Rectory Lane
Rickmansworth
Herts WD3 1FD   T/F 020 8428 0037
E info@collectivedance.co.uk
W www.collectivedance.co.uk

CONTI Italia ACADEMY OF THEATRE ARTS
Full-time 3 year & 1 year Musical Theatre Courses
Dance Teacher Training with Performing Arts Course
Italia Conti House, 23 Goswell Road
London EC1M 7AJ
F 020 7253 1430   T 020 7608 0044
E admin@italiaconti.co.uk
W www.italiaconti.com

COUNCIL FOR DANCE EDUCATION & TRAINING (CDET) THE
Old Brewer's Yard, 17-19 Neal Street
Covent Garden, London WC2H 9UY
F 020 7240 2547   T 020 7240 5703
E info@cdet.org.uk
W www.cdet.org.uk

CPA COLLEGE
The Studios, 219B North Street
Romford RM1 4QA
F 01708 766077   T 01708 766007
E agency@cpastudios.co.uk
W www.cpastudios.co.uk

D & B SCHOOL OF PERFORMING ARTS
Central Studios
470 Bromley Road
Bromley, Kent BR1 4PN
F 020 8697 8100   T 020 8698 8880
E bonnie@dandbmanagement.com
W www.dandbperformingarts.co.uk

DANCE BASE NATIONAL CENTRE FOR DANCE
14-16 Grassmarket
Edinburgh EH1 2JU
F 0131 225 5234   T 0131 225 5525
E dance@dancebase.co.uk
W www.dancebase.co.uk

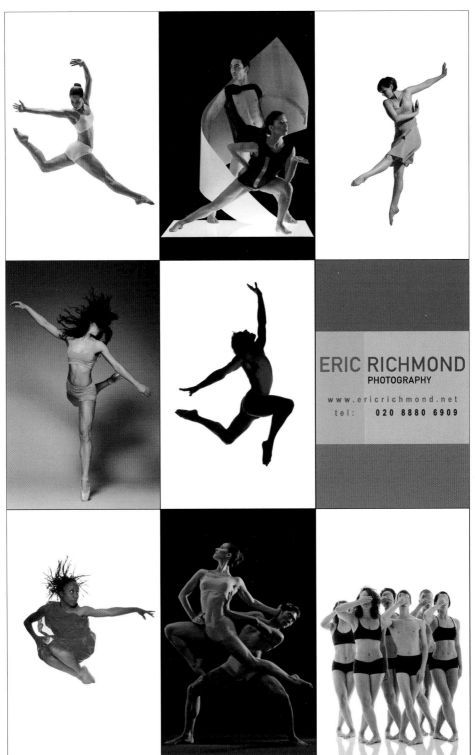

ERIC RICHMOND
PHOTOGRAPHY

www.ericrichmond.net
tel: 020 8880 6909

DANCE HOUSE
20 St Andrew's Street
Glasgow G1 5PD   T 0141 552 2442
E info@dancehouse.org
W www.dancehouse.org

DANCE RESEARCH COMMITTEE - IMPERIAL SOCIETY OF TEACHERS OF DANCING
Training in Historical Dance
c/o Ludwell House, Charing
Kent TN27 0LS
F 01233 712768   T 01233 712469
E n.gainesarmitage@tiscali.co.uk
W www.istd.org

DANCEWORKS
Also Fitness, Yoga & Martial Arts Classes
16 Balderton Street, London W1K 6TN   T 020 7629 6183
E info@danceworks.net
W www.danceworks.net

DAVIES Siobhan STUDIOS
Daily Professional Classes. Open Dance & Body Conditioning Classes for Wider Community
85 St George's Road, London SE1 6ER
F 020 7091 9669   T 020 7091 9650
E info@siobhandavies.com
W www.siobhandavies.com

DIRECTIONS THEATRE ARTS CHESTERFIELD LTD
1A-2A Sheffield Road, Chesterfield
Derbyshire S41 7LL   T/F 01246 854455
E julie.cox5@btconnect.com
W www.directionstheatrearts.org

D M ACADEMY
The Studios, Briggate
Shipley, Bradford, West Yorks BD17 7BT
F 01274 592502   T 01274 585317
E info@dmacademy.co.uk
W www.dmacademy.co.uk

DUFFILL Drusilla THEATRE SCHOOL
Grove Lodge, Oakwood Road
Burgess Hill
West Sussex RH15 0HZ
F 01444 232680   T 01444 232672
E drusilladschool@btclick.com
W www.drusilladuffilltheatreschool.co.uk

EAST LONDON DANCE
Stratford Circus, Theatre Square
London E15 1BX
F 020 8279 1054   T 020 8279 1050
E office@eastlondondance.org
W www.eastlondondance.org

EDINBURGH'S TELFORD COLLEGE
350 West Granton Road
Edinburgh EH5 1QE
F 0131 559 4111   T 0131 559 4000
E mail@ed-coll.ac.uk
W www.ed-coll.ac.uk

ELIE Mark DANCE FOUNDATION
Portobello Dance School
The Tabernacle, Powis Square
London W11 2AY   M 07947 484021
E markeliedancefoundation@uk2.net
W www.portobellodance.org.uk

ELMHURST SCHOOL FOR DANCE
249 Bristol Road, Edgbaston
Birmingham B5 7UH
F 0121 472 6654   T 0121 472 6655
E enquiries@elmhurstdance.co.uk
W www.elmhurstdance.co.uk

ENGLISH NATIONAL BALLET SCHOOL
Carlyle Building
Hortensia Road
London SW10 0QS
F 020 7376 3404   T 020 7376 7076
E info@enbschool.org.uk
W www.enbschool.org.uk

EXCEL SCHOOL OF PERFORMING ARTS
KT Summit House, 100 Hanger Lane
Ealing, London W5 1EZ   T 020 8799 6168
E excel@kt.org
W www.ktioe-excel.org

EXPRESSIONS ACADEMY OF PERFORMING ARTS
3 Newgate Lane, Mansfield
Nottingham NG18 2LB
F 01623 647337   T 01623 424334
E expressions-uk@btconnect.com
W www.expressionsperformingarts.co.uk

FANTASY FEET DANCE & MUSICAL THEATRE ACADEMY
16 Llwyn Yr Eos Grove, Penyard
Merthyr Tydfil
Mid Glamorgan, Wales CF47 0GD
M 07894 164104   M 07947 345434
E fantasyfeetdanceacademy@yahoo.co.uk
W www.fantasyfeetdance.co.uk

GEORGIE SCHOOL OF THEATRE ARTS
101 Lane Head Road
Shepley
Huddersfield
West Yorkshire HD8 8DB   T/F 01484 606994
E donna.george@virgin.net

GREASEPAINT ANONYMOUS
4 Gallus Close, Winchmore Hill
London N21 1JR
F 020 8882 9189   T 020 8886 2263
E info@greasepaintanonymous.co.uk

HAMMOND SCHOOL THE
Hoole Bank, Mannings Lane
Chester CH2 4ES
F 01244 305351   T 01244 305350
E info@thehammondschool.co.uk
W www.thehammondschool.co.uk

HARRIS Paul
Contact: Paul Harris®. Choreography. Movement for Actors Tuition in Period & Contemporary Social Dance
24 Montana Gardens, Sutton
Surrey SM1 4FP
M 07958 784462   T 020 8722 8798
E office@paulharris.uk.com
W www.paulharris.uk.com

ISLINGTON ARTS FACTORY
2 Parkhurst Road, London N7 0SF
F 020 7700 7229   T 020 7607 0561
E info@islingtonartsfactory.org
W www.islingtonartsfactory.org

Stella Mann College of PERFORMING ARTS LIMITED

Stella Mann College has been invited to offer places under the Government's Dance and Drama Awards scheme.

This College offers the opportunity to study for the National Diploma in either Professional Dance or Professional Musical Theatre, both validated by Trinity College, London.

Course accredited by the Council for Dance Education and Training.

Funded by **ypla** Young People's Learning Agency

TRINITY COLLEGE LONDON

CDET COUNCIL FOR DANCE EDUCATION & TRAINING

Photo by Peter Teigen

Stella Mann College promotes individuality and difference and welcomes applications from people from under-represented groups.

10 Linden Road, Bedford, Bedfordshire, MK40 2DA.   Tel: 01234 213331   Fax: 01234 217284
e-mail: info@stellamanncollege.co.uk   www.stellamanncollege.co.uk

...stretch yourself to the max!

LABAN
Creekside, London SE8 3DZ
F 020 8691 8400   T 020 8691 8600
E info@laban.org
W www.laban.org

LAINE THEATRE ARTS
The Studios, East Street
Epsom, Surrey KT17 1HH
F 01372 723775   T 01372 724648
E webmaster@laine-theatre-arts.co.uk
W www.laine-theatre-arts.co.uk

LEARN SALSA, CHA CHA CHA & MERENGUE WITH PATRICE
The Hendon Methodist Church
The Burroughs
Hendon Central Station
London NW4   M 07748 676670
E salsawithpatrice@gmail.com
W www.myspace.com/salsaisback

LEE Lynn THEATRE SCHOOL THE
48 Brook Road, Benfleet
Essex SS7 5JF   T 01268 795863
E lynn@leetheatre.fsnet.co.uk

LIVERPOOL THEATRE SCHOOL
Musical Theatre & Professional Classes
19 Aigburth Road, Liverpool
Merseyside L17 4JR
F 0151 728 9582   T 0151 728 7800
E info@liverpooltheatreschool.co.uk
W www.liverpooltheatreschool.co.uk

LONDON CONTEMPORARY DANCE SCHOOL
Full-time Vocational Training at Degree & Postgraduate Level
16 Flaxman Terrace, London WC1H 9AT
F 020 7121 1145   T 020 7121 1111
E lcds@theplace.org.uk
W www.lcds.ac.uk

LONDON SCHOOL OF CAPOEIRA
Unit 1-2 Leeds Place, Tollington Park
London N4 3RF   T 020 7281 2020
E info@londonschoolofcapoeira.co.uk
W www.londonschoolofcapoeira.co.uk

LONDON STUDIO CENTRE
42-50 York Way, London N1 9AB
F 020 7837 3248   T 020 7837 7741
E info@london-studio-centre.co.uk
W www.london-studio-centre.co.uk

MANN Stella COLLEGE OF PERFORMING ARTS LTD
Professional Training Course for Performers & Teachers
10 Linden Road, Bedford
Bedfordshire MK40 2DA
F 01234 217284   T 01234 213331
E info@stellamanncollege.co.uk
W www.stellamanncollege.co.uk

MGA ACADEMY OF PERFORMING ARTS THE
The MGA Company
1 St Colme Street
Edinburgh EH11 2RZ   T 0131 466 9392
E info@themgacompany.com
W www.themgaacademy.com

MIALKOWSKI Andrzej - BALLROOM & LATIN AMERICAN
Choreographer. Teacher. IDTA Member
Step By Step Dance School
54 Henry Street, Northampton
Northamptonshire NN1 4JE
M 07849 331430   T 01604 239755
E info@danceschool-stepbystep.com
W www.danceschool-stepbystep.com

MIDLANDS ACADEMY OF DANCE & DRAMA
Century House, Building B
428 Carlton Hill, Nottingham NG4 1QA   T/F 0115 911 0401
E admin@maddcollege.supanet.com
W www.maddcollege.co.uk

MILLENNIUM PERFORMING ARTS LTD
29 Thomas Street, Woolwich
London SE18 6HU   T 020 8301 8744
E info@md2000.co.uk
W www.md2000.co.uk

NEW LONDON PERFORMING ARTS CENTRE
Performing Arts Classes (3-19 yrs). All Dance Styles
GCSE Course. RAD & ISTD Exams
76 St James Lane, Muswell Hill
London N10 3DF
F 020 8444 4040   T 020 8444 4544
E nlpac@aol.com
W www.nlpac.co.uk

NORTH LONDON DANCE STUDIO
843-845 Green Lanes
Winchmore Hill
London N21 2RX
F 020 8364 2009   T 020 8360 5700
E thedancestudio@btopenworld.com

NORTHERN ACADEMY OF PERFORMING ARTS
Anlaby Road, Hull HU1 2PD
F 01482 212280   T 01482 310690
E napa@northernacademy.org.uk
W www.northernacademy.org.uk

NORTHERN BALLET SCHOOL
The Dancehouse
10 Oxford Road
Manchester M1 5QA
F 0161 237 1408   T 0161 237 1406
E enquiries@northernballetschool.co.uk
W www.northernballetschool.co.uk

NORTHERN SCHOOL OF CONTEMPORARY DANCE THE
98 Chapeltown Road, Leeds LS7 4BH   T 0113 219 3000
E info@nscd.ac.uk
W www.nscd.ac.uk

PAUL'S THEATRE SCHOOL
Ardleigh House
42 Ardleigh Green Road
Hornchurch, Essex RM11 2LG   T 01708 447123
E info@paulstheatreschool.com
W www.paulstheatreschool.com

PERFORMERS COLLEGE
Southend Road, Corringham
Essex SS17 8JT
F 01375 672353   T 01375 672053
E lesley@performerscollege.co.uk
W www.performerscollege.co.uk

PINEAPPLE DANCE STUDIOS
7 Langley Street, London WC2H 9JA
F 020 7836 0803   T 020 7836 4004
E studios@pineapple.uk.com
W www.pineapple.uk.com

PLACE THE
Robin Howard Dance Theatre
17 Duke's Road
London WC1H 9BY
F 020 7121 1142   T 020 7121 1000
E info@theplace.org.uk
W www.theplace.org.uk

PROFESSIONAL TEACHERS OF DANCING
Contact: Mellissa Harrop
Quay West Business Centre
Quay Lane
Gosport, Hants PO12 4LJ   T 023 9260 4285
E ptdenquiries@msn.com
W www.ptdance.com

RAMBERT SCHOOL OF BALLET & CONTEMPORARY DANCE
Clifton Lodge
St Margaret's Drive
Twickenham, Middlesex TW1 1QN
F 020 8892 8090   T 020 8892 9960
E info@rambertschool.org.uk
W www.rambertschool.org.uk

RIDGEWAY STUDIOS PERFORMING ARTS COLLEGE
Fairley House, Andrews Lane
Cheshunt, Herts EN7 6LB
F 01992 633844   T 01992 633775
E info@ridgewaystudios.co.uk
W www.ridgewaystudios.co.uk

RIVERSIDE REFLECTIONS BATON TWIRLING TEAM
34 Knowle Avenue, Bexleyheath
Kent DA7 5LX
M 07958 617976   T/F 01322 410003
E c.johnson717@ntlworld.com
W www.riverside-reflections.webs.com

ROEBUCK Gavin
Classical Ballet
51 Earls Court Square
London SW5 9DG   T 020 7370 7324
E info@gavinroebuck.com

ROJO Y NEGRO
Argentine Tango School of Dance
52 Lloyd Baker Street
Clerkenwell
London WC1X 9AA   T 020 8520 2726
E info@rojoynegroclub.com
W www.rojoynegroclub.com

ROYAL ACADEMY OF DANCE
36 Battersea Square, London SW11 3RA
F 020 7924 3129   T 020 7326 8000
E info@rad.org.uk
W www.rad.org.uk

SAFREY ACADEMY OF PERFORMING ARTS
10 St Julians Close, London SW16 2RY
F 020 8488 9121   T 020 8664 6676
E info@safreyarts.co.uk
W www.mbkonline.co.uk

TIFFANY THEATRE COLLEGE
969-973 London Road
Leigh on Sea, Essex SS9 3LB   T 01702 710069
E info@tiffanytheatrecollege.com
W www.tiffanytheatrecollege.com

URDANG ACADEMY THE
Finsbury Town Hall, Rosebery Avenue, London EC1R 4RP
F 020 7278 6727   T 020 7713 7710
E info@theurdangacademy.com
W www.theurdangacademy.com

VALLÉ ACADEMY OF PERFORMING ARTS
The Vallé Academy Studios
Wilton House, Delamare Road
Cheshunt, Herts EN8 9SG
F 01992 622868   T 01992 622862
E enquiries@valleacademy.co.uk
W www.valleacademy.co.uk

WHITEHALL PERFORMING ARTS CENTRE
Rayleigh Road, Leigh-on-Sea
Essex SS9 5UU   T/F 01702 529290

YOUNG Sylvia THEATRE SCHOOL
1 Nutford Place, London W1H 5YZ
F 020 7258 3915   T 020 7258 2330
E syoung@syts.co.uk
W www.syts.co.uk

ALRA (ACADEMY OF LIVE AND RECORDED ARTS)
Studio 24, The Royal Victoria Patriotic Building
John Archer Way
London SW18 3SX
F 020 8875 0789   T 020 8870 6475
E info@alra.co.uk
W www.alra.co.uk

ARTS EDUCATIONAL SCHOOLS LONDON
14 Bath Road, London W4 1LY
F 020 8987 6699   T 020 8987 6666
E receptionist@artsed.co.uk
W www.artsed.co.uk

BIRMINGHAM SCHOOL OF ACTING
Level 0, Millennium Point
Curzon Street
Birmingham B4 7XG
F 0121 331 7221   T 0121 331 7220
E info@bsa.bcu.ac.uk
W www.bsa.bcu.ac.uk

BRISTOL OLD VIC THEATRE SCHOOL
1-2 Downside Road, Clifton
Bristol BS8 2XF
F 0117 980 9258   T 0117 973 3535
E enquiries@oldvic.ac.uk
W www.oldvic.ac.uk

CENTRAL SCHOOL OF SPEECH & DRAMA, UNIVERSITY OF LONDON
Eton Avenue, Swiss Cottage
London NW3 3HY   T 020 7722 8183
E enquiries@cssd.ac.uk
W www.cssd.ac.uk

CONTI Italia ACADEMY OF THEATRE ARTS
Avondale, 72 Landor Road
London SW9 9PH
F 020 7737 2728   T 020 7733 3210
E acting@lsbu.ac.uk
W www.italiaconti-acting.co.uk

CYGNET TRAINING THEATRE
New Theatre, Friars Gate
Exeter, Devon EX2 4AZ   T/F 01392 277189
E cygnetarts@btconnect.com
W www.cygnetnewtheatre.com

DRAMA CENTRE LONDON
Central Saint Martins College of Art & Design
10 Back Hill
London EC1R 5EN
F 020 7514 8777   T 020 7514 8778
E drama@arts.ac.uk
W www.csm.arts.ac.uk/drama

DRAMA STUDIO LONDON
Grange Court, 1 Grange Road
London W5 5QN
F 020 8566 2035   T 020 8579 3897
E admin@dramastudiolondon.co.uk
W www.dramastudiolondon.co.uk

EAST 15 ACTING SCHOOL
Hatfields, Rectory Lane
Loughton IG10 3RY
F 020 8508 7521   T 020 8508 5983
E east15@essex.ac.uk
W www.east15.ac.uk

GSA, GUILDFORD SCHOOL OF ACTING
University of Surrey, Stag Hill Campus
Guildford, Surrey GU2 7XH   T 01483 560701
E gsaenquiries@gsa.surrey.ac.uk
W www.gsauk.org

GUILDHALL SCHOOL OF MUSIC & DRAMA
Silk Street, Barbican
London EC2Y 8DT
F 020 7256 9438   T 020 7628 2571
E info@gsmd.ac.uk
W www.gsmd.ac.uk

LAMDA
155 Talgarth Road, London W14 9DA
F 020 8834 0501   T 020 8834 0500
E enquiries@lamda.org.uk
W www.lamda.org.uk

LIVERPOOL INSTITUTE FOR PERFORMING ARTS THE
Mount Street, Liverpool L1 9HF
F 0151 330 3131   T 0151 330 3000
E reception@lipa.ac.uk
W www.lipa.ac.uk

MANCHESTER SCHOOL OF THEATRE AT MANCHESTER METROPOLITAN UNIVERSITY
The Mabel Tylecote Building
Cavendish Street
Manchester M15 6BG   T 0161 247 1305
W www.theatre.mmu.ac.uk

MOUNTVIEW
Academy of Theatre Arts
Ralph Richardson Memorial Studios
1 Kingfisher Place
Clarendon Road, London N22 6XF
F 020 8829 0034   T 020 8881 2201
E enquiries@mountview.org.uk
W www.mountview.org.uk

OXFORD SCHOOL OF DRAMA THE
Sansomes Farm Studios
Woodstock, Oxford OX20 1ER
F 01993 811220   T 01993 812883
E info@oxforddrama.ac.uk
W www.oxforddrama.ac.uk

QUEEN MARGARET UNIVERSITY, EDINBURGH
Queen Margaret University Drive
Musselburgh
East Lothian EH21 6UU
F 0131 474 0001   T 0131 474 0000
E admissions@qmu.ac.uk
W www.qmu.ac.uk

ROSE BRUFORD COLLEGE
Lamorbey Park, Burnt Oak Lane
Sidcup, Kent DA15 9DF
F 020 8308 0542   T 020 8308 2600
E enquiries@bruford.ac.uk
W www.bruford.ac.uk

ROYAL ACADEMY OF DRAMATIC ART
62-64 Gower Street, London WC1E 6ED
F 020 7323 3865   T 020 7636 7076
E reception@rada.ac.uk
W www.rada.org

ROYAL SCOTTISH ACADEMY OF MUSIC & DRAMA
100 Renfrew Street
Glasgow G2 3DB   T 0141 332 4101
E registry@rsamd.ac.uk
W www.rsamd.ac.uk

ROYAL WELSH COLLEGE OF MUSIC & DRAMA
Drama Department
Castle Grounds
Cathays Park, Cardiff CF10 3ER
F 029 2039 1301   T 029 2039 1361
E admissions@rwcmd.ac.uk
W www.rwcmd.ac.uk

THE CONFERENCE OF DRAMA SCHOOLS

The Conference of Drama Schools comprises Britain's 22 leading Drama Schools. CDS exists to set and maintain the highest standards of training within the vocational drama sector and to make it easier for prospective students to understand the range of courses on offer and the application process. CDS member schools offer courses in Acting, Musical Theatre, Directing and Technical Theatre training.

CDS members offer courses which are:
Professional – you will be trained to work in the theatre by staff with professional experience and by visiting professionals.
Intensive – courses are full-time
Work Orientated – you are being trained to do a job – these courses are practical training for work.

CDS publishes *The Conference of Drama Schools – Guide to Professional Training in Drama and* *Technical Theatre 2011* and *The CDS Guide to Careers Backstage*.

For links to CDS schools please visit the website at **www.drama.ac.uk**

The full texts of both guides are available on the website – if you would like a hard copy please contact French's Theatre Bookshop, by phone on 020 7255 4300 or by emailing **theatre@samuelfrench-london.co.uk** or by visiting the shop at 52 Fitzroy Street, London, W1T 5JR. Single copies will be sent free of charge to UK addresses.
To contact CDS please visit the website or write to the Executive Secretary, CDS Ltd, P.O. Box 34252, London NW5 1XJ.

in association with

A B ACADEMY THEATRE SCHOOL
Act Out Ltd
22 Greek Street
Stockport, Cheshire SK3 8AB — T/F 0161 429 7413
E ab22actout@aol.com

ABI ACTING MA BA Hons STSD
Drama School Tutor/Actor for one-to-one Coaching
47 Hardinge Road
London NW10 3PN — M 07977 050223
E stephanie.schonfield@googlemail.com

ABOMELI TUTORING
*Contact: Charles Abomeli BA LLAM. Development Coach
Stage & Screen Acting Technique*
E charlesabm@aol.co.uk — M 07960 954904
W www.charlesabomeli.com

ACADEMY ARTS LTD THE
PO Box 54435, London E10 7AY — T 020 8539 1151
E info@academyarts.co.uk
W www.academyarts.co.uk

ACADEMY OF CREATIVE TRAINING
8-10 Rock Place
Brighton
East Sussex BN2 1PF — T 01273 818266
E info@actbrighton.org
W www.actbrighton.org

ACADEMY OF THE SCIENCE OF ACTING AND DIRECTING THE
9-15 Elthorne Road
London N19 4AJ
F 020 7272 0026 — T 020 7272 0027
E info@asad.org.uk
W www.asad.org.uk

ACADEMY SCHOOL OF PERFORMING ARTS THE
Dance. Drama. Singing
M 07983 981186 — T 0161 287 9700
E theacademy@ntlworld.com
W www.academy-sopa.co.uk

ACKERLEY STUDIOS OF SPEECH, DRAMA & PUBLIC SPEAKING
*Contact: Margaret Christina Parsons (Principal)
Drama. Speech*
4th Floor, Hanover House, Hanover Street
Liverpool L1 3DZ — T 0151 709 5995

ACT 2 CAM
14 Percy Road, Whitley Bay, Newcastle
Tyne and Wear NE26 2AX — T 0191 280 1345
E info@act2cam.com
W www.act2cam.com

ACT ONE DRAMA STUDIO
PO Box 4483, Sheffield S10 9DX — T 0114 266 7209
E info@actonedramastudio.co.uk
W www.actonedramastudio.co.uk

ACT UP
Acting Classes for Everyone. Acting Workshops. Audition Technique. Pre-Drama School (18+ yrs). Public Speaking Vocal Coaching
Unit 88, Battersea Business Centre
99-109 Lavender Hill, London SW11 5QL
F 020 7924 6606 — T 020 7924 7701
E info@act-up.co.uk — W www.act-up.co.uk

ACTING ANGEL THE
Acting & Audition Workshops. Career Coaching. Industry Talks & Training Products for Young Adult & Graduate Actors
E info@theactingangel.co.uk — M 07807 103295
W www.theactingangel.co.uk

ACTING AUDITION SUCCESS
Contact: Philip Rosch, Association of Guildhall Teachers FVCM LALAM ATCL LGSM ANE BA Hons. Auditions for Top UK Drama Schools. Audition Speeches. Commercial Castings Effective Sight-reading. Expert Career Guidance Private Acting Classes. RADA Acting Exams
53 West Heath Court
North End Road, London NW11 7RG — T 020 8731 6686
E philiprosch1@hotmail.com — W www.philiprosch.com

Gloria Lytton

Former Actress
Qualified Speech Therapist
Teacher at R.A.D.A. 1972-1986

Remedial Voice and Speech Work
Speaking with Confidence
Public Speaking
Audition Coaching

For people from all backgrounds
and walks of life

Tel: 020-8441 3118

www.zoenathenson.com

ZOË NATHENSON
SCHOOL OF FILM ACTING

- **FILM ACTING, AUDITION TECHNIQUE & SIGHT READING**
- **GROUP WORKSHOPS AND INTENSIVE COURSES AVAILABLE**

Zoe Nathenson School of Film Acting
55 St James' Lane, London N10 3DA
Mobile: 07956 833 850 Tel: 020 8883 7554
Email: zoe.act@btinternet.com

ACTING BUDDY
E info@actingbuddy.com
W www.actingbuddy.com
T 020 7558 8020

ACTING COACH SCOTLAND
2nd Floor, 19 Queen Street
Glasgow, Lanarkshire G20 6HQ
E mark@actingcoachscotland.co.uk
W www.actingcoachscotland.co.uk
T/F 0800 7569535

ACTION LAB
Contact: Miranda French, Peter Irving. Part-time Acting Courses & Private Coaching. London & West Dorset
M 07976 393023
E miranda@mirandafrench.com
M 07979 623987

ACTOR WORKS THE
Contact: Daniel Brennan, Wendy Smith. Courses: 1 Year Intensive (Evening & Weekend), 1 Year Intensive (Day), 1 Year Part-time (Evening), 10 Weeks (Saturday). Drama School (Over 18s)
First Floor, Raine House
Raine Street, Wapping, London E1W 3RJ
E ask@theactorworks.co.uk
W www.theactorworks.co.uk
T 020 7702 0909

ACTORS CENTRE THE
Accent/Dialect Coaching. Acting for Camera. Audition Technique. Beginners & Professional Workshops. Meisner Shakespeare. Singing. Television Presenting
1A Tower Street
London WC2H 9NP
E reception@actorscentre.co.uk
W www.actorscentre.co.uk
T 020 7632 8001

ACTORS PLATFORM
Casting Director Workshops. Weekly. London
7 Brookfield Road
West Kirby
Wirral CH48 4EJ
E melissa@actorsplatform.com
W www.actorsplatform.com
M 07849 999035

ACTORS STUDIO
Acting Workshops. Audition Technique. Dialect/Accent Coaching. Elocution. Improvisation. Language Tutoring. Private Acting Classes. Public Speaking. Stage School for Children. Vocal Coaching
Pinewood Film Studios
Pinewood Road
Iver Heath, Bucks SL0 0NH
F 01753 655622
E info@actorsstudio.co.uk
W www.actorsstudio.co.uk
T 01753 650951

Unit 10, 21 Wren Street
London WC1X 0HF

ACTORS STUDIO MERSEYSIDE
1 Maryland Street
Liverpool L1 9DE
E asm@performersproductions.co.uk
W www.actorsstudiomerseyside.co.uk
T 0151 708 4000

ACTOR'S TEMPLE THE
13-14 Warren Street
London W1T 5LG .
E info@actorstemple.com
W www.actorstemple.com
T 020 3004 4537

LSDA
LONDON SCHOOL OF DRAMATIC ART

The London School of Dramatic Art offers a
range of comprehensive courses designed to
develop individual creative talents and provide
a thorough grounding in all aspects of
performance as part of a student's preparation
for a working life as an actor

020 7581 6100   www.lsda-acting.com

infopage

Why do I need drama training?

The entertainment industry is an extremely competitive one, with thousands of performers competing for a small number of jobs. In such a crowded market, professional training will increase an actor's chances of success, and professionally trained artists are also more likely to be represented by agencies. Drama training can begin at any age and should continue throughout an actor's career.

I have already trained to be an actor. Why do I need further training?

Drama training should not cease as soon as you graduate or get your first job. Throughout your career you should strive to enhance your existing skills and keep up-to-date with the techniques new actors are being taught, even straight after drama school, in order to retain a competitive edge. You must also be prepared to learn new skills for specific roles if required. Ongoing drama training and classes can help you stay fit and active, and if you go through a period of unemployment you can keep your mind and body occupied, ready to take on your next job.

What kind of training is available?

For the under 18's, stage schools provide specialist training in acting, singing and dancing. They offer a variety of full and part-time courses. After 18, students can attend drama school. The standard route is to take a three-year, full-time course, in the same way you would take a university degree. Some schools also offer one or two-year courses.

What is the Conference of Drama Schools (CDS)?

The Conference of Drama Schools was founded in 1969 and comprises Britain's twenty two leading Drama Schools. It exists in order to strengthen the voice of the member schools, to set and maintain the highest standards of training within the vocational drama sector, and to make it easier for prospective students to understand the range of courses on offer and the application process. The twenty two member schools listed in the section 'Drama Schools (Conference Of)' offer courses in Acting, Musical Theatre, Directing and Technical Theatre training. For more information you can visit their website www.drama.ac.uk

What is NCDT?

The National Council for Drama Training was established in 1976 and is a unique collaborative partnership of employers in the theatre, broadcast and media industry, employee representatives and training providers. Its aim is to champion and support professional drama training and education working to safeguard the highest standards and quality assurance through accreditation for vocational drama courses in the UK. This provides students with the confidence that the courses they choose are recognised by the drama profession as being relevant to the purposes of their employment. For more information please see www.ncdt.co.uk

How should I use these listings?

The following listings provide up-to-date contact details for a wide range of performance courses, classes and coaches. Every company listed is done so by written request to us. Some companies have provided contact names, areas of specialisation and a selection of courses on offer.

I want to apply to join a full-time drama course. Where do I start?

Your first step should be to research as many different courses as possible. Have a look on each school's website and request a prospectus. Ask around to find out where other people have trained or are training now and who they recommend. You would be advised to begin your search by considering CDS courses. Please refer to the *CDS Guide to Professional Training in Drama & Technical Theatre* for a description of each school, its policy and the courses it offers together with information about funding, available from www.drama.ac.uk

What types of courses are available?

Drama training courses generally involve three-year degree or diploma courses or one-year postgraduate courses if you have already attended university or can demonstrate a certain amount of previous experience. Alternatively, short-term or part-time foundation courses are available, which can serve as an introduction to acting but are not a substitute for a full-time drama course.

When should I apply?

Deadlines for applications to drama courses vary between schools so make sure you check each school's individual deadlines. Most courses start in September. If the school you are considering requires you to apply via UCAS, you must submit your application between mid-September 2010 and 15th January 2011 to guarantee that your application will be considered for a course beginning in 2011. You can apply after that until 30th June, but the school is then under no obligation to consider your application.

See www.ucas.ac.uk/students/startapplication/whentoapply or contact the individual school for more details.

What funding is available to me?

Drama courses are unavoidably expensive. Most students have to fund their own course fees and other expenses, whether from savings, part-time work or a student loan. However, if you are from a low-income household you may qualify for a maintenance grant from the government to cover some of the costs. Some NCDT accredited courses offer a limited number of students Dance and Drama Awards (DaDA) scholarships, introduced to increase access to dance, drama and stage management training for talented students. These scholarships include help with both course fees and living expenses. Find out what each school offers in terms of potential financial support before applying. Visit www.ncdt.co.uk/guidetotraining/funding for a useful guide to drama school funding.

Another possibility is to raise funds from a charity, trust or foundation. As with applying to agents and casting professionals for representation and work, do your research first and target your letters to explain how your needs meet each organisation's objectives, rather than sending a generalised letter to everyone. You are much more likely to be considered if you demonstrate that you know the background of the organisation and what they can offer performers. You will find further advice and a list of charities and foundations you could approach at www.ncdt.co.uk/guidetotraining/funding/fundraising

How can my child become an actor?

If your child is interested in becoming an actor, they should try to get as much practical experience as possible. They could also join a stage school or sign with an agent. Contact details for stage schools can be found among the listings on the following pages. Please also see the 'Agents – Children's & Teenagers'' section for more information.

What about other forms of training?

Building on your initial acting course is essential for both new and more experienced actors. There are so many new skills you can learn – you could take stage fighting classes, hire a vocal coach, attend singing and dance lessons, and many more. These will enhance your CV and will give you a competitive edge. It is also extremely useful to take occasional 'refresher' courses on audition skills, different acting techniques and so on in various forms such as one-to-one lessons, one-off workshops or evening classes, to make sure you are not rusty when your next audition comes along.

Where can I find more information?

The Actors Centre runs approximately 1700 classes and workshops a year to encourage performers to develop their talent throughout their career in a supportive environment. They also run introductory classes for people who are interested in becoming actors but currently have no training or experience. Visit their website www.actorscentre.co.uk for more information. You may also want to refer to the 'Dance Training & Professional Classes' to add additional skills to your CV as well as keep fit. If you are interested in a career behind rather than in front of the camera or stage, please see the *CDS Guide to Careers Backstage*, available from www.drama.ac.uk

info**page**

Janine Snape is Assistant Casting Director at the Royal Shakespeare Company and a member of the Casting Directors Guild of Great Britain and Ireland.

Pursuing a career in the performing arts is a brave choice. The industry grows increasingly competitive each year thanks to the continual interest in the perceived glamorous lives of our most successful actors and celebrities. With the amount of work on offer remaining fairly static and more and more people being attracted to the industry every day, it can be a tough world to survive in. Diving into this turmoil and keeping yourself afloat takes passion and talent, combined with skill, endurance and the confidence in your abilities that can often only be achieved through training.

Entering the industry and ascending to become an 'overnight star' is a rarity and most of the time it simply isn't true. It's a romantic and exciting idea to believe in but delve into the background of those overnight success stories and you'll often discover years of plain old hard work and determination behind them.

Whether you are walking into an audition room, performing in a show or approaching life generally, we want you to shine to your full potential and enjoy yourself. Performers are story-tellers who absorb information and experiences and have the ability to communicate with and engage an audience. This requires a vocal clarity that can only be achieved through training, along with empathy, imagination and an emotional truth that comes from life experience. A good solid foundation of training will provide you with the tools to support your performance and give you the freedom to be relaxed and expressive in your work.

There are many forms of training available and the quality and range on offer is exceptional. Working with a voice coach can teach you breath control and rhythm, movement practitioners can show you methods to remain supple and how to move in a space, working with a singing teacher can provide you with the technique to help you make it through an eight show week and still be able to speak at the end of it. These are just a few examples of the range of practitioners working in the industry and a small and general selection of the myriad tools they can provide you with. Whether it be CDS training, additional training after graduating, or on-the-job training, make the most of what's on offer, practise it and apply it when you can.

On a practical note, going into an audition knowing you have the income to support yourself will help you relax and perform to your best ability on the day. Standing in front of a room full of people and being asked to switch on and perform when you desperately need the job to pay for your next meal is a lot of pressure to put yourself under. Taking on work outside the industry is another part of being an actor. Look at it positively: apart from providing an income, a job beyond performing also offers you the chance to observe the world and others from a different perspective. A job can teach you practical skills that may carry over into your life as a performer, such as how to work in a team and engage with people in an environment other than an audition or rehearsal room. Life really can be stranger than fiction and even in the dullest of jobs you may come across some vibrant characters that inspire you as a performer. Life experience contributes to you being a well-rounded company member and individual, and will provide you with material to draw on and add texture to your performance.

Despite the fact that at any one time a large percentage of performers are 'out of work', the reality is the work never stops. Continuing with your training, attending workshops, auditioning, networking and talking to your peers, reading, seeing shows, watching film and TV, listening to music and seeking out new experiences are all part of the job. Immerse yourself in life and culture. Stay curious, keep yourself motivated, mentally stimulated and in good condition so you are ready to work at the drop of a hat. You may not always know what you are doing from one day to the next and that can be both daunting and exciting. It's important to use the time you have to invest in yourself by continually working on and adding to your skills. Remain as open-minded, positive and versatile as you can be. The possibilities are endless and you want to be ready to take advantage of all the opportunities that arise.

Please visit www.rsc.org.uk for further information on the Royal Shakespeare Company.

infopage

Members of the Conference of Drama Schools offer their students the highest quality training in the industry. Graduates from these schools are in a strong position to advise anyone thinking of following in their path. We have asked two recent graduates from CDS schools to share their thoughts on the benefits of drama training.

Photo: Peter Simpkin

Andrew Gower recently graduated from the Oxford School of Drama where he achieved a National Diploma in Professional Acting. He won the Spotlight Prize at the Spotlight Showcase 2010.

I still remember the exact moment in a GCSE drama lesson when I first thought: "I like this a lot." I gradually realised that this could be the career for me. I decided to audition for drama school, but like a lot of students I didn't know what to expect.

Unfortunately, at the beginning of my course I didn't receive a Dance and Drama Award, so funding came from savings and a career development loan. However, I believe not receiving the award made me work harder and appreciate every day and every lesson at the school. Thankfully, at the beginning of my second year when I wasn't sure if I would be able to fund my course further, I finally received a DaDA award.

My time at drama school is filled with highlights. I've had the opportunity to play some amazing characters and work on some great classic and modern texts with some inspiring directors. I suppose it sounds clichéd, but I would recommend reading and watching as much theatre as you possibly can. The Oxford School of Drama has taught me that you can never take it easy in this profession – you have to keep working at it.

I've had an amazing time since my school's showcase and the Spotlight Showcase and have signed with a great agency. I am now enjoying meeting casting directors and auditioning for some exciting roles. I'm really looking forward to (and have my fingers crossed for) my first job. I feel excited about using all the skills I have soaked up in the past three years at drama school and I can't wait to learn more out there in the industry!

Photo: Fatimah Namdar

Vivienne Bell recently graduated from Central School of Speech and Drama where she studied for a BA in Acting for Stage and Screen, achieving a First Class Honours degree. She won the Highly Commended Actor award at the Spotlight Showcase 2010.

I've wanted to act since I was a little girl and have always had a vivid imagination and a passion for words. Going into amateur dramatics as a child was a natural progression from acting out stories in the garden to my dolls. I auditioned for drama school after a couple of years out of education; I wanted to feel ready and gain some life experience first, so I worked, travelled, studied, fell in love etc.

I always knew I wanted to go to Central. This was mainly based on my admiration for their alumni; many of my favourite actors had attended the school and I wished to follow in their footsteps. When I visited the school throughout the audition process, I could see myself there and I was convinced it was the place for me.

From my experience, I would say that keeping an open mind is vital throughout your training. In the beginning, I struggled to combine instinct and technique. The training at Central is excellent because it teaches you a whole range of different techniques and skills, so you can find out what works for you as an actor and can develop your own process. I feel that Central have prepared me well for life in the industry: I 'own' my work; I feel confident; I have a solid base of skills and practice; and I trust my instincts 'in the moment'. The advice I would give to anyone studying at drama school would be to aim to surprise yourself every day. Have courage, have faith in yourself and enjoy your craft!

ACTORS' THEATRE SCHOOL
Foundation Course
32 Exeter Road, London NW2 4SB
F 020 8450 1057   T 020 8450 0371
E info@theactorstheatreschool.co.uk
W www.theactorstheatreschool.co.uk

ACTS
Ayres-Clark Theatre School
c/o 12 Gatward Close, Winchmore Hill
London N21 1AS   T 020 8360 0352
E actsn21@talktalk.net

ADVANCED PERFORMERS STUDIO
Riverside Studios, Crisp Road
London W6 9RL   T 020 8237 1080
E info@associatedstudios.co.uk
W www.associatedstudios.co.uk

AI CORPORATE
Artist Networking Consultancy
PO Box 708, Nundah
Queensland 4012, Australia   T +61 412 794 281
E info@aicorporate.com.au
W www.aicorporate.com.au

ALEXANDER Helen
Audition Technique. Drama School Entry
14 Chestnut Road, Raynes Park
London SW20 8EB   T 020 8543 4085
E helen-alexander@virginmedia.com

ALL EXPRESSIONS THEATRE SCHOOL
153 Waverley Avenue, Twickenham
Middlesex TW2 6DJ   T 020 8898 3321
E info@allexpressions.co.uk
W www.allexpressions.co.uk

ALLSORTS - DRAMA
Part-time Courses & Drama Training (3-18 yrs)
Kensington, Notting Hill, Hampstead, Fulham, Putney
34 Crediton Road
London NW10 3DU   T/F 020 8969 3249
E info@allsortsdrama.com
W www.allsortsdrama.com

ALRA (ACADEMY OF LIVE & RECORDED ARTS)
See DRAMA SCHOOLS (Conference of)

AMERICAN MUSICAL THEATRE ACADEMY OF LONDON
11 Plough Yard, London EC2A 3LP   T 020 7247 7110
E info@americanacademy.co.uk
W www.americanacademy.co.uk

AMERICAN VOICES
Contact: Lynn Bains. Acting Teacher & Director. American Accent/Dialect Coach
20 Craighall Crescent, Edinburgh EH6 4RZ   M 07875 148755
E mail@lynnbains.com

AND ALL THAT JAZZ
Contact: Eileen Hughes. Accompanist. Vocal Coaching
165 Gunnersbury Lane, Acton Town
London W3 8LJ   T 020 8993 2111

ARABESQUE SCHOOL OF PERFORMING ARTS
Quarry Lane, Chichester PO19 8NY   T/F 01243 531144
E arabesqueschool@aol.com
W www.aspauk.com

ARDEN SCHOOL OF THEATRE THE
Contact: Victoria Muir (Administrator). Professional Stage Practice in Acting Studies & Musical Theatre
HNC in Drama. FD in Theatre Practice
The Manchester College, Nicholls Campus
Hyde Road, Manchester M12 6BA
F 0161 279 7199   T 0161 279 7257
E vmuir@themanchestercollege.ac.uk

ARTEMIS SCHOOL OF SPEECH & DRAMA
Peredur Centre of The Arts, West Hoathly Road
East Grinstead, West Sussex RH19 4NF   T/F 01342 321330
E office@artemisspeechanddrama.org.uk
W www.artemisspeechanddrama.org.uk

ARTEMIS STUDIOS
30 Charles Square, Bracknell
Berkshire RG12 1AY   T 01344 429403
E info@artemis-studios.co.uk
W www.artemis-studios.co.uk

ARTS EDUCATIONAL SCHOOLS LONDON
See DRAMA SCHOOLS (Conference of)

ASH Samantha Jane
Acting Workshops. Short Films
43 Eustace Street, Chadderton
Oldham OL9 0ED   M 07805 091361
E brunettebunny13@hotmail.co.uk

ASHCROFT ACADEMY OF DRAMATIC ART THE
Dance ISTD. Drama LAMDA. Singing (4-18 yrs)
Malcolm Primary School, Malcolm Road
Penge, London SE20 8RH
M 07799 791586   T/F 0844 8005328
E geraldi.gillma@btconnect.com
W www.ashcroftacademy.com

explore different techniques and new ways of working in over 1700 classes a year, taught by top industry professionals

extend your skills and your networks with advanced workshops and groundbreaking labwork led by leading actors and directors

excel at your craft with one-to-one tuition and expert advice, all at prices that won't break the bank

The Actors Centre has been the UK's premiere resource for actors for over 30 years.

Discover what becoming a member can do for you and your career at www.actorscentre.co.uk

the actors centre

VOICE CONSULTANT & COACH
Jessica Higgs
Tel: 020-7359 7848 Mobile: 079-4019 3631
Vocal technique, voice & text
sight-reading and auditions

ASHFORD Clare BSc PGCE LLAM ALAM (Recital) ALAM (Acting)
20 The Chase, Coulsdon
Surrey CR5 2EG   T 020 8660 9609
E clareashford@handbag.com

AUDITION COACH
Contact: Martin Harris. Acting Workshops. Audition Techniques. Group Evening Classes. Private Acting Classes
32 Baxter Road, Sale, Manchester M33 3AL
M 07788 723570   T 0161 969 1444
E martin@auditioncoach.co.uk
W www.auditioncoach.co.uk

AUDITIONS: A PRACTICAL GUIDE
W www.auditionsapracticalguide.com

AVERY-CLARK Kenneth
Musical Theatre. Voice Coach
32 Brookfield Road, London E9 5AH   T 020 8525 0111

BAC (Battersea Arts Centre)
Young People's Theatre Workshops & Performance Projects (12-25 yrs)
Lavender Hill, London SW11 5TN
F 020 7978 5207   T 020 7326 8219
E bacypt@bac.org.uk   W www.bac.org.uk

BARRITT Marcia ACIL
Jamaican Patwa' Language Coach
19 Turnstone Close, Ickenham
Uxbridge, Middlesex UB10 8NW   M 07854 644108
E mbarritt@btinternet.com
W www.marciabarritt.co.uk

BATE Richard MA (Theatre) LGSM (TD) PGCE (FE) Equity
Audition Technique. Drama School Entry
Vocal & Acting Training
Apt 1, Broom Hall, High Street, Broom
Biggleswade, Bedfordshire SG18 9ND   M 07940 589295
E rich.bate@yahoo.co.uk

BATES Esme
BA Hons Drama Education, Central School of Speech & Drama. Children's Casting Director. LAMDA Associate. LAMDA Exam Coach. Play in a week Specialist
Youth Theatre Director
2 Barons Court, Western Elms Avenue
Reading, Berks RG30 2BP
M 07941 700941   T 0118 958 9330
E esmebates@btinternet.com

BENCH Paul MEd LGSM ALAM FRSA LJBA (Hons) PGCE ACP (Lings) (Hons) MASC (Ph) MIFA (Reg)
Audition Technique. Corporate Vocal Presentation. LAMDA Exams, Grades to Diploma Level. Private Acting Classes Public Speaking. Stress Management. Vocal Coaching
1 Whitehall Terrace, Shrewsbury
Shropshire SY2 5AA   T/F 01743 233164
E pfbench@aol.com
W www.paulbench.co.uk

BENSKIN Eileen
Dialect Coach
M 07785 791715   T 020 8455 9750

BERKERY Barbara
Dialogue/Dialect Coach for Film & Television   T 020 7281 3139

BEST THEATRE ARTS
PO Box 749, St Albans AL1 4YW   T 01727 759634
E bestarts@aol.com
W www.besttheatrearts.com

BIG ACT THE
Unit 1FA, Gate C, Knorr-Bremse Business Park
Douglas Road, Bristol BS15 8HJ   T 0870 8810367
E info@thebigact.com
W www.thebigact.com

BIG ACT THEATRE SCHOOL THE
90 Chapel Way, Epsom Downs, Epsom, Surrey KT18 5SY
M 07816 524066   T 01737 211541
E lucy@bigacttheatre.co.uk
W www.bigacttheatre.co.uk

BIG LITTLE THEATRE SCHOOL
Acting Examination & Audition Prep (LAMDA). Early Years Drama & Dance. Performance in Education Workshops Professional Development Programme. RAD Ballet, ISTD Tap & Modern. Singing Technique Classes & Private Lessons Skills Development Classes. Summer Schools. Youth Theatre Companies
Garnet House, 2A Harvey Road
Bournemouth, Dorset BH5 2AD   T 01202 434499
E info@biglittle.biz
W www.biglittle.biz

BIRD COLLEGE
Drama/Musical Theatre College
The Centre, 27 Station Road, Sidcup, Kent DA15 7EB
F 020 8308 1370   T 020 8300 6004
E admin@birdcollege.co.uk
W www.birdcollege.co.uk

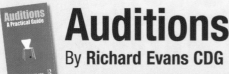

RICK LIPTON DIALECT, DIALOGUE AND VOICE COACH

- American Accent Coaching from an American in London
- Digital Recordings of your sessions provided
- Film, Television, Theatre, Auditions, Private Lessons
- 10+ years experience, 1000+ actors trained and coached

07961445247   rl@ricklipton.com   www.ricklipton.com

BIRMINGHAM SCHOOL OF ACTING
See DRAMA SCHOOLS (Conference of)

BIRMINGHAM THEATRE SCHOOL THE
The Old Rep Theatre
Station Street, Birmingham B5 4DY   T 0121 643 3300
E info@birminghamtheatreschool.co.uk
W www.birminghamtheatreschool.co.uk

BODENS STUDIOS
Contact: Adam Boden. Acting Workshops. Audition Technique
Dancing. Improvisation. Part-time Performing Arts Classes
Singing
Bodens Studio & Agency
99 East Barnet Road
New Barnet, Herts EN4 8RF
F 020 8449 5212   T 020 8447 0909
E info@bodenstudios.com
W www.bodenstudios.com

BOWDEN ACADEMY OF DRAMATIC ARTS THE
Suite 3, Merley House
Merley House Lane
Wimborne, Dorset BH21 3AA   M 07902 253499
E admin@bowdenacademy.co.uk
W www.bowdenacademy.co.uk

BOWES Sara
Child Acting Coach for Film & Commercials
25 Holmes Avenue, Hove BN3 7LA   M 07830 375389
E sara@sarabowes.com

BOYD Beth
Private Acting Coaching
10 Prospect Road, Long Ditton
Surbiton, Surrey KT6 5PY   T 020 8398 6768

BRADSHAW Irene
Private Coach. Voice & Audition Preparation
Flat F, Welbeck Mansions, Inglewood Road
West Hampstead, London NW6 1QX
M 07949 552915   T 020 7794 5721
E irene@irenebradshaw.fsnet.co.uk
W www.voice-power-works.co.uk

BRAITHWAITE'S ACROBATIC SCHOOL
8 Brookshill Avenue, Harrow Weald
Middlesex   T 020 8954 5638

BRANSTON Dale
Audition Technique. Singing Teacher
Ground Floor Flat, 16 Fernwood Avenue
Streatham, London SW16 1RD
M 07767 261713   T 020 8696 9958
E branpickle@yahoo.co.uk

BRIDGE THEATRE TRAINING COMPANY THE
Cecil Sharp House, 2 Regent's Park Road
London NW1 7AY
F 020 7424 9118   T 020 7424 0860
E admin@thebridge-ttc.org
W www.thebridge-ttc.org

BRIGHTON PERFORMERZONE
Contact: William Pool (ARCM)
Singing. Tuition. Workshops
33A Osmond Road, Hove
East Sussex BN3 1TD   M 07973 518643
E info@performerzone.co.uk
W www.performerzone.co.uk

BRIGHTON SCHOOL OF MUSIC & DRAMA
96 Claremont Road, Seaford
East Sussex BN25 2QA   T 01323 492918
E carolenuabest@aol.com

BRISTOL OLD VIC THEATRE SCHOOL
See DRAMA SCHOOLS (Conference of)

**B.R.I.T. SCHOOL FOR PERFORMING ARTS
& TECHNOLOGY THE**
60 The Crescent
Croydon CR0 2HN
F 020 8665 8676   T 020 8665 5242
E admin@brit.croydon.sch.uk
W www.brit.croydon.sch.uk

BRITISH AMERICAN DRAMA ACADEMY
14 Gloucester Gate, Regent's Park
London NW1 4HG
F 020 7487 0731   T 020 7487 0730
E info@badaonline.com
W www.badaonline.com

BROWN Michael BA MFA
Acting Technique (Meisner). Audition Technique/Preparation
Improvisation. Physical Performance Skills (Lecoq)
Private Acting Coach. Theatre Styles Workshops
75 Palmerston Road
London SW14 7QA   M 07963 171385
E brown.michaelanthony@gmail.com

CAMERON BROWN Jo PGDVS
Dialect. Dialogue. Voice Coaching for Films, Stage, Television
& Auditions
E jocameronbrown@hotmail.com   M 07970 026621

CAMM Howard
Opera Repetiteur
4 Picton Avenue, Billingham
Stockton-on-Tees, Teesside TS22 5BP   M 07805 599685
E howardcamm@googlemail.com

CAMPBELL Jon
36 Fentiman Road, London SW8 1LF   M 07854 697971
E joncampbell@joncampbell.co.uk
W www.joncampbell.co.uk

CAMPBELL Ross ARCM Dip RCM (Perf)
Head of Singing & Music, GSA. Professor, Royal Academy of
Music. Accompanist. Music Director. Singing Coach
17 Oldwood Chase, Farnborough
Hants GU14 0QS
M 07956 465165   T 01252 510228
E rosscampbell@ntlworld.com

CYGNET TRAINING THEATRE Patron Peter Brook

PROFESSIONAL ACTING TRAINING

CYGNET students train and tour as a company playing at a wide variety of venues. The training gives high priority to voice technique, musical skills and the acting methods of Stanislavsky and Michael Chekhov.

The Tempest

ENTRY (over 18) by audition workshop and interview

Apply (with SAE) to: New Theatre, Friars Gate, Exeter EX2 4AZ

Member of The Conference of Drama Schools   Registered Charity No. 1081824

CAPITAL ARTS THEATRE SCHOOL
Contact: Kathleen Shanks
Wyllyotts Centre
Darkes Lane
Potters Bar, Herts EN6 2HN
M 07885 232414   T/F 020 8449 2342
E capitalarts@btconnect.com

CAPITAL SCREEN ARTS (CSA)
Courses in Screen-Acting & Meisner Technique. Private Coaching, 1 year Part-time Programme & 10 Week Courses
First Floor
75 Brownlow Road
London N11 2BN   M 07583 175120
E info@capitalscreenarts.co.uk
W www.capitalscreenarts.co.uk

CAPO FERRO FIGHT ENSEMBLE
168 Richmond Road, Sheffield
Yorkshire S13 8TG   M 07791 875902
E cassonsue@hotmail.com

CARAVANSERAI PRODUCTIONS & ACTING STUDIO
Unit 30, Grand Union Centre
West Row, London W10 5AS   T 020 8968 3769
E info@caravanseraiproductions.com
W www.caravanseraiproductions.com

CARSHALTON COLLEGE
Nightingale Road
Carshalton, Surrey SM5 2EJ
F 020 8544 4440   T 020 8544 4444
E cs@carshalton.ac.uk
W www.carshalton.ac.uk

COURT
Theatre Training Company

train for a life in the theatre by working in the theatre...

BA (Hons) Acting
Accelerated 2 Year Course
(subject to validation)

P.G. Dipl.
- **Technical Theatre**
- **Acting**
1 Year Courses

address: Court Theatre Training Company, The Courtyard Theatre, Bowling Green Walk, 40 Pitfield St, London N1 6EU
phone/fax: 020 7739 6868   **email:** info@thecourtyard.org.uk   **web:** www.thecourtyard.org.uk

CELEBRATION THEATRE COMPANY FOR THE YOUNG
Contact: Neville Wortman. Summer Week Intensive Course
Acting Workshops. Audition Technique. Dialect/Accent
Coaching. Drama School (over 18's). Elocution. Improvisation
Language Tutoring. Private Acting Classes. Public Speaking
48 Chiswick Staithe
London W4 3TP
M 07976 805976   T 020 8994 8886
E neville@speakwell.co.uk
W www.speakwell.co.uk

CELEBRITY TALENT ACADEMY
2A Tileyard Studios, Tileyard Road
Kings Cross, London N7 9AH   T 0845 1162355
E celebritytalentacademy@gmail.com
W www.celebritytalentacademy.com

CENTRAL SCHOOL OF SPEECH & DRAMA, UNIVERSITY OF LONDON
See DRAMA SCHOOLS (Conference of)

CENTRE STAGE ACADEMY THEATRE SCHOOL
9 Beech Grove, Midhurst
West Sussex GU29 9JA   M 07773 416593
E brett.east@hotmail.com
W www.csa-theatreschool.co.uk

CENTRE STAGE SCHOOL OF PERFORMING ARTS
Students (4-18 yrs). North London
The Croft, 7 Cannon Road
Southgate, London N14 7HE
F 020 8886 7555   T 020 8886 4264
E carole@centrestageuk.com
W www.centrestageuk.com

CENTRESTAGE SCHOOL OF PERFORMING ARTS
All Day Saturday Classes. Drama School Auditions
Private Coaching for Professionals. Summer Courses
Centrestage House
117 Canfield Gardens
London NW6 3DY   T 020 7328 0788
E vickiwoolf@centrestageschool.co.uk
W www.centrestageschool.co.uk

Holy Trinity School, Trinity Walk
London NW3 5SQ

CHARACTER CREATION THEATRE
Performing Arts Classes For All
310 Hope Mill
Pollard Street East
Manchester, Lancashire M4 7JA   M 07592 050400
E charactercreationtheatre@gmail.com
W www.charactercreationtheatre.co.uk

CHARD Verona LRAM Dip RAM (Musical Theatre)
Teacher at Central School of Speech & Drama. Singing Tutor
Ealing House
33 Hanger Lane
London W5 3HJ   T 020 8992 1571
E verona@veronachard.com

CHARKHAM Esta
16 British Grove
Chiswick, London W4 2NL   T 020 8741 2843
E esta@clara.co.uk

CHARRINGTON Tim
Dialect/Accent Coaching
54 Topmast Point
Strafford Street, London E14 8SN
M 07967 418236   T 020 7987 3028
E tim.charrington@googlemail.com

CHASE Stephan PRODUCTIONS LTD
Private Coach for Acting, Auditions, Public Speaking & Script
Work. Originator of Managing Authentic Presence
The Studio
22 York Avenue
London SW14 7LG   T 020 8878 9112
E stephan@stephanchase.com
W www.stephanchase.com

CHEKHOV Michael CENTRE UK
Acting Workshops. Audition/Casting Technique. Film/
Television Acting. Private Acting Sessions. Vocal Training
Group Training: The Awakening, The Deepening
E admin@michaelchekhov.org.uk
W www.michaelchekhov.org.uk

CHRISKA STAGE SCHOOL
37-39 Whitby Road
Ellesmere Port
Cheshire L64 8AA   T 01928 739166
E chrisbooth41@hotmail.com
W www.chriska.co.uk

CHRYSTEL ARTS THEATRE SCHOOL
Part-time classes for Children, Teenagers & Young Adults in
Dance, Drama & Musical Theatre. ISTD & LAMDA Examinations
Edgware Parish Hall
Rectory Lane, Edgware
Middlesex HA8 7LG
T 020 8952 6010   T 01494 785589
E chrystelarts@waitrose.com

CHUBBUCK TECHNIQUE
Private Coaching. Workshops
E coaching@chubbucktechnique.co.uk   T 020 7732 1774
W www.chubbucktechnique.co.uk

CHURCHER Mel MA
Acting & Vocal Coach
E melchurcher@hotmail.com   M 07778 773019
W www.melchurcher.com

CHURCHER Teresa (Life Coach MASC)
Acting & Audition Workshops. Career & Life Coaching,
Industry Talks & Training Products for Young Adult &
Graduate Actors
London, Milton Keynes & Northampton
E info@theactingangel.co.uk   M 07807 103295
W www.theactingangel.co.uk

CIRCOMEDIA
Centre for Contemporary Circus & Physical Performance
Britannia Road, Kingswood
Bristol BS15 8DB   T/F 0117 947 7288
E info@circomedia.com
W www.circomedia.com

CIRCUS MANIACS SCHOOL OF CIRCUS ARTS
Full & Part-time Courses. One-to-One Act Development
Production Support
Unit 62, Basepoint Business Centre, Oakfield Close
Tewkesbury Bus Park, Tewkesbury, Gloucestershire GL20 8SD
M 07977 247287   T 01684 854412
E info@circusmaniacs.com   W www.circusmaniacs.com

CITY LIT THE
Accredited & Non-Accredited Part-time & Full-time Day &
Evening Courses. Acting Workshops. Audition Technique
Bi-Media. Camera Training. Dancing. Dialect/Accent Coaching
Directing. Elocution Coaching. Improvisation. Presenting
Professional Preparation. Public Speaking. Role-play Training
Singing. Story Telling
Keeley Street
Covent Garden, London WC2B 4BA   T 020 7492 2542
E drama@citylit.ac.uk   W www.citylit.ac.uk

CLEMENTS Anne MA LGSM FRSA
Audition Technique. Back to Basics for Professional Actors
Dialect/Accent Coaching. Preparation for Drama School Entry
Vocal Coaching
Hampstead   T 020 7435 1211
E woodlandcreature10@hotmail.com

COLDIRON M J
Audition Preparation & Presentation Skills
Private Coaching
54 Millfields Road
London E5 0SB   T 020 8533 1506
E jiggs@blueyonder.co.uk
W www.web.me.com/mcoldiron

COLGAN Valerie
Audition Technique. Voice Production
The Green, 17 Herbert Street
London NW5 4HA   T 020 7267 2153

COMBER Sharrone BA (Hons) MAVS (CSSD) PGCE
Audition Technique. Dialect/Accent Coaching. Elocution
Presentation Skills. Private Acting Classes. Public Speaking
Vocal Coaching
E sharronecomber@hotmail.com   M 07752 029422

Dee Forrest PGDVS Dip.DV. VOICE COACH

DIALECTS: FILMS & TV - www.projecturvoice.com

AUDITIONS • PROJECTION • DIALECTS • INTERPRETATION

VOCAL PROBLEMS • PHONETICS • PRESENTATION SKILLS

Tel: 01273-204779   Mob: 07957 211065   E-mail: dee_forrest@yahoo.com

Sessions in London & Brighton NLP Coaching

COMEDY COACH
Contact: Jack Milner
43 Church Street, Chesham
Buckinghamshire HP5 1HU   T 01494 772908
E jack@jackmilner.com
W www.jackmilner.com

COMPLETE WORKS CREATIVE COMPANY LTD THE
The Old Truman Brewery
91 Brick Lane, London E1 6QL
F 020 7247 7405   T 020 7377 7280
E theatre@tcw.org.uk
W www.tcw.org.uk

CONTI Italia ACADEMY OF THEATRE ARTS
See DRAMA SCHOOLS (Conference of)

CONTI Italia ACADEMY OF THEATRE ARTS
Italia Conti House, 23 Goswell Road
London EC1M 7AJ
F 020 7253 1430   T 020 7608 0044
E info@italiaconti.co.uk
W www.italiaconti-acting.co.uk

CORNER Clive AGSM LRAM
Qualified Teacher. Audition Training. Private Coaching
'The Belenes', 60 Wakeham
Portland DT5 1HN   T 01305 860267
E cornerassociates@aol.com

CORONA THEATRE SCHOOL
3 Thameside Centre, Kew Bridge Road
Brentford, Middlesex TW8 0HF   T 020 8758 2553
E info@coronatheatreschool.com
W www.coronatheatreschool.com

COURT THEATRE TRAINING COMPANY
The Courtyard Theatre, Bowling Green Walk
40 Pitfield Street, London N1 6EU   T/F 020 7739 6868
E info@thecourtyard.org.uk
W www.thecourtyard.org.uk

COX Gregory BA Joint Hons
Bristol Old Vic Graduate with 30 Years' Experience
Audition Coaching. Drama Coaching. Sight Reading Skills.
Voice Work
South West London   M 07931 370135
E gregoryedcox@hotmail.com

COX Jerry MA PGCE BA (Hons)
Acting Coach. Audition Technique. Preparation/Entry for
Drama School. Private Acting Classes
4 Stevenson Close, London EN5 1DR   M 07957 654027
E jerrymarwood@hotmail.com

CPA COLLEGE
Full-time 3 yr Performing Arts College
The Studios, 219B North Street
Romford, Essex RM1 4QA
F 01708 766077   T 01708 766007
E college@cpastudios.co.uk
W www.cpastudios.co.uk

CREATIVE PERFORMANCE LTD
Mobile Workshop in Circus Skills & Drama TIE. Events
Management for Libraries, Schools, Youth Clubs
& Play Schemes
20 Pembroke Road
North Wembley
Middlesex HA9 7PD   T 020 8908 0502
E creative.performance@yahoo.co.uk

CROWE Ben
Accent Coach. Acting/Audition Tuition
25 Holmes Avenue, Hove BN3 7LA   M 07952 784911
E bencrowe@hotmail.co.uk

CYGNET TRAINING THEATRE
See DRAMA SCHOOLS (Conference of)

D & B SCHOOL OF PERFORMING ARTS
Central Studios
470 Bromley Road, Bromley BR1 4PN
F 020 8697 8100   T 020 8698 8880
E bonnie@dandbmanagement.com
W www.dandbperformingarts.co.uk

DALLA VECCHIA Sara
Italian Teacher
13 Fauconberg Road, London W4 3JZ   M 07877 404743

DAVIDSON Clare
30 Highgate West Hill, London N6 6NP   T 020 8348 0132
E clare@claredavidson.co.uk
W www.claredavidson.co.uk

DE BURGH Luan BA (Hons) MA. MA Dip
Accent Softening. Elocution. Improvisation. Presentation
Skills. Public Speaking. Vocal Coaching. Voice & Text
E luan@luandeburgh.com   M 07976 809693
W www.luandeburgh.com

DEBUT THEATRE SCHOOL OF PERFORMING ARTS
12 Tenterfields House
Meadow Road
Apperley Bridge, Bradford BD10 0LQ   T 01274 618288
E jacqui.debut@btinternet.com
W www.debuttheatreschool.co.uk

DE COURCY Bridget
Singing Teacher
19 Muswell Road, London N10   T 020 8883 8397
E bridgetdecourcy@fsmail.net

De FLOREZ Jane LGSM PG Dip
Singing Teacher: Auditions. Classical. Jazz. Musical Theatre
Waterloo, London SE1 8LT   T 020 7803 0835
E janedeflorez@fsmail.net
W www.singingteacherlondon.com

DIGNAN Tess MA
Audition, Text & Voice Coach
004 Oregon Building
Deals Gateway
Lewisham SE13 7RR   T 020 8691 4275
E dignan@tess.orangehome.co.uk

1 Year Acting Course

Accredited by NCDT
Validated by Trinity College London
Member of the Conference of Drama Schools
Dance and Drama Awards Scheme

2 Year Acting Course

Validated by Trinity College London
Member of the Conference of Drama Schools
Dance and Drama Awards Scheme

4 Week Summer Acting Course

Intensive training for the
acting profession, for postgraduate
and mature students

The teaching is passionate, personal
and always relevant

We teach you not just how to act,
but how to be an actor

DRAMA STUDIO LONDON
Grange Court, 1 Grange Road, London, W5 5QN

020 8579 3897
admin@dramastudiolondon.co.uk
www.dramastudiolondon.co.uk

ACTING
CHARACTERISATION
STAGECRAFT
TV AND SCREEN
RADIO
TEXT ANALYSIS
MOVEMENT
IMPROVISATION
PHYSICAL THEATRE
VOICE AND ACCENTS
SINGING
WORK & AUDITIONS

DRAMA STUDIO LONDON

DI LACCIO Gabriela
Singing Teacher & Coach
165 Gunnersbury Lane
London W3 8LJ   T 020 8993 2111

DIRECTIONS THEATRE ARTS (CHESTERFIELD) LTD
Musical Theatre School & College
Studios: 1A/2A Sheffield Road
Chesterfield, Derby S41 7LL
M 07973 768144   T/F 01246 854455
E geoffrey.cox@btconnect.com
W www.directionstheatrearts.org

DOGGETT Antonia
Flat 2/2, 131 Queen Margaret Drive
Glasgow G20 8PD   M 07814 155090
E antonia.doggett@googlemail.com

DONKER CURTIUS Jill
W www.jilldonkercurtius.co.uk   M 07970 753289

DRAMA ASSOCIATION OF WALES
Summer Courses for Amateur Actors & Directors
The Old Library, Singleton Road
Splott, Cardiff CF24 2ET   T 029 2045 2200
E gary@dramawales.org.uk

DRAMA CENTRE LONDON
See DRAMA SCHOOLS (Conference of)

DRAMA COACHING
Audition Technique. Text Analysis
Trinity Guildhall Examinations
Vocal Presentation Skills
256 Earlsfield Road
London SW18 3DY   M 07950 720868
E euniceroberts1@gmail.com

DRAMA STUDIO EDINBURGH THE
Children's Weekly Drama Workshops
19 Belmont Road
Edinburgh EH14 5DZ   T 0131 453 3284
E info@thedramastudio.com
W www.thedramastudio.com

DRAMA STUDIO LONDON
See DRAMA SCHOOL (Conference of)

DRAMA TRAINING UK - ALISON MEAD
77 Victoria Road
Bromley BR2 9PL   T 020 8402 7858
E info@dramatraininguk.co.uk
W www.dramatraininguk.co.uk

DULIEU John
Acting Coach. Audition & Role Preparation
16 Fernwood Avenue, Streatham
London SW16 1RD
M 07803 289599   T 020 8696 9958
E john_dulieu@yahoo.com

DUNMORE Simon
Acting & Audition Tuition
E simon.dunmore@btinternet.com
W www.simon.dunmore.btinternet.co.uk

DURRENT Peter
Audition & Rehearsal Pianist. Vocal Coach
Blacksmiths Cottage
Bures Road, Little Cornard
Sudbury, Suffolk CO10 0NR   T 01787 373483

DYSON Kate LRAM
Audition Technique Coaching. Drama
39 Arundel Street, Kemptown BN2 5TH
M 07812 949875   T 01273 607490
E kate.dyson@talktalk.net

EARNSHAW Susi THEATRE SCHOOL
The Bull Theatre
68 High Street, Barnet, Herts EN5 5SJ
F 020 8364 9618   T 020 8441 5010
E info@sets.org.uk
W www.susiearnshaw.co.uk

EAST 15 ACTING SCHOOL
See DRAMA SCHOOLS (Conference of)

EASTON Helena BPSA MA ATC (CSSD)
Acting Coach
103 Red Square, Carysfort Road
London N16 9AG   M 07985 931473
E helena.easton@gmail.com

EASTON Lydia
Singing Teacher
72 Palmerston Road, London N22 8RF   M 07977 511621
E lydzeaston@yahoo.com

ECOLE INTERNATIONALE DE THEATRE JACQUES LECOQ
Contact: Rita Leys. Acting Workshops
Drama School (over 21 yrs). Mime. Movement & Creative
Theatre. Play Writing
57 rue du Faubourg Saint-Denis, 75010 Paris
F 00 331 45 23 40 14   T 00 331 47 70 44 78
E contact@ecole-jacqueslecoq.com
W www.ecole-jacqueslecoq.com

EDINBURGH LIGHTING & SOUND SCHOOL (ELSS)
c/o Black Light
West Shore Trading Estate
West Shore Road, Edinburgh EH5 1QF   T 0131 551 0204
E contact@edinburghlightingandsoundschool.co.uk
W www.edinburghlightingandsoundschool.co.uk

ELLIOTT CLARKE THEATRE SCHOOL & COLLEGE
Full-time Vocational & Evening Classes
35 Sefton Street, Liverpool L8 5SL   T 0151 709 3323
E contact@elliottclarke.co.uk

EXCEL SCHOOL OF PERFORMING ARTS
KT Summit House, 100 Hanger Lane
Ealing W5 1EZ   T 020 8799 6168
E excel@kt.org
W www.ktioe-excel.org

EXPRESSIONS ACADEMY OF PERFORMING ARTS
3 Newgate Lane
Mansfield, Notts NG18 2LB
F 01623 647337   T 01623 424334
E expressions-uk@btconnect.com
W www.expressionsperformingarts.co.uk

FAIRBROTHER Victoria MA CSSD LAMDA Dip
Audition Technique. Improvisation. Private Acting Classes
Public Speaking. Vocal Coaching
15A Devonport Road, Shepherd's Bush
London W12 8NZ   M 07877 228990
E victoriafairbrother1@hotmail.com

FAITH Gordon BA IPA Dip REM Sp MCHC (UK) LRAM
Speech
1 Wavel Mews, Priory Road
London NW6 3AB   T 020 7328 0446
W www.gordonfaith.co.uk/voice.htm

FBI AGENCY
Acting Classes for Everyone
PO Box 250, Leeds LS1 2AZ
M 07515 567309   T/F 07050 222747
E j.spencer@fbi-agency.co.uk
W www.fbi-agency.co.uk

FERRIS Anna MA (Voice Studies, CSSD)
Audition Technique. Private Acting Classes. Vocal Coaching
Gil'cup Leaze, Hilton
Blandford Forum, Dorset DT11 0DB   T 01258 881098
E atcferris@googlemail.com

FERRIS ENTERTAINMENT PERFORMING ARTS
London. Belfast. Cardiff
Number 8, 132 Charing Cross Road
London WC2H 0LA   T 0845 4724725
E info@ferrisentertainment.com
W www.ferrisentertainment.com

FINBURGH Nina
Sight Reading Specialist (Masterclasses & Individuals)
Audition Technique (Equity Members only)
1 Buckingham Mansions
West End Lane, London NW6 1LR   T 020 7435 9484
E ninafinburgh@aol.com

FOOTSTEPS THEATRE SCHOOL
Dance, Drama & Singing Training
1st Floor, Morrisons Enterprise
5 Bradford Road
Bradford, West Yorkshire BD10 8EW   T/F 01274 616535
E helen@footsteps.fslife.co.uk

City Lit offers a wide range of part-time acting and related courses in Central London

- Acting and Dance classes
- Agent and Casting directors Master-classes
- Method and Meisner classes
- TV Presenting, Radio, Voice-over and Camera workshops
- Story-telling, Stand-up Comedy, Performing Magic
- Weekend workshops
- Technical Theatre Skills (Foundation & Access)
- Stage fighting - Beginners and Advanced classes
- Musical Theatre Diploma
- Advanced Performance Diploma

city lit
The centre for adult learning

Over 400 part-time courses for adults available ranging from beginners to professionals.

Call the Drama, dance and speech department on 020 7492 2542 or e-mail: drama@citylit.ac.uk

Request a course guide at www.citylit.ac.uk

FORD Carole Ann ADVS
Acting Coach. Communication Skills
N10 2AL   T 020 8815 1832
E emko2000@aol.com

FORREST Dee
Deputy Head of Voice, Mountview. Audition Technique
Accent Reduction. Clarity & Elocution. Confidence Building/
NLP. Dialect/Accent Coaching for Film & Television. Public
Speaking. RP. Vocal Coaching
London & Brighton Studios
20 Landseer Road, Hove BN3 7AF
M 07957 211065   T 01273 204779
E dee_forrest@yahoo.com
W www.projecturvoice.com

FRANKLIN Michael
Meisner Technique
Correspondence:
c/o Spotlight, 7 Leicester Place
London WC2H 7RJ   T/F 020 8979 9185
E info@acteach.info

FRANKLYN Susan
Audition Speeches. Confidence. Interview Technique
Presentation. Sight Reading
M 07780 742891   T 01306 884913

FRIEZE Sandra
English & Foreign Actors
London Area NW3/NW6   M 07802 865305

MARJ MCDAID
BSocSc PGDVS
voice consultant and coach

speech - singing - dialects: speciality irish
mechanics of the voice - estill
psychodynamics of the voice - wolfsohn, gestalt

020 7923 4929
marjmcdaid@hotmail.com
www.voicings.co.uk

FURNESS Simon
Contact: Simon Furness. Actor Training (Sanford Meisner Technique). Acting Workshops. Audition Preparation & Technique. Private Acting Classes
c/o The Actors' Temple
13-14 Warren Street
London W1T 5LG   M 07702 619665
E simonfurness@googlemail.com

GLASGOW ACTING ACADEMY
Contact: Maureen Cairns, Allan Jones
2nd Floor
34 Argyle Arcade Chambers
Buchanan Street, Glasgow G2 8BD   T 0141 222 2942
E info@glasgowactingacademy.com

GLYNNE Frances THEATRE STUDENTS
Flat 9, Elmwood
6 The Avenue, Hatch End
Middlesex HA5 4EP   M 07950 918355
E franandmo@gmailcom

GMA TELEVISION PRESENTER TRAINING
Presenting for Television, Radio, Live Events. Autocue Improvisation. Scriptwriting. Talkback. Vocal Coaching
86 Beverley Gardens
Maidenhead, Berks SL6 6SW
M 07769 598625   T 01628 673078
E geoff@gma-training.co.uk

GRAYSON John
Acting Workshops. Audition Technique. Improvisation Private Acting Classes. Public Speaking. Singing Vocal Coaching
2 Jubilee Road, St Johns
Worcester WR2 4LY   M 07702 188031
E jgbizzybee@btinternet.com

GREASEPAINT ANONYMOUS
Youth Theatre & Training Company
Part-time Theatre Workshops Run Weekly through School Term Time. Holiday Courses at Easter & Summer Acting Workshops. Dancing. Singing (4-30 yrs)
4 Gallus Close, Winchmore Hill
London N21 1JR
F 020 8882 9189   T 020 8886 2263
E info@greasepaintanonymous.co.uk

GREGORY Paul
RSC & RNT Actor/Drama Coach
4302 Teesdale Avenue
Studio City, CA 91604, USA
M 001 310 218 2733   T 001 818 308 6557
E pgregory789@yahoo.co.uk

GREVILLE Jeannine THEATRE SCHOOL
Melody House
Gillott's Corner, Henley-on-Thames
Oxon RG9 1QU   T 01491 572000
E info@jgdance.co.uk
W www.jgdance.co.uk

GROUT Philip
Theatre Director. Drama Coaching. Tuition for Students & Professionals
81 Clarence Road
London N22 8PG   T 020 8881 1800
E philipgrout@hotmail.com

GSA, GUILDFORD SCHOOL OF ACTING
See DRAMA SCHOOLS (Conference of)

GUILDHALL SCHOOL OF MUSIC & DRAMA
See DRAMA SCHOOLS (Conference of)

HANCOCK Allison LLAM
Acting. Audition Coach. Dramatic Art. Elocution Speech Correction. Voice
38 Eve Road
Isleworth
Middlesex TW7 7HS   T/F 020 8891 1073

HARLEQUIN STUDIOS PERFORMING ARTS SCHOOL
Drama & Dance Training
122A Phyllis Avenue
Peacehaven
East Sussex BN10 7RQ   T 01273 581742

HARRIS Sharon NCSD LRAM LAM STSD IPA Dip DA (London Univ)
Speech & Drama Specialist Teacher
Private Acting Coach for Screen and Stage. Training for RADA LAMDA and ESB Exams. Audition Technique. Drama School and National Youth Theatre Audition Prepapration
71 The Avenue, Watford
Herts WD17 4NU
M 07956 388716   T 01923 211644
E theharrisagency@btconnect.com

HARRISON Abigail
Audition & Acting Coach
E creativeacting@hotmail.co.uk   M 07847 420882

HARRISON RUTHERFORD Lucie MA Voice Studies, BA (Hons) Drama
Acting Coach. Voice Teacher
11 Thorne Passage
London SW13 0PA   M 07773 798440
E info@lucieharrison.co.uk
W www.lucieharrison.co.uk

HASS Leona
Vocal Coach
12 Silverton Road, London W6 9NY   M 07801 270745
E info@apstudios.co.uk
W www.apstudios.co.uk

HEALING VOICES
Contact: Felicitas Ste. Croix
Singing. Voice Coach. Coaches many Actors, Church Musicians & other Professional Singers in the UK France & USA
E healing.voices@yahoo.com   M 07939 143721

HESTER John LLCM (TD)
Member of The Society of Teachers of Speech & Drama
Acting Courses for All Ages. Acting Workshops. Audition
Technique. Dialect/Accent Coaching. Drama School Auditions
(over 18s). Elocution Coaching. Private Acting Classes. Public
Speaking. Stage School for Children. Vocal Coaching
105 Stoneleigh Park Road
Epsom, Surrey KT19 0RF   T 020 8393 5705
E hjohnhester@aol.com

HIGGS Jessica
Voice
41A Barnsbury Street, London N1 1PW
M 07940 193631   T 020 7359 7848

H. J. A. (HERBERT JUSTICE ACADEMY)
Inspiration House
38 Croydon Road
Beckenham, Kent BR3 4BJ
F 020 8650 8365   T 020 8249 3299
E mail@hjaworld.com
W www.hjaworld.com

HOFFMANN-GILL Daniel
Acting & Audition Tuition
M 07946 433903   T 020 8888 6045
E danielhg@gmail.com

HONEYBORNE Jack
Accompanist. Coach
The Studio, 165 Gunnersbury Lane
London W3 8LJ   T 020 8993 2111

HOPE STREET LTD
Professional Development Opportunities for Emerging
& Established Artists
13A Hope Street, Liverpool L1 9BQ
F 0151 709 3242   T 0151 708 8007
E peter@hope-street.org
W www.hope-street.org

HOPNER Ernest LLAM
Elocution. Public Speaking. Vocal Coaching
70 Banks Road, West Kirby CH48 0RD   T 0151 625 5641

HOUSEMAN Barbara
Ex-RSC Voice Dept, Associate Director Young Vic
Acting. Confidence. Text. Voice
E barbarahouseman@hotmail.com   M 07767 843737
W www.barbarahouseman.com

HOWARD Ashley BA MA
Voice Coach
5 St John's Street, Aylesbury, Bucks HP20 1BS   M 07821 213752
E ashleyhowardvoicecoach@yahoo.co.uk
W www.ashleyhoward.yolasite.com

HUGHES Dewi
Accents. Auditions. Bodywork. Text. Voice
Flat 2, 4 Fielding Road, London W14 0LL   M 07836 545717
E dewi.hughes@gmail.com

HUGHES-D'AETH Charlie
RSC Voice Coach
Acting Workshops. Audition Techniques. Public Speaking
22 Osborne Road, Brighton BN1 6LQ   M 07811 010963
E chdaeth@aol.com

IMPULSE COMPANY THE
Meisner-Based Core Training
PO Box 158, Twickenham TW1 3WG   T/F 07525 264173
E info@impulsecompany.co.uk

INDEPENDENT THEATRE WORKSHOP THE
8 Terminus Mills
Clonskeagh, Dublin 6, Ireland   T 00 353 1 2600831
E info@independent-theatre-workshop.com
W www.independent-theatre-workshop.com

INTERACT
Contact: Lauren Bigby (LGSM)
Acting Workshops. Audition Technique. Elocution Coaching
Private Acting Classes
Public Speaking
18 Knightbridge Walk, Billericay
Essex CM12 0HP   M 07961 982198
E renbigby@hotmail.com

INTERNATIONAL SCHOOL OF SCREEN ACTING
3 Mills Studios, Unit 3
24 Sugar House Lane
London E15 2QS   T 020 8555 5775
E office@screenacting.co.uk
W www.screenacting.co.uk

JACK Andrew
Dialect Coach
Vrouwe Johanna
24 The Moorings, Willows Riverside
Windsor, Berks SL4 5TG   M 07836 615839
W www.andrewjack.com

JACK Paula
Dialect Coach. Language Specialist
Vrouwe Johanna
24 The Moorings, Willows Riverside
Windsor, Berks SL4 5TG   M 07836 615839
W www.paulajack.com

JAM THEATRE COMPANY
21 Beechtree Avenue
Marlow, Bucks SL7 3NH   T 01628 487773
E office@jamtheatre.co.uk
W www.jamtheatre.co.uk

JAMES Linda RAM Dip Ed IPD LRAM
Dialect & Speech Coach
25 Clifden Road, Brentford
Middlesex TW8 0PB   T 020 8568 2390

JAQUARELLO Roland BA
Audition Technique. Drama School Entrance. Radio Coaching
41 Parfrey Street
London W6 9EW   T/F 020 8741 2446
E roland@jaquarellofulham.freeserve.co.uk
W www.rolandjaquarello.com

JIGSAW PERFORMING ARTS SCHOOLS
Head Office:
64-66 High Street
Barnet, Herts EN5 5SJ   T 020 8447 4530
E admin@jigsaw-arts.co.uk
W www.jigsaw-arts.co.uk

JINGLES Jo
1 Boismore Road
Chesham, Bucks HP5 1SH   T 01494 778989
E headoffice@jojingles.co.uk
W www.jojingles.com

JONES Desmond
Courses in Dynamic Acting, The Total Actor. Introduction to Mime & Physical Theatre. Physical Story Telling for the Theatre. Private Classes & Consultant - Freelance Choreography. Coach. Director. Teacher
20 Thornton Avenue
London W4 1QG   T/F 020 8747 3537
E enquiries@desmondjones.com
W www.desmondjones.com

JUDE'S DRAMA ACADEMY & MANAGEMENT
Manor House
Oldham Road
Springhead, Oldham OL4 4QJ   T 0161 624 5378
E judesdrama@yahoo.co.uk
W www.judesdrama.co.uk

KENT YOUTH THEATRE
Contact: Richard Andrews
Stage & Screen Academy. Courses in Drama, Dance, Musical Theatre, Singing, Film Acting/Making. Improvisation Private Acting Classes. Stage School for Children
Office: Mulberry Croft
Mulberry Hill, Chilham CT4 8AJ
M 07967 580213   T/F 01227 730177
E richard@kentyouththeatre.co.uk
W www.kentyouththeatre.co.uk

KERR Louise
Voice Coach
20A Rectory Road, London E17 3BQ
M 07780 708102   T 020 8509 2767
E louise@louisekerr.com
W www.resonancevoice.com

KIRKLEES COLLEGE
Courses in Acting, Dance & Musical Theatre (BTec)
Highfields Annexe
New North Road
Huddersfield HD1 5NN   T 01484 437047
E info@kirkleescollege.ac.uk

KNYVETTE Sally
Drama School Preparation. Drama Tuition. All Levels
52 Burnfoot Avenue
London SW6 5EA — M 07958 972425
E salkny@aol.co.uk

KRIMPAS Titania
Audition Technique. Drama School (over 18's)
One-to-one Tuition
The Garden Flat
23 Lambolle Road
London NW3 4HS — M 07957 303958
E titania@krimpas.freeserve.co.uk

KSA PERFORMING ARTS
Beckenham Halls
4 Bromley Road, Beckenham BR3 5JE — T 01342 322121
E info@ksapa.co.uk
W www.ksapa.co.uk

LAINE THEATRE ARTS
Contact: Betty Laine
The Studios, East Street
Epsom, Surrey KT17 1HH
F 01372 723775 — T 01372 724648
E info@laine-theatre-arts.co.uk
W www.laine-theatre-arts.co.uk

LAMDA
See DRAMA SCHOOLS (Conference of)

LAMONT DRAMA SCHOOL & CASTING AGENCY
Contact: Diane Lamont
Acting Skills. Audition Technique Coaching. Part-time Lessons
2 Harewood Avenue
Ainsdale, Merseyside PR8 2PH — M 07736 387543
E diane@lamontcasting.co.uk
W www.lamontcasting.co.uk

LAURIE Rona
Coach for Auditions. Voice & Speech Technique
Flat 1, 21 New Quebec Street
London W1H 7SA — T 020 7262 4909

LEAN David Lawson BA Hons PGCE
Acting Tuition for Children. LAMDA Exams
Licensed Chaperone
72 Shaw Drive, Walton-on-Thames
Surrey KT12 2LS — T 01932 230273
E dlawsonlean@aol.com
W www.davidlawsonlean.com

LEE THEATRE SCHOOL THE
Office: 126 Church Road
Benfleet, Essex SS7 4EP — T 01268 795863
E lynn@leetheatre.fsnet.co.uk
W www.lynnlee.co.uk

LESLIE Maeve
Classical & Musicals. Presentations. Singing
Voice Production
60 Warwick Square
London SW1V 2AL — T 020 7834 4912

LEVENTON Patricia BA Hons
Audition & Dialect Coach
113 Broadhurst Gardens
West Hampstead, London NW6 3BJ
M 07703 341062 — T 020 7624 5661
E patricia@lites2000.com

LIEDERCOACH.COM
Contact: Jurgen Schwarz
German Singing for Lieder, Recitals & Opera. German Speech
for Film, Television & Theatre
E contact@liedercoach.com — T 020 3411 4951
W www.liedercoach.com

LINCOLN ACADEMY OF DRAMATIC ARTS
6-18 yrs
Sparkhouse Studios
Rope Walk
Lincoln, Lincs LN6 7DQ
F 01522 837201 — T 01522 837242
E info@lada.org.uk
W www.lada.org.uk/academy

Jurgen Schwarz German Speech Consultant and Coach

German Speech for Film, TV and Theatre • German Singing for Lieder, Recitals and Opera
t: 020 3411 4951 e: contact@liedercoach.com www.liedercoach.com

LIPTON Rick
Dialect/Accent Coaching
14 Lock Road, Richmond
Surrey TW10 7LH   M 07961 445247
E info@ricklipton.com
W www.ricklipton.com

LIVERPOOL INSTITUTE FOR PERFORMING ARTS THE
See DRAMA SCHOOLS (Conference of)

LIVINGSTON Dione LRAM FETC
*Audition Technique. Dialect/Accent Coaching. Elocution
Coaching. Improvisation. Language Tutoring. Private Acting
Classes. Public Speaking. Vocal Coaching*
7 St Luke's Street,
Cambridge CB4 3DA   T 01223 365970

LLOYD Gabrielle
*Audition Technique. Drama School Entrance. LAMDA Exams
Private Acting Classes. Public Speaking. Vocal Coaching*
Southwest London
E gubilloyd@hotmail.com   T 020 8946 4042

LOCATION TUTORS NATIONWIDE
*Fully Qualified/Experienced Teachers Working with Children
on Film Sets & Covering all Key Stages of National Curriculum*
16 Poplar Walk
Herne Hill SE24 0BU
F 020 7207 8794   T 020 7978 8898
E locationtutorsnationwide@googlemail.com
W www.locationtutors.co.uk

LONDON ACTORS WORKSHOP
Workshop Studio Based in Endell Street, Covent Garden
Enquiries:
29B Battersea Rise
London SW11 1HG   M 07748 846294
E info@londonactorsworkshop.co.uk
W www.londonactorsworkshop.co.uk

LONDON DRAMA SCHOOL
Acting. Singing. Speech Training
30 Brondesbury Park, London NW6 7DN
F 020 8830 4992   T 020 8830 0074
E enquiries@startek-uk.com
W www.startek-uk.com

**LONDON INTERNATIONAL SCHOOL OF PERFORMING
ARTS**
The Old Lab, 3 Mills Studios
Three Mill Lane, London E3 3DU
F 020 8215 3392   T 020 8215 3390
E welcome@lispa.co.uk
W www.lispa.co.uk

LONDON REPERTORY COMPANY ACADEMY
27 Old Gloucester Street
London WC1N 3XX   T/F 020 7258 1944
E academy@londonrepertorycompany.com
W www.londonrepertorycompany.com/academy

LONDON SCHOOL OF DRAMATIC ART
*Foundation & Advanced Diplomas in Acting (Full & Part-time)
Drama School (over 18s). Short Summer Courses*
4 Bute Street
South Kensington
London SW7 3EX   T 020 7581 6100
E enquiries@lsda-acting.com
W www.lsda-acting.com

LONDON SCHOOL OF FILM, MEDIA & PERFORMANCE
Regent's College, Inner Circle
Regent's Park, London NW1 4NS
F 020 7487 7425   T 020 7487 7505
E lsfmp@regents.ac.uk
W www.regents.ac.uk/lsfmp

LONDON SCHOOL OF MUSICAL THEATRE
83 Borough Road
London SE1 1DN   T/F 020 7407 4455
E enquiries@lsmt.co.uk

LONDON STUDIO CENTRE
*Courses in Theatre Dance (3 yrs), Full-time, BA. Evening &
Saturday Classes. Summer Course*
42-50 York Way, London N1 9AB
F 020 7837 3248   T 020 7837 7741
E info@london-studio-centre.co.uk
W www.london-studio-centre.co.uk

LONG OVERDUE THEATRE SCHOOL THE
5 Kings Chase, Andover
Hants SP10 3TH   M 07875 309868
E school@longoverdue.co.uk
W www.longoverdue.co.uk

LONGMORE Wyllie
19 Torbay Road
Manchester M21 8XE   T 0161 881 6440
E info@wyllielongmore.co.uk
W www.wyllielongmore.co.uk

MACKINNON Alison
Accent. Audition Preparation. Presentation. Voice
London SE6
E alison.mackinnon@bruford.ac.uk   M 07973 562132

MADDERMARKET THEATRE
Contact: Education Officer
Education Department
St John's Alley
Norwich NR2 1DR
F 01603 661357   T 01603 628600
E mmtedu@btconnect.com
W www.maddermarket.co.uk

MANCHESTER SCHOOL OF ACTING
29 Ardwick Green North
Manchester M12 6DL   T/F 0161 273 4738
E actorclass@aol.com
W www.manchesterschoolofacting.co.uk

GUILDFORD SCHOOL OF ACTING

Photo: Steve Porter

Courses for 2011 entry

Undergraduate:

- BA (Hons) Acting or Musical Theatre [3 years]
- National Diploma in Professional Acting or Musical Theatre [3 years]*
- 3 Year BA (Hons) Professional Productions Skills
- 2 Year Trinity National Diploma in Professional Production Skills
- 1 Year AP(e)L Trinity National Diploma in Professional Production Skills
- 1 Year BA (Hons) Professional Productions Skills [Extension to 1 and 2 Year Courses]

Postgraduate:

- MA Acting [1 year]
- MA Musical Theatre [1 year]
- MA Practice of Voice and Singing [1 year]

* Diploma courses validated by Trinity College London
Fully funded places available from Dance and Drama Awards for Trinity Diplomas
(option to top up to BA [Hons] with extra fee) and Higher Education Funding Council
for England on 3 year courses
All vocational courses accredited by the National Council for Drama Training

Member of CDS

Funded by

Young People's
Learning Agency

UNIVERSITY OF
SURREY

CDS

For an application form/further details contact:-
Guildford School of Acting
Stag Hill Campus, University of Surrey, Guildford GU2 7XH UK

Tel: (01483) 560701 Fax: (01483) 684070
Email: gsaenquiries@gsa.surrey.ac.uk Web: www.gsauk.org

MANCHESTER SCHOOL OF THEATRE AT MANCHESTER METROPOLITAN UNIVERSITY
See DRAMA SCHOOLS (Conference of)

MARLOW Chris
Voice & Speech Teacher
RDDC, 52 Bridleway
Waterfoot, Rossendale
Lancashire BB4 9DS   M 07792 309992
E rddc@btinternet.com
W www.rddc.co.uk

MARLOW Jean LGSM
32 Exeter Road
London NW2 4SB   T 020 8450 0371

MARTIN Liza GRSM GRSM (Recital) ARMC (Singing & Piano)
Piano Accompanist. Singing Tuition   T 020 8348 0346

MARTIN Mandi SINGING TECHNIQUE
Currently Coaching at Millennium Dance 2000 & Bodywork at Cambridge Performing Arts
90 School Lane
Bushey
Hertfordshire WD23 1BX   M 07811 758656
E mandi.martin@sky.com

MASTERS PERFORMING ARTS COLLEGE LTD
Musical Theatre/Dance Course
Arterial Road, Rayleigh
Essex SS6 7UQ   T 01268 777351
E info@mastersperformingarts.co.uk

MAVERICK YOUTH ACADEMY
12 Lydney Grove, Northfield
Birmingham B31 1RB   M 07531 138248
E academy@mavericktheatre.co.uk
W www.mavericktheatre.co.uk

MAY Maggie DRAMA
The Epsom Playhouse
Ashley Avenue
Epsom, Surrey KT18 5AL   M 07984 745323
E office@maggiemayltd.com
W www.maggiemayltd.com

McDAID Marj
1 Chesholm Road
Stoke Newington, London N16 0DP
M 07815 993203   T 020 7923 4929
E marjmcdaid@hotmail.com
W www.voicings.co.uk

McDONAGH Melanie MANAGEMENT (ACADEMY OF PERFORMING ARTS & CASTING AGENCY)
14 Apple Tree Way
Oswaldtwistle
Accrington, Lancashire BB5 0FB
M 07909 831409   T 01254 392560
E mcdonaghmgt@aol.com
W www.mcdonaghmanagement.co.uk

McKEAND Ian
Audition Technique. Drama School Entry
12 Linnet Close, Birchwood
Lincoln LN6 0JQ   T 01522 805966
E ian.mckeand@ntlworld.com
W http://homepage.ntlworld.com/ian.mckeand1

McKELLAN Martin
Acting Workshops. Dialect/Accent Coaching. Private Acting Classes. Vocal Coaching
Covent Garden
London WC2H 9PA   T 020 7240 0145
E martinmckellan@yahoo.co.uk

MEAD Alison
E info@dramatraininguk.co.uk   T 020 8402 7858
W www.dramatraininguk.co.uk

MELLECK Lydia
Pianist & Coach for Auditions & Repertoire, RADA, Mountview Accompanist. Singing for Beginners
Vocal Coaching. Workshops on Sondheim
10 Burgess Park Mansions
London NW6 1DP   T 020 7794 8845
E lyd.muse@yahoo.co.uk

MGA ACADEMY OF PERFORMING ARTS THE
The MGA Company
1 St Colme Street
Edinburgh EH11 2RZ   T 0131 466 9392
E info@themgacompany.com
W www.themgaacademy.com

MICHEL Hilary ARCM
Accompanist. Audition Songs. Diction & Languages for Songs Piano, Recorder & Singing Teacher. Technique. Theory Vocal Coach
82 Greenway
Totteridge, London N20 8EJ
M 07775 780182   T 020 8343 7243
E hilarymich@hotmail.com

MILLER Christie
Acting & Life Coach
32 Brookfield Road
London E9 5AH   T 020 8525 0111
E christie.miller@btinternet.com
W www.christiemillercoaching.com

MILLER Robin
Audition Technique. Dialect/Accent Coaching
South West London
E robinjenni@hotmail.com   M 07957 627677

MONTAGE THEATRE ARTS
Contact: Judy Gordon (Artistic Director). Dance. Drama Singing. Children & Adults
The Albany, Douglas Way
London SE8 4AG   T 020 8692 7007
E office@montagetheatre.com
W www.montagetheatre.com

MOORE Stefanie BA Hons LLAM
Audition Preparation. Public Speaking. Voice and Text
119 Francis Road
London E10 6PL   M 07751 564223
E stef@tinbobbin.com
W www.tinbobbin.com

MORGAN Katie BA (Hons) PG dip PGCE
Private Acting Coach
Audition Preparation. Devising. Drama School Entry.
Improvisation. Meisner Technique. Working the Text.
London   M 07956 344255
E katie080@hotmail.com

MORLEY ADULT EDUCATION COLLEGE
Acting School Programme. Day & Evening LOCN Accredited
61 Westminster Bridge Road
London SE1 7HT   T 020 7450 1925
E dominic.grant@morleycollege.ac.uk
W www.morleycollege.ac.uk

MORRISON Elspeth
Accent & Dialect Coach   M 07790 919870
E elsp.morrison@talk21.com

MORRISON Stuart MA Voice Studies (CSSD) FVCM (Hons) PGCE (Drama)
Voice & Speech Coach
24 Deans Walk
Old Coulsdon
Surrey CR5 1HR   M 07867 808648
E stuartvoicecoach@yahoo.co.uk
W www.voiceandspeech.org.uk

MOUNTVIEW
See DRAMA SCHOOLS (Conference of)

MRS WORTHINGTON'S WORKSHOPS
Part-time Performing Arts for Children (6-16 yrs)
16 Ouseley Road
London SW12 8EF   T 020 8767 6944

MTA (The Musical Theatre Academy)
The Drill Hall
16 Chenies Street
London WC1E 7EX
M 07904 987493   T 020 8882 8181
E info@themta.co.uk
W www.thetma.co.uk

Jill Donker Curtius MA

Dip Ed. Dramatic Art
CSSD/University of London

MA Actor Training and Coaching
CSSD/University of London

Association of Lamda Teachers

• Audition coaching for drama school entry
• Confidence building and practical support throughout the auditioning process
• Up to date monologue choice according to age and type

Recent entries:
LAMDA
Mountview Academy
Guildford School of Acting
Arts Educational
Oxford School of Drama
CSSD

m: 07970753289   www.jilldonkercurtius.co.uk

MURRAY Barbara LGSM LALAM
129 Northwood Way, Northwood
Middlesex HA6 1RF   T 01923 823182

MUSICAL KIDZ THEATRE COMPANY THE
Spires Meade, 4 Bridleways
Wendover, Bucks HP22 6DN
F 01296 623696   M 07989 353673
E themusicalkidz@aol.com
W www.themusicalkidz.co.uk

MUSICAL THEATRE SCHOOL AT BRISTOL ACADEMY OF PERFORMING ARTS
Academy Theatre, Market Place
Shepton Mallet, Somerset BA4 5AZ   T 01749 347984
E info@musicaltheatreschool.com
W www.musicaltheatreschool.com

NATHENSON Zoe
Audition Technique. Film Acting. Sight Reading Group Classes
55 St James's Lane, London N10 3DA   M 07956 833850
E zoe.act@btinternet.com
W www.zoenathenson.com

NEIL Andrew
Audition Technique. Private Acting Classes. Public Speaking
2 Howley Place, London W2 1XA
M 07979 843984   T/F 020 7262 9521
E andrewneil@talktalk.net

NEW LONDON PERFORMING ARTS CENTRE
Courses in Performing Arts (3-19 yrs). Dance. Drama GCSE Courses LAMDA ISTD & RAD
76 St James Lane
Muswell Hill, London N10 3DF
F 020 8444 4040   T 020 8444 4544
E nlpac@aol.com
W www.nlpac.co.uk

NEWNHAM Caryll
Singing Teacher
35 Selwyn Crescent, Hatfield, Herts AL10 9NL
M 07976 635745   T 01707 267700
E caryll@ntlworld.com

NICHOLAS Paul SCHOOL OF ACTING & PERFORMING ARTS
Thornton Little Theatre, Thornton
Cleveleys, Lancashire FY5 3SZ   T 01253 851144
E info@pnsa.co.uk
W www.pnsa.co.uk

NOBLE Penny PSYCHOTHERAPY
Character-Centred Counselling & Training. Character Development. Performance Support. Safe Emotion Memory Work. Script Work. Self-esteem & Confidence
8 Shaftesbury Gardens, Victoria Road
North Acton, London NW10 6LJ   M 07506 579895
E pennynobletherapy@googlemail.com
W www.pennynoblepsychotherapy.com

NORTHERN ACADEMY OF PERFORMING ARTS
Anlaby Road, Hull HU1 2PD
F 01482 212280   T 01482 310690
E napa@northernacademy.org.uk
W www.northernacademy.org.uk

NORTHERN FILM & DRAMA
Acting Workshops. Audition Technique. Dancing. Drama School (over 18s). Film & Television Training. Improvisation Private Acting Classes. Stage School for Children
PO Box 76, Leeds LS25 9AG   T/F 01977 681949
E info@northernfilmanddrama.com
W www.northernfilmanddrama.com

NPAS @ THE STUDIOS
Docklands, Dublin 1, Ireland   T/F 00 353 1 8944660
E info@npas.ie
W www.npas.ie

OLLERENSHAW Maggie BA (Hons) Dip Ed
Acting Workshops. Audition Technique. Career Guidance Private Acting. Television & Theatre Coaching
151D Shirland Road
London W9 2EP
M 07860 492699   T 020 7286 1126
E maggieoll@aol.com

OLSON Lise
American Accents. Practical Voice. Vocal Coaching Working with Text
Midlands Based
c/o Birmingham School of Acting
Millennium Point, Curzon Street
Birmingham B4 7XG   T 0121 331 7220
E lise.olson@bcu.ac.uk

OMOBONI Lino
Private Acting Classes
2nd Floor
12 Weltje Road, London W6 9TG
M 07525 187468   T/F 020 8741 2038
E bluewand@btinternet.com

OPEN VOICE
Contact: Catherine Owen
Auditions. Consultancy. Personal Presentations
9 Bellsmains
Gorebridge
Near Edinburgh EH23 4QD   T 01875 820175

OPPOSITE LEG LTD
Contact: David Windle
Acting Workshops. Classroom Presence for Teachers. Corporate Voice & Body Training. Improvisation. Presentation Skills Training. Private Acting Classes. Public Speaking Teenage Drama Workshops. Vocal Coaching
132 Bethwin Road
London SE5 0YY   M 07950 824123
E david@oppositeleg.co.uk
W www.oppositeleg.co.uk

SCREEN ACTING

STEFAN GRYFF (DGGB) (LLB)

"I believe that for film and TV an actors quality is more important than their level of talent."

I will provide:

- Individual or group tuition in camera acting
- Preparation of show reels for Casting Directors and Agents
- Special training for beginners and artists unused to camera acting
- Rehearsal & workshops for experienced actors currently employed in TV or film

Marble Arch Studio
Tel: 020 7723 8181

ORAM Daron
Senior Voice Teacher, Arts Educational Schools
Audition Preparation. Dialect/Accent Coaching
Voice Coaching
W4/SE10
E darono@yahoo.com   M 07905 332497

OSBORNE HUGHES John
Spiritual Psychology of Acting
Miracle Tree Productions Training Department
51 Church Road
London SE19 2TE
M 07801 950916   T 020 8653 7735
E johughes@miracletreeproductions.com
W www.spiritualpsychologyofacting.com

OSCARS THEATRE ACADEMY
Contact: Paula Danholm
Oscars Management
Spring Bank House
1 Spring Bank, New North Road
Huddersfield, West Yorkshire HD1 5NR   T 01484 545519
E oscars.college@virgin.net

OXFORD SCHOOL OF DRAMA THE
See DRAMA SCHOOLS (Conference of)

PALMER Jackie STAGE SCHOOL
30 Daws Hill Lane, High Wycombe, Bucks HP11 1PW
F 01494 510479   T 01494 510597
E jackie.palmer@btinternet.com
W www.jackiepalmer.co.uk

Heini Schneebeli
Photographer

Studio / location

020 7482 6568
07801 263 880

Roger Lloyd Pack   Jehane Markham Trio

PARKES Frances MA AGSM
Contact: Frances Parkes, Sarah Upson. Dialect/Accent
Coaching. Interview Skills for Castings. Presenting. Private
Acting Classes. Public Speaking. Speak English Clearly
Programme for Actors with English as a Second Language
Suite 5, 3rd Floor
1 Harley Street, London W1G 9QD
T 01782 827222 (Upson Edwards)   T/F 020 8542 2777
E frances@maxyourvoice.com
W www.maxyourvoice.com

PAUL'S THEATRE SCHOOL
Ardleigh House, 42 Ardleigh Green Road
Hornchurch, Essex RM11 2LG   T 01708 447123
E info@paulstheatreschool.com
W www.paulstheatreschool.com

PERFORMANCE BUSINESS THE
78 Oatlands Drive, Weybridge
Surrey KT13 9HT   T 01932 888885
E michael@theperformance.biz
W www.theperformance.biz

PERFORMANCE FACTORY STAGE SCHOOL THE
c/o Forge Fach Centre, Hebron Road
Swansea SA6 5EJ   T 01792 849565
E info@tpfwales.com
W www.theperformancefactorywales.com

PERFORMERS COLLEGE
Contact: Brian Rogers, Susan Stephens
Southend Road, Corringham
Essex SS17 8JT
F 01375 672353   T 01375 672053
E pdc@dircon.co.uk
W www.performerscollege.co.uk

PERFORMERS THEATRE SCHOOL
Hope Street, Liverpool L1 9DE   T 0151 708 4000
E info@performerstheatre.co.uk
W www.performerstheatre.co.uk

Royal Victoria Patriotic Buildings
London SW18   T 020 8479 3000

PILATES INTERNATIONAL LTD
Pilates Teacher Training (NVQ3 - Cert). Physical Coaching
Unit 1, Broadbent Close
20-22 Highgate High Street
London N6 5JG   T/F 020 8348 1442
E pilates@pilatesinternational.co.uk
W www.pilatesinternational.co.uk

POLLYANNA CHILDREN'S TRAINING THEATRE
1 Knighten Street
Wapping, London E1W 1PH   T 020 7481 1911
E pollyanna_mgmt@btinternet.com
W www.pollyannatheatre.org

POLYDOROU Anna
147C Fernhead Road
Maida Hill
Queens Park W9 3ED   M 07833 545292
E annahebe@yahoo.co.uk

POOR SCHOOL
242 Pentonville Road, London N1 9JY   T 020 7837 6030
E acting@thepoorschool.com
W www.thepoorschool.com

PRECINCT THEATRE THE
Units 2/3 The Precinct
Packington Square, London N1 7UP
F 020 7359 3660   T 020 7359 3594
E theatre@breakalegman.com
W www.breakalegman.com

PRICE Janis R.
Voice Coach
E janis@janisprice.sfnet.co.uk   M 07977 630829

PRIMOATTO PRODUCTIONS
2/21 Culmington Road, Ealing
London W13 9NJ   M 07830 120536
E mg@primoattoproductions.com
W www.primoattoproductions.com

QUEEN MARGARET UNIVERSITY, EDINBURGH
See DRAMA SCHOOLS (Conference of)

QUESTORS THEATRE EALING THE
12 Mattock Lane, London W5 5BQ
F 020 8567 2275   T 020 8567 0011
E jane@questors.org.uk
W www.questors.org.uk

RAVENSCOURT THEATRE SCHOOL
See CORONA THEATRE SCHOOL

RAW TALENT TRAINING
Contact: Helen Raw
Courses: Acting for Film, TV & Theatre Cold Reading &
Audition Technique. Monologue & Character Development.
Improvisation & Scene Study. Beginner to Advanced Actors
E info@rawtalenttraining.co.uk   T 0131 510 0133
W www.rawtalenttraining.co.uk

MOUNTVIEW
ACADEMY OF THEATRE ARTS

Ralph Richardson Memorial Studios, Kingfisher Place,
Clarendon Road, Wood Green, London N22 6XF

Musical Theatre

Acting

Technical Theatre

Stage Management · Lighting · Sound · Design · Construction

Undergraduate &
Postgraduate Courses
Plus an exciting programme of
Part-time and Summer Courses

Tel: 020 8881 2201
Fax: 020 8829 0034
enquiries@mountview.org.uk
www.mountview.org.uk

CDS MEMBER

Mountview is committed to equal opportunities.

TESS DIGNAN MA
VOICE AND ACTING COACH
All Audition Preparation Assisted
All Enquiries Welcome m: 07528 576915 **e:** dignan@tess.orangehome.co.uk

• RBC • RADA • LAMDA
• RSC • RNT • NTS
• FILM • TV • WEST END

RAZZAMATAZ THEATRE SCHOOLS
2nd Floor
Atlas Works, Nelson Street
Denton Holme, Carlisle CA2 5NB   T 01228 550129
E franchise@razzamataz.co.uk
W www.razzamataz.co.uk

RC-ANNIE LTD
Dramatic Fight Services. Theatrical Blood Supplies
34 Pullman Place
London SE9 6EG   T 020 8123 5936
E info@rc-annie.com
W www.rc-annie.com

REBEL SCHOOL OF THEATRE ARTS
& CASTING AGENCY LTD
Based in Leeds & Huddersfield
PO Box 169, Huddersfield HD8 1BE   M 07808 803637
E suerebeltheatre@aol.com
W www.rebelschool.co.uk

RED ONION PERFORMING ARTS CENTRE
Dance. Drama. Vocal Training Theatre School (3 yrs-Adult)
806 High Street, Leyton
London E10   T 020 8520 3975
E info@redonion.uk.com
W www.redonion.uk.com

REDROOFS THEATRE SCHOOL
26 Bath Road, Maidenhead
Berks SL6 4JT
T 01628 822982 (Holiday Times)   T 01628 674092
E sam@redroofs.co.uk
W www.redroofs.co.uk

REFLECTIONS AGENCY
34 Knowle Avenue, Bexleyheath
Kent DA7 5LX
M 07958 617976   T/F 01322 410003
E c.johnson717@ntlworld.com
W www.riverside-reflections.webs.com

REP COLLEGE THE
17 St Mary's Avenue
Purley on Thames
Berks RG8 8BJ   T 0118 942 1144
E tudor@repcollege.co.uk
W www.repcollege.co.uk

RICHARDSON ASSOCIATES
The Mill House, 3 Clough Mill
Walsden, West Yorkshire OL14 7QX   T 01706 812420
E russell@richardsonassoc.co.uk
W www.russrichardson.co.uk

RICHMOND DRAMA SCHOOL
1 Year Course
Richmond Adult College
Parkshot
Richmond, Surrey TW9 2RE   T 020 8439 8944
E mark.woolgar@racc.ac.uk

RIDGEWAY STUDIOS PERFORMING ARTS COLLEGE
Fairley House
Andrews Lane
Cheshunt, Herts EN7 6LB
F 01992 633844   T 01992 633775
E info@ridgewaystudios.co.uk
W www.ridgewaystudios.co.uk

RISING STARS DRAMA SCHOOL
PO Box 6281
Dorchester
Dorset DT1 9BB   T 0845 2570127
E info@risingstarsdramaschool.co.uk
W www.risingstarsdramaschool.co.uk

ROFFE Danielle
Acting Workshops. Audition Technique. Dialect/Accent Coaching. Drama School (over 18s). Elocution. Private Acting Classes. Public Speaking. Vocal Coaching
E danielle@danielleroffe.com   M 00 61 40406566 (Australia)

ROSCH Philip
Association of Guildhall Teachers, FVCM LALAM ATCL LGSM ANEA BA Hons. Auditions for Top UK Drama Schools. Audition Speeches. Effective Sight-reading. Commercial Castings Expert Career Guidance. Private Acting Classes
RADA Acting Exams
53 West Heath Court
London NW11 7RG   T 020 8731 6686
E philiprosch1@hotmail.com
W www.philiprosch.com

ROSE BRUFORD COLLEGE
See DRAMA SCHOOLS (Conference of)

ROSS David ACTING ACADEMY
Contact: David Ross
Acting Workshops. Audition Technique. Dialect/Accent Coaching. Drama School Preparation. Improvisation Stage School for Children. Vocal Coaching
8 Farrier Close
Sale, Cheshire M33 2ZL   M 07957 862317
E info@davidrossacting.com
W www.davidrossacting.com

ROSSENDALE DANCE & DRAMA CENTRE
Contact: Chris Marlow
LAMDA LCM TCL Grade & Diploma Courses & Exams. Acting Workshops. Audition Technique. Dancing. Dialect/Accent Coaching. Drama School (over 18s). Elocution. Improvisation Private Acting Classes. Public Speaking. Stage School for Children. Vocal Coaching
52 Bridleway
Waterfoot
Rossendale, Lancs BB4 9DS   T 01706 211161
E rddc@btinternet.com

ROYAL ACADEMY OF DRAMATIC ART
See DRAMA SCHOOLS (Conference of)

Janis R Price

MA TRAINING ACTORS VOICE
Guildhall School of Music & Drama

Original Qualification in Speech & Language Therapy
Central School of Speech & Drama (now not practising)

VOICE ~ SPEECH ~ TEXT   IN ALL PERFORMANCE SPACES

COMPANY WORK & INDIVIDUAL CLIENTS

07977 630829 janis@janisprice.fsnet.co.uk

ROYAL ACADEMY OF MUSIC
Musical Theatre Department
Marylebone Road, London NW1 5HT   T 020 7873 7483
E mth@ram.ac.uk
W www.ram.ac.uk

ROYAL SCOTTISH ACADEMY OF MUSIC & DRAMA
See DRAMA SCHOOLS (Conference of)

ROYAL WELSH COLLEGE OF MUSIC & DRAMA
See DRAMA SCHOOLS (Conference of)

RUMBELOW Sam
Acting & Method Acting Coach
84 Union Road, London SW4 6JU   T 020 7622 9742
E samson@methodacting.co.uk
W www.methodacting.co.uk

RYDER Richard
Voice & Accent Coach
9 Kamen House
17-21 Magdalen Street
London SE1 2RH   M 07967 352551
E richard_j_ryder@hotmail.com

SALES Stephanie
61 Brookfield Rd, Chiswick, London W4 1DF   T 020 8995 9127
E steph@stephaniesales.co.uk
W www.stephaniesales.co.uk/dramacoaching

SAMUELS Marianne
Accents. Text & Business Voice. Voice Coach
Ealing, West London   M 07974 203001
E mariannemicallef@hotmail.com

Three Year Acting Course

One Year Acting Course

Accredited by the National
Council for Drama Training

Dance and Drama Awards
available

**THE
OXFORD
SCHOOL
OF
DRAMA**

Six Month Foundation Course in Acting

Six Month Foundation Course in
Musical Theatre

For prospectus or further information

The Oxford School of Drama
Sansomes Farm Studios
Woodstock, OX20 1ER

www.oxforddrama.ac.uk
info@oxforddrama.ac.uk
Telephone: 01993 812883

A member of the
Conference of
Drama Schools

Funded by:

Leading learning and skills

The Oxford School of Drama Trust is a registered charity
The Foundation Courses are run by The Oxford School of Drama Limited

John Colclough A d v i s o r y

Practical independent guidance for actors and actresses

t: 020 8873 1763   e: john@johncolclough.org.uk   www.johncolclough.co.uk

SCALA SCHOOL OF PERFORMING ARTS
*Audition Technique. Dancing. Dialect/Accent Coaching
Improvisation. Singing. Stage School for Children
Vocal Training*
Office: 42 Rufford Avenue
Yeadon, Leeds LS19 7QR
F 0113 250 8806   T 0113 250 6823
E office@scalakids.com
W www.scalakids.com

SCHER Anna THEATRE
St Silas Church, Penton St, London N1 9UL   T 020 3093 5422
E enquiries@nicknightmanagement.com
W www.nicknightmanagement.com

SCREEN COMBAT SCHOOL
27 High Street
Kincardine, Alloa FK10 4RJ   T 01259 731010
E info@clanranald.org
W www.clanranald.org

SEMARK Rebecca LLAM
*Accent, Dialect, Elocution & Vocal Coaching. Audition
Technique. Drama School (over 18s). Drama School
Preparation. LAMDA Exams. Private Acting Classes. Public
Speaking. Stage School for Children*
Epping, Essex   M 07956 850330
E rebecca@semark.biz
W www.semark.biz

SHAW Phil
*Actors' Consultancy Service. Audition Technique
Voice Coaching*
Suite #476, 2 Old Brompton Road
South Kensington, London SW7 3DQ   T 020 8715 8943
E shawcastlond@aol.com

SHENEL Helena
Singing Teacher
80 Falkirk House
165 Maida Vale, London W9 1QX
T 020 7328 2921   T 020 7724 8793

SHINE TIME MUSICAL THEATRE & ACTING
*Contact: Laura Green. Audition Technique. Dancing. Drama
School Preparation. Improvisation. LAMDA Acting Solo
Examinations. Musical Theatre & Acting Holiday Workshops.
Private Acting Classes. Singing. Stage School for Children.
Vocal Coaching*
Flat 10, Valentine House, Church Road
Guildford, Surrey GU1 4NG   M 07880 721689
E shinetime@hotmail.co.uk
W www.shinetimeworkshops.com

SHOWSONG ACCOMPANIST
165 Gunnersbury Lane, London W3 8LJ   T 020 8993 2111

SIMMONS Jacki BA (Hons) PGCE MA (CSSD)
Audition Technique. Private Acting Classes
16 Tower Terrace, London N22 6SX   M 07989 389183
E jacki_@hotmail.com

SIMMONS Ros MA
Auditions. Dialects/Accents. Presentations. Voice
The Real Speaking Company
120 Hillfield Avenue
Crouch End, London N8 7DN
M 07957 320572   T 020 8347 8089
E info@realspeaking.co.uk
W www.realspeaking.co.uk

SIMPKIN Heather
Morriston, Fairmile
Henley-on-Thames, Oxon RG9 2JX   T 01491 574349
E heathersimpkin@btinternet.com

SINGER Sandra ASSOCIATES
*LAMDA & ISTD Exams. Acting Workshops. Audition Technique
Dancing. Dialect/Accent Coaching. Part-time Drama School
(over 18s). Improvisation. Private Acting Classes. Singing
Stage School for Children. Vocal Coaching*
21 Cotswold Road
Westcliff-on-Sea
Essex SS0 8AA   T 01702 331616
E sandrasingeruk@aol.com
W www.sandrasinger.com

SINGER STAGE SCHOOL
*Part-time Vocational Stage School & Summer School. Adult
Classes (16+ yrs) for Singing, Acting & Tap. Acting Workshops
Audition Technique. Dancing. Dialect/Accent Coaching. Drama
School (over 18s). Improvisation. ISTD. Private Acting Classes
Singing. Stage School for Children. Vocal Coaching*
Office: 21 Cotswold Road
Westcliff-on-Sea
Essex SS0 8AA   T 01702 331616
E sandrasingeruk@aol.com
W www.sandrasinger.com

SOCIETY OF TEACHERS OF SPEECH & DRAMA THE
Registered Office:
73 Berry Hill Road
Mansfield, Notts NG18 4RU   T 01623 627636
E ann.k.jones@btinternet.com
W www.stsd.org.uk

SPEAK EASILY
32 Bloomsbury Street, London WC1B 3QJ   T 020 7717 9649
E info@speak-easily.com
W www.speak-easily.com

SPEAKE Barbara STAGE SCHOOL
East Acton Lane, London W3 7EG
F 020 8743 2746   T 020 8743 1306
E speakekids3@aol.com

**SPEED Anne-Marie Hon ARAM MA (Voice Studies) CSSD
ADVS BA**
*Vanguard Estill Practitioner. Accents. Auditions. Coaching
Vocal Technique - Speaking & Singing*
E anne-marie.speed@virgin.net   M 07957 272554
W www.thevoiceexplained.com

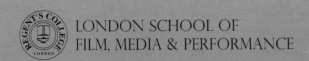

LONDON SCHOOL OF
FILM, MEDIA & PERFORMANCE

ACT ON AMBITION
IN A CREATIVE AND SUPPORTIVE LEARNING ENVIRONMENT

ACTING FOUNDATION COURSE 1 YEAR

Gain the skills to audition for drama school or undertake university-level study. This intensive course includes a Mock Audition Workshop with a professional director.

JANUARY AND SEPTEMBER ENTRY

BA (HONS) ACTING & GLOBAL THEATRE 3 YEAR

Develop your acting skills and undertake a challenging study of world theatre cultures. Includes exciting study period abroad in Australia, the Czech Republic or the USA.

SEPTEMBER ENTRY

MORE INFORMATION
REGENTS.AC.UK/LSFMP
COME TO AN OPEN DAY / SCHOLARSHIPS AVAILABLE

London School of Film, Media & Performance
Regent's College Inner Circle, Regent's Park, London, NW1 4NS, UK
Tel   +44 (0) 20 7487 7505   **Fax**   +44 (0) 20 7487 7425
Email lsfmp@regents.ac.uk   **Web** www.regents.ac.uk/lsfmp

GORDON FAITH B.A., IPA., Dip.R.E.M. Sp., L.R.A.M.
SPEECH AND VOICE TEACHER
• Ex BBC Repertory • All Speech Work Undertaken

020-7328 0446   www.gordonfaith.co.uk   1 Wavel Mews, Priory Rd. London NW6 3AB

SPIRITUAL PSYCHOLOGY OF ACTING THE
51 Church Road, London SE19 2TE   T 020 8653 7735
E info@spiritualpsychologyofacting.com
W www.spiritualpsychologyofacting.com

SPONTANEITY SHOP THE
85-87 Bayham Street
London NW1 0AG   T 020 7788 4080
E info@the-spontaneity-shop.com
W www.the-spontaneity-shop.com

STAGE2 YOUTH THEATRE
Based at:
Millennium Point
Curzon Street, Birmingham B4 7XG
E info@stage2.org
W www.stage2.org

Administration:
12 Valentine Road, Kings Heath
Birmingham, West Midlands B14 7AN   M 07961 018841

STAGE 84 YORKSHIRE SCHOOL OF PERFORMING ARTS
Evening & Weekend Classes & Summer Schools
Old Bell Chapel, Town Lane, Idle
West Yorks BD10 8PR
M 07785 244984   T 01274 569197
E valeriejackson@stage84.com

STAGE CENTRAL THEATRE ARTS
St John Fisher High School
North Yorkshire HG2 8PT
M 07940 014448   T 01423 331478
E darren@stagecentral.co.uk
W www.stagecentral.co.uk

STAGECOACH TRAINING CENTRES FOR THE PERFORMING ARTS
The Courthouse, Elm Grove
Walton-on-Thames, Surrey KT12 1LZ
F 01932 222894   T 01932 254333
E mail@stagecoach.co.uk
W www.stagecoach.co.uk

STAGEFIGHT
138 Wilden Lane, Stourport-on-Severn
Worcestershire DY13 9LP   M 07813 308672
E raph@stagefight.co.uk
W www.stagefight.co.uk

STE. CROIX Felicitas
Former Assistant to Jack Waltzer. Audition Preparation
Chekhov. Meisner. Meyerhold. Sense Memories. Coaches
many Professional Actors & Singers in the UK, France & USA
E felicitasstecroix@yahoo.com   M 07939 143721

STEPHENSON Sarah GMusRNCM PGDip RNCM
Accompanist. Audition Preparation. Vocal Coach
8A Edgington Road
Streatham, London SW16 5BS
M 07957 477642   T 020 8425 1225
E s.stephenson@ntlworld.com

STEWART Carola LRAM NCSD LUD
Audition Technique. CV Advice. Dialect/Accent Coaching
Elocution. Interview Technique. LAMDA Exams. Private Acting
Classes. Public Speaking
13 Church Lane
East Finchley
London N2 8DX   T 020 8444 5994
E carolastewart@msn.com

STIRLING ACADEMY
Contact: Glen Mortimer
Acting Workshops. Audition Techniques. Audition Training
for Camera. Drama School (over 18's). Improvisation. Private
Acting Classes. Showreels
490 Halliwell Road, Bolton
Lancashire BL1 8AN
F 0844 4128689   T 0845 0176500
E admin@stirlingacademy.co.uk
W www.stirlingacademy.co.uk

STOCKTON RIVERSIDE COLLEGE
Education & Training
Harvard Avenue, Thornaby
Stockton TS17 6FB   T 01642 865400
W www.stockton.ac.uk

STOMP! THE SCHOOL OF PERFORMING ARTS
Stage School for Children. Street Dance. Acting & Singing
Classes (6-19 yrs). Evenings & Weekends
Mill Hill & Finchley Areas
c/o Suite 2
Fiboard House
5 Oakleigh Gardens, London N20 9AB   T 020 8446 9898
E stompschoolnw7@aol.com
W www.stompschool.com

STREETON Jane
Singing Teacher, RADA
24 Richmond Road, Leytonstone
London E11 4BA   T 020 8556 9297
E janestreetonsop@aol.com

STUDIOS THE
Office: 47 Furze Platt Road
Maidenhead SL6 7NF   T 01628 777853
E julie.fox@virgin.net

SUPERSTARS IN THE MAKING
81 Tynewydd Road, Barry
Vale of Glamorgan CF62 8BA   M 07545 565425
E superstars@radio.fm
W www.superstarsinthemaking.com

SUPPORT ACT SERVICES
Contact: Ian McCracken
Services for Actors including Stage Combat Instruction
193 Church Road
Northolt UB5 5BE   M 07980 300927
E info@supportact.co.uk
W www.supportact.co.uk

TALENT TIME THEATRE SCHOOL
Show Company
Parkwood Health & Fitness Centre
Darkes Lane, Potters Bar, Herts EN6 1AA
M 07930 400647   M 07904 771980
E talenttimeyouth@aol.com
W www.talenttimetheatre.com

TALENTED KIDS PERFORMING ARTS SCHOOL & AGENCY
Contact: Maureen V. Ward
*Acting Workshops. Audition Technique. Dance. Drama School
(over 18s). Elocution. Improvisation. Musical Theatre. Singing.
Stage School for Children. Vocal Coaching*
23 Burrow Manor, Calverstown
Kilcullen
Co. Kildare, Ireland
M 00 353 872480348   T/F 00 353 45 485464
E talentedkids@hotmail.com
W www.talentedkidsireland.com

TEAM ACTIVATE
Auditions & Presentation Skills. Activity-based Workshops
E teamactivate@fastmail.fm   M 07837 712323
W www.teamactivate.com

THAT'S A WRAP PERFORMING ARTS SCHOOL
*Accompanist. Acting Workshops. Audition Technique. Dialect
& Accent Coaching. Elocution. Improvisation. Private Acting
Classes. Singing. Stage School for Children*
The Actors Studio
Pinewood Studios, Pinewood Road
Iver Heath, Bucks SL0 0NH   T 01753 650951
E info@actorsstudio.co.uk
W www.actorsstudio.co.uk

THEATRETRAIN
Annual West End Productions Involving all Pupils (6-18 yrs)
Orchard Studio, PO Box 42
Hitchin, Herts SG4 8FS   T 01327 300498
E admin@theatretrain.co.uk
W www.theatretrain.co.uk

TIP TOE STAGE SCHOOL
Dance, Drama, Singing & Performing Arts Part-time Training
For correspondence only:
65 North Road
South Ockendon, Essex RM15 6QH   M 07914 899438
E julieecarter@aol.com
W www.tiptoestageschool1.piczo.com

WARD CASTING

wardcasting.com / 0208 886 5676

Career advice, mentoring & development + Assisting with all your casting needs + Specialising in the 18-30 age range

TO BE OR NOT TO BE
Contact: Anthony Barnett
LAMDA Exams. Showreels. Theatre/Audition Pieces. TV/Film
Acting Technique
40 Gayton Road, King's Lynn
Norfolk PE30 4EL   M 07958 996227
E tony@tobeornottobe.org.uk
W www.showreels.org.uk

TODD Paul
Audition Technique. Acting. Drumming. Improvisation
Vocal Coaching
3 Rosehart Mews
London W11 3JN
M 07813 985092   T 020 7229 9776
E paultodd@talk21.com

TOMORROW'S TALENT
Theatre Training for Students (3-18+ yrs)
Based in Chelmsford, Essex   T 01202 526667
E enquiries@tomorrowstalent.co.uk
W www.tomorrowstalent.co.uk

TOP HAT STAGE SCHOOL
Part-time Theatre Arts Training in Hertfordshire (4-17 yrs)
Schools in Potters Bar, Welwyn, Stevenage, St Albans
& Hertford
PO Box 860, St Albans
Herts AL1 9BR   T/F 01727 812666
E admin@tophatstageschool.co.uk
W www.tophatstageschool.co.uk

TOP TV ACADEMY
Presenter Training. Researcher Workshop
Elstree Film & TV Studios
Shenley Road
Hertfordshire WD6 1JG   M 07971 284958
E liz@toptvacademy.co.uk
W www.toptvacademy.co.uk

TRING PARK SCHOOL FOR THE PERFORMING ARTS
Dance, Drama & Musical Theatre Training School (8-19 yrs)
Tring Park, Tring
Herts HP23 5LX   T 01442 824255
E info@tringpark.com
W www.tringpark.com

TROLLOPE Ann
Voice/Acting Coach
Harpsford, St. Peters Lane
Solihull B92 0DR   M 07943 816276
E ann-t@uwclub.net

TROTTER William BA MA PGDVS
25 Thanet Lodge
Mapesbury Road
London NW2 4JA   T/F 020 8459 7594
E william.trotter@ukspeech.co.uk
W www.ukspeech.co.uk

TUCKER John
Accents. Auditions. Role Preparation. Singing Lessons.
Voice Coaching
503 Mountjoy House, Barbican
London EC2Y 8BP   M 07903 269409
E mail@john-tucker.com
W www.john-tucker.com

TURNBULL Mark
E markturnbull14@btinternet.com   M 07742 070122

TV ACTING CLASSES
Contact: Elisabeth Charbonneau
E ejcharbonneau@aol.com   M 07885 621061

TWICKENHAM THEATRE WORKSHOP
FOR CHILDREN
29 Campbell Road, Twickenham
Middlesex TW2 5BY   T 020 8898 5882

URQUHART Moray
Private Coaching for Auditions, Schools, Showbiz etc
61 Parkview Court
London SW6 3LL   T 020 7731 3604
E nmuphelps@yahoo.co.uk

VALLÉ ACADEMY OF PERFORMING ARTS
The Vallé Academy Studios
Wilton House
Delamare Road
Cheshunt, Herts EN8 9SG
F 01992 622868   T 01992 622862
E enquiries@valleacademy.co.uk
W www.valleacademy.co.uk

VERRALL Charles
19 Matilda Street, London N1 0LA   T 020 7833 1971
E info@charlesverrall.com
W www.learntoact.com

VISUAL NOISE ARTS CENTRE & WHITE NOISE CASTING
Performing Arts Centre
19 Preston Old Road
Blackpool
Lancs FY3 9PR   T 01253 696990
E info@visualnoiseuk.com

VIVIAN Michael
Acting Workshops. Audition Technique. Improvisation
Private Acting Classes. Public Speaking
15 Meredyth Road
Barnes, London SW13 0DS
M 07958 903911   T 020 8876 2073
E vivcalling@aol.com

VOCAL CONFIDENCE
Contact: Alix Longman. Fast, Effective Vocal Technique for
Speech, Singing & Presentation. Audition Preparation
E alix@vocalconfidence.com   M 07958 450382
W www.vocalconfidence.com

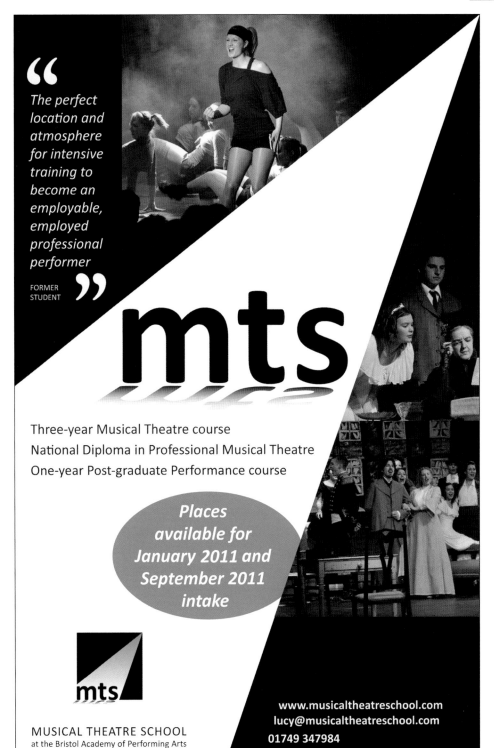

The perfect location and atmosphere for intensive training to become an employable, employed professional performer

FORMER STUDENT

mts

Three-year Musical Theatre course
National Diploma in Professional Musical Theatre
One-year Post-graduate Performance course

Places available for January 2011 and September 2011 intake

mts

MUSICAL THEATRE SCHOOL
at the Bristol Academy of Performing Arts

www.musicaltheatreschool.com
lucy@musicaltheatreschool.com
01749 347984

VOICE & ACCENT COACHING
7 Dodcott Barns, Burleydam
Whitchurch SY13 4BQ   M 07723 620728
E voice@carohetherington.co.uk
W www.carohetherington.co.uk

VOICE MASTER
Creators of the Hudson Voice Technique, the only Technique
in the World for Voiceovers, Actors & Autocue
88 Erskine Hill, London NW11 6HR   T 020 8455 2211
E stevehudson@voicemaster.co.uk
W www.voicemaster.co.uk

VOICE TAPE SERVICES INTERNATIONAL
Professional Management. Voice-Over Direction & CDs
80 Netherlands Road
New Barnet, Herts EN5 1BS
F 020 8441 4828   T 020 8440 4848
E info@vtsint.co.uk
W www.vtsint.co.uk

VOICES AND PERFORMANCE
Contact: Julia Gaunt ALCM TD-Musical Theatre
116 Nottingham Road, Selston
Nottinghamshire   M 07712 624083
E joolsmusicbiz@aol.com
W www.joolsmusicbiz.com

VOICES LONDON
Auditions. Technique. Vocal Coaching
36 Wigmore Street, London W1U 2BP
M 07775 810572   T 01279 655542
E info@voicesvocal.co.uk
W www.voicesvocal.co.uk

VOXTRAINING LTD
Demo CDs. Voice-Over Training
20 Old Compton Street
London W1D 4TW   T 020 7434 4404
E info@voxtraining.com
W www.voxtraining.com

WALLACE Elaine BA
Voice
249 Goldhurst Terrace, London NW6 3EP   T 020 7625 4049
E im@voicebiz.biz

WALSH Anne
Accents. Dialect. Speech
45B Windsor Road, Willesden Green
London NW2 5DT
M 07932 440043   T 020 8459 8071

WALSH Genevieve
Acting Tuition. Audition Coaching
37 Kelvedon House, Guildford Road
Stockwell, London SW8 2DN   T 020 7627 0024

WALTZER Jack
Professional Acting Workshops
5 Minetta Street Apt 2B
New York NY 10012
T 001 (212) 840 1234   M 07847 126318 (London)
E jackwaltzer@hotmail.com
W www.jackwaltzer.com

WARD CASTING LTD
Studio 5, 155 Commercial Street
London E1 6BJ   T 020 8886 5676
E casting@wardcasting.com
W www.wardcasting.com

WEAKLIAM Brendan PGDipMusPerf BMusPerf DipABRSM
Singing Teacher. Voice Coach
23 Alders Close, Wanstead
London E11 3RZ   M 07724 558955
E brenweakliam@hotmail.com

WEBB Bruce
Audition Technique. Singing
Abbots Manor, Kirby Cane
Bungay, Suffolk NR35 2HP   T 01508 518703

WELBOURNE Jacqueline
Choreographer. Circus Trainer. Consultant
c/o Circus Maniacs
Unit 62, Basepoint Business Centre
Oakfield Close
Tewkesbury Business Park
Tewkesbury, Gloucestershire GL20 8SD
M 07977 247287   T 01684 854412
E jackie@circusmaniacs.com
W www.circusmaniacs.com

WEST END WORKSHOPS
Arts Workshops. Audition Coaching
E info@westendworkshops.co.uk   T 01202 526667
W www.westendworkshops.co.uk

WESTMINSTER KINGSWAY COLLEGE
Performing Arts
Regent's Park Centre
Longford Street
London NW1 3HB
F 020 7391 6400   T 0870 0609800
E courseinfo@westking.ac.uk
W www.westking.ac.uk

WHITE Chris
Head of Acting Rose Bruford, BSA, Italia Conti
E chrisjohnwhite40@aol.com   M 07971 234829

WHITE Susan BA TEFL LGSM MA Voice Studies Distinction
Coach of Spoken Voice & Personal Presence. Summer Pause
Voice Days for Individuals.
Central London
E susan@per-sona.com   T 020 7244 0402
W www.per-sona.com

WHITEHALL PERFORMING ARTS CENTRE
Rayleigh Road, Leigh-on-Sea
Essex SS9 5UU   T 01702 529290
E info@whitehallcollege.co.uk

WHITWORTH Geoffrey LRAM MA
Piano Accompanist
789 Finchley Road
London NW11 8DP   T 020 8458 4281

WILDER Andrea
23 Cambrian Drive
Colwyn Bay
Conwy LL28 4SL
F 07092 249314   M 07919 202401
E andrea@awagency.co.uk
W www.awagency.co.uk

WILSON Holly
3 Worple Street, Mortlake
London SW14 8HE   T 020 8878 0015
E hbwilson@faxmail.co.uk

HOLLY WILSON
LLAM. Actor. Teacher-London Drama Schools.
Voice, Speech & Drama, Audition coaching. Private tuition.
Tel: 020-8878 0015

WIMBUSH Martin Dip GSMD
Audition Technique. Drama School Entry. Elocution
Public Speaking. Vocal Coaching
Flat 4, 289 Trinity Road, Wandsworth Common
London SW18 3SN   T 020 8877 0086
E martinwimbush@btinternet.com
W www.martinwimbush.com

WIMBUSH Martin Dip GSMD
31 Winchelsea Road
Rye, East Sussex TN31 7EJ   T 020 8877 0086
E martinwimbush@btinternet.com
W www.martinwimbush.com

WINDSOR Judith Ph. D
American Accents/Dialects
Woodbine, Victoria Road, Deal, Kent CT14 7AS
F 01782 728004   T 01782 827222
E sarah.upson@voicecoach.tv

WOOD Tessa Teach Cert AGSM CSSD PGDVS
Voice Coach
43 Woodhurst Road, London W3 6SS   T 020 8896 2659
E tessaroswood@aol.com

WOODHOUSE Alan AGSM ADVS
Acting Coach. Acting Workshops. Elocution. Private Acting
Classes. Public Speaking. Voice Coach
33 Burton Road, Kingston upon Thames
Surrey KT2 5TG   M 07748 904227
E alanwoodhouse50@hotmail.com
W www.woodhouse-voice.co.uk

WOODHOUSE Nan (Playwright & Honorary FLAM)
LGSM (Hons Medal) LLAM LLCM (TD) ALCM
                                   M 07812 921625

WORTMAN Neville
Speech Coach. Voice Training
11 Mandeville Place, London W1U 3AJ
M 07976 805976   T 020 8994 8886
E wortman.speakwell@btinternet.com
W www.speakwell.co.uk

WYNN Madeleine
Acting Workshops. Audition Technique. Directing & Acting
Coach. Drama School (over 18s). LAMDA Exams. Private Acting
Classes. Public Speaking
40 Barrie House, Hawksley Court
Albion Road, London N16 0TX   T 01394 450265
E madeleine@onetel.com

YOUNG Sylvia THEATRE SCHOOL
Acting Workshops
Audition Technique. Dancing. Improvisation. Singing
Stage School for Children. Summer Schools
Vocal Coaching
1 Nutford Place
London W1H 5YZ
F 020 7258 3915   T 020 7258 2330
E syoung@syts.co.uk
W www.syts.co.uk

YOUNG ACTORS THEATRE
70-72 Barnsbury Road
London N1 0ES
F 020 7833 9467   T 020 7278 2101
E info@yati.org.uk
W www.yati.org.uk

YOUNGSTAR TELEVISION & FILM ACTING SCHOOL
Part-time Schools across the UK (8-20 yrs)
Head Office
5 Union Castle House
Canute Road
Southampton SO14 3FJ
F 023 8045 5816   T 023 8047 7717
E info@youngstar.tv
W www.youngstar.tv

YOUNGSTARS THEATRE SCHOOL & AGENCY
Contact: Coralyn Canfor-Dumas
Part-time Children's Theatre School:
Commercials, Film, Stage, Television, Voice-Overs (4-16 yrs)
Dancing. Drama. Singing
4 Haydon Dell
Bushey, Herts WD23 1DD
M 07966 176756   T 020 8950 5782
E youngstarsagency@gmail.com

ZANDER Peter
Acting for Stage, Screen, Radio & Opera. Audition Technique
Breathing. Drama School Preparation. Improvisation. Mime
Movement. Posture. Private Acting Classes. Public Speaking
Relaxation. Speech Tutoring (English & German)
Voice Coaching
22 Romilly Street
London W1D 5AG
M 07920 125509   T 020 7437 4767
E peterzan.berlin@virgin.net

Michael Vivian Actor ▌ Director ▌ Writer
Productions at Arts Ed., Mountview, Guildford & Central
Also QDOS, UK Productions & various reps.
Voice Speech & Drama, Audition Coaching, Private Tuition
Tel: 020-8876 2073 Mob: 07958-903911

F

Festivals
Film & Video Facilities
Film, Radio, Television & Video
   Production Companies
Film & Television Schools
Film & Television Studios

24:7 THEATRE FESTIVAL
25-31 July 2011
PO Box 247, Manchester M60 2ZT   T 0845 4084101
E info@247theatrefestival.co.uk
W www.247theatrefestival.co.uk

ALDEBURGH FESTIVAL OF MUSIC AND THE ARTS
10-26 June 2011
Aldeburgh Music
Snape Maltings Concert Hall
Snape Bridge, Nr Saxmundham, Suffolk IP17 1SP
BO 01728 687110   T 01728 687100
E enquiries@aldeburgh.co.uk
W www.aldeburgh.co.uk

BARBICAN INTERNATIONAL THEATRE EVENT (BITE)
Year-Round Festival
Barbican Theatre, Silk Street
London EC2Y 8DS
F 020 7382 7377   T 020 7382 7372
E theatre@barbican.org.uk
W www.barbican.org.uk

BATH INTERNATIONAL MUSIC FESTIVAL
25 May - 5 June 2011
Bath Festivals, Abbey Chambers
Kingston Buildings, Bath BA1 1NT
BO 01225 463362   T 01225 462231
E info@bathfestivals.org.uk
W www.bathmusicfest.org.uk

BATH LITERATURE FESTIVAL
26 February - 6 March 2011
Bath Festivals,
Abbey Chambers
Kingston Buildings, Bath BA1 1LY
BO 01225 463362   T 01225 462231
E info@bathfestivals.org.uk
W www.bathlitfest.org.uk

BRIGHTON DOME & FESTIVAL LTD
7-22 May 2011
Contact: Andrew Comben (Chief Executive)
12A Pavilion Buildings, Castle Square
Brighton BN1 1EE
BO 01273 709709   T 01273 700747
E info@brightonfestival.org
W www.brightonfestival.org

BUXTON FESTIVAL
9-27 July 2011
3 The Square, Buxton
Derbyshire SK17 6AZ
BO 0845 1272190   T 01298 70395
E info@buxtonfestival.co.uk
W www.buxtonfestival.co.uk

CHESTER SUMMER MUSIC FESTIVAL
End June - Mid July 2011
Contact: Kate Sawallisch
(Festival Manager)
Chester Festivals Ltd
Chester Railway Station
1st Floor, West Wing Offices
Station Road, Chester CH1 3NT
BO 0845 2417868   T 01244 405631
E k.sawallisch@chesterfestivals.co.uk
W www.chesterfestivals.co.uk/site/music

[CONTACTS 2011]

What do I need to know about the listed festivals?

The festivals listed in this section are all dedicated to creative and performing arts. Festivals are an opportunity for like-minded people to gather together to appreciate and learn from both well-established and new and up-and-coming acts and performers.

Why should I get involved?

Being a spectator at a festival is a chance to see others in action and to see a variety of shows that are not necessarily mainstream. This is an opportunity to see talent in its rawest form, which is exactly why casting directors often attend drama festivals: they may spot someone who is just what they are looking for, who would otherwise have gone unnoticed in a pile of CVs.

Taking part in festivals will be something else to add to your CV and will help develop your skills. This not only means performance skills but social skills as well: you will meet hundreds of new faces with the same passion for their work as you, so this is a great opportunity to make friends and useful contacts in the industry.

What do I need to bear in mind?

Before committing to performing at a festival, there are a number of issues to take into consideration. You will usually be unpaid and you will have to set aside enough money to fund the time spent rehearsing for and performing at the festival, not to mention travel, accommodation and food expenses. Not only that, you must also consider that you will be putting yourself out of the running for any paid work offered to you during this time. Make sure you let your agent know the dates you will be unavailable for work. You may find it helpful to refer to Equity's advice leaflet *Low Pay/No Pay* which is available at http://www.equity.org.uk/Documents/Public/low%20pay%20no%20pay%202010.pdf

You may be required to not just perform but help out with any odd jobs involved with your show, such as setting up the stage and handing out flyers. If you are considering taking your own show to a festival, you will have to think well in advance about entrance fees, choosing and hiring a suitable venue, publicising your show, casting if necessary, finding technicians, buying or hiring props, costumes, sets, and so on. You must weigh up the financial outlays and potential headaches with the learning and networking opportunities that come with being involved in festivals.

How can I get involved?

If you are a performer at a festival, casting professionals could be there looking for you! Let them know that you will be performing and where and when. Send them a covering letter giving details and enclose your CV and headshot if you have not already done so in previous correspondence. You could do the same with agents if you are currently searching for new representation.

Spotlight members performing at the Edinburgh Fringe Festival can access a number of free services including a series of career advice seminars, one-on-one advice sessions with a Spotlight expert and free Wi-Fi. For full information or to book tickets for seminars please visit www.edfringe.com from June onwards and enter 'Spotlight' in the show/performer field. For full information or to book tickets for one-on-one sessions please visit www.spotlight.clickbook.net then click on the 'Edinburgh Festival 1 on 1's' tab to see available times.

Most festivals have websites which you can browse for further information on what to expect and how to get involved. Even if you simply go as a spectator to a festival, you will learn a lot and will have the opportunity to network. If you are performing in or organising a show, make sure you know exactly what you are letting yourself in for and make the most of your time there!

infopage

NSDF is a week-long celebration of theatre and live performance. The festival includes the most exceptional student theatre from across the UK, alongside workshops, masterclasses and performances from a diverse mix of extraordinary professionals. Chris Thorpe is an NSDF Selector, writer, deviser and performer. He writes and translates stage plays, screenplays and drama for BBC Radio 4.

Never in the whole of human history have there been fewer reasons to leave the house.

I sit here, writing this, streaming an album by a band I hadn't heard of until I saw them referenced in a bulletin board post about five minutes ago. I'm doing that until the film I could have got the bus into town, and paid a tenner to see at the pictures, has finished downloading. Then I'll watch it without interacting with a single other human being whose needs and priorities might conceivably conflict with my own. And after that the lovely man in the supermarket lorry will drop off enough food for the next week, and maybe the postman will turn up with that book on, I don't know, the Faroe Islands or Kazakhstani Punk Bands or something that I ordered yesterday because it just looked interesting. Then I'll update my status to reflect the facts above, and check back an hour or so later to see if anyone cares. Life is easy.

But for some reason, festivals still exist. Like Jeff Bridges, they abide. Because some things can't be replicated. Some things can't just be delivered or piped in fibre-optically. Some things you have to do a little bit of work for.

Some unkillable impulse still means that (most of us) have this need to get together from time to time. A need to check in and remind each other that we're still alive, and still capable of being re-energised and surprised by the world.

At the National Student Drama Festival in 2010 there were over 50 performances from some of the UK's most exciting emerging artists - all of whom were either in some form of education or had left education the previous year. That statement isn't meant to be patronisingly inclusive, suggesting that within the raw, unshaped talent of the selected shows lies the kernel of future artists to be nurtured and developed. The technicians involved, the performers, designers, directors and musicians involved aren't fighting for a place in some mythical club of professionals who are somehow supremely talented (read *lucky*) enough to have translated their passion into a career - and although some of the students at the festival probably look at it this way, they're wrong. By virtue of making the art that they bring, and their commitment to continue making it, the students are already artists. They're only emerging because they've just started.

Of course the students involved in the shows and, more vitally, the students who come without being involved in a show (and make up the lifeblood of the festival) benefit from the fact that the non-students who come to the festival - the Visiting Artists who run over 180 workshops - have been at it a bit longer. But it's not a meeting of mentors and pupils; it's a true exchange of experience. Punchdrunk stick around for a week to make a haunting site-specific, Akala fuses Hip Hop and Shakespeare, Mike Leigh or Christopher Eccleston answer questions about the reality of their jobs openly and honestly, Methuen talk about the state of playwrighting, Filter and Slung Low bring their own ideas about fostering a company dynamic and style - this is just a tiny selection of what's at the festival. And all these things would be interesting and informative if they were in the spirit of formal education, but it's the fact they're at a festival in which attendees are committed to the group, to the level playing field, to peer-to-peer dialogue and to honest exchange that makes the whole thing so valuable. Everyone creates and feeds off the energy regardless of their perceived position in the 'outside' world. The festival context is everything.

This touches on the durability of the festival as a form in a world where it's increasingly easy to shut yourself in. Whether it's Manchester International's huge international challenge to their audience to try something different, the variety of Latitude, the open lack of compromise of All Tomorrow's Parties, or the free-for-all of Edinburgh, the one thing that the best festivals have in common is that they demand investment. Investment in travel: mental and physical. Investment in risk. Investment of artists in throwing their work open to all-comers and of audiences in stepping through the door to try something they might not have heard of, that might be disagreeable, alienating, delighting - life-changing, even.

Festivals are a way of coping with the fact that other human beings exist. And, you know, *celebrating* that fact. Bring it on.

Please visit www.nsdf.org.uk for further information.

Rupert Lazarus recently graduated from the University of Leeds with a BA Hons in Theatre and Performance. At NSDF 2010 he won the Spotlight Award for Most Promising Actor.

The one question I am constantly asked is *why*. Why an actor? Why do any of us want to embark upon the tight rope that is a career in performance? The precarious nature of such a profession must keep supportive parents awake at night. Although my conviction wavers on the *why*, all I know is that it is this or nothing.

Photo: Sandy Pond-Jones

Becoming a student of drama has only added fuel to that furnace by giving me the initial tools and knowledge to question its subjectivity. The degree itself provided little actor training and as a result, opportunities to work with theatrical texts came about through my own endeavours. The endless theatrical opportunities provided by my peers and university societies firstly etched into me that this was something I wanted to do and secondly led me to NSDF. Under the guidance, imagination and vision from my director we were able to create a character that was both loved and hated, respected and corrupted, absurdly content in his nihilism. Performing with talented colleagues made long hours fade into short minutes; standing alongside exceptional talent armed me with the confidence that our show would excel. My only regret is that I did not go earlier.

Being given the chance to perform in front of the likes of Mike Leigh and Mark Ravenhill was a privilege, accentuated further by the environment that is NSDF; an environment that encourages communication, discussion and debate. As the glory of this unique event faded I found myself considering once again the *why*. The beauty of theatre lies in the memory; it is transient, it passes, actors sculpt in snow. But within those memories I feel my heart smile, and chasing that smile provides me with the answer.

Rachel Helen Shaw recently graduated from the University of Leeds with a BA Hons in Theatre and Performance. At NSDF 2010 she won the Spotlight Award for Most Promising Actress.

My mother was the one who believed in my acting ability. My own belief had been lost somewhere at school between the name calling and the whispering that I'm sure we are all too familiar with. She encouraged me to enrol in performance at Hull College and my tutor there motivated me to study it further at university. It is only now that I have been thrown into the 'real world' that I finally understand how much of a performer lives inside me. I feel scared, daunted, anxious, overwhelmed, but I honestly cannot imagine

Photo: Richard Clifton

doing anything else with my life.

I have been fortunate throughout my education to be given frequent opportunities to work professionally with Hull Truck Theatre and freelance writer Dave Windass. I also have the advantage of an agent, a privilege many performers dream of graduating with. However, the National Student Drama Festival has been one of the best events in my life so far. Although I cannot stress the significance of being able to perform for countless celebrated industry professionals, the festival offered so much more than simply an opportunity to act. The Auditioning for Camera workshop has already changed the way I interview for television. The skills discovered in the Actors' Physical Choices workshop are demonstrated in my current performance *Thinspiration*, a one woman show in which I portray the bipolar lifestyle of an anorexic. The workshops alone are invaluable.

I would recommend NSDF to any aspiring performers. It offers more than you could imagine and in the week you spend there you live in another world: a creative place which allows you to truly celebrate your chosen profession. It is a week which has given me the belief I have needed in myself to survive in this precarious industry: a priceless souvenir.

NSDF is essential, I was inspired by all the drive, idealism and commitment.
Christopher Eccleston

The Sunday Times National Student Drama Festival is a week-long celebration of theatre and live performance, including the most exceptional student theatre from across the UK, workshops, masterclasses and performances from a diverse mix of extraordinary professionals.

NSDF10's Visiting Artists included Akala, ATG, Belt Up, John Caird, Christopher Eccleston, Filter, Gandini Company, Graeae, Hip Hop Shakespeare, IdeasTap, ITC, Stephen Jeffreys, Terry King, Mike Leigh, Methuen Drama, National Theatre Studio, NYT, Punchdrunk, Mark Ravenhill, The Roundhouse, RSC, Showstopper!, Stage Electrics and Tamasha.

NSDF11 is **the** place for students seeking involvement with drama and the creative industries and is open to anyone aged sixteen and over and up to a year after graduating.

NSDF is amazing. I now know how to improve and my confidence has grown tenfold with the humbling and inspiring advice and compliments of some amazing people like Mike Leigh and Mark Ravenhill (who then came to the pub quiz after.) Simply extraordinary.
Ashley Scott Layton, Student Director

WWW.NSDF.ORG.UK
Scarborough 9–15 Apr 2011
Photographs © by Allan Titmuss

CHICHESTER FESTIVITIES (Not Chichester Festival Theatre)
24 June - 10 July 2011 (Provisional)
Canon Gate House, South Street
Chichester, West Sussex PO19 1PU
F 01243 528356   T 01243 785718
E info@chifest.org.uk
W www.chifest.org.uk

DANCE UMBRELLA
October 2011
Dance Umbrella brings brave new dance to London as part of its leading international dance festival
1 Brewery Square, London SE1 2LF
F 020 8741 7902   T 020 8741 4040
E mail@danceumbrella.co.uk
W www.danceumbrella.co.uk

EDINBURGH FESTIVAL FRINGE
5-29 August 2011
Festival Fringe Society Ltd, 180 High Street
Edinburgh EH1 1QS
BO 0131 226 0000   T 0131 226 0026
W www.edfringe.com

EDINBURGH INTERNATIONAL FESTIVAL
12 August - 4 September 2011
The Hub, Castlehill
Edinburgh EH1 2NE   BO 0131 473 2000
E boxoffice@eif.co.uk
W www.eif.co.uk

HARROGATE INTERNATIONAL FESTIVAL
15-31 July 2011
Raglan House, Raglan Street
Harrogate, North Yorkshire HG1 1LE
F 01423 521264   T 01423 562303
E info@harrogate-festival.org.uk
W www.harrogate-festival.org.uk

HENLEY FRINGE TRUST THE
18-23 July 2011
Aston Farm House, Remenham Lane
Henley on Thames, Oxon RG9 3DE   M 07742 059762
E info@henleyfringe.org
W www.henleyfringe.org

KING'S LYNN FESTIVAL
17-30 July 2011
5 Thoresby College, Queen Street
King's Lynn, Norfolk PE30 1HX
F 01553 767688   T 01553 767557
W www.kingslynnfestival.org.uk

LIFT
Biennial Festival
Trinity Buoy Wharf, 60 Orchard Place
London E14 0JW
F 020 7093 1304   T 020 7093 6340
E kate@liftfestival.com
W www.liftfestival.com

LLANDOVERY THEATRE ARTS FESTIVAL
Autumn 2011
Director: Jaqueline Harrison
Llandovery Theatre, Stone Street
Llandovery, Carmarthenshire SA20 0DQ   T 01550 720113
W www.llandoverytheatre.com

11-13 MARCH 2011, OLYMPIA, LONDON

PERFORM 2011

PERFORMSHOW.CO.UK

PERFORM 2011 is the new exciting show for aspiring actors, singers and anyone looking for a career in theatre and performance (London's Olympia 11-13 March 2011).

The event offers the opportunity to meet 30 exhibitors, including top schools, courses, colleges, associations, agents, photographers and casting directories - all the industry professionals that can help enhance your education, skills and start an exciting career.

There will be **25 free fabulous workshops** to choose from, covering important and practical topics for a performer's career such as audition tips, singing and acting surgery, your body on stage, acting for the camera, presenting skills, getting the perfect head-shot and many more. The full programme can be found online.

4,000 likeminded visitors are expected. This is a great opportunity to network and find new exciting people to work with or learn from.

For more information about ***PERFORM 2011*** please visit

www.performshow.co.uk

Box office opens in December. We recommend you register online for regular updates and to be the first to register for our free workshops as spaces are limited!

SPOTLIGHT
at the
Edinburgh Festival Fringe

Spotlight will be in Edinburgh in 2011 for the festival and as usual we've got lots to offer our members:

Free Seminars

Essential career tips and advice from Spotlight experts and casting professionals. Last year's seminars included 'How to be a Professional Actor', 'Meet the Casting Director' and 'So You Want To Be An Actor'. For full information or to book tickets please visit www.edfringe.com and put 'Spotlight' in the show/performer field.

Free Careers Advice For Actors, Dancers, and Presenters

Informal fifteen minute 1-on-1 sessions offering personalised career advice from Spotlight. For full information or to book tickets please visit www.spotlight.clickbook.net then click on the 'Edinburgh Festival 1 on 1's' tab to see available times.

Free Wi-Fi

Free Spotlight Wi-Fi access is available to all.

Spotlight Performers Facebook Group

If you are performing at the festival you can post up flyers, show details and photos on the Spotlight Performers Facebook Group so that your fellow performers can come and see your show!

LUDLOW FESTIVAL SOCIETY LTD
27 June - 12 July 2011
Festival Office, Castle Square
Ludlow, Shropshire SY8 1AY
BO 01584 872150
E admin@ludlowfestival.co.uk
W www.ludlowfestival.co.uk
T 01584 875070

MOVE IT 2011
10-13 March 2011
Olympia Exhibition Centre
Warwick Road
London SW5 9TA
E info@moveitdance.co.uk
W www.moveitdance.co.uk
T 020 7288 6463

PERFORM 2011
11-13 March 2011
Olympia Exhibition Centre
Warwick Road
London SW5 9TA
E info@performshow.co.uk
W www.performshow.co.uk
T 020 7288 6463

SUNDAY TIMES NATIONAL STUDENT DRAMA FESTIVAL THE
9-15 April 2011
Scarborough. Contact: Holly Kendrick (Director)
Woolyard, 54 Bermondsey Street
London SE1 3UD
E info@nsdf.org.uk
W www.nsdf.org.uk

TAIWAN CINEFEST LONDON
March 2011
c/o Cinefest Productions
1st Floor, Albion Mills
18 East Tenter Street
London E1 8DN
E s.flynn@taiwancinefest.com
W www.taiwancinefest.com
M 07932 364665

ULSTER BANK BELFAST FESTIVAL AT QUEEN'S
14-29 October 2011
8 Fitzwilliam Street
Belfast BT9 6AW
F 028 9097 1336
E festivalservice@qub.ac.uk
W www.belfastfestival.com
T 028 9097 1034

ULSTER BANK DUBLIN THEATRE FESTIVAL
29 September - 16 October 2011
Contact: Shauna Lyons
44 East Essex Street
Temple Bar, Dublin 2, Ireland
F 00 353 1 6797709
E marketing@dublintheatrefestival.com
W www.dublintheatrefestival.com
T 00 353 1 6778439

WINCHESTER HAT FAIR, FESTIVAL OF STREET THEATRE
1-3 July 2011
5A Jewry Street, Winchester
Hampshire SO23 8RZ
E info@hatfair.co.uk
W www.hatfair.co.uk
T 01962 849841

ACTOR'S ONE-STOP SHOP THE
Showreels for Performing Artists
First Floor, Above The Gate Pub
Station Road, London N22 7SS   T 020 8888 7006
E info@actorsonestopshop.com
W www.actorsonestopshop.com

ALBANY THE
Douglas Way, London SE8 4AG
F 020 8469 2253   T 020 8692 4446
E hires@thealbany.org.uk
W www.thealbany.org.uk

ANVIL POST PRODUCTION
Contact: Mike Anscombe (Studio Manager)
Perivale Park, Horsenden Lane South
Perivale UB6 7RL   T 020 8799 0555
E mike.anscombe@technicolor.com
W www.technicolor.com

ARRI MEDIA
3 Highbridge, Oxford Road
Uxbridge, Middlesex UB8 1LX
F 01895 457101   T 01895 457100
E info@arrimedia.com
W www.arrimedia.com

ASCENT MEDIA LTD
Post-Production Facilities
Film House, 142 Wardour Street
London W1F 8DD
F 020 7878 7800   T 020 7878 0000
W www.ascentmedia.co.uk

CENTRAL FILM FACILITIES
Film Unit Drivers & Transport
c/o Myddle Cottage
Plaish, Church Stretton
Shropshire SY6 7HX
M 07966 421878   T 01694 771544
E mansell323@btinternet.com
W www.centralfilmfacilities.com

CENTRELINE VIDEO LTD
138 Westwood Road, Tilehurst
Reading RG31 6LL   T 0118 941 0033
W www.centrelinevideo.com

CHANNEL 2020 LTD
2020 House, 26-28 Talbot Lane
Leicester LE1 4LR
F 0116 222 1113   T 0844 8402020
E info@channel2020.co.uk
W www.channel2020.co.uk

The Clerkenwell Workshops
27/31 Clerkenwell Close
London EC1R 0AT

CLICKS MEDIA STUDIOS
Contact: Peter Snell
Amp House, Grove Road
Rochester, Kent ME2 4BX   T 01634 723838
E info@clicksmediastudios.com
W www.clicksmediastudios.com

CRYSTAL MEDIA
28 Castle Street, Edinburgh EH2 3HT
F 0131 240 0989   T 0131 240 0988
E hello@crystal-media.co.uk
W www.crystal-media.co.uk

DE LANE LEA
Film & TV Sound Dubbing & Editing Suite
75 Dean Street, London W1D 3PU
F 020 7432 3838   T 020 7432 3800
E solutions@delanelea.com
W www.delanelea.com

DENMAN PRODUCTIONS
*3D Computer Animation. Film/Video CD Business Card
Showreels*
60 Mallard Place
Strawberry Vale
Twickenham TW1 4SR   T 020 8891 3461
E info@denman.co.uk
W www.denman.co.uk

DIVERSE PRODUCTION LTD
Pre & Post-Production
Network House, 1 Ariel Way
London W12 7SL
F 020 3189 3200   T 020 7603 4567
E reception@diverse.tv
W www.diverse.tv

EXECUTIVE AUDIO VISUAL
*DVD Editing & Duplication Service
Photography Services*
E chris.jarvis60@gmail.com   T 020 7723 4488

FROME SILK MILL STUDIOS
Westbrook House, 33 Vicarage Street
Frome BA11 1PU
M 07811 440584   T 01373 473246
E silkmillstudios@macace.net

GREENPARK PRODUCTIONS LTD
Film & Video Archives
Illand, Launceston
Cornwall PL15 7LS
F 01566 782127   T 01566 782217
E info@greenparkimages.co.uk
W www.greenparkimages.co.uk

HARLEQUIN PRODUCTIONS
Suite 5, Woodville Court
31 Sylvan Road
London SE19 2SG   T 020 8653 2333
E neill@harlequinproductions.co.uk
W www.harlequinproductions.co.uk

HARVEY HOUSE FILMS LTD
Animation. Full Pre/Post Production. Graphics. Showreels
71 Southfield Road, London W4 1BB   M 07968 830536
E chris@harveyhousefilms.co.uk
W www.harveyhousefilms.co.uk

HUNKY DORY PRODUCTIONS LTD
Crew. Facilities. Also Editing: Non-Linear
57 Alan Drive, Barnet
Herts EN5 2PW
M 07973 655510   T 020 8440 0820
E adrian@hunkydory.tv
W www.hunkydory.tv

MPC (THE MOVING PICTURE COMPANY)
Post-Production
127 Wardour Street, London W1F 0NL
F 020 7287 5187   T 020 7434 3100
E mailbox@moving-picture.com
W www.moving-picture.com

OCEAN OPTICS
Underwater Camera Sales & Operator Rental
Archer Fields, Burnt Mills Industrial Estate
Basildon, Essex SS13 1DL
F 01268 523795   T 01268 523786
E optics@oceanoptics.co.uk
W www.oceanoptics.co.uk

ONSIGHT LTD
Trading as Axis Films. Film Equipment Rental
Shepperton Studios, Studios Road
Middlesex TW17 0QD
F 01932 592246   T 01932 592244
E axisfilms@onsight.co.uk
W www.onsight.co.uk

PANAVISION UK
The Metropolitan Centre, Bristol Road
Greenford, Middlesex UB6 8GD
F 020 8839 7300   T 020 8839 7333
W www.panavision.co.uk

PEDIGREE PUNKS
Compositing. Editing. Encoding. Mastering to All Formats
Shooting Crews
49 Woolstone Road, Forest Hill
London SE23 2TR
F 020 8291 5801   T 020 8314 4580
E video@pedigree-punks.com
W www.pedigree-punks.com

PLACE THE
Robin Howard Dance Theatre
17 Duke's Road
London WC1H 9PY
F 020 7121 1142   T 020 7121 1000
E info@theplace.org.uk
W www.theplace.org.uk

PRO-LINK RADIO SYSTEMS LTD
Radio Microphones & Communications
5, B Block
Saxon Business Park
Hanbury Road, Bromsgrove
Worcestershire B60 4AD
F 01527 577757   T 01527 577788
E service@prolink-radio.com
W www.prolink-radio.com

RICH TV LTD
Houldsworth Mill
Houldsworth Street
Reddish, Stockport
Cheshire SK5 6DA   T 0161 975 6207
E sales@richtv.co.uk
W www.richtv.co.uk

SALON LTD
Editing Equipment Hire. Post-Production
12 Swainson Road
London W3 7XB   T 020 8746 7611
E hire@salonrentals.com
W www.salonrentals.com

SOUNDHOUSE THE
10th Floor, Astley House
Quay Street, Manchester M3 4AE
F 0161 832 7266   T 0161 832 7299
E mail@thesoundhouse.com
W www.thesoundhouse.tv

TEN80MEDIA
Studio 517 Foleshill Road
Coventry, West Midlands CV6 5AU   M 07814 406251
E info@ten80media.com
W www.ten80media.com

VIDEO INN PRODUCTION
AV Equipment Hire
Glebe Farm
Wooton Road
Quinton, Northampton NN7 2EE   T 01604 864868
E post@videoinn.co.uk
W www.videoinn.co.uk

VSI - VOICE & SCRIPT INTERNATIONAL
Dubbing. DVD Encoding & Authoring Facilities. Editing
Subtitling. Voice-overs
132 Cleveland Street
London W1T 6AB
F 020 7692 7711   T 020 7692 7700
E info@vsi.tv
W www.vsi.tv

W6 STUDIO
Editing Facilities. Photography. Video Production
359 Lillie Road, Fulham
London SW6 7PA   T 020 7385 2272
E kazkam@w6studio.fsnet.co.uk
W www.w6studio.co.uk

30 BIRD PRODUCTIONS
Citylife, 182-190 Newmarket Road
Cambridge CB5 8HE   M 07970 960995
E info@30birdproductions.org
W www.30birdproductions.org

303 PRODUCTIONS
11 D'Arblay Street, London W1T 8DT
F 020 7434 1955   T 020 7494 0955
E henry@303productions.co.uk

1066 PRODUCTIONS
8 Blackstone House, Off Bowen Drive
West Dulwich, London SE21 8NY   T 020 7193 6156
E admin@1066productions.com
W www.1066productions.com

ACADEMY
16 West Central Street, London WC1A 1JJ
F 020 7240 0355   T 020 7395 4155
E post@academyfilms.com
W www.academyfilms.com

AGILE FILMS
Unit 1, 68-72 Redchurch Street
London E2 7DP   T 020 7000 2882
E info@agilefilms.com
W www.agilefilms.com

ALGERNON LTD
24B Cleveleys Road, London E5 9JN
F 0870 1388516   M 07092 805026
E info@algernonproductions.com
W www.algernonproductions.com

AN ACQUIRED TASTE TV CORP
51 Croham Road, South Croydon CR2 7HD
F 020 8686 5928   T 020 8686 1188
E cbennetttv@aol.com

APTN
The Interchange, Oval Road
Camden Lock, London NW1 7DZ
F 020 7413 8312   T 020 7482 7400

ARIEL PRODUCTIONS LTD
Contact: By Post
46 Melcombe Regis Court, 59 Weymouth Street
London W1G 8NT

ARLINGTON PRODUCTIONS LTD
Cippenham Court, Cippenham Lane
Cippenham, Nr Slough, Berkshire SL1 5AU
F 01753 691785   T 01753 516767

ASCENT 142
Film House, 142 Wardour Street, London W1F 8DD
F 020 7878 7870   T 020 7878 0000
W www.ascentmedia.co.uk

ASF PRODUCTIONS LTD
Contact: Alan Spencer, Malcolm Bubb. Commercials.
Corporate Videos. Documentaries. Feature Films. Films
38 Clunbury Court, Manor Street
Berkhamsted, Herts HP4 2FF   M 07770 277637
E info@asfproductions.co.uk

ASHFORD ENTERTAINMENT CORPORATION LTD THE
Contact: Frazer Ashford. By e-mail. Documentaries. Drama
Feature Films. Films. Television
20 The Chase, Coulsdon
Surrey CR5 2EG   T 0844 3510042
E info@ashford-entertainment.co.uk
W www.ashford-entertainment.co.uk

AVALON TELEVISION LTD
4A Exmoor Street, London W10 6BD
F 020 7598 7313   T 020 7598 8000

BAILEY Catherine LTD
110 Gloucester Avenue, Primrose Hill
London NW1 8JA   T 020 7483 3330
W www.cbltd.net

BANANA PARK LTD
Animation Production Company
Banana Park, 6 Cranleigh Mews
London SW11 2QL
F 020 7738 1887   T 020 7228 7136
E studio@bananapark.co.uk
W www.bananapark.co.uk

BARFORD PRODUCTIONS
206-212 St John Street
Clerkenwell
London EC1V 4JY   T 020 7324 1466
E info@barford.co.uk
W www.barford.co.uk

BBC WORLDWIDE LTD
Media Centre, Media Village
201 Wood Lane W12 7TQ   T 020 8433 2000
W www.bbcworldwide.com

BLACKBIRD PRODUCTIONS
6 Molasses Row, Plantation Wharf
Battersea, London SW11 3UX   T 020 7924 6440
E enquiries@blackbirdproductions.co.uk

BLUE FISH MEDIA
E ideas@bfmedia.co.uk
W www.bfmedia.co.uk

BRUNSWICK FILMS LTD
Formula One Motor Racing Archive
Brunswick House, 26 Macroom Road
Maida Vale, London W9 3HY
F 020 8960 4997   T 020 8960 0066
E info@brunswickfilms.com
W www.brunswickfilms.com

BRYANT WHITTLE LTD
49 Federation Road, Abbey Wood
London SE2 0JT   T 020 8311 8752
E amanda@bryantwhittle.com
W www.bryantwhittle.com

BURDER FILMS
37 Braidley Road, Meyrick Park
Bournemouth BH2 6JY   T 01202 295395
E burderfilms@aol.com
W www.johnburder.co.uk

CALDERDALE TELEVISION
12 South Avenue, Fartown
Huddersfield HD2 1BY   T 01484 432389
E ctv@calderdaletv.co.uk

CARDINAL BROADCAST
Room 114, N&P Building
Pinewood Studios
Iver Heath, Bucks SL0 0NH   T 01753 639210
W www.cardinalbroadcast.com

CAST YOU
20 Berkeley Street
Mayfair, London W1J 6HF
F 0870 2583250   T 0844 2572327
E info@castyou.co.uk
W www.castyou.co.uk

CELTIC FILMS ENTERTAINMENT LTD
3-4 Portland Mews, London W1F 8JF
F 020 7494 9134   T 020 7494 6886
E info@celticfilms.co.uk
W www.celticfilms.co.uk

CENTRAL OFFICE OF INFORMATION
Moving Image
Hercules House, Hercules Road
London SE1 7DU
F 020 7261 8776   T 020 7261 8220
E eileen.newton@coi.gsi.gov.uk
W www.coi.gov.uk

CENTRE SCREEN PRODUCTIONS
Eastgate, Castle Street
Castlefield, Manchester M3 4LZ
F 0161 832 8934   T 0161 832 7151
E info@centrescreen.co.uk
W www.centrescreen.co.uk

CHANNEL 2020 LTD
2020 House, 26-28 Talbot Lane
Leicester LE1 4LR
F 0116 222 1113   T 0844 8402020
E info@channel2020.co.uk
W www.channel2020.co.uk

CHANNEL TELEVISION PRODUCTION
The Television Centre
La Pouquelaye, St Helier
Jersey JE1 3ZD
F 01534 816817   T 01534 816816
E production@channeltv.co.uk
W www.channelonline.tv

CHANNEL X LTD
4 Candover Street, London W1W 7DJ
F 020 7580 8016   T 0845 9002940
E firstname.lastname@channelx.co.uk
W www.channelx.co.uk

CHILDREN'S FILM & TELEVISION FOUNDATION LTD
E annahome@cftf.org.uk   M 07887 573479

CINEMANX LTD
3rd Floor, 12 Great Portland Street
London W1W 8QN
F 020 7636 5481   T 020 7637 2612

CLASSIC MEDIA
1A Colonels Lane, Chertsey
Surrey KT16 8RH
F 01932 563207   T 01932 561316
E lyn.beardsall@classic-media-group.com

CLASSIC MEDIA
3rd Floor, Royalty House
72-74 Dean Street, London W1D 3SG
F 020 8762 6299   T 020 8762 6200
E enquiries@classicmedia.tv
W www.classicmedia.tv

CLAW FILMS LTD
11-15 Betterton Street, London WC2H 9BP
F 020 7470 8810   T 020 7470 8809
E info@clawfilms.com
W www.clawfilms.com

CLEVER BOY MEDIA LTD
Pinewood Film Studios, Pinewood Road
Iver Heath, Bucks SL0 0NH   T 01753 650951
E info@screenactingcloseup.com
W www.screenactingcloseup.com

COLLINGWOOD O'HARE PRODUCTIONS LTD
10-14 Crown Street, Acton
London W3 8SB
F 020 8993 9595   T 020 8993 3666
E info@crownstreet.co.uk
W www.collingwoodohare.com

COMMERCIAL BREAKS
Anglia House, Norwich NR1 3JG
F 0844 8816790   T 0844 8816789
E commercialbreaks@itv.com
W www.commercialbreaks.co.uk

COMMUNICATOR LTD
Omnibus Business Centre, 39-41 North Road
London N7 9DP   T 020 7700 0777
E info@communicator.ltd.uk

COMPLETE WORKS CREATIVE COMPANY LTD THE
The Old Truman Brewery, 91 Brick Lane
London E1 6QL
F 020 7247 7405   T 020 7377 0280
E film@tcw.org.uk
W www.tcw.org.uk

COMTEC LTD
Tandridge Court Farm, Tandridge Lane
Oxted, Surrey RH8 9NJ
F 0844 8805239   T 0844 8805238
E info@comtecav.co.uk
W www.comtecav.co.uk

COURTYARD PRODUCTIONS
TV Production Company
Little Postlings Farmhouse, Four Elms
Kent TN8 6NA   T 01732 700324
E courtyard@mac.com

CPL PRODUCTIONS LTD
38 Long Acre, London WC2E 9JT
F 020 7836 9633   T 020 7240 8101
E info@cplproductions.co.uk
W www.cplproductions.co.uk

CREATIVE PARTNERSHIP THE
13 Bateman Street, London W1D 3AF
F 020 7437 1467   T 020 7439 7762
W www.creativepartnership.co.uk

CROFT TELEVISION
Croft House, Progress Business Centre, Whittle Parkway
Slough, Berkshire SL1 6DQ
F 01628 668791   T 01628 668735
E nick@croft-tv.com
W www.croft-tv.com

CROSSROADS FILMS
2nd Floor, 83 Long Acre, London WC2E 9NG
F 020 7395 4849   T 020 7395 4848
E info@crossroadsfilms.co.uk
W www.crossroadsfilms.co.uk

CUPSOGUE PICTURES
40 Hayway, Irthlingborough
Wellingborough NN9 5QP   T 020 3411 2058
E enquiries@cupsoguepictures.com
W www.cupsoguepictures.com

CUTHBERT Tony PRODUCTIONS
Suite 14, 7 Dials Court
3 Shorts Gardens, London WC2H 9AT   T 020 7836 3432
E tonycuthbert@btconnect.com
W www.tonycuthbert.com

DALTON FILMS LTD
127 Hamilton Terrace, London NW8 9QR   T 020 7328 6169
E dalton@robdal.demon.co.uk

DANCETIME LTD
1 The Orchard, Chiswick
London W4 1JZ   T/F 020 8742 0507
E berry@tabletopproductions.com
W www.tabletopproductions.com

DARLOW SMITHSON PRODUCTIONS LTD
Highgate Studios, 53-79 Highgate Road
London NW5 1TL
F 020 7482 7039   T 020 7482 7027
E mail@darlowsmithson.com
W www.darlowsmithson.com

DIALOGICS
249-251 Kensal Road, London W10 5DB   T 020 8960 6069
E dialogue@dialogics.com
W www.dialogics.com

DIDA MEDIA
Provides Remote Casting. Represents Up-and-coming Talents
89 Fleet Street, London EC4Y 1DH   T 020 7353 4205
E info@didamedia.com
W www.didamedia.com

DISNEY Walt COMPANY THE
3 Queen Caroline Street, Hammersmith, London W6 9PE
F 020 8222 2795   T 020 8222 1000
W www.disney.co.uk

DLT ENTERTAINMENT UK LTD
10 Bedford Square, London WC1B 3RA
F 020 7636 4571   T 020 7631 1184

DRAMATIS PERSONAE LTD
Contact: Nathan Silver, Nicolas Kent
19 Regency Street, London SW1P 4BY   T 020 7834 9300
E ns@nathansilver.com

DREAMING WILL INITIATIVE THE
PO Box 38155, London SE17 3XP   T/F 020 7793 9755
E londonswo@hotmail.com
W www.lswproductions.co.uk

ECOSSE FILMS LTD
Brigade House, 8 Parsons Green, London SW6 4TN
F 020 7736 3436   T 020 7371 0290
E info@ecossefilms.com
W www.ecossefilms.com

EDGE PICTURE COMPANY LTD THE
20-22 Shelton Street, London WC2H 9JJ
F 020 7836 6949   T 020 7836 6262
E ask.us@edgepicture.com
W www.edgepicture.com

EFFINGEE PRODUCTIONS LTD
Contact: Lesley Kiernan. By e-mail. Television
PO Box 7615, Glasgow G42 2FY   T 0141 443 9301
E info@effingee.com
W www.effingee.com

ENDEMOL UK PLC
Including Endemol UK Productions, Initial, Brighter Pictures,
Victoria Real, Remarkable & Zeppotron
Shepherds Building Central
Charecroft Way
Shepherd's Bush, London W14 0EE
F 0870 3331800   T 0870 3331700
E info@endemol.com
W www.endemol.com

ENLIGHTENMENT INTERACTIVE
East End House, 24 Ennerdale
Skelmersdale WN8 6AJ   T 01695 727555
W www.trainingmultimedia.co.uk

EON PRODUCTIONS LTD
Eon House, 138 Piccadilly, London W1J 7NR
F 020 7408 1236   T 020 7493 7953

EXTRA DIGIT LTD
10 Wyndham Place, London W1H 2PU
W www.extradigit.com

EYE FILM & TELEVISION
Epic Studios, 112-114 Magdalen Street
Norwich NR3 1JD   T 0845 6211133
E production@eyefilmandtv.co.uk
W www.eyefilmandtv.co.uk

FARNHAM FILM COMPANY THE
34 Burnt Hill Road, Lower Bourne, Farnham GU10 3LZ
F 01252 725855   T 01252 710313
E info@farnfilm.com
W www.farnfilm.com

FEELGOOD FICTION LTD
49 Goldhawk Road, London W12 8QP
F 020 8740 6177   T 020 8746 2535
E feelgood@feelgoodfiction.co.uk
W www.feelgoodfiction.co.uk

FERRIS ENTERTAINMENT FILMS
London. Belfast. Cardiff
Number 8, 132 Charing Cross Road
London WC2H 0LA   T 0845 4724725
E info@ferrisentertainment.com
W www.ferrisentertainment.com

FESTIVAL FILM & TELEVISION LTD
Festival House, Tranquil Passage, London SE3 0BJ
F 020 8297 1155   T 020 8297 9999
E info@festivalfilm.com
W www.festivalfilm.com

FILM & GENERAL PRODUCTIONS LTD
Contact: Davina Belling
3 Bradbrook House, Studio Place
London SW1X 8EL   T 020 7235 4495

FILMS OF RECORD LTD
6 Angler Lane, Kentish Town, London NW5 3DG
F 020 7284 0626   T 020 7428 3100
W www.filmsofrecord.com

FIREFLY PRODUCTIONS
Twin Oaks, Hale Purlieu, Fordingbridge SP6 2NN
M 07956 675276   T 01725 514462
E theonlyfirefly@aol.com
W www.fireflyproductions.info

FIRST WRITES THEATRE COMPANY LTD
First Writes Radio Drama Company
Lime Kiln Cottage, High Starlings
Banham, Norfolk NR16 2BS
F 01953 888974   T 01953 888525
E ellen@first-writes.co.uk
W www.first-writes.co.uk

FLASHBACK TELEVISION LTD
58 Farringdon Road, London EC1R 3BP
F 020 7253 8765   T 020 7253 8768
E mailbox@flashbacktv.co.uk
W www.flashbacktelevision.com

FLYING DUCKS GROUP
Duck HQ, The Old Mill, The Upper Hattons
Pendeford Hall Lane
Coven WV9 5BD   T 01902 842888
E enquiries@flyingducks.biz
W www.flyingducks.biz

FOCUS PRODUCTIONS PUBLICATIONS
58 Shelley Road, Stratford-upon-Avon
Warwickshire CV37 7JS
F 01789 294845   T 01789 298948
E maddern@focuspublishers.co.uk
W www.focusproductions.co.uk

FORSTATER Mark PRODUCTIONS
11 Keslake Road, London NW6 6DJ   M 07771 665382
E mforstater@msn.com

FREMANTLEMEDIA TALKBACKTHAMES
1 Stephen Street, London W1T 1AL
F 020 7691 6100   T 020 7691 6000
W www.freemantlemedia.com

FRICKER Ian (FILMS) LTD
146 Strand, London WC2R 1JD
F 020 7836 3078   T 020 7836 3090
E mail@ianfricker.com

FULMAR TELEVISION & FILM LTD
Pascoe House, 54 Bute Street
Cardiff Bay, Cardiff CF10 5AF
F 029 2045 5111   T 029 2045 5000

FUNNY FACE FILMS LTD
8A Warwick Road, Hampton Wick
Surrey KT1 4DW   M 07506 365433
E stevendrew40@hotmail.com

GALA PRODUCTIONS LTD
25 Stamford Brook Road, London W6 0XJ
F 020 8741 2323   T 020 8741 4200
E info@galaproductions.co.uk
W www.galaproductions.co.uk

GALLEON FILMS LTD
Greenwich Playhouse, Station Forecourt
189 Greenwich High Road
London SE10 8JA   T/F 020 8310 7276
E alice@galleontheatre.co.uk
W www.galleonfilms.co.uk

GAMMOND Stephen ASSOCIATES
24 Telegraph Lane, Claygate
Surrey KT10 0DU   T 01372 460674

GAY Noel TELEVISION LTD
Shepperton Studios, Studios Road
Shepperton, Middlesex TW17 0QD
F 01932 592172   T 01932 592569
E charles.armitage@virgin.net

GHA GROUP
33 Newman Street, London W1T 1PY
F 020 7636 4448   T 020 7439 8705
E sales@ghagroup.co.uk
W www.ghagroup.co.uk

GLASS PAGE LTD THE
15 De Montfort Street, Leicester LE1 7GE
F 0116 249 2188   T 0116 249 2199
E info@glass-page.com
W www.glass-page.com

GOLDHAWK ESSENTIAL
Radio Productions
20 Great Chapel Street, London W1F 8FW
F 020 7287 3597   T 020 7439 7113
E enquiries@goldhawk.eu

GRANT NAYLOR PRODUCTIONS LTD
Room 964, David Lean Buildings
Shepperton Studios, Studios Road, Shepperton
Middlesex TW17 0QD
F 01932 592484   T 01932 592175

GREAT GUNS LTD
43-45 Camden Road, London NW1 9LR
F 020 7692 4422   T 020 7692 4444
E reception@greatguns.com
W www.greatguns.com

GUERILLA FILMS LTD
35 Thornbury Road, Isleworth, Middlesex TW7 4LQ
F 020 8758 9364   T 020 8758 1716
E david@guerilla-films.com
W www.guerilla-films.com

HAMMERWOOD FILM PRODUCERS
110 Trafalgar Road, Portslade
Sussex BN41 1GS   T 01273 277333
E filmangels@freenetname.co.uk
W www.filmangel.co.uk

HANDS UP PRODUCTIONS LTD
7 Cavendish Vale, Sherwood
Nottingham NG5 4DS   M 07767 828451
E marcus@handsuppuppets.com
W www.handsuppuppets.com

HARBOUR PICTURES
21-25 St Annes Court, London W1F 0BJ
F 020 7494 4885   T 020 7287 6289
E info@harbourpictures.com
W www.harbourpictures.com

HARTSWOOD FILMS
Twickenham Studios
The Barons, St Margaret's
Twickenham, Middlesex TW1 2AW
F 020 8607 8744   T 020 8607 8736
W www.hartswoodfilms.co.uk

HEAD Sally PRODUCTIONS
Twickenham Film Studios
The Barons, St Margaret's
Twickenham, Middlesex TW1 2AW
F 020 8607 8964   T 020 8607 8730
E admin@shpl.demon.co.uk

HEAVY ENTERTAINMENT LTD
111 Wardour Street, London W1F 0UH
F 020 7494 1100   T 020 7494 1000
E info@heavy-entertainment.com
W www.heavy-entertainment.com

Television & Film Production
Studio and Production Offices for Hire

13 Colquhoun Avenue, Hillington Park, Glasgow, G52 4BN
Tel: 0141 443 9301 Fax: 0141 882 5003
www.effingee.com

Effingee Productions Ltd

HERMES ENTERTAINMENT INC
Based in Paris & London
72/6 Grove Lane, Camberwell Green
London SE5 8TW   M 07875 628299
E moneymodeste@yahoo.com

HIT ENTERTAINMENT LTD
5th Floor, Maple House
149 Tottenham Court Road
London W1T 7NF
F 020 7388 9321   T 020 7554 2500
E creative@hitentertainment.com
W www.hitentertainment.com

HOLMES ASSOCIATES & OPEN ROAD FILMS
The Studio, 37 Redington Road
London NW3 7QY   T 020 7813 4333
E holmesassociates@blueyonder.co.uk

HUNGRY MAN LTD
1-2 Herbal Hill, London EC1R 5EF
F 020 7239 4589   T 020 7239 4550
E ukreception@hungryman.com
W www.hungryman.com

HUNKY DORY PRODUCTIONS LTD
57 Alan Drive, Barnet, Herts EN5 2PW
M 07973 655510   T 020 8440 0820
E adrian@hunkydory.tv
W www.hunkydory.tv

HURRICANE FILMS LTD
17 Hope Street, Liverpool L1 9BQ
F 0151 707 9149   T 0151 707 9700
E info@hurricanefilms.co.uk
W www.hurricanefilms.net

IAMBIC MEDIA LTD
89 Whiteladies Road, Clifton
Bristol BS8 2NT
F 0117 923 8343   T 0117 923 7222
E admin@iambic.tv

ICE PRODUCTIONS LTD
Warwick Corner, 42 Warwick Road
Kenilworth, Warwickshire CV8 1HE   T 01926 864800
E web@ice-productions.com
W www.ice-productions.com

ICON FILMS LTD
1-2 Fitzroy Terrace, Bristol BS6 6TF
F 0117 973 3890   T 0117 317 1717
W www.iconfilms.co.uk

INFORMATION TRANSFER LTD
Training Video Packages
Burleigh House, 15 Newmarket Road
Cambridge CB5 8EG
F 01223 310200   T 01223 312227

ISIS PRODUCTIONS LTD
Goldcrest Post, 1 Lexington Street
London W1F 9AF   T 020 7220 2929
W www.isis-productions.com

JACKSON Brian FILMS LTD
39-41 Hanover Steps, St George's Fields
Albion Street, London W2 2YG
F 020 7262 5736   T 020 7402 7543
W www.brianjacksonfilms.com

J. I. PRODUCTIONS
90 Hainault Avenue, Giffard Park
Milton Keynes, Bucks MK14 5PE   M 07732 476409
E jasonimpey@live.com
W www.jasonimpey.co.uk

JMS GROUP LTD THE
Park Farm Studios, Hethersett
Norwich, Norfolk NR9 3DL
F 01603 812255   T 01603 811855
E info@jms-group.com
W www.jms-group.com

KNOWLES Dave FILMS LTD
Contact: Jenny Knowles. Corporate, Training & Project
Documentary Video Productions
34 Ashleigh Close, Hythe SO45 3QP   T 023 8084 2190
E mail@dkfilms.co.uk
W www.dkfilms.co.uk

LALICE FILMS
58 Chiswick Lane, London W4 2LA
F 020 8747 1212   T 020 8797 1610
E stagewx41@live.com

LANDSEER PRODUCTIONS LTD
27 Arkwright Road, London NW3 6BJ   T 020 7794 2523
E ken@landseerproductions.com
W www.landseerfilms.com

LEFT EYE BLIND
Contact: Aurora Fearnley. By e-mail. Commercials. Drama
Music Videos. Promos. Television
Studio 81, Kirkstall Road
Leeds LS3 1LH   M 07816 954492
E aurora@lefteyeblind.com
W www.lefteyeblind.com

LIME PICTURES
Campus Manor, Childwall
Abbey Road, Liverpool L16 0JP
F 0151 722 6839   T 0151 722 9122

LOOKING GLASS FILMS LTD
103 Brittany Point, Ethelred Estate
Kennington, London SE11 6UH   T/F 020 7735 1363
E lookingglassfilm@aol.com

LOOP COMMUNICATION AGENCY THE
Suite 302, QC 30, Queen Charlotte Street, Bristol BS1 4HJ
F 0117 311 2041   T 0117 311 2040
E mail@theloopagency.com

MALLINSON TELEVISION PRODUCTIONS
Commercials
29 Lynedoch Street, Glasgow G3 6EF
F 0141 332 6190   T 0141 332 0589
E shoot@mtp.co.uk

MANIC TV & FILM PRODUCTIONS
77 Brick Lane, Spitalfields, London E1 6QL   T 020 3246 0088
E info@manictv.co.uk
W www.manictv.co.uk

MANSFIELD Mike TELEVISION LTD/MANSFIELD PRODUCTIONS LTD
The Gatehouse, 4 Ellerton Road
London SW20 0EP   T 020 8947 6884
E mikemantv@aol.com

MANS Johnny PRODUCTIONS LTD
PO Box 196, Hoddesdon, Herts EN10 7WG
F 01992 470516   T 01992 470907
E johnnymansagent@aol.com
W www.johnnymansproductions.co.uk

MARTIN William PRODUCTIONS
The Studio, Tubney Warren Barns
Tubney, Oxfordshire OX13 5QJ
F 01865 390148   T 01865 390258
E info@wmproductions.co.uk
W www.wmproductions.co.uk

MAVERICK TELEVISION
Progress Works, Heath Mill Lane, Birmingham B9 4AL
F 0121 771 1550   T 0121 771 1812
E mail@mavericktv.co.uk
W www.mavericktv.co.uk

MAX MEDIA
Contact: Martin Franks. Drama. Comedy. Corporate
The Lilacs, West End, Woodhurst, Huntingdon
Cambridge PE28 3BH
F 01487 825299   T 01487 823608
E martin@therealmaxmedia.com
W www.therealmaxmedia.com

MBP TV
Saucelands Barn, Coolham, Horsham, West Sussex RH13 8QG
F 01403 741647   T 01403 741620
E info@mbptv.com
W www.mbptv.com

McINTYRE Phil ENTERTAINMENTS
3rd Floor, 85 Newman Street, London W1T 3EU
F 020 7291 9000   T 020 7291 9001
E info@mcintyre-ents.com

MENTORN
77 Fulham Palace Road, London W6 8JA
F 020 7258 6888   T 020 7258 6800
E reception@mentorn.tv

MET FILM PRODUCTION
Ealing Studios, Ealing Green, London W5 5EP
F 020 8280 9111   T 020 8280 9127
E anetta@metfilm.co.uk
W www.metfilm.co.uk

MINAMON FILM
Contact: Min Clifford. By e-mail/Telephone
Corporate Videos. Documentaries. Drama. Films
117 Downton Avenue, London SW2 3TX   T 020 8674 3957
E studio@minamonfilm.co.uk
W www.minamonfilm.co.uk

MINISTRY OF VIDEO
Contact: Chris, Andy. By e-mail/Telephone. Casting Videos
Children's Entertainment. Commercials. Corporate Videos
Live Events. Live Stage Productions. Music Videos. Showreels
1533 High Road, Whetstone
London N20 9PP   T 020 8369 5956
E info@ministryofvideo.co.uk
W www.ministryofvideo.co.uk

MISTRAL FILMS LTD
31 Oval Road, London NW1 7EA
F 020 7284 0547   T 020 7284 2300
E info@mistralfilm.co.uk

MONITON PICTURES
1st Floor, George House
36 North Hanover Street
Glasgow G1 2AD   M 07753 865511
E andy@monitonpictures.com
W www.monitonpictures.com

MOVE A MOUNTAIN PRODUCTIONS
5 Ashchurch Park Villas
London W12 9SP   T 020 8743 3017
E mail@moveamountain.com
W www.moveamountain.com

MURPHY Patricia FILMS LTD
Lock Keepers Cottage
Lyme Street, London NW1 0SF
F 020 7485 0555   T 020 7267 0007
E office@patriciamurphy.co.uk

NEAL STREET PRODUCTIONS LTD
1st Floor
26-28 Neal Street, London WC2H 9QQ
F 020 7240 7099   T 020 7240 8890
E post@nealstreetproductions.com

NEW MOON TELEVISION
63 Poland Street, London W1F 7NY
F 020 7479 7011   T 020 7479 7010
E production@new-moon.co.uk
W www.new-moon.co.uk

NEW PLANET FILMS LTD
PO Box 640, Pinner HA5 9JB   T 020 8426 1090
E info@newplanetfilms.com
W www.newplanetfilms.com

NEXUS PRODUCTIONS LTD
Animation, Mixed Media, Live Action & Interactive Production
for Commercials, Broadcast, Pop Promos & Title Sequences
113-114 Shoreditch High Street
London E1 6JN
F 020 7749 7501   T 020 7749 7500
E info@nexusproductions.com
W www.nexusproductions.com

NFD PRODUCTIONS LTD
Contact: By Post/e-mail/Telephone. Children's Entertainment
Commercials. Corporate Videos. Drama. Films. Television
Short Films. Showreels
PO Box 76, Leeds LS25 9AG
M 07966 473455   T/F 01977 681949
E info@nfdproductions.com
W www.nfdproductions.com

OMNI PRODUCTIONS LTD
14-16 Wilson Place, Bristol BS2 9HJ   T 0117 954 7170
E info@omniproductions.co.uk
W www.omniproductions.co.uk

ON COMMUNICATION/ONTV OXFORD & LONDON
Work across all Media in Business Communications
11-12 St James's Square
London SW1Y 4LB   T 020 7104 2110
E info@oncommunication.com
W www.oncommunication.com

5 East St Helen Street
Abingdon, Oxford OX14 5EG
F 01235 530581   T 01235 537400

ON SCREEN PRODUCTIONS LTD
Ashbourne House, 33 Bridge Street
Chepstow, Monmouthshire NP16 5GA
F 01291 636301   T 01291 636300
E action@onscreenproductions.co.uk
W www.onscreenproductions.com

OPEN MIND PRODUCTIONS
27 York Road, Teddington
Middlesex TW11 8SL   T 0845 8909192
E production.manager@openmind.co.uk

OPEN SHUTTER PRODUCTIONS LTD
Contact: John Bruce. Documentaries. Drama. Film. Television
100 Kings Road, Windsor, Berkshire SL4 2AP
M 07753 618875   T 01753 841309
E openshutterproductions@googlemail.com

OVC MEDIA LTD
Contact: Eliot M. Cohen. By e-mail. Animation
Documentaries. Drama. Feature Films. Films. Television
88 Berkeley Court, Baker Street
London NW1 5ND
F 020 7723 3064   T 020 7402 9111
E eliot@ovcmedia.com
W www.ovcmedia.com

P4FILMS
Film & Video for Television, Commercials. Corporate
Cheltenham Film Studios, Hatherley Lane
Cheltenham, Gloucestershire GL51 6PN   T 01242 542760
E info@p4films.com
W www.p4films.com

PAPER MOON PRODUCTIONS
Wychwood House, Burchetts Green Lane
Littlewick Green Maidenhead
Berkshire SL6 3QW   T/F 01628 829819
E insight@paper-moon.co.uk

PARADINE David PRODUCTIONS LTD
The Penthouse
346 Kensington High Street, London W14 8NS
F 020 7602 0411   T 020 7371 3111
E mail@paradine-productions.com

PARHAM PRODUCTIONS
Ardleigh House, 42 Ardleigh Green Road
Hornchurch, Essex RM11 2LG   T 01708 447123
E info@paulstheatreschool.com
W www.paulstheatreschool.com

PARK VILLAGE LTD
1 Park Village East, London NW1 7PX
F 020 7388 3051   T 020 7387 8077
E info@parkvillage.co.uk

PASSION PICTURES LTD
Animation. Documentary. Television
3rd Floor, 33-34 Rathbone Place
London W1T 1JN
F 020 7323 9030   T 020 7323 9933
E info@passion-pictures.com

PATHE PICTURES LTD
4th Floor, 6 Ramillies Place, London W1F 7TY
F 020 7631 3568   T 020 7323 5151
W www.pathe.co.uk

PENSIVE PENGUIN PRODUCTIONS
37 Oldstead Grove, Ferncrest
Bolton, Lancs BL3 4XW   T 01204 848333
E glenmortimer@btinternet.com
W www.shadowhawkinternational.com/seeingsmokephotos.htm

PICTURE PALACE FILMS LTD
13 Egbert Street, London NW1 8LJ
F 020 7586 9048   T 020 7586 8763
E info@picturepalace.com
W www.picturepalace.com

PIER PRODUCTIONS LTD
8 St Georges Place
Brighton BN1 4GB   T 01273 691401
E info@pierproductionsltd.co.uk

PINBALL LONDON
London N5 2JZ   M 07941 474721
E paula@pinballonline.co.uk
W www.pinballonline.co.uk

PODCAST COMPANY THE
101 Wardour Street
London W1F 0UG   M 07956 468344
E info@thepodcastcompany.co.uk
W www.thepodcastcompany.co.uk

268 Regents Park Road, Finchley
London N3 3HN   M 07956 468344

POSITIVE IMAGE LTD
25 Victoria Street, Windsor
Berkshire SL4 1HE
F 01753 830878   T 01753 842248
E theoffice@positiveimage.co.uk

POTBOILER PRODUCTIONS LTD
9 Greek Street, London W1D 4DQ
F 020 7287 5228   T 020 7734 7372
E info@potboiler.co.uk
W www.potboiler.co.uk

POZZITIVE TELEVISION LTD
Paramount House, 162-170 Wardour Street
London W1F 8AB
F 020 7437 3130   T 020 7734 3258
E pozzitive@pozzitive.co.uk
W www.pozzitive.co.uk

PREACHY PRODUCTIONS
14 Richborne Terrace, London SW8 1AU   M 07905 928543
E info@preachyfilms.com

PRETTY CLEVER PICTURES
Hurst Cottage, Old Buddington Lane
Hollist Lane, Eastbourne
Midhurts, West Sussex GU29 0QN
M 07836 616981   T 01730 817899
E pcpics@globalnet.co.uk

PRISM ENTERTAINMENT
Television Production & Website Design Company
The Clockhouse
220 Latimer Road, London W10 6QY
F 020 8969 1012   T 020 8969 1212
E info@prism-e.com
W www.prismentertainment.co.uk

PRODUCERS THE
8 Berners Mews, London W1T 3AW
F 020 7636 4099   T 020 7636 4226
E info@theproducersfilms.co.uk
W www.theproducersfilms.co.uk

PSA FILMS
52 The Downs, Altrincham WA14 2QJ
F 0161 924 0022   T 0161 924 0011
E andy@psafilms.co.uk

PVA MANAGEMENT LTD
County House, St Marys Street
Worcester WR1 1HB
F 01905 610709   T 01905 616100
E films@pva.co.uk
W www.pva.co.uk

QUADRILLION
The Old Barn, Kings Lane
Cookham Dean, Berkshire SL6 9AY   T 01628 487522
E enqs@quadrillion.tv
W www.quadrillion.tv

READ Rodney
45 Richmond Road, Twickenham
Middlesex TW1 3AW
M 07956 321550   T 020 8891 2875
E rodney_read@blueyonder.co.uk
W www.rodney-read.com

RECORDED PICTURE COMPANY LTD
24 Hanway Street, London W1T 1UH
F 020 7636 2261   T 020 7636 2251
E rpc@recordedpicture.com

RED KITE ANIMATION
89 Giles Street, Edinburgh EH6 6BZ
F 0131 553 6007   T 0131 554 0060
E info@redkite-animation.com
W www.redkite-animation.com

RED ROSE CHAIN
Gippeswyk Hall, Gippeswyk Avenue
Ipswich, Suffolk IP2 9AF   T 01473 288886
E info@redrosechain.co.uk
W www.redrosechain.co.uk

REDWEATHER PRODUCTIONS
Easton Business Centre
Felix Road, Bristol BS5 0HE
F 0117 941 5851   T 0117 941 5854
E info@redweather.co.uk
W www.redweather.co.uk

REEL THING LTD THE
20 The Chase, Coulsdon
Surrey CR5 2EG   T 0844 3576393
E info@reelthing.tv
W www.reelthing.tv

REPLAY LTD
*Contact: Danny Scollard. Animation. Corporate Videos
Documentaries. Drama. E-Learning. Live Events. Script
Writing. Web Design*
Museum House
25 Museum Street
London WC1A 1JT   T 020 7637 0473
E sales@replayfilms.co.uk
W www.replayfilms.co.uk

REUTERS LTD
The Thompson Reuters Building
South Collonade
Canary Wharf, London E14 5EP   T 020 7250 1122

REVERE ENTERTAINMENT
91 Berwick Street, London W1F 0NE
F 020 7292 7391   T 020 7292 8370

RIVERSIDE TV STUDIOS
Riverside Studios, Crisp Road
London W6 9RL
F 020 8237 1121   T 020 8237 1123
E info@riversidetv.co.uk
W www.riversidetv.co.uk

ROEBUCK PRODUCTIONS
Commer House, Station Road
Tadcaster, North Yorkshire LS24 9JF
F 01937 835901   T 01937 835900
E john@roebuckproductions.com
W www.roebuckproductions.com

ROOKE Laurence PRODUCTIONS
14 Aspinall House
155 New Park Road
London SW2 4EY
M 07765 652058   T 020 8674 3128

RSA FILMS
42-44 Beak Street, London W1F 9RH
F 020 7734 4978   T 020 7437 7426
W www.rsafilms.com

SANDS FILMS
82 St Marychurch Street, London SE16 4HZ
F 020 7231 2119   T 020 7231 2209
E info@sandsfilms.co.uk
W www.sandsfilms.co.uk

SCALA PRODUCTIONS LTD
2nd Floor, 37 Foley Street
London W1W 7TN   T 020 7637 5720
E scalaprods@aol.com

SCIMITAR FILMS LTD
219 Kensington High Street
London W8 6BD
F 020 7602 9217   T 020 7734 8385
E winner@ftech.co.uk

SCREEN FIRST LTD
Funnells Farm, Down Street
Nutley, East Sussex TN22 3LG   T 01825 712034
E paul.madden@virgin.net

SEPTEMBER FILMS LTD
Glen House, 22 Glenthorne Road
Hammersmith, London W6 0NG
F 020 8741 7214   T 020 8563 9393
E september@septemberfilms.com

SEVEN STONES MEDIA LTD
The Old Butcher's Shop, St Briavels
Gloucestershire GL15 6TA   T 01594 530708
E info@sevenstonesmedia.com

SEVENTH ART PRODUCTIONS
63 Ship Street, Brighton BN1 1AE
F 01273 323777   T 01273 777678
E info@seventh-art.com
W www.seventh-art.com

SHED PRODUCTIONS
2 Holford Yard, London WC1X 9HD
F 020 7239 1011   T 020 7239 1010
E shed@shedproductions.com
W www.shedproductions.com

SHELL FILM & VIDEO UNIT
Shell Centre, York Road
London SE1 7NA   T 020 7934 3318
E jane.poynor@shell.com

SIGHTLINE
Video for the Web. For Promotion, Training, E-Learning, DVDs, Interactive CD-ROM, Touch Screens & Websites
Dylan House
Town End Street
Godalming, Surrey GU7 1BQ
F 01483 861516   T 01483 861555
E action@sightline.co.uk
W www.sightline.co.uk

SILK SOUND
Commercials. Corporate Videos. Documentaries
13 Berwick Street, London W1F 0PW
F 020 7494 1748   T 020 7434 3461
E bookings@silk.co.uk
W www.silk.co.uk

SILVER PRODUCTIONS LTD
Bridge Farm, Lower Road
Britford, Salisbury
Wiltshire SP5 4DY
F 01722 336227   T 01722 336221
W www.silver.co.uk

SINDIBAD FILMS LTD
Tower House, 226 Cromwell Road
London SW5 0SW   T 020 7259 2707
E info@sindibad.co.uk
W www.sindibad.co.uk

SMITH & WATSON PRODUCTIONS
The Gothic House
Fore Street
Totnes, Devon TQ9 5EH
F 01803 864219   T 01803 863033
E info@smithandwatson.com
W www.smithandwatson.com

SNEEZING TREE FILMS
1st Floor, 37 Great Portland Street
London W1W 8QH
F 020 7580 1957   T 020 7436 8036
E firstname@sneezingtree.com
W www.sneezingtree.com

SOLOMON THEATRE COMPANY
High Street, Damerham
Fordingbridge, Hants SP6 3EU   T/F 01725 518760
E office@solomon-theatre.co.uk
W www.solomon-theatre.co.uk

SONY PICTURES
25 Golden Square, London W1F 9LU
F 020 7533 1015   T 020 7533 1000

SPACE CITY PRODUCTIONS
79 Blythe Road, London W14 0HP
F 020 7371 4001   T 020 7371 4000
E info@spacecity.co.uk
W www.spacecity.co.uk

SPEAKEASY PRODUCTIONS LTD
Wildwood House
Stanley, Perth PH1 4NH
F 01738 828419   T 01738 828524
E info@speak.co.uk
W www.speak.co.uk

SPECIFIC FILMS LTD
25 Rathbone Street, London W1T 1NQ
F 020 7636 6886   T 020 7580 7476
E info@specificfilms.com

SPIRAL PRODUCTIONS LTD
Unit 17-18, The Dove Centre
109 Bartholomew Road
London NW5 2BJ
F 020 7485 1845   T 020 7428 9948
E info@spiral.co.uk
W www.spiral.co.uk

STAFFORD Jonathan PRODUCTIONS
Shepperton Studios
Studios Road
Shepperton, Middlesex TW17 0QD
F 01932 592617   T 01932 562611
E jon@staffordproductions.com

STAMP PRODUCTIONS
10 Margaret Street, London W1W 8RL   T 020 3178 2367
E ben@stamp-productions.co.uk
W www.stamp-productions.com

STANDFAST FILMS
The Studio, 14 College Road
Bromley, Kent BR1 3NS   T 020 8466 5580

STANTON MEDIA
6 Kendal Close, Aylesbury
Bucks HP21 7HR   T 01296 489539
E info@stantonmedia.com
W www.stantonmedia.com

STONE PRODUCTIONS CREATIVE LTD
Lakeside Studio
62 Mill Street
St Osyth, Essex CO16 8EW
F 01255 822160   T 01255 822172
E kevin@stone-productions.co.uk
W www.stone-productions.co.uk

STUDIO AKA
Animation
30 Berwick Street, London W1F 8RH
F 020 7437 2309   T 020 7434 3581
W www.studioaka.co.uk

TABARD PRODUCTIONS LTD
Contact: John Herbert. By e-mail
Corporate Videos. Documentaries
Adam House, 7-10 Adam Street
London WC2N 6AA
F 020 7497 0850   T 020 7497 0830
E johnherbert@tabard.co.uk
W www.tabardproductions.com

TABLE TOP PRODUCTIONS
Contact: Ben Berry. By e-mail
Drama. Feature Films
1 The Orchard, Bedford Park
Chiswick, London W4 1JZ
T/F 020 8742 0507   T 020 8994 1269
E berry@tabletopproductions.com

TAKE 3 PRODUCTIONS LTD
72-73 Margaret Street
London W1W 8ST   T 020 7637 2694
E mail@take3.co.uk
W www.take3.co.uk

TAKE FIVE PRODUCTIONS
37 Beak Street, London W1F 9RZ
F 020 7287 3035   T 020 7287 2120
E info@takefivestudio.com
W www.takefivestudio.com

TALKBACKTHAMES
20-21 Newman Street, London W1T 1PG
F 020 7861 8001   T 020 7861 8000
W www.talkbackthames.tv

TALKING PICTURES
Pinewood Studios, Pinewood Road
Iver Heath, Bucks SL0 0NH
F 01865 890504   T 01753 655744
E info@talkingpictures.co.uk
W www.talkingpictures.co.uk

TANDEM CREATIVE
Contact: By e-mail
Corporate Videos. Documentaries
Charleston House, 13 High Street
Hemel Hempstead, Herts HP1 3AA
F 01442 219250   T 01442 261576
E info@tandem.tv
W www.tandem.tv

THEATRE WORKSHOP
Film. Theatre
34 Hamilton Place, Edinburgh EH3 5AX
F 0131 220 0112   T 0131 225 7942
W www.theatre-workshop.com

THIN MAN FILMS
9 Greek Street, London W1D 4DQ
F 020 7287 5228   T 020 7734 7372
E info@thinman.co.uk

TIGER ASPECT PRODUCTIONS
5 Soho Square, London W1D 3QA
F 020 7434 1798   T 020 7434 6700
E general@tigeraspect.co.uk
W www.tigeraspect.co.uk

TKO COMMUNICATIONS LTD
A Division of The Kruger Organisation Inc
PO Box 130, Hove
Sussex BN3 6QU
F 01273 540969   T 01273 550088
E tkoinc@tkogroup.com

TOP BANANA
The Studio, Stourbridge
West Midlands DY9 0HA
F 01562 700930   T 01562 700404
E info@top-b.com
W www.top-b.com

TOPICAL TELEVISION LTD
61 Devonshire Road
Southampton SO15 2GR
F 023 8033 9835   T 023 8071 2233

TRAFALGAR 1 LTD
Contact: Hasan Shah. By Post/e-mail
Documentaries. Feature Films. Film. Music Videos. Television
153 Burnham Towers, Fellows Road
London NW3 3JN
F 020 7483 0662   T 020 7722 7789
E t1ltd@blueyonder.co.uk

TVF
375 City Road, London EC1V 1NB
F 020 7833 2185   T 020 7837 3000

TV PRODUCTION PARTNERSHIP LTD
4 Fullerton Manor
Fullerton, Hants SP11 7LA   T 01264 861440
E dbj@tvpp.tv
W www.tvpp.tv

TWOFOUR
Corporate Videos. Documentaries. Live Events. Television
Twofour Studios
Estover, Plymouth PL6 7RG
F 01752 727450   T 01752 727400
E enq@twofour.co.uk
W www.twofour.co.uk

TYBURN FILM PRODUCTIONS LTD
Cippenham Court, Cippenham Lane
Cippenham, Nr Slough, Berkshire SL1 5AU
F 01753 691785   T 01753 516767

VECTOR PRODUCTIONS
Inspiring Corporate Video & Television Production
Moulton Park Industrial Estate
Northampton NN3 6AQ
T 0845 0535400 (Midlands)   T 020 7193 5655 (London)
E production@vectortv.co.uk
W www.vectortv.co.uk

VERA PRODUCTIONS LTD
165 Wardour Street, London W1F 8WW
F 020 7292 1481   T 020 7292 1480
E phoebe@vera.co.uk

VIDEOADVERT.COM
Mead Haze, Lower Cookham Road
Maidenhead, Berkshire SL6 8JL   M 07990 543290
E info@videoadvert.com
W www.videoadvert.com

VIDEO ARTS
6-7 St Cross Street, London EC1N 8UA
F 020 7400 4900   T 020 7400 4800
E info@videoarts.co.uk

VIDEO ENTERPRISES
Contact: Maurice Fleisher
Corporate Videos. Documentaries. Live Events. Television
12 Barbers Wood Road
High Wycombe, Bucks HP12 4EP
M 07831 875216   T 01494 534144
E videoenterprises@ntlworld.com
W www.videoenterprises.co.uk

VIDEOTEL PRODUCTIONS
Corporate Videos
84 Newman Street, London W1T 3EU
F 020 7299 1818   T 020 7299 1800

VILLAGE PRODUCTIONS
4 Midas Business Centre, Wantz Road
Dagenham, Essex RM10 8PS
F 020 8593 0198   T 020 8984 0322
E village000@btclick.com

VISION MANAGEMENT
1 The Old Farmhouse, Mosley Hall Farm
Knutsford, Cheshire WA16 8RB   T 01565 621912
E nell10_@hotmail.com

VSI - VOICE & SCRIPT INTERNATIONAL
132 Cleveland Street, London W1T 6AB   T 020 7692 7700
E info@vsi.tv
W www.vsi.tv

W3KTS LTD
10 Portland Street, York YO31 7EH   T 01904 647822
E chris@w3kts.com

W6 STUDIO
359 Lillie Road, Fulham, London SW6 7PA
F 020 7381 5252   T 020 7385 2272
E kazkam@w6studio.fsnet.co.uk
W www.w6studio.co.uk

WALKING FORWARD LTD
Studio 6, Aberdeen Centre
22-24 Highbury Grove, London N5 2EA   T/F 020 7359 5249
E info@walkingforward.co.uk
W www.walkingforward.co.uk

WALKOVERS VIDEO LTD
Facilities. Production
Kington Langley, Chippenham
Wiltshire SN15 5NR   T 01249 750428
E walkoversvideo@btinternet.com

WALSH BROS LTD
Contact: By e-mail
Animation. Documentaries. Drama. Feature Films. Films
Television
29 Trafalgar Grove, Greenwich
London SE10 9TB   T/F 020 8858 6870
E info@walshbros.co.uk
W www.walshbros.co.uk

WALSH Steve PRODUCTIONS LTD
Contact: Wendy Wolfcarius
Animation. Feature Films. Films. Television
352 Banbury Road
Oxford OX2 7PP
F 020 7580 6567   T 020 7580 6553
E info@steve-walsh.com
W www.steve-walsh.com

WARNER BROS PRODUCTIONS LTD
Warner Suite
Leavesden Studios
South Way, Leavesden, Herts WD25 7LT
F 01923 685221   T 01923 685222

WARNER SISTERS PRODUCTIONS LTD
Ealing Studios, Ealing Green
London W5 5EP   T 020 8567 6655
E ws@warnercini.com

WEST DIGITAL
Broadcast Post-Production
65 Goldhawk Road, London W12 8EG
F 020 8743 2345   T 020 8743 5100
E luci@westdigital.co.uk

WHITEHALL FILMS
10 Lower Common South
London SW15 1BP
F 020 8788 2340   T 020 8785 3737
E mwhitehall@msn.com

WINNER Michael LTD
219 Kensington High Street
London W8 6BD
F 020 7602 9217   T 020 7734 8385
E winner@ftech.co.uk

WORKING TITLE FILMS LTD
26 Aybrook Street, London W1U 4AN
F 020 7307 3001   T 020 7307 3000

WORLD PRODUCTIONS & WORLD FILM SERVICES LTD
2nd Floor
12-14 St Christopher's Place
London W1U 1NH
F 020 3179 1801   T 020 3179 1800
W www.world-productions.com

WORLD WIDE PICTURES
Unit 30, 10-50 Willow Street
London EC2A 4BH
F 020 7613 6581   T 020 7613 6580
E info@worldwidepictures.tv
W www.worldwidepictures.tv

WORLD'S END TELEVISION
16-18 Empress Place, London SW6 1TT
F 020 7386 4901   T 020 7386 4900
E info@worldsendproductions.com
W www.worldsendproductions.com

WORTHWHILE MOVIE LTD
Providing the services of Bruce Pittman as Film Director
191 Logan Avenue, Toronto
Ontario, Canada M4M 2NT   T 001 (416) 469 0459
E bruce.pittman@sympatico.ca

XINGU FILMS
12 Cleveland Row, London SW1A 1DH
F 020 7451 0601   T 020 7451 0600

ZEPHYR FILMS LTD
33 Percy Street, London W1T 2DF
F 020 7255 3777   T 020 7255 3555
E info@zephyrfilms.co.uk

infopage

What are Film & Television Schools?

The schools listed in this section offer various courses to those who wish to become part of the behind-camera world of the entertainment industry. These courses include filmmaking, producing, screenwriting and animation, to name a few. Students taking these courses usually have to produce a number of short films in order to graduate. The following advice has been divided into two sections: for potential students and for actors.

Advice For Filmmakers/Writers:

Why should I take a course?

The schools listed here offer courses which enable a budding filmmaker or script writer to develop their skills with practical training. These courses are designed to prepare you for a career in a competitive industry. They also provide you with an opportunity to begin networking and making contacts with industry professionals.

How should I use these listings?

Research a number of schools carefully before applying to any courses. Have a look at the websites of the schools listed first to get an idea of the types of courses on offer, what is expected from students, and the individual values of each school. Request a prospectus from the school if they do not have full details online. Word of mouth recommendations are invaluable if you know anyone who has attended or taught at a school. You need to decide what type of course suits you - don't just sign up for the first one you read about. See what is available and give yourself time to think about the various options.

Advice For Actors:

Why should I get involved?

Student films can offer new performers the chance to develop skills and experience in front of a camera, learning scripts, working with other actors and working with crew members. Making new contacts and learning how to get on with those you are working with, whether in front of or behind camera, is a vital part of getting along in the acting community.

In addition, you are likely to receive a certain amount of exposure from the film. The student filmmaker may show it to teachers, other students, other actors, and most importantly directors when applying for jobs, and you would normally be given your own copy of the film which you can show to agents or casting directors if requested, or use a clip of it in your showreel (see below).

For more experienced actors, working on a student film can offer the opportunity to hone existing skills and keep involved within the industry. It can also be useful to observe new actors and keep up-to-date with new training ideas and techniques.

How do I get involved?

It may be helpful to see if the schools' websites have any advice for actors interested in being considered for parts in student films and suggesting how they should make contact. If there is no advice of this kind, it would be worth either phoning or e-mailing to ask if the school or its students would consider actors previously unknown to them. If this is the case, ask who CVs and headshots should be sent to, and whether they would like to see a showreel or voicereel (for animation courses).

If you are asked to play a role in a student film, make sure you are not going to a student's home and that someone knows where you are going and when. Equity also recommends that actors request a contract when working on any film; you could receive payment retrospectively if the film becomes a success. You may find it helpful to refer to Equity's advice leaflet *Low Pay/No Pay* which is available at http://www.equity.org.uk/Documents/Public/low%20pay%20no%20pay%202010.pdf

Should I use a clip of a student film on my showreel?

Casting directors would generally prefer to see some form of showreel than none at all. If you do not have anything else you can show that has been professionally broadcast, or do not have the money to get a showreel made from scratch, then a student film is an acceptable alternative. See the 'Promotional Services' section for more information on showreels.

Where can I find more information?

Students and actors may want to visit Shooting People's website www.shootingpeople.org for further advice and daily e-mail bulletins of student/short film and TV castings. Filmmakers can upload their films to the site for others to view.

BRIGHTON FILM SCHOOL
Contact: Senior Lecturer Franz von Habsburg FBKS (BAFTA)
Member of the National Association for Higher Education
in the Moving Image (NAHEMI) & the University Film Video
Association (UFVA). Part-time Day or Evening Film Directors'
Courses includes Screen Writing, Cinematography etc
E info@brightonfilmschool.org.uk   T 01273 302166
W www.brightonfilmschool.org.uk

LEEDS METROPOLITAN UNIVERSITY
MA in Film Making. BA (Hons) in Film & Moving Image
Production. Cert HE/FdA in Film & Television Production
BA (Hons) in Animation
Northern Film School
Electric Press, 1 Millennium Square
Leeds LS2 3AD
F 0113 812 8080   T 0113 812 0000
E filmenquiries@leedsmet.ac.uk
W www.leedsmet.ac.uk

LONDON COLLEGE OF COMMUNICATION
Film & Video Course
Elephant & Castle, London SE1 6SB
F 020 7514 6843   T 020 7514 6569
E info@lcc.arts.ac.uk
W www.lcc.arts.uk

LONDON FILM ACADEMY
The Old Church, 52A Walham Grove
London SW6 1QR
F 020 7381 6116   T 020 7386 7711
E info@londonfilmacademy.com
W www.londonfilmacademy.com

LONDON FILM SCHOOL THE
2-year MA Course in Film Making. 1-year MA in Screenwriting
24 Shelton Street, London WC2H 9UB
F 020 7497 3718   T 020 7836 9642
E info@lfs.org.uk
W www.lfs.org.uk

MIDDLESEX UNIVERSITY
School of Arts & Education
Television Production, Trent Park Campus
Bramley Road, London N14 4YZ   T 020 8411 5000
W www.mdx.ac.uk

NATIONAL FILM AND TELEVISION SCHOOL
MA & Diploma Courses in the Key Filmmaking Disciplines
Short Courses for Freelancers
Beaconsfield Studios
Station Road
Beaconsfield, Bucks HP9 1LG
F 01494 674042   T 01494 731425
E info@nfts.co.uk
W www.nfts.co.uk

NORTHERN FILM SCHOOL
Electric Press Building, 1 Millennium Square
Leeds LS2 3AD   T 0113 812 8000
E s.golay@leedsmet.ac.uk
W www.northernfilmschool.co.uk

UNIVERSITY FOR THE CREATIVE ARTS
Undergraduate Degree Courses in Animation, Broadcast
Media, Film Production & Journalism
Falkner Road
Farnham, Surrey GU9 7DS   T 01252 892883
E enquiries@ucreative.ac.uk
W www.ucreative.ac.uk

UNIVERSITY OF WESTMINSTER SCHOOL OF MEDIA ARTS & DESIGN
Undergraduate courses in Film & Television Production &
Contemporary Media Practice. Postgraduate Courses in
Screenwriting & Producing, Film & Television; Theory, Culture
& Industry
Admissions & Enquiries: Watford Road
Northwick Park, Harrow
Middlesex HA1 3TP   T 020 7911 5000
W www.wmin.ac.uk/filmschool

3 MILLS STUDIOS
Three Mill Lane
London E3 3DU
F 08715 944028
E info@3mills.com
W www.3mills.com
T 020 7363 3336

ANIMAL PROMOTIONS
White Rocks Farm, Underriver
Sevenoaks, Kent TN15 0SL
F 01732 763767
E happyhoundschool@yahoo.co.uk
W www.animalpromotions.co.uk
M 07778 156513

ARDMORE STUDIOS LTD
Herbert Road, Bray
Co. Wicklow, Ireland
F 00 353 1 2861894
E film@ardmore.ie
W www.ardmore.ie
T 00 353 1 2862971

BBC TELEVISION
Television Centre, Wood Lane
Shepherds Bush
London W12 7RJ
T 020 8743 8000

BRAY FILM STUDIOS
Down Place, Water Oakley
Windsor, Berkshire SL4 5UG
F 01628 623000
T 01628 622111

BRIGHTON FILM STUDIOS LTD
The Brighton Forum
95 Ditchling Road
Brighton BN1 4ST
E franz@brightonfilmstudios.com
W www.brightonfilmstudios.com
T 01273 302166

CAPITAL STUDIOS
Wandsworth Plain, London SW18 1ET
F 020 8877 0234
E info@capitalstudios.com
W www.capitalstudios.com
M 07974 921018

CLAPHAM ROAD STUDIOS
Animation. Live Action
161 Clapham Road
London SW9 0PU
T 020 7582 9664

EALING STUDIOS
Ealing Green, London W5 5EP
F 020 8758 8658
E info@ealingstudios.com
W www.ealingstudios.com
T 020 8567 6655

ELSTREE STUDIOS
Shenley Road
Borehamwood
Herts WD6 1JG
F 020 8905 1135
E info@elstreestudios.co.uk
W www.elstreestudios.co.uk
T 020 8953 1600

LONDON STUDIOS THE
London Television Centre
Upper Ground
London SE1 9LT
F 020 7157 5757
E sales@londonstudios.co.uk
W www.londonstudios.co.uk
T 020 7157 5555

PINEWOOD STUDIOS
Pinewood Road, Iver Heath
Buckinghamshire SL0 0NH
W www.pinewoodgroup.com
T 01753 651700

REUTERS TELEVISION
The Reuters Thompson Building
South Colonnade
Canary Wharf, London E14 5EP
T 020 7250 1122

RIVERSIDE STUDIOS
Crisp Road, London W6 9RL
F 020 8237 1001
E info@riversidestudios.co.uk
W www.riversidestudios.co.uk
T 020 8237 1000

SANDS FILMS COSTUMES LTD/ROTHERHITHE STUDIOS
82 St Marychurch Street
London SE16 4HZ
F 020 7231 2119
E info@sandsfilms.co.uk
W www.sandsfilms.co.uk
T 020 7231 2209

SARM WEST STUDIOS LTD
Contact: Julie Bateman
8-10 Basing Street
London W11 1ET
F 020 7221 9247
E julie@spz.com
W www.sarmstudios.com
T 020 7229 1229

SHEPPERTON STUDIOS
Studios Road
Shepperton
Middlesex TW17 0QD
F 01932 568989
W www.pinewoodgroup.com
T 01932 562611

TEDDINGTON STUDIOS
Broom Road
Teddington
Middlesex TW11 9NT
F 020 8943 4050
W www.pinewoodgroup.com
T 020 8977 3252

TWICKENHAM FILM STUDIOS LTD
The Barons
St Margaret's
Twickenham
Middlesex TW1 2AW
F 020 8607 8889
E enquiries@twickenhamstudios.com
W www.twickenhamstudios.com
T 020 8607 8888

Film London

Supports over 1,000 film, TV and
advertising projects every year.
Make us your first point of contact
for filming in the capital.

www.filmlondon.org.uk

Good Digs Guide
Compiled By Janice Cramer and David Banks

This is a list of digs recommended by those who have used them.

To keep the list accurate please send recommendations for inclusion to

GOOD DIGS GUIDE
Spotlight
7 Leicester Place
London WC2H 7RJ
Alternatively, please email contacts@spotlight.com

If you are a digs owner wishing to be listed, your application must contain a recommendation from a performer who has stayed in your accommodation.

ABERDEEN
Milne, Mrs A
5 Sunnyside Walk, Aberdeen AB24 3NZ   T 01224 638951

ABERDEEN
Woods, Pat
62 Union Grove, Aberdeen AB10 6RX   T 01224 586324

AYR
Dunn, Sheila
The Dunn-Thing Guest House
13 Park Circus
Ayr KA7 2DJ
M 07887 928685   T 01292 284531

BATH
Hutton, Mrs Celia
Bath Holiday Homes, Terranova
Shepherds Walk, Bath BA2 5QT
E bhh@virgin.net   T 01225 830830
W www.bathholidayhomes.co.uk

BATH
Tapley, Jane
Camden Lodgings, 3 Upper Camden Place
Bath BA1 5HX   T 01225 446561
E peter@tapley.ws

BELFAST
McCully, Mrs S
28 Eglantine Avenue, Belfast BT9 6DX
M 07985 947673   T 028 9068 2031
E shealaghmccully@hotmail.com

BIRMINGHAM
Hurst, Mr P
41 King Edward Road, Mosley
Birmingham B13 8HR   T 0121 449 8220
E phurst1com@aol.com

BIRMINGHAM
Mountain, Marlene P
268 Monument Road, Edgbaston
Birmingham B16 8XF   T 0121 454 5900

BIRMINGHAM
Wilson, Mrs
17 Yew Tree Road, Edgbaston
Birmingham B15 2LX   T 0121 440 5182

BLACKPOOL
Lees, Jean
Ascot Flats, 6 Hull Road
Central Blackpool FY1 4QB   T 01253 621059

BLACKPOOL
Somerset Apartments
22 Barton Avenue, Blackpool FY1 6AP   T/F 01253 346743
W www.blackpool-somerset-apartments.co.uk

BLACKPOOL
Waller, Veronica & Bob
The Brooklyn Hotel, 7 Wilton Parade
Blackpool FY1 2HE   T 01253 627003
W enquiries@brooklynhotel.co.uk

BOLTON
Duckworth, Paul
19 Burnham Avenue, Bolton BL1 6BD
M 07762 545129   T 01204 495732
E pauljohnathan@msn.com

BOLTON
White, Mrs M
20 Heywood Gardens, Great Lever
Bolton BL3 6RB   T 01204 531589

BOURNEMOUTH
Sitton, Martin
Flat 2, 9 St Winifreds Road
Meyrick Park, Bournemouth BH2 6NX   T 01202 293318

[CONTACTS 2011]

BRADFORD
Smith, Theresa
8 Moorhead Terrace, Shipley
Bradford BD18 4LA   T 01274 778568
E theresaannesmith@hotmail.com

BRIGHTON
Benedict, Peter
19 Madeira Place, Brighton BN2 1TN
M 07752 810122   T 020 7703 4104
E peter@peterbenedict.co.uk   W www.madeiraplace.co.uk

BRIGHTON
Chance, Michael & Drinkel, Keith
6 Railway Street, Brighton BN1 3PF
M 07876 223359   T 01273 779585
E mchance@lineone.net

BRIGHTON
Cleveland, Carol
13 Belgrave Street, Brighton BN2 9NS
M 07973 363939   T 01273 602607
E info@carolcleveland.com

BRIGHTON
Dyson, Kate
39 Arundel Street, Kemptown BN2 5TH
M 07812 949875   T 01273 607490
E kate.dyson@talktalk.net

BRISTOL
Ham, Phil & Jacqui
78 Stackpool Road, Bristol BS3 1NN
M 07956 962422   T 0117 902 5213
E jacquic@tiptopmusic.com

BRISTOL
Walsh, Karen
The Courtyard, 8 Royal York Crescent
Clifton, Bristol BS8 4JZ   M 07966 282398

BURY ST EDMUNDS
Bird, Mrs S
30 Crown Street, Bury St Edmunds
Suffolk IP33 1QU   T 01284 754492

BURY ST EDMUNDS
Harrington-Spier, Sue
39 Well Street, Bury St Edmunds
Suffolk IP33 1EQ   T 01284 768986
E sue.harringtonspier@googlemail.com

BUXTON
Kitchen, Mrs G
Silverlands Holiday Apartments
c/o 156 Brown Edge Road, Buxton, Derbyshire SK17 7AA
T 01298 79381   T 01298 26555
E swiftcaterequip2@aol.com

CAMBRIDGE
Dunn, Anne
The Dovecot, 1 St Catherine's Hall, Coton, Cambs CB23 7GU
M 07774 131797   T 01954 210291
E dunn@annecollet.fsnet.co.uk

CANTERBURY
Ellen, Nikki
Crockshard Farmhouse, Wingham
Canterbury CT3 1NY   T 01227 720464
E crockshard_bnb@yahoo.com   W www.crockshard.com

CARDIFF
Blade, Mrs Anne
25 Romilly Road, Canton
Cardiff CF5 1FH   T 029 2022 5860

CARDIFF
Drew, Brian
5 Westbury Terrace, Victoria Park
Canton, Cardiff CF5 1FZ   T 029 2037 7512

CARDIFF
Kelly, Sheila
166 Llandaff Road, Canton
Cardiff CF11 9PX   T 029 2039 5078
E mgsmkelly1@yahoo.co.uk

CARDIFF
Kennedy, Rosie
Duffryn Mawr Cottages, Pendoylan
Vale of Glamorgan   M 07746 946118
E rosie.kennedy@ukonline.co.uk
W www.duffrynmawrcottages.co.uk

CARDIFF
Lewis, Nigel
66 Donald Street, Roath, Cardiff CF24 4TR
M 07813 069822   T 029 2049 4008
E nigel.lewis66@btinternet.com

CHESTERFIELD
Cook, Linda & Chris
27 Tennyson Avenue, Chesterfield, Derbyshire
M 07929 850561   T 01246 202631
E chris_cook@talk21.com

CHESTERFIELD
Foston, Mr & Mrs
Anis Louise Guest House, 34 Clarence Road
Chesterfield S40 1LN   T 01246 235412
E anislouise@gmail.com
W www.anislouiseguesthouse.co.uk

CHESTERFIELD
Popplewell, Mr & Mrs
Alfred House, 23 Tennyson Avenue
Chesterfield, Derbyshire S40 4SN   T 01246 201738

CHICHESTER
Potter, Iain & Lyn
Hunston Mill Cottages, Selsey Road
Chichester PO20 1AU   T 01243 783375
E hunstonmill@aol.com   W www.hunstonmill.co.uk

COVENTRY
Snelson, Paddy & Bob
Banner Hill Farmhouse, Rouncil Lane
Kenilworth CV8 1NN   T 01926 852850

DARLINGTON
Bird, Mrs
Gilling Old Mill, Gilling West
Richmond, N Yorks DL10 5JD   T 01748 822771
E admin@yorkshiredales-cottages.com

DARLINGTON
Graham, Anne
Holme House, Piercebridge
Darlington DL2 3SY   T 01325 374280
E graham.holmehouse@gmail.com   W www.holmehouse.com

DARLINGTON
Reception
George Hotel, Piercebridge
Darlington DL2 3SW   T 01325 374576
W www.georgeontees.co.uk

DERBY
Boddy, Susan
St Wilfrids, Church Lane
Barrow-upon-Trent, Derbyshire DE73 7HB   T 01332 701384

DUNDEE
Hill, Mrs J
Ash Villa, 216 Arbroath Road
Dundee DD4 7RZ   T 01382 450831
E ashvilla_guesthouse@talk21.com

EASTBOURNE
Allen, Peter
Flat 1, 16 Enys Road
Eastbourne BN21 2DN
M 07712 439289   T 01323 730235

EASTBOURNE
Dullaway, Lisa
No. 3, 3 Cavendish Place
Eastbourne, East Sussex BN21 3EJ
M 07950 707464   T 01323 731258
E cavendish3@hotmail.co.uk

EASTBOURNE
Guess, Maggie
3 Hardy Drive, Langney Point
Eastbourne, East Sussex BN23 6ED
M 07710 273288   T 01323 736689
E guesswhom@btinternet.com

EDINBURGH
ACS Properties
(Short Term Letting in Edinburgh)
Office: 7 St Martins Place, Haddington
East Lothian EH41 4NF
M 07875 667752   T 01620 840900
E ashley@acs-properties.com
W www.acs-properties.com

EDINBURGH
Glen Miller, Edna
25 Bellevue Road, Edinburgh EH7 4DL   T 0131 556 4131

EDINBURGH
Stobbart, Joyce
84 Bellevue Road, Edinburgh EH7 4DE
M 07740 503951   T 0131 222 9889 (Daytime)
E joyms@btinternet.com

EDINBURGH
Tyrrell, Helen
9 Lonsdale Terrace, Edinburgh EH3 9HN
M 07929 960510   T 0131 229 7219
E helen.tyrrell@vhscotland.org.uk

GLASGOW
Baird, David W
6 Beaton Road, Maxwell Park, Glasgow G41 4LA
M 07842 195597   T 0141 423 1340
E b050557@yahoo.com

GLASGOW
Leslie-Carter, Simon
52 Charlotte Street, Glasgow G1 5DW
F 01436 810520   T 0845 2305252
E slc@52charlottestreet.co.uk
W www.52charlottestreet.co.uk

INVERNESS
Blair, Mrs
McDonald House Hotel, 1 Ardross Terrace
Inverness IV3 5NQ   T 01463 232878

INVERNESS
Kerr-Smith, Jennifer
Ardkeen Tower, 5 Culduthel Road
Inverness IV2 4AD   T 01463 233131

IPSWICH
Ball, Bunty
56 Henley Road, Ipswich IP1 3SA   T 01473 256653

IPSWICH
Bennett, Liz
Gayfers, Playford, Ipswich IP6 9DR   T 01473 623343
E lizzieb@clara.co.uk

IPSWICH
Hyde-Johnson, Anne
64 Benton Street, Hadleigh
Ipswich, Suffolk IP7 5AT   T 01473 823110

ISLE OF WIGHT
Ogston, Sue
Windward House, 69 Mill Hill Road
Cowes, Isle of Wight PO31 7EQ   T 01983 280940
E sueogston1@tiscali.co.uk

KESWICK
Bell, Miss A
Flat 4, Skiddaw View
Penrith Road, Keswick CA12 5HF   M 07740 949250

LEEDS
Baker, Mrs M
2 Ridge Mount (off Cliff Road)
Leeds LS6 2HD   T 0113 275 8735
E ridgemountleeds@googlemail.com

LEEDS
Byrne, Ralph
16 Oakwell Crescent, Leeds LS8 4AF
M 07763 572183   T 0113 249 5303
E ralphjbyrne@googlemail.com

LEEDS
Cannon, Rosie
14 Toronto Place, Chapel Allerton
Leeds LS7 4LJ
M 07969 832955   T 0113 262 1070

LINCOLN
Carnell, Andrew
Tennyson Court Cottages, 3 Tennyson Street
Lincoln LN1 1LZ
T 01522 569892   T 0800 9805408
E andrew@tennyson-court.co.uk
W www.tennyson-court.co.uk

LINCOLN
Sharpe, Mavis S
Bight House, 17 East Bight, Lincoln LN2 1QH   T 01522 534477

LIVERPOOL
de Leng, Ms S
7 Beach Lawn, Waterloo
Liverpool L22 8QA   T 0151 476 1563
E deleng@blueyonder.co.uk

LIVERPOOL
Double, Ross
5 Percy Street, Liverpool L8 7LT   T 0151 708 8821

LIVERPOOL
Maloney, Anne
16 Sandown Lane, Wavertree, Liverpool L15 8HY
M 07977 595040   T 0151 734 4839

LLANDUDNO
Blanchard, Mr D & Mrs A
Oasis Hotel, 4 Neville Crescent
Central Promenade, Llandudno LL30 1AT   T 01492 877822
E ann@oasis-hotel.co.uk

LONDON
Allen, Mrs I
Flat 2, 9 Dorset Square, London NW1 6QB   T 020 7723 3979

LONDON
Cardinal, Maggie
17A Gaisford Street, London NW5 2EB   T 020 7681 7376

LONDON
Kempton, Victoria
66 Morley Avenue, London N22 6NG
M 07946 344697   T 020 8888 5595
E vjkempton@onetel.com

LONDON
Long, Hilary
56 Sutlej Road, Charlton, London SE7 7DB
F 07092 315384   T 020 8856 5023
E rainbowtheatrelondoneast@yahoo.co.uk

LONDON
Maya, Ms Y
23 Lena Crescent, London N9 0FB   M 07958 461468

LONDON
Mesure, Nicholas
16 St Alfege Passage, Greenwich
London SE10 9JS   T 020 8853 4337

LONDON
Montagu, Beverley
13 Hanley Road, London N4 3DU   T 020 7263 3883

LONDON
Rothner, Stephanie
44 Grove Road, North Finchley, London N12 9DY
M 07956 406446   T 020 8446 1604

LONDON
Shaw, Lindy
11 Baronsmede, London W5 4LS   T 020 8567 0877
E lindy.shaw@talktalk.net

LONDON
Walsh, Genevieve
37 Kelvedon House, Guildford Road
Stockwell, London SW8 2DN   T 020 7627 0024

LONDON
Warren, Mrs Sally
28 Prebend Gardens, Chiswick
London W4 1TW   T 020 8994 0560

MALVERN
Emuss, Mrs
Priory Holme, 18 Avenue Road
Malvern WR14 3AR   T 01684 568455
E treemuss@fsmail.net

MALVERN
Martin, Mr N
37 Quest Hills Road, Malvern WR14 1RL
M 07979 851529   T 01684 562442
E nick@questhills.co.uk

MALVERN
McLeod, Mr & Mrs
Sidney House, 40 Worcester Road
Malvern WR14 4AA   T 01684 574994
E info@sidneyhouse.co.uk   W www.sidneyhouse.co.uk

MANCHESTER
Cox, Lucia
22 Woodlawn Court, Manchester M16 9RH
M 07805 337742   T 0161 860 6005
E lougrand76@hotmail.com

MANCHESTER
Dyson, Mrs Edwina
33 Danesmoor Road, West Didsbury
Manchester M20 3JT   T 0161 434 5410
E edwinadyson@hotmail.com

MANCHESTER
Halliwell, C
29 Merchants Quay, Manchester M50 3XF
M 07841 259258   T 0161 872 5076

MANCHESTER
Heaton, Miriam
58 Tamworth Avenue, Whitefield
Manchester M45 6UA   T 0161 773 4490

MANCHESTER
Higgins, Mark & Tanzey, Mathew
103 The Arthouse, 43 George Street
The Gay Village, Manchester M1 4AB
M 07904 520898   T 0161 234 0705
E icenlemon30@hotmail.com
W www.theatredigsmanchester.co.uk

MANCHESTER
Jones, Miss P M
Forget-me-not Cottages, Whitefield
Manchester M45 7SU   T 0161 766 9243

MANCHESTER
Prichard, Fiona & John
45 Bamford Road, Didsbury, Manchester M20 2QP
M/F 07771 965651   T 0161 434 4877

MANCHESTER
Twist, Susan
45 Osborne Road, Levenshulme
Manchester M19 2DU   T 0161 225 1591

MILFORD HAVEN
Henricksen, Bruce & Diana
Belhaven House Hotel Ltd, 29 Hamilton Terrace
Milford Haven SA73 3JJ
M 07825 237386   T 01646 695983
E brucehenricksen@mac.com   W www.westwaleshotel.com

NEWCASTLE UPON TYNE
The Manager
Rosebery Hotel, 2 Rosebery Crescent
Jesmond, Newcastle upon Tyne NE2 1ET   T 0191 281 3363
W www.roseberyhotel.co.uk

NEWPORT
Price, Mrs Dinah
Great House, Isca Road
Old Village, Caerleon, Gwent NP18 1QG   T 01633 420216
E dinahprice123@btinternet.com
W www.greathousebb.co.uk

NORWICH
Busch, Julia
8 Chester Street, Norwich NR2 2AY
M 07920 133250   T 01603 612833
E juliacbusch@aol.com

NOTTINGHAM
Davis, Barbara
3 Tattershall Drive, The Park
Nottingham NG7 1BX   T 0115 947 4179

NOTTINGHAM
Offord, Mrs
5 Tattershall Drive, The Park
Nottingham NG7 1BX   T 0115 947 6924

NOTTINGHAM
Santos, Mrs S
Eastwood Farm, Hagg Lane
Epperstone, Nottingham NG14 6AX   T 0115 966 3018
E info@eastwoodfarm.co.uk

NOTTINGHAM
Seymour Road Studios Bed & Breakfast
42 Seymour Road, West Bridgford
Nottingham NG2 5EF   M 07946 208211
E fran@seymourroadstudios.co.uk

NOTTINGHAM
Walker, Christine
18A Cavendish Crescent North, The Park
Nottingham NG7 1BA   T 0115 947 2485
E walker.ce@virgin.net

OXFORD
Petty, Susan
74 Corn Street
Witney, Oxford OX28 6BS   T 01993 703035

PETERBOROUGH
Smith, J
Fen-Acre, 20 Barber Drove North
Crowland, Peterborough PE6 0BE
M 07759 661896   T 01733 211847
E julie@fen-acreholidaylet.com
W www.fen-acreholidaylet.com

PLYMOUTH
Ball, Fleur
3 Hoe Gardens, Plymouth PL1 2JD   T 01752 670967
E fleurball@blueyonder.co.uk

PLYMOUTH
Carson, Mr & Mrs
6 Beech Cottages, Parsonage Road
Newton Ferrers, Nr Plymouth PL8 1AX   T 01752 872124
E beechcottages@aol.com

PLYMOUTH
Humphreys, John & Sandra
Lyttleton Guest House (Self Catering)
4 Crescent Avenue
Plymouth PL1 3AN   T 01752 220176

PLYMOUTH
Mead, Teresa
Ashgrove House, 218 Citadel Road
The Hoe, Plymouth PL1 3BB   T 01752 664046
E ashgroveho@aol.com

PLYMOUTH
Spencer, Hugh & Eloise
10 Grand Parade, Plymouth PL1 3DF
M 07966 41283   T 01752 664066
E hugh.spencer@hotmail.com

POOLE
Saunders, Mrs
1 Harbour Shallows
15 Whitecliff Road
Poole BH14 8DU   T 01202 741637
E saunders.221@btinternet.com

SALISBURY
Brumfitt, Ms S
26 Victoria Road, Salisbury
Wilts SP1 3NG   T 01722 334877

SHEFFIELD
Slack, Penny
Rivelin Glen Quarry
Rivelin Valley Road
Sheffield S6 5SE   T 0114 234 0382
E pennyslack@aol.com
W www.quarryhouse.org.uk

SOUTHSEA & PORTSMOUTH
Tyrell, Wendy
Douglas Cottage, 27 Somerset Road
Southsea PO5 2NL   T 023 9282 1453

STOKE-ON-TRENT
Hindmoor, Mrs
Verdon Guest House (Self Catering and B&B)
44 Charles Street
Hanley, Stoke-on-Trent ST1 3JY   T 01782 264244

STOKE-ON-TRENT
Meredith, Mr K
2 Bank End Farm Cottage
Hammond Avenue
Brown Edge, Stoke-on-Trent
Staffs ST6 8QU   T 01782 502160
E kenmeredith@btinternet.com

STRATFORD-UPON-AVON
Caterham House
58-59 Rother Street
Stratford-upon-Avon CV37 6LT   T 01789 267309
E caterhamhousehotel@btconnect.com

TAUNTON
Parker, Sue
Admirals Rest
5 Taunton Road
Bridgwater TA6 3LW   T 01278 458580

TAUNTON
Read, Mary
Pyreland Farm, Cheddon Road
Taunton, Somerset TA2 7QX   T 01823 334148

WESTCLIFF
Hussey, Joy
42A Ceylon Road
Westcliff-on-Sea SS0 7HP   M 07946 413496
E annjayhussey@googlemail.com

WINCHESTER
South Winchester Lodges
The Green
South Winchester Golf Club
Winchester, Hampshire SO22 5QX   T 01962 820490

WOLVERHAMPTON
Nixon, Sonia
39 Stubbs Road, Pennfields
Wolverhampton WV3 7DJ   T 01902 339744

WOLVERHAMPTON
Riggs, Peter A
'Bethesda', 56 Chapel Lane
Codsall
Nr Wolverhampton WV8 2EJ
M 07930 967809   T 01902 844068

WORTHING
Stewart, Mollie
School House
11 Ambrose Place
Worthing BN11 1PZ   T 01903 206823

WORTHING
Symonds, Mrs Val
23 Shakespeare Road
Worthing BN11 4AR
M 07951 183252   T 01903 201557

YORK
Blacklock, Tom
155 Lowther Street, York YO3 7LZ   T 01904 620487

YORK
Blower, Iris & Dennis
Dalescroft Guest House
10 Southlands Road
York YO23 1NP   T 01904 626801
E info@dalescroft-york.co.uk
W www.dalescroft-york.co.uk

YORK
Harrand, Greg
Hedley House Hotel & Apts
3 Bootham Terrace, York YO30 7DH   T 01904 637404
E greg@hedleyhouse.com

Please note that while Spotlight takes every care in screening the companies featured in this section, it cannot be held responsible for services or treatments received.

ALEXANDER ALLIANCE
Alexander Technique. Audition & Voice Coaching
3 Hazelwood Drive
St Albans, Herts   T 01727 843633
E bev.keech@ntlworld.com
W www.alextech.co.uk

ALEXANDER CENTRE THE Bloomsbury
Alexander Technique
Bristol House
80A Southampton Row
London WC1B 4BB   T 020 7404 5348
E enquiries@alexcentre.com
W www.alexcentre.com

ALEXANDER TECHNIQUE
Contact: Jackie Coote MSTAT
27 Britannia Road, London SW6 2HJ   T 020 7731 1061
E jackiecoote@alexandertec.co.uk
W www.alexandertec.co.uk

ALEXANDER TECHNIQUE
Contact: Robert Macdonald
13 Ascot Lodge, Greville Place
London NW6 5JD   M 07956 852303
W www.voice.org.uk

ALL ABOUT TEETH LTD
The Club Room, Miserden
Gloucestershire GL6 7JA   T 01285 821220
E nicolas@ceramiccentre.com

ALTERED IMAGE LIFE COACHING
Primrose Cottage, 6 Lee Place
Ilfracombe EX34 9BQ
F 08709 133624   M 07050 644101
E lifecoach@merseymail.com
W www.alteredimage2.co.uk

ARTS CLINIC THE
*Personal & Professional Development
Psychological Counselling*
14 Devonshire Place, London W1G 6HX
F 020 7224 6256   T 020 7935 1242
E mail@artsclinic.co.uk

ASPEY ASSOCIATES
*Executive Coaching. Human Resources
Management & Team Training*
90 Long Acre, Covent Garden
London WC2E 9RZ   T 0845 1701300
E hr@aspey.com
W www.aspey.com

AURA DENTAL SPA
5 Queens Terrace
London NW8 6DX   T 020 7722 0040
E info@auradentalspa.com
W www.auradentalspa.com

BODY CLINIC THE
Skincare Specialists
Harley Street W1G
South Woodford E18
Gidea Park RM2   T 0800 5424809
E info@thebodyclinic.co.uk
W www.thebodyclinic.co.uk

BODYWISE YOGA & NATURAL HEALTH CENTRE
119 Roman Road, London E2 0QN   T 020 8981 6938
E info@bodywisehealth.org
W www.bodywisehealth.org

[CONTACTS 2011]

infopage

How should I use these listings?

You will find a variety of companies in this section which could help you enhance your health and wellbeing physically and mentally. They include personal fitness and lifestyle coaches, counsellors, exercise classes and beauty consultants amongst others. It is worth researching any company or service you are considering using. Many of these listings have websites which you can browse. Even if you feel you have your career and lifestyle under control, you may still find the following advice helpful:

Your body is part of your business

Your mental and physical health is vital to your career as a performer. Just from a business perspective, your body is part of your promotional package and it needs to be maintained. Try to keep fit and eat healthily to enhance both your outward appearance and your inner confidence. This is particularly important if you are unemployed. You need to ensure that if you are suddenly called for an audition you look suitable for and feel positive about the part you are auditioning for.

Injury

Keeping fit also helps you to minimise the risk of an injury during a performance. The last thing you want to do is to be prevented from working. An injury is more likely to occur if you are inflexible and unprepared for sudden physical exertion. If you do pick up an injury or an illness you will want to make sure it does not get any worse by getting treatment with a specialist.

Mental health

Mental health is just as important as bodily health. Just as you would for any physical injury or illness, if you suffer from a psychological problem such as stage fright, an addiction or depression, you should make sure that you address your concerns and deal with the issues involved. You may need to see a counsellor or a life coach for guidance and support.

Unemployment

If you are unemployed, it can be difficult to retain a positive mindset. The best thing you can do is to keep yourself occupied. You could join a dance or drama class, which would help to maintain your fitness levels as well as developing contacts and keeping involved within the industry. Improve your CV by learning to speak a new language or play a musical instrument. Think about taking on temporary or part-time work outside of acting to earn money until the next job comes along, or you could put yourself forward for acting work in a student film (see 'Film & Television Schools' for more information).

Where can I find more information?

For more information on health and wellbeing you may wish to contact the British Association for Performing Arts Medicine (BAPAM) www.bapam.org.uk. You may also find their article on the next page helpful. Please refer to the 'Drama Training, Schools & Coaches' and 'Dance Training & Professional Classes' sections if you are interested in taking drama or dance courses or lessons to improve your fitness, keep your auditioning skills sharp between jobs and/or stay occupied and motivated.

Please note that while Spotlight takes every care in screening the companies and individuals featured in this section, it cannot be held responsible for services or treatments received.

Actors who are never out of work are rare creatures. But you can use your resting periods to invest in your physical and mental health. Here are a few suggestions from BAPAM, the charity that provides free health-assessment clinics and reduced-price treatments to artists with performance-related health problems.

Look after your health on a budget

If you can't justify the cost of keeping up your gym membership, go for cheaper forms of exercise:

- **Walk or cycle** instead of driving or using public transport. If you haven't ridden a bike for years, build your confidence by taking a course.
- **Run** in the open air instead of on a treadmill at a gym. It's much better to be in the fresh air - and it's more sociable.
- **Swimming** is a cheap and effective form of exercise. Think about taking lessons to make your stroke more efficient and avoid putting unnecessary pressure on your joints - especially your neck.
- **Team sports** combine fresh air and being sociable; now could be the time to take up football or netball again. Be careful, though - you wouldn't want a sports injury to come between you and your next job!
- Learn a technique to help with **posture**, such as Alexander Technique, Feldenkrais or Pilates. Techniques that are taught one-to-one can be expensive, but you can often find taster sessions at adult education colleges.
- **Take a refresher** in all those stagecraft skills (breathing; warm-up exercises; stage fighting) you learned at drama school. Enrol on a short course or read some books. When the next job comes up you need to be in peak condition and able to perform safely.

Think about your diet while you're resting

Everyone knows that eating well has a positive effect on your mental and physical wellbeing - especially important when you need to keep your spirits up.

- Learn about **healthy eating**, and expand your repertoire of recipes. Farmers' markets save money and you'll learn what's in season. Then you can maintain good habits when you're running around or on tour.
- If you ration your **treats**, you make them more special. If a treat becomes a daily habit you won't enjoy real treats so much.
- Now is the time to **phase out junk food.** Why spend money on processed food when you could eat so much better for less? See the BAPAM factsheet *Sensible eating for performers*.
- Don't rely on **alcohol** to keep you going. You develop expectations around alcohol, and that will take its toll on your liver (and your wallet!). Try to make a drink last longer, or alternate alcohol and water over the course of an evening. See the BAPAM factsheet *The drinks are on me!* for more information about drinking responsibly.

Invest in your mental health too

- Think strategically about your career. Do a **skills audit**, remembering all the skills you've accumulated (numeracy, fundraising, any IT skills). Be creative about how you can put them to use, and fill any skill gaps. Focusing on something developmental can take your mind off your current circumstances.
- Use quiet periods to **organise** your paperwork and electronic filing systems. You will feel empowered when you know everything is in order; it saves time and stress when you do get busy if you already have a workable system in place. Learn to use **spreadsheets** to keep track of your finances. You'll save yourself endless headaches when it's time to file your tax return, *and* you'll save yourself money on an accountant.
- **Volunteering** is great for stopping you feeling isolated. Try and find an activity that involves **physical exercise** - such as working in a community garden. It might even lead to a job!
- Remember, there's no need to suffer alone if being out of work is beginning to get you down. A few sessions with a **counsellor** can make a big difference. Check out the BAPAM Directory online at www.bapam.org.uk to locate a performer-friendly counsellor in your area.

To find out more about performance-related health issues and BAPAM services, please see the website www.bapam.org.uk

infopage

Maria Yacoob is a dance teacher, choreographer, and writer. She teaches jazz classes at Pineapple Dance Studios, works as a choreographer for stage and television, has been a dance critic for the BBC, and regularly writes about dance for magazines.

Here's a question: why should you, the readers of Contacts, take regular dance classes? Well, here are three answers: dancing is good for your body, it's good for your career, and it's good for your soul. These compelling calls to physically express yourself hold true whether dance is your speciality, a third string to your performing bow, or an activity you only embark upon after sufficient alcoholic lubrication at a party.

First of all, let's consider a key tool of any performer's trade – your body. It goes without saying that performance of any kind requires an adequate level of physical fitness.

For dancers, the levels you achieve at the end of your training can only improve, or even be maintained, if you take regular dance classes between, and indeed during, jobs. Ballet dancers belonging to the world's top companies take class every morning before going into rehearsals or performances – an example all dancers would do well to follow. Loss of flexibility is often cited as the big downside of stopping regular training, but strength and stamina are usually the first things to go. And less obviously (but just as noticeably to those hosting auditions) the repetition of movement that improves technique, placement and accuracy is lost without regular upkeep.

For part-time or non-dancers, the physical benefits of dance include improved flexibility, strength, and stamina. But why choose dance classes as opposed to swimming, yoga or pumping iron at the gym?

Because as well as being a great way to keep fit, dance is, of course, a performing art. Right now, after years of being sidelined as niche entertainment, dance is enjoying the time of its life. It's the subject of prime time television shows, cinematic musicals like *Mamma Mia!* are smashing records, and the success of the West End is flying in the face of the recession, thanks to musicals.

So now, more than ever, if you want to get the job, you need to dance. And if you already dance, you'd do well to equip yourself in a variety of styles, from ballet to hip-hop to ballroom. Pineapple is the perfect place to pick up new moves, with open classes at every level in almost every form of dance. And the structure of most classes – where the teacher requires students to pick up a chunk of choreography and immediately perform it – is perfect training for the audition process.

But if that sounds more daunting than delightful to those less confident with their coordination, don't worry. Start with beginner classes, and remember the third reason for dancing – it's good for the soul.

All exercise releases endorphins, but none can induce happiness quite like dance can. It's a unique and potent mix of accomplishing the steps, losing yourself in the music, feeling the hot, sweaty collective energy of the class, and using your body to express pure emotion. It's why dance has been a part of all societies since tribal Africa. It's why thousands of people traipse into nightclubs every weekend to dance away the stresses and strains of the 9-5 week.

It's also why dance classes are the perfect antidote to the seemingly insecure and sometimes solitary day-to-day existence of a 'between jobs' performer. During those periods when you're waiting for your agent to call, dance classes will give you a bit of structure to your day, a reason to get out of bed, a social life, an easy way to feel good about yourself.

So, what are you waiting for? Put on your dancing shoes and hit the (studio) floor...

Please visit www.pineapple.uk.com for further information about Maria's jazz classes and all other classes at Pineapple.

BOXMOOR HOUSE DENTAL PRACTICE
451 London Road
Hemel Hempstead HP3 9BE
F 01442 244454   T 01442 253253
E d-gardner@btconnect.com

BREATHE FITNESS PERSONAL TRAINING
22A Station Approach, Hayes
Bromley, Kent BR2 7EH   M 07840 180094
E anthony@breathefitness.uk.com
W www.breathefitness.uk.com

BURGESS Chris
Counselling & Psychotherapy for Performing Artists
The Chandlery
55 Westminster Bridge Road
London SE1 7QY   M 07985 011694
E chrisburgess@netcom.co.uk

BURT Andrew
Counselling
74 Mill Hill Road, London W3 8JJ   T 020 8992 5992
E burt.counsel@tiscali.co.uk
W www.andrewburtcounselling.co.uk

COGNATIVE BEHAVIOURAL THERAPY (CBT)
West/North London
E info@therapycbt.co.uk
W www.therapycbt.co.uk

CONSTRUCTIVE TEACHING CENTRE LTD
Alexander Technique Teacher Training
18 Lansdowne Road
London W11 3LL   T 020 7727 7222
E constructiveteachingcentre@gmail.com
W www.constructiveteaching.com

CORTEEN Paola MSTAT
Alexander Technique
10A Eversley Park Road, London N21 1JU   T 020 8882 7898
E pmcorteen@yahoo.co.uk

COURTENAY Julian
NLP Hypnotherapy
42 Langdon Park Road, London N6 5QG   M 07973 139376
E julian@mentalfitness.uk.com

CRAIGENTINNY DENTAL CARE
57 Duddington Crescent, Milton Road
Edinburgh EH15 3AY   T 0131 669 2114
E dentist@craigentinny.co.uk
W www.craigentinny.co.uk

CROWE Sara
Holistic Massage. Pregnancy Treatment. Reflexology
25 Holmes Avenue
Hove BN3 7LB   M 07830 375389
E saracrowe77@gmail.com

DAVIES Siobhan STUDIOS
Treatment Room
85 St George's Road, London SE1 6ER
F 020 7091 9669   T 020 7091 9650
E info@siobhandavies.com
W www.siobhandavies.com

DREAM
Massage, Reflexology & Yoga for Events,
the Workplace & Home
117B Gaisford Street, London NW5 2EG   M 07973 731026
E heidi@dreamtherapies.co.uk
W www.dreamtherapies.co.uk

EDGE OF THE WORLD HYPNOTHERAPY & NLP
Contact: Graham Howes
ASHPH GHR Registered. GHSC Regulated. Gastric Band/Weight
Loss Hypnotherapy Specialist Help for Performers: Anxiety,
Audition/Stage Fright, Problems with Line Learning, Stress.
Quit Smoking
Central London, Essex/Suffolk
M 07960 755626   T 01206 391050
E info@edgehypno.com
W www.edgehypno.com

EDWARDS Simon MCA Hyp
Hypnotherapy for Professionals in Film, Stage & Television
Flat 7, Boatrace Court
Mortlake High Street
London SW14 8HL   M 07889 333680
E simonedwardsltd@googlemail.com
W www.simonedwards.com

ELITE SPORTS SKILLS
Personal Training. Sports Coaching. Level 4 in Fitness &
Coaching
E esskills@hotmail.com   M 07527 504052
W www.elitesportsskills.com

ENLIGHTENED SELF INTEREST
45 Hyde Park Square, London W2 2JT   M 07986 629537
E shevlin-elmore@lcch.co.uk

EXPERIENTIAL FOCUSING THERAPY SESSIONS
Contact: Dr Greg Madison
93-95 Gloucester Place, London W1   M 07941 300871
E info@gregmadison.net
W www.gregmadison.net

40 Wilbury Road, Brighton BN1

EXPLORING U COUNSELLING LTD
The Workshop, 9 Hall Street
Long Melford, Nr Sudbury
Suffolk CO10 9JF   M 07841 979450
E euc@exploringUcounselling.co.uk
W www.exploringUcounselling.co.uk

FABULOUS-LIFESTYLES
25 Brookland Hill, London NW11 6DU   M 07958 984195
E nicci@fabulous-lifestyles.com
W www.fabulous-lifestyles.com

FAITH Gordon BA DHC MCHC (UK)
Focusing. Hypnotherapy. Obstacles to Performing
Positive Affirmation
1 Wavel Mews, Priory Road
West Hampstead, London NW6 3AB   T 020 7328 0446
W www.gordonfaith.co.uk/voice.htm

FIT 4 THE PART
Contact: Jon Trevor
Celebrity Trainer. Lifestyle Guru, Media Presenter
North London
M 07702 590464   T 0845 4380486
E info@jontrevor.com
W www.jontrevor.com

FITNESS COACH THE
Contact: Jamie Baird
Agua at The Sanderson
50 Berners Street
London W1T 3NG
M 07970 782476   T 020 7300 1414
E jamie@thefitnesscoach.com

FLEUR DE VIE
Hilton Hall, Hilton Lane
Essington, Staffordshire WV11 2BQ   M 07548 896333
E susan@cmc-technologies.co.uk

HAMMOND John B. Ed (Hons) ICHFST
Fitness Consultancy. Sports & Relaxation Massage
4 Glencree, Billericay
Essex CM11 1EB
M 07703 185198   T/F 01277 632830

HARLEY STREET VOICE CENTRE THE
The Harley Street ENT Clinic
109 Harley Street
London W1G 6AN
F 020 7935 7701   T 020 7224 2350
E info@harleystreetent.com
W www.harleystreetent.com

HILLSHYPNOTHERAPY
30 Tudor Road, Godmanchester
Huntingdon, Cambs PE29 2DP   M 07590 466949
E adamcharleshills@gmail.com

HYL ENERGISER
10 Little Newport Street
London WC2H 7JJ   M 07768 321092
E info@hylenergiser.com
W www.hylenergiser.com

HYPNOSIS WORKS
19 Glengall Road, London SE15 6NJ   T 020 7237 5815
E sssp@hypnosisdoeswork.net
W www.hypnosisdoeswork.net

INSPIRATIONAL WELLBEING
Energy Healer
131 Woodland Grove, Epping
Essex CM16 4NG   T 01992 576565
E inspirationalwellbeing@gmail.com
W www.inspirationalwellbeing.com

INTOUCH LONDON
Mobile Massage Therapist
E jade@intouch-london.com   M 07917 057078
W www.intouch-london.com

JEEVES SERVICES (UK) LTD
Lifestyle Management
Allerton, 5A New Church Road
Sutton Coldfield B73 5RT   M 07812 992726
E dani@jeevesservices.com
W www.jeevesservices.com

JLP FITNESS
*Boxing. Kick/Muay-Thai Boxing. Personal Training
Group Sessions*
E jlp@jacquileepryce.com   M 07930 304809

JOINT PERFORMANCE OSTEOPATHY
Metis @ The Long Dock
Drury Lane
London WC2B 5SP   M 07957 165070
E info@jointperformance.co.uk
W www.jointperformance.co.uk

JOSHI CLINIC THE
Holistic Healthcare
57 Wimpole Street, London W1G 8YW
F 020 7486 9622   T 020 7487 5456
E info@joshiclinic.co.uk
W www.joshiclinic.co.uk

LIFE COACHING
*Contact: Dr Elspeth Reid. Including Career, Relationship &
Self-Confidence Coaching*
102 Clarence Road
Wimbledon SW19 8QD   T 020 8879 7676
E coach@elspethreid.com
W www.elspethreid.com

LIFE PRACTICE UK LTD
Specialists in Behavioural Change
Woodlands, Preston Road
Gosmore, Hitchin
Herts SG4 7QS   T/F 01462 451473
E info@lifepractice.co.uk
W www.lifepractice.co.uk

LUCAS Hazel
Qualified Holistic Masseur
119 Brightwell Avenue
Westcliff-on-Sea
Essex SS0 9EQ   M 07870 862939
E onedaylucas@blueyonder.co.uk

MAGIC KEY PARTNERSHIP THE
Contact: Lyn Burgess. Life Coach
151A Moffat Road, Thornton Heath
Surrey CR7 8PZ   T 0845 1297401
E lyn@magickey.co.uk
W www.magickey.co.uk

MATRIX ENERGY FIELD THERAPY
Accredited Healer
Deal Castle House, 31 Victoria Road
Deal, Kent CT14 7AS
M 07762 821828   T 01304 379466
E donnie@lovingorganization.org

McCALLION Anna
Alexander Technique
Flat 2, 11 Sinclair Gardens
London W14 0AU   T 020 7602 5599
E hildegarde007@yahoo.com

MINDSCI CLINIC
Clinical Hypnotism
34 Willow Bank, Ham
Richmond, Surrey TW10 7QX   T/F 020 8948 2439
E bt@mindsci-clinic.com
W www.mindsci-clinic.com

NOBLE Penny PSYCHOTHERAPY
8 Shaftesbury Gardens, Victoria Road
North Acton, London NW10 6LJ   M 07506 579895
E pennynobletherapy@googlemail.com
W www.pennynoblepsychotherapy.com

NORTON Michael R.
Implant/Reconstructive Dentistry
104 Harley Street, London W1G 7JD
F 020 7486 9119   T 020 7486 9229
E linda@nortonimplants.com
W www.nortonimplants.com

NUTRITIONAL THERAPY FOR PERFORMERS
Contact: Vanessa May BSc. CNHC NTC & BANT Reg
18 Oaklands Road
Ealing
London W7 2DR   M 07962 978763
E vanessa@wellbeingandnutrition.co.uk
W www.wellbeingandnutrition.co.uk

OGUNLARU Rasheed
Life & Business Coach
The Coaching Studio, 223A Mayall Road
London SE24 0PS   T 020 7207 1082
E rasheed@rasaru.com
W www.rasaru.com

PEAK PERFORMANCE TRAINING
Contact: Tina Reibl
Hypnotherapy. NLP. Success Strategies
42 The Broadway, Maidenhead
Berkshire SL6 1LU   T 01628 633509
E tina.reibl@tesco.net
W www.maidenhead-hypnotherapy.co.uk

POLAND Ken DENTAL STUDIOS
Film/Stage Dentistry
1 Devonshire Place, London W1G 6HH
F 020 7486 3952   T 020 7935 6919
E robpoland@btconnect.com

PSYCHOTHERAPY & MEDICAL HYPNOSIS
Contact: Karen Mann DCH DHP. Including Performance
Improvement & Let Go of the Past
10 Harley Street, London W1G 9PF   T 020 7794 5843
E emailkarenmann@googlemail.com
W www.karenmann.co.uk

ROBERTS Dan PERSONAL TRAINING
38 Calverton Street
London SW1V 3AU   M 07958 774541
E info@danrobertstraining.com

RUOK4SPEX.COM
PO Box 1027, PE12 0SQ
E info@ruok4spex.com
W www.ruok4spex.com

SEYRI Kayvan MSc NSCA-CPT*D CSCS *D
NASM-PES CES
Athletic Performance Specialist. Master Personal Trainer
E info@ultimatefitpro.com   M 07881 554636
W www.ultimatefitpro.com

SHENAS Dr DENTAL STUDIO
51 Cadogan Gardens, Sloane Square
Chelsea, London SW3 2TH   T 020 7589 2319
E info@shenasdental.co.uk
W www.shenasdental.co.uk

SHER SYSTEM THE
Helping Skin with Acne & Rosacea
PO Box 573, Staines, Middlesex TW18 9FJ
F 01784 463410   T 01784 227805
E skincare@sher.co.uk
W www.sher.co.uk

SHIATSU HEALTH CENTRE
Moving Arts Base
134 Liverpool Road
London N1 1LA   M 07905 504418
E japaneseyoga@btinternet.com
W www.shiatsuhealth.com

SMILE NW
Contact: Dr Veronica Morris (Cosmetic & General Dentist)
17 Hallswelle Parade, Finchley Road
Temple Fortune, London NW11 0DL
F 020 8458 5681   T 020 8458 2333
E enquiries@smile-nw.co.uk
W www.smile-nw.co.uk

SMILE SOLUTIONS
Dental Practice
24 Englands Lane
London NW3 4TG
F 020 7449 1769   T 020 7449 1760
E enquiries@smile-solutions.info
W www.smile-solutions.info

SMILEMORE DENTAL CARE
Cosmetic Dentistry. Dental Hygienist. Implants. Invisalign
Orthodontics. Porcelain Veneers. Tooth Whitening
63 St Johns Wood High Street
London NW8 7NL   T 020 7586 1210
E paul.abrahams@smilemoredentalcare.com
W www.smilemoredentalcare.com

SMILESTUDIO
First Floor, Wingate House
93-107 Shaftesbury Avenue
London W1D 5DY   T 020 7439 0888
W www.smile-studio.co.uk

STAT (The Society of Teachers of the Alexander Technique)
1st Floor Linton House
39-51 Highgate Road
London NW5 1RS
F 020 7482 5435   T/F 020 7482 5135
E enquiries@stat.org.uk
W www.stat.org.uk

THEATRICAL DENTISTRY
Contact: Richard D. Casson (Cosmetic Dentist)
6 Milford House
7 Queen Anne Street
London W1G 9HN   T/F 020 7580 9696
E smile@richardcasson.com
W www.richardcasson.com

TOP NOTCH NANNIES
142 Buckingham Palace Road
London SW1W 9TR
T 020 7881 0893   T 020 7824 8209
E jean@topnotchnannies.com
W www.topnotchnannies.com

VITAL TOUCH LTD THE
210 Creighton Avenue
London N2 9BJ   M 07976 263691
E suzi@thevitaltouch.com
W www.thevitaltouch.com

WALK-IN BACKRUB
On-site Massage Company
14 Neals Yard, London WC2H 9DP   T/F 020 7436 9875
E info@walkinbackrub.co.uk
W www.walkinbackrub.co.uk

WELLBEING
Contact: Leigh Jones. Personal Training. Tai Chi. Yoga
22 Galloway Close, Broxbourne
Herts EN10 6BU   M 07957 333921
E williamleighjones@hotmail.com

WOODFORD HOUSE DENTAL PRACTICE
162 High Road, Woodford Green
Essex IG8 9EF
F 020 8504 1393   T 020 8504 2704
E info@improveyoursmile.co.uk
W www.improveyoursmile.co.uk

O

**Opera Companies
Organisations**

p268

OPERA COMPANIES

CARL ROSA OPERA
359 Hackney Road
London E2 8PR
F 020 7613 0859
E info@carlrosaopera.co.uk
W www.carlrosaopera.co.uk

T 020 7613 0777

CLOCKWORK OPERA
406 Vesta Court
City Walk
London SE1 4BP
E info@clockworkopera.com
W www.clockworkopera.com

T 020 7060 3004

CO-OPERA CO PRODUCTIONS
5 Orchard Business Centre
Kangley Bridge Road
London SE26 5AQ
E info@co-opera-co.org
W www.co-opera-co.org

T 0845 1235664

ENGLISH NATIONAL OPERA
London Coliseum
St Martin's Lane
London WC2N 4ES
F 020 7845 9277
W www.eno.org

T 020 7836 0111

ENGLISH TOURING OPERA
Contact: James Conway
1st Floor
52-54 Rosebery Avenue
London EC1R 4RP
F 020 7713 8686
E admin@englishtouringopera.org.uk
W www.englishtouringopera.org.uk

T 020 7833 2555

GLYNDEBOURNE FESTIVAL OPERA
Glyndebourne, Lewes
East Sussex BN8 5UU
W www.glyndebourne.com

T 01273 812321

GRANGE PARK OPERA
24-26 Broad Street
Alresford
Hampshire SO24 9AQ
E info@grangeparkopera.co.uk
W www.grangeparkopera.co.uk

T 01962 737360

GUBBAY Raymond LTD
Dickens House
15 Tooks Court
London EC4A 1QH
F 020 7025 3751
E info@raymondgubbay.co.uk
W www.raymondgubbay.co.uk

T 020 7025 3750

KENTISH OPERA
Lakefield Farm House
Ide Hill Road
Bough Beech TN8 7PW
E sl.sweald@fsmail.net
W www.kentishopera.fsnet.co.uk

T 01732 700339

MUSIC THEATRE LONDON
c/o Capriol Films
The Old Reading Room
The Street, Brinton
Melton Constable, Norfolk NR24 2QF   M 07831 243942
E info@capriolfilms.co.uk
W www.capriolfilms.co.uk

OPERA DELLA LUNA
7 Cotmore House
Fringford
Bicester, Oxfordshire OX27 8RQ
F 01869 323533   T 01869 325131
E enquiries@operadellaluna.org
W www.operadellaluna.org

OPERA NORTH
Grand Theatre, 46 New Briggate
Leeds LS1 6NU
F 0113 244 0418   T 0113 243 9999
E info@operanorth.co.uk
W www.operanorth.co.uk

OPERAUK
177 Andrewes House
Barbican, London EC2Y 8BA   T 020 7628 0025
E rboss4@aol.com
W www.operauk.co.uk

PEGASUS OPERA COMPANY LTD
The Brix, St Matthew's
Brixton Hill, London SW2 1JF   T/F 020 7501 9501
E admin@pegopera.org
W www.pegopera.org

PIMLICO OPERA
24 Broad Street, Alresford
Hampshire SO24 9AQ   T 01962 737360
E pimlico@grangeparkopera.co.uk
W www.grangeparkopera.co.uk

PMB PRESENTATIONS LTD
Vicarage House
58-60 Kensington Church Street
London W8 4DB
F 020 7368 3338   T 020 7368 3337
E p@triciamurraybett.com
W www.pmbpresentations.co.uk

ROYAL OPERA THE
Royal Opera House
Covent Garden
London WC2E 9DD   T 020 7240 1200
W www.roh.org.uk

SCOTTISH OPERA
39 Elmbank Crescent
Glasgow G2 4PT   T 0141 248 4567
W www.scottishopera.org.uk

WELSH NATIONAL OPERA
Wales Millennium Centre
Bute Place, Cardiff CF10 5AL
F 029 2063 5099   T 029 2063 5000
E marketing@wno.org.uk
W www.wno.org.uk

A STAGE KINDLY
Supports the future of new musicals from around the world
7 Northiam, Cromer Street
London WC1H 8LB   M 07947 074887
E astagekindly@aol.com
W www.astagekindly.com

ABTT (ASSOCIATION OF BRITISH THEATRE TECHNICIANS)
4th Floor, 55 Farringdon Road, London EC1M 3JB
F 020 7242 9303   T 020 7242 9200
E office@abtt.org.uk
W www.abtt.org.uk

ACTORS' ADVISORY SERVICE
Provides Advice to Actors, Agents, Photographers etc
29 Talbot Road, Twickenham
Middlesex TW2 6SJ   T 020 8287 2839

ACTORS' BENEVOLENT FUND
6 Adam Street, London WC2N 6AD
F 020 7836 8978   T 020 7836 6378
E office@abf.org.uk
W www.actorsbenevolentfund.co.uk

ACTORS CENTRE (LONDON) THE
Charity. 1700 Classes a year for professional actors
Advice & information. Introductory Courses
1A Tower Street, London WC2H 9NP   T 020 7632 8001
E reception@actorscentre.co.uk
W www.actorscentre.co.uk

ACTORS CENTRE NORTH
Contact: Maggie Lackey. Charity. Provides Advice, Support
& Information. Workshops in continuing professional
development for professionally trained actors
21-23 Oldham Street, Manchester M1 1JG   T/F 0161 819 2513
E info@actorscentrenorth.com
W www.actorscentrenorth.com

ACTORS' CHARITABLE TRUST
Provides Advice & Support. Grants for Actors' Children
58 Bloomsbury Street, London WC1B 3QT
F 020 7637 3368   T 020 7636 7868
E robert@tactactors.org

ACTORS' CHURCH UNION
St Paul's Church, Bedford Street
London WC2E 9ED   T 020 7240 0344
E actors-church.union@tiscali.co.uk

ADVERTISING ASSOCIATION
7th Floor North, Artillery House
11-19 Artillery Row, London SW1P 1RT
F 020 7222 1504   T 020 7340 1100
E aa@adassoc.org.uk
W www.adassoc.org.uk

AGENTS' ASSOCIATION (Great Britain)
54 Keyes House, Dolphin Square, London SW1V 3NA
F 020 7821 0261   T 020 7834 0515
E association@agents-uk.com
W www.agents-uk.com

ARTS & BUSINESS
Nutmeg House, 60 Gainsford Street
Butlers Wharf, London SE1 2NY
F 020 7407 7527   T 020 7378 8143
E head.office@aandb.org.uk
W www.aandb.org.uk

ARTS CENTRE GROUP
c/o Paintings In Hospitals
51 Southwark Street, London SE1 1RU
T 020 7407 1881   T 0845 4581881
E info@artscentregroup.org.uk
W www.artscentregroup.org.uk

ARTS COUNCIL ENGLAND
14 Great Peter Street, London SW1P 3NQ
F 020 7608 4100   T 0845 3006200
W www.artscouncil.org.uk

ARTS COUNCIL OF NORTHERN IRELAND
MacNeice House, 77 Malone Road, Belfast BT9 6AQ
F 028 9066 1715   T 028 9038 5200
E info@artscouncil-ni.org
W www.artscouncil-ni.org

ARTS COUNCIL OF WALES THE
Bute Place, Cardiff CF10 5AL
F 029 2041 1400   T 0845 8734900
E info@artswales.org.uk
W www.artswales.org.uk

ARTSLINE
Disability Access Information Service
c/o 21 Pine Court, Wood Lodge Gardens
Bromley BR1 2WA   T 020 7388 2227
E admin@artsline.org.uk
W www.artsline.org.uk

ASSOCIATION OF LIGHTING DESIGNERS
PO Box 680, Oxford OX1 9DG   M 07817 060189
E office@ald.org.uk
W www.ald.org.uk

ASSOCIATION OF MODEL AGENTS
11-29 Fashion Street, London E1 6PX   T 020 7422 0699
E amainfo@btinternet.com

BASCA - BRITISH ACADEMY OF SONGWRITERS, COMPOSERS & AUTHORS
2nd Floor, British Music House
26 Berners Street, London W1T 3LR
F 020 7636 2212   T 020 7636 2929
E info@basca.org.uk
W www.basca.org.uk

BFI SOUTH BANK
Belvedere Road, South Bank
London SE1 8XT   T 020 7928 3535
W www.bfi.org.uk

BRITISH ACADEMY OF FILM & TELEVISION ARTS
195 Piccadilly, London W1J 9LN
F 020 7292 5868   T 020 7734 0022
E membership@bafta.org
W www.bafta.org

BRITISH ACADEMY OF FILM & TELEVISION ARTS / LOS ANGELES
8533 Melrose Avenue, West Hollywood, CA 90069, USA
F (310) 854 6002   T (310) 652 4121
E office@baftala.org
W www.baftala.org

BRITISH ACADEMY OF STAGE & SCREEN COMBAT
Suite 280, 10 Great Russell Street
London WC1B 3BQ   M 07981 806265
E info@bassc.org
W www.bassc.org

BRITISH ASSOCIATION FOR PERFORMING ARTS MEDICINE (BAPAM)
Charity
4th Floor, Totara Park House
34-36 Gray's Inn Road, London WC1X 8HR   T 020 7404 8444
E clinic@bapam.org.uk
W www.bapam.org.uk

BRITISH ASSOCIATION OF DRAMATHERAPISTS THE
Waverley, Battledown Approach
Cheltenham, Glos GL52 6RE   T 01242 235515
E enquiries@badth.org.uk
W www.badth.org.uk

WE CAN HELP ACTORS' CHILDREN

Are you:

- **a professional actor?**
- **the parent of a child under 21?**
- **having trouble with finances?**

Please get in touch for a confidential chat.

The Actors' Charitable Trust
020 7636 7868
robert@tactactors.org

TACT can help in many ways: with regular monthly payments, one-off grants, and long-term support and advice.
We help with clothing, child-care, music lessons, school trips, special equipment and adaptations, and in many other ways.

Our website has a link to a list of all the theatrical and entertainment charities which might be able to help you if you do not have children: www.tactactors.org

TACT

TACT, 58 Bloomsbury Street, London C1B 3QT.
Registered charity number 206809.

BRITISH BOARD OF FILM CLASSIFICATION
3 Soho Square, London W1D 3HD
F 020 7287 0141   T 020 7440 1570
W www.bbfc.co.uk

BRITISH COUNCIL
Arts Group
10 Spring Gardens, London SW1A 2BN   T 020 7389 3194
E arts@britishcouncil.org
W www.britishcouncil.org/arts

BRITISH EQUITY COLLECTING SOCIETY
Guild House, Upper St Martin's Lane
London WC2H 9EG   T 020 7670 0350
E becs@equity.org.uk
W www.equitycollecting.org.uk

BRITISH FILM INSTITUTE
21 Stephen Street, London W1T 1LN
F 020 7436 0165   T 020 7255 1444
W www.bfi.org.uk

BRITISH LIBRARY SOUND ARCHIVE
96 Euston Road, London NW1 2DB
F 020 7412 7441   T 020 7412 7676
E sound-archive@bl.uk
W www.bl.uk/soundarchive

BRITISH MUSIC HALL SOCIETY
Contact: Daphne Masterton (Secretary). Charity
45 Mayflower Road, Park Street
St Albans, Herts AL2 2QN   T 01727 768878
W www.music-hall-society.com

CATHOLIC ASSOCIATION OF PERFORMING ARTS
Contact: Ms Molly Steele (Hon Secretary). By Post (SAE)
1 Maiden Lane, London WC2E 7NB   T 020 7240 1221
E secretary@caapa.org.uk

CELEBRITY BULLETIN THE
8-10 Wiseton Road, London SW17 7EE
F 020 8672 2282   T 020 8672 3191
E enquiries@celebrity-bulletin.co.uk

CHILDREN'S FILM & TELEVISION FOUNDATION LTD
E annahome@cftf.org.uk   M 07887 573479

CIDA (CREATIVE INDUSTRIES DEVELOPMENT AGENCY)
*Professional Development & Business Support for Artists &
Creative Businesses*
Media Centre, Huddersfield
West Yorkshire HD1 1RL
F 01484 483150   T 01484 483140
E info@cida.org
W www.cida.org

CINEMA & TELEVISION BENEVOLENT FUND (CTBF)
22 Golden Square, London W1F 9AD
F 020 7437 7186   T 020 7437 6567
E charity@ctbf.co.uk
W www.ctbf.co.uk

CINEMA EXHIBITORS' ASSOCIATION
22 Golden Square, London W1F 9JW
F 020 7734 6147   T 020 7734 9551
E cea@cinemauk.ftech.co.uk
W www.cinemauk.org.uk

CLUB FOR ACTS & ACTORS
Incorporating Concert Artistes Association
20 Bedford Street, London WC2E 9HP
T 020 7836 3172 (Office)   T 020 7836 2884 (Members)
E office@thecaa.org
W www.thecaa.org

COMPANY OF CRANKS
1st Floor, 62 Northfield House
Frensham Street, London SE15 6TN   M 07963 617981
E mimetic16@yahoo.com
W www.mimeworks.com

CONCERT ARTISTES ASSOCIATION
See CLUB FOR ACTS & ACTORS

CONFERENCE OF DRAMA SCHOOLS
*Contact: Saul Hyman. Comprises Britain's 22 Leading Drama
Schools. Publishes the Guide to Professional Training in
Drama & Technical Theatre*
PO Box 34252, London NW5 1XJ
E info@cds.drama.ac.uk
W www.drama.ac.uk

**COUNCIL FOR DANCE EDUCATION & TRAINING
(CDET) THE**
Old Brewer's Yard, 17-19 Neal Street, London WC2H 9UY
F 020 7240 2547   T 020 7240 5703
E info@cdet.org.uk
W www.cdet.org.uk

**CPMA (Co-operative Personal Management
Association)**
The Secretary, c/o 62 Foulden Road
London N16 7UR   M 07876 641582
E cpmauk@yahoo.co.uk
W www.cpma.coop

CRITICS' CIRCLE THE
c/o Catherine Cooper Events
48 De Walden House, Allitsen Road
St John's Wood, London NW8 7BA   T 020 7483 1181
W www.criticscircle.org.uk

D'OYLY CARTE OPERA COMPANY
First Floor, 295 Kennington Road
London SE11 4QE
F 020 7820 0240   T 0844 6060007
E ian@doylycarte.org.uk
W www.doylycarte.org.uk

DANCE HOUSE
20 St Andrews Street, Glasgow G1 5PD   T 0141 552 2442
E info@dancehouse.org
W www.dancehouse.org

DANCE UK
*Including the Healthier Dancer Programme & 'The UK
Choreographers' Directory'. Professional Body & Charity,
providing Advice, Information & Support*
The Urdang, The Old Finsbury Town Hall
Rosebery Avenue, London EC1R 4QT
F 020 7833 2363   T 020 7713 0730
E info@danceuk.org
W www.danceuk.org

DENVILLE HALL
*Provides residential & nursing care to actors & other
theatrical professions*
62 Ducks Hill Road, Northwood
Middlesex HA6 2SB
T 01923 820805 (Residents)   T 01923 825843 (Office)
E denvillehall@yahoo.com
W www.denvillehall.org.uk

DIRECTORS UK
Inigo Place, 31 & 32 Bedford Street, London WC2E 9ED
F 020 7845 9700   T 020 7240 0009
E info@directors.uk.com
W www.directors.uk.com

DRAMA ASSOCIATION OF WALES
Specialist Drama Lending Library
The Old Library, Singleton Road
Splott, Cardiff CF24 2ET   T 029 2045 2200
E teresa@dramawales.org.uk

DRAMATURGS' NETWORK
Network of Professional Dramaturgs
E info@dramaturgy.co.uk   M 07939 270566
W www.dramaturgy.co.uk

ENGLISH FOLK DANCE & SONG SOCIETY
Cecil Sharp House, 2 Regent's Park Road, London NW1 7AY
F 020 7284 0534   T 020 7485 2206
E info@efdss.org
W www.efdss.org

EQUITY CHARITABLE TRUST
Plouviez House, 19-20 Hatton Place
London EC1N 8RU
F 020 7242 7995   T 020 7831 1926
E info@equitycharitabletrust.org.uk

FILM LONDON
Suite 6.10, The Tea Building
56 Shoreditch High Street, London E1 6JJ
F 020 7613 7677   T 020 7613 7676
E info@filmlondon.org.uk
W www.filmlondon.org.uk

GLASGOW FILM OFFICE
Free Advice & Liaison Support for all Productions
City Chambers, Glasgow G2 1DU
F 0141 287 0311   T 0141 287 0424
E info@glasgowfilm.com

GRAND ORDER OF WATER RATS
328 Gray's Inn Road, London WC1X 8BZ
F 020 7278 1765   T 020 7278 3248
E info@gowr.net
W www.gowr.net

GROUP LINE
Group Bookings for London Theatre
22-24 Torrington Place, London WC1E 7HJ
F 020 7436 6287   T 020 7580 6793
E tix@groupline.com
W www.groupline.com

HAMMER FILMS PRESERVATION SOCIETY
Fan Club
14 Kingsdale Road
Plumstead
London SE18 2DG   T 020 8854 7383
E braystudios@live.com

INDEPENDENT THEATRE COUNCIL (ITC)
Professional Body offering Advice, Information, Support & Political Representation
12 The Leathermarket
Weston Street
London SE1 3ER
F 020 7403 1745   T 020 7403 1727
E admin@itc-arts.org
W www.itc-arts.org

INTERNATIONAL CENTRE FOR VOICE THE
Central School of Speech & Drama
Eton Avenue, London NW3 3HY
E icv@cssd.ac.uk
W www.icvoice.co.uk

IRVING SOCIETY THE
Contact: Michael Kilgarriff (Hon. Secretary)
10 Kings Avenue
London W5 2SH   T 020 8566 8301
E secretary@theirvingsociety.org.uk
W www.theirvingsociety.org.uk

ITC
See INDEPENDENT THEATRE COUNCIL

ITV PLC
London Television Centre, Upper Ground
London SE1 9LT   T 020 7157 3000
W www.itv.com

❖

THE RALPH AND MERIEL RICHARDSON FOUNDATION

Please support us as we provide grants to help actors, their spouses and children in distress.
It is easy to include the Foundation in your will or send a donation to the address below.

If you are an actor and need our help, or know someone who does,
you can contact us in confidence.

ADDRESS: c/o Suite 23, 19 Cavendish Square, London W1A 2AW
Web: sirralphrichardson.org.uk E-Mail: manager@sirralphrichardson.org.uk

LONDON SCHOOL OF CAPOEIRA THE
Units 1 & 2 Leeds Place
Tollington Park
London N4 3RF T 020 7281 2020
E info@londonschoolofcapoeira.co.uk
W www.londonschoolofcapoeira.co.uk

LONDON SHAKESPEARE WORKOUT
PO Box 31855, London SE17 3XP T/F 020 7793 9755
E londonswo@hotmail.com
W www.lswproductions.co.uk

MANDER & MITCHENSON THEATRE COLLECTION
Jerwood Library of the Performing Arts
King Charles Building
Old Royal Naval College, Greenwich, London SE10 9JF
F 020 8305 9426 T 020 8305 4424
E kdavis@tcm.ac.uk

NATIONAL ASSOCIATION OF YOUTH THEATRES (NAYT)
Contact: Jo Harker. Founded in 1982, NAYT works with over
1,000 groups & individuals to support the development
of youth theatre activity through information & support
services, advocacy, training, participation & partnerships
Arts Centre, Vane Terrace
Darlington
County Durham DL3 7AX
F 01325 363313 T 01325 363330
E nayt@btconnect.com
W www.nayt.org.uk

NATIONAL CAMPAIGN FOR THE ARTS
1 Kingly Street, London W1B 5PA
F 020 7287 4777 T 020 7287 3777
E nca@artscampaign.org.uk
W www.artscampaign.org.uk

NATIONAL COUNCIL FOR DRAMA TRAINING
249 Tooley Street, London SE1 2JX T 020 7407 3686
E info@ncdt.co.uk
W www.ncdt.co.uk

NATIONAL RESOURCE CENTRE FOR DANCE
University of Surrey, Guildford
Surrey GU2 7XH
F 01483 689500 T 01483 689316
E nrcd@surrey.ac.uk
W www.surrey.ac.uk/nrcd

NODA (National Operatic & Dramatic Association)
Charity, providing Advice, Information & Support. Largest
umbrella body for amateur theatre in the UK offering
advice & assistance on all aspects of amateur theatre plus
workshops, summer school and social events
Noda House, 58-60 Lincoln Road
Peterborough PE1 2RZ
F 01733 319506 T 01733 865790
E info@noda.org.uk W www.noda.org.uk

NORTH WEST PLAYWRIGHTS
Charity. Provides Advice, Information & Support. Regional
Agency Developing & Supporting Scriptwriters in All Media
18 Express Networks
1 George Leigh Street
Manchester M4 5DL T/F 0161 237 1978
E newplaysnw@hotmail.com
W www.northwestplaywrights.co.uk

OFCOM
Ofcom Media Office, Riverside House
2A Southwark Bridge Road, London SE1 9HA T 0300 1234000
E ofcomnews@ofcom.org.uk
W www.ofcom.org.uk

PACT
*Trade Association for Independent Television, Feature Film &
New Media Production Companies*
3rd Floor Fitzrovia House
153-157 Cleveland Street
London W1T 6QW   T 020 7380 8230
E info@pact.co.uk
W www.pact.co.uk

PERFORMING RIGHT SOCIETY LTD
29-33 Berners Street
London W1T 3AB
F 020 7306 4455   T 020 7580 5544
W www.prsformusic.com

RICHARDSON Ralph & Meriel FOUNDATION
c/o Suite 23
19 Cavendish Square
London W1A 2AW
F 020 7664 4489   T 020 7636 1616
E manager@sirralphrichardson.org.uk
W www.sirralphrichardson.org.uk

ROYAL TELEVISION SOCIETY
5th Floor, Kildare House
3 Dorset Rise, London EC4Y 8EN
F 020 7822 2811   T 020 7822 2810
E info@rts.org.uk
W www.rts.org.uk

ROYAL THEATRICAL FUND
11 Garrick Street, London WC2E 9AR
F 020 7379 8273   T 020 7836 3322
E admin@trtf.com

SAMPAD SOUTH ASIAN ARTS
Promotes the appreciation & practice of South Asian Arts
c/o Mac, Cannon Hill Park
Birmingham B12 9QH   T 0121 446 3260
E info@sampad.org.uk
W www.sampad.org.uk

SCOTTISH SCREEN
249 West George Street, Glasgow G2 4QE
F 0141 302 1711   T 0141 302 1700
E info@scottishscreen.com
W www.scottishscreen.com

SCRIPT
*West Midlands Playwrights, Scriptwriters. Provides Training,
Development & Support*
Unit 107 The Greenhouse, The Custard Factory
Gibb Street, Birmingham B9 4AA   T 0121 224 7415
E info@scriptonline.net
W www.scriptonline.net

SOCIETY OF AUTHORS
*Trade Union for Professional Writers. Providing Advice,
Funding, Information & Support*
84 Drayton Gardens, London SW10 9SB   T 020 7373 6642
E info@societyofauthors.org
W www.societyofauthors.org

SOCIETY OF BRITISH THEATRE DESIGNERS
Professional Body. Charity. Providing Advice & Information
RBC, Burnt Oak Lane
Sidcup, Kent DA15 9DF   T 020 8308 2664
E admin@theatredesign.org.uk
W www.theatredesign.org.uk

SOCIETY OF LONDON THEATRE (SOLT)
32 Rose Street, London WC2E 9ET
F 020 7557 6799   T 020 7557 6700
E enquiries@solttma.co.uk

SOCIETY OF TEACHERS OF SPEECH & DRAMA THE
Registered Office: 73 Berry Hill Road
Mansfield, Nottinghamshire NG18 4RU   T 01623 627636
E ann.k.jones@btinternet.com
W www.stsd.org.uk

SOCIETY OF THEATRE CONSULTANTS
27 Old Gloucester Street
London WC1N 3AX   T 020 7419 8767
W www.theatreconsultants.org.uk

STAGE CRICKET CLUB
39-41 Hanover Steps, St George's Fields
Albion Street, London W2 2YG
F 020 7262 5736   T 020 7402 7543
E brianjfilm@aol.com
W www.stagecc.co.uk

STAGE GOLFING SOCIETY
Sudbrook Park, Sudbrook Lane
Richmond, Surrey TW10 7AS   T 020 8940 8861
E sgs@richmondgolfclub.co.uk

STAGE MANAGEMENT ASSOCIATION
Providing Advice, Information & Support. Supports,
represents & promotes stage management and all its
practitioners. Provides help finding work, training &
networking opportunities & advice
89 Borough High Street, London SE1 1NL   T 020 7403 7999
E admin@stagemanagementassociation.co.uk
W www.stagemanagementassociation.co.uk

STAGE ONE (Operating Name of The Theatre Investment Fund Ltd)
32 Rose Street, London WC2E 9ET
F 020 7557 6799   T 020 7557 6737
E enquiries@stageone.uk.com
W www.stageone.uk.com

THEATRE WRITING PARTNERSHIP
Nottingham Playhouse, Wellington Circus
Nottingham NG1 5AF   T 0115 947 4361
E info@theatrewritingpartnership.org.uk

THEATREMAD (Theatre: Making A Difference)
The Make a Difference Trust raises funds to support people
living with HIV, AIDS & other long-term medical conditions
UK Charity Registration No. 1124014
c/o The Make A Difference Trust, 1st Floor
54 Greek Street, Soho, London W1D 3DS
F 020 7734 0646   T 020 7734 5683
E office@madtrust.org.uk
W www.madtrust.org.uk

THEATRES TRUST THE
Contact: Kate Carmichael (Resources Officer). National
Advisory Public Body for Theatres, Protecting Theatres
for Everyone. Charity. Social Membership. Provides Advice,
Support & Information
22 Charing Cross Road, London WC2H 0QL
F 020 7836 3302   T 020 7836 8591
E info@theatrestrust.org.uk
W www.theatrestrust.org.uk

THEATRICAL GUILD THE
Charity for Backstage & Front of House Staff
Ambassadors Theatre, West Street
London WC2H 9ND   T 020 7395 5460
E admin@ttg.org.uk
W www.ttg.org.uk

THEATRICAL MANAGEMENT ASSOCIATION
See TMA

TMA (Theatrical Management Association)
32 Rose Street, London WC2E 9ET
F 020 7557 6799   T 020 7557 6700
E enquiries@solttma.co.uk
W www.tmauk.org

TYA - UK CENTRE OF ASSITEJ
Contact: Paul Harman. International Association of Theatre
for Children & Young People. Network for makers &
promoters of professional theatre for young audiences
16 Victoria Embankment
Darlington DL1 5JR   T 01325 483259
E youngtheatreportal8@gmail.com
W www.tya-uk.org

UK CHOREOGRAPHERS' DIRECTORY THE
See DANCE UK

UK FILM COUNCIL
10 Little Portland Street
London W1W 7JG
F 020 7861 7862   T 020 7861 7861
E info@ukfilmcouncil.org.uk
W www.ukfilmcouncil.org.uk

UK THEATRE CLUBS
54 Swallow Drive
London NW10 8TG   T 020 8459 3972
E uktheatreclubs@aol.com

UNITED KINGDOM COPYRIGHT BUREAU
110 Trafalgar Road, Portslade
East Sussex BN41 1GS   T 01273 277333
E info@copyrightbureau.co.uk
W www.copyrightbureau.co.uk

VARIETY & LIGHT ENTERTAINMENT COUNCIL
54 Keyes House, Dolphin Square
London SW1V 3NA
F 020 7821 0261   T 020 7798 5622

VARIETY CLUB CHILDREN'S CHARITY
Variety Club House, 93 Bayham Street
London NW1 0AG
F 020 7428 8111   T 020 7428 8100
E info@varietyclub.org.uk
W www.varietyclub.org.uk

WILLIAMS Tim AWARDS
In memory of LSW's late musical director. Seeking to support
excellence in the composition of theatrical song
PO Box 31855
London SE17 3XP   T 020 7793 9755
E londonswo@hotmail.com
W www.lswproductions.co.uk

WOMEN IN FILM AND TELEVISION
Contact: Rebecca Brand. WFTV is the premier membership
organisation for women working in the Film, Television
and Digital Media industries in the UK. Provides Advice,
Information, Social Membership & Support
Unit 2, Wedgewood Mews
12-13 Greek Street
London W1D 4BB
F 020 7287 1500   T 020 7287 1400
E info@wftv.org.uk
W www.wftv.org.uk

YOUTH MUSIC THEATRE UK (YMT)
40 Parkgate Road, Battersea
London SW11 4JH   T 0844 4154858
E mail@ymtuk.org
W www.youthmusictheatreuk.org

PHOTOGRAPHERS

ACTORHEADSHOTS.CO.UK
M 07740 507970
E info@actorheadshots.co.uk
W www.actorheadshots.co.uk

ADALSTEINSSON Einar
M 07964 016698
W www.headshots.halfyeti.com

AH IMAGE STUDIO
E andrea@ahimagestudio.com
W www.ahimagestudio.com

AHB PHOTOGRAPHY
M 07957 101333
W www.ahbasit.com

ALLEN Stuart
M 07776 258829
W www.stuartallenphotos.com

AM LONDON
M 07974 188105
T 020 7193 1868
W www.am-london.com

ANKER Matt
M 07835 241835
W www.mattanker.com

ANNAND Simon
M 07884 446776
W www.simonannand.com

AW HEADSHOTS
M 07816 317038
W www.awheadshots.com

BACON Ric
M 07970 970799
W www.ricbacon.co.uk

BAKER Chris
T 020 8441 3851
W www.chrisbakerphotographer.com

BANELLO Annalisa
M 07958 490253
W www.annalisabanello.com

BERLE Ian
M 07931 909342
W www.ianberlephotography.com

BISHOP Brandon
M 07931 383830
T 020 7275 7468
W www.brandonbishopphotography.com

Photographers

Each photographer listed in this section has taken an advertisement in this edition. See Index to Advertisers pages to view each advertisement.

Promotional Services
(CVs, Showreels, Websites etc)
Properties & Trades
Publications (Print & Online)

[CONTACTS 2011]

BRITTON Anthony
M 07944 681251
T 01784 488343
E anthony-britton@btconnect.com
W www.anthonybritton.co.uk

BURNETT Sheila
T 020 7289 3058
W www.sheilaburnett-photography.com

CABLE Paul
M 07958 932764
E info@paulcable.com
W www.paulcable.com

CARTER Charlie
T 020 8222 8742
E charlie@charliecarter.com
W www.charliecarter.com

CHAMBERS Jonathan
M 07869 289048
E info@jonathanchambersphotography.com
W www.jonathanchambersphotography.com

CLARK John
M 07702 627237
T 020 8854 4069
E info@johnclarkphotography.com
W www.johnclarkphotography.com

CLEARVISION IMAGERY
M 07879 491106
M 07719 587292
W www.clearvisionimagery.co.uk

CLIFF Mike
M 07539 644579
W www.mikecliffphotography.co.uk

CURTIS Michael
M 07816 110110
E info@michael-curtis.com
W www.michael-curtis.com

DAWKES Nicholas
M 07787 111997
E studio@nicholasdawkesphotography.co.uk
W www.nicholasdawkesphotography.co.uk

de WOOLFSON Luke
M 07968 761232
E photography@lukedewoolfson.com
W www.lukedewoolfson.com

GARDEN Henrietta
M 07973 825734
E henri.garden@blueyonder.co.uk

GIBB Adrian
T 020 7639 6215
E adriangibb@googlemail.com
W www.adriangibb.co.uk

GREGAN Nick
M 07774 421878
T 020 8533 3003
E info@nickgregan.com
W www.nickgregan.com

GROGAN Claire
M 07932 635381
T 020 7272 1845
E claire@clairegrogan.co.uk
W www.clairegrogan.co.uk

HARRISON-CRIPPS Alex
M 07977 529641
W www.alexharrisoncripps.co.uk

HARRISON-JONES Scott
M 07885 752868

HCK PHOTOGRAPHY
M 07956 612338
E info@hck-photography.co.uk
W www.hck-photography.co.uk

HEADSHOT LONDON
M 07940 444641
W www.headshotlondon.co.uk

HOLDING Rob
M 07703 472660
E rob@robholding.co.uk
W www.robholding.co.uk

HUGHES Jamie
M 07850 122977
E jamie@jamiehughesphotography.com
W www.jamiehughesphotography.com/headshots

HULL Anna
T 020 7498 5023
W www.annahullphotography.com

HUNTER Remy
M 07766 760724
W www.remyhunter.co.uk

JAMES Katherine
M 07734 680543
E info@katherine-james.com
W www.katherine-james.com

JAMES Nick
M 07961 122030
W www.nickjamesphotography.co.uk

How do I find a photographer?

Having a good quality, up-to-date promotional headshot is crucial for every performer. Make sure you choose your photographer very carefully: do some research and try to look at different examples. Photographers' adverts run throughout this book, featuring many sample shots, although to get a real feel for their work you should also try to see their portfolio or website since this will give a more accurate impression of the quality of their photography.

If you live in or around London, please feel free to visit the Spotlight offices and look through current editions of our directories to find a style you like. We also have nearly sixty photographers' portfolios available for you to browse, many of them from photographers listed over the next few pages. Our offices are open Monday - Friday, 10.00am - 5.30pm at 7 Leicester Place, London WC2H 7RJ (nearest tube is Leicester Square).

What should I expect from the photo shoot?

When it comes to your photo shoot, bear in mind that a casting director, agent or production company will want to see a photo of the 'real' you. Keep your appearance as neutral as possible so that they can imagine you in many different roles, rather than type-casting yourself from the outset and limiting your opportunities.

Your eyes are your most important feature, so make sure they are visible: face the camera straight-on and try not to smile too much because it makes them harder to see. Wear something simple and avoid jewellery, hats, scarves, glasses or props, since these will all add character. Do not wear clothes that detract from your face such as polo necks, big collars, busy patterns or logos. Always keep your hands out of the shot.

Also consider the background: some photographers like to do outdoor shots. A contrast between background and hair colour works well, whereas dark backgrounds work less well with dark hair, and the same goes for light hair on light backgrounds.

Which photograph should I choose?

When you get your contact sheet back from the photographer, make sure you choose a photo that looks like you - not how you would like to look. If you are unsure, ask friends or your agent for an honest opinion. Remember, you will be asked to attend meetings and auditions on the basis of your photograph, so if you turn up looking completely different you will be wasting everyone's time.

Due to copyright legislation, you must always credit the photographer when using the photo.

How should I submit my photo to Spotlight and to casting professionals?

All photographs submitted to Spotlight must be of the highest possible quality, otherwise casting professionals will not see you in the best possible light. If you are sending your photo by hard copy, we would expect a 10 x 8 sized print, which is the industry standard. It is not necessary to provide an original print: a high quality, clear focused repro is fine. If you are sending a digital image by e-mail or disk, we have certain technical specifications which can be found on our website (see below). We would recommend that you follow similar guidelines when sending your headshot directly to casting professionals.

What are Spotlight portfolio photographs?

Every Spotlight performer can also add extra photographs onto their web page, in addition to their principal photograph. These are called portfolio photos, and they give you the opportunity to show yourself in a range of different shots and/or roles. Members can upload up to 15 digital photos to their online CV free of charge by logging on to www.spotlight.com with their update PIN.

Please visit www.spotlight.com/artists/multimedia/photoguidelines for further information.

JAMIE Matt
M 07976 890643
W www.mattjamie.co.uk/portraits

JEFFERSON Paris
M 07825 047773
W www.parisjefferson.com

KOWALIK Piotr
M 07946 323631
W www.piotrkowalik.co.uk

LADENBURG Jack
M 07932 053743
E info@jackladenburg.co.uk
W www.jackladenburg.co.uk

LATIMER Carole
T 020 7727 9371
E carole@carolelatimer.com
W www.carolelatimer.com

LAWTON Steve
M 07973 307487
W www.stevelawton.com

LE MAY Pete
M 07703 649246
W www.petelemay.co.uk

LEGEND PHOTOGRAPHY
M 01424 430055
W www.legend-photography.com

M.A.D. PHOTOGRAPHY
M 07949 581909
T 020 8363 4182
W www.mad-photography.co.uk

MERCHANT Natasha
M 07932 618111
T 020 8653 5399
W www.natashamerchant.com

MILLER BETTS Joanna
M 07779 145999
W www.joannamillerbetts.com

MOLLIÈRE Pascal
M 07713 242948
T 020 8406 9185
E info@pascalphoto.co.uk
W www.pascalphoto.co.uk

MOUNT Gemma
M 07976 824923
W www.gemmamountphotography.com

MULHOLLAND Ruth
M 07939 516987
W www.ruthmulholland.com

NAMDAR Fatimah
M 07973 287535
T 020 8341 1332
E fnamdar@mac.com
W www.fatimahnamdar.com

NOHO STUDIOS
M 07889 895510
E michael@nohostudios.co.uk
W www.nohostudios.co.uk

O'REGAN Dominic
M 07795 560370
E dom@dominicoregan.co.uk
W www.dominicoregan.co.uk

PARADISE Andy
M 07957 392980
E andy@hereslookingatyou.co.uk
W www.hereslookingatyou.co.uk

PIELAK Alex
M 07817 750560
E alex@alexpielak.com
W www.alexpielak.com

POLLARD Michael
T 0161 456 7470
E info@michaelpollard.co.uk
W www.michaelpollard.co.uk

POWER Eliza
M 07590 370261
E eliza@elizapower.co.uk
W www.elizapower.co.uk

PRICE David
M 07950 542494
E info@davidpricephotography.co.uk
W www.davidpricephotography.co.uk

PROCTOR Carl
M 07956 283340
E carlphotos@btconnect.com
W www.carlproctorphotography.com

RAFIQUE Harry
M 07986 679498
W www.hr-photographer.co.uk

RDF PHOTOGRAPHY
M 07967 211871
E rfairclough@mac.com
W www.rdfphotography.co.uk

RECTOR Ben
M 07770 467791
E ben@benrector.com
W www.benrector.com

RICARDO Mat
M 07743 494675
E hello@matricardophotography.com
W www.matricardophotography.com

RICHMOND Eric
T 020 8880 6909
W www.ericrichmond.net

ROBARTS Gigi
M 07908 725944
E gigifoto2@aol.com

RUOCCO Alex
M 07732 293231
W www.alexruoccophotography.co.uk

SAINT Martin
M 07912 091318
T 020 8503 3159
E info@martinsaint.com
W www.martinsaint.com

SAVAGE Robin
M 07901 927597
E contact@robinsavage.co.uk
W www.robinsavage.co.uk

SAYER Howard
M 07860 559891
E howard@howardsayer.com
W www.howardsayer.com

SCHNEEBELI Heini
M 07801 263880
T 020 7482 6568

SCOTT Karen
M 07958 975950
E info@karenscottphotography.com
W www.karenscottphotography.com

SHAKESPEARE LANE Catherine
T 020 7226 7694
W www.csl-art.co.uk

SILVA Nuno
M 07939 500757
E info@nunosilvastudios.com
W www.nunosilvastudios.com

SIMPKIN Peter
M 07973 224084
T 020 8364 2634
E petersimpkin@aol.com
W www.petersimpkin.co.uk

STILL Rosie
M 07597 946252
T 020 8857 6920
E rosie@rosiestillphotography.co.uk
W www.rosiestillphotography.co.uk

SUMMERS Caroline
M 07931 301234
T 020 7223 7669
E carolinesummers@mac.com
W www.gallery.me.com/carolinesummers

ULLATHORNE Steve
M 07961 380969
E steve@steveullathorne.com
W www.steveullathorne.com

VALENTINE Vanessa
M 07904 059541
W www.vanessavalentinephotography.com

VERASTEGUI Ana
M 07818 067557
E anaphotography@me.com
W www.anartphoto.com

WEBSTER Caroline
M 07867 653019
E caroline@carolinewebster.co.uk
W www.carolinewebster.co.uk

WHARLEY Michael
M 07961 068759
W www.michaelwharley.co.uk

WILKINSON Howard
M 07947 345305
T 01706 645203
W www.howardwilkinsonphotography.co.uk

WILL C
M 07712 669953
T 020 8438 0303
E billy_snapper@hotmail.com
W www.london-photographer.com

WINDHAM Marco
M 07768 330027
W www.flickr.com/photos/marcowindham

WORKMAN Robert
T 020 7385 5442
W www.robertworkman.demon.co.uk

10X8PRINTS.COM
E info@10x8prints.com   T 020 3137 6108
W www.10x8prints.com

A1 VOX LTD
Audio Clips. Demo CDs. ISDN Links. Spoken Word Audio
20 Old Compton Street
London W1D 4TW   T 020 7434 4404
E info@a1vox.com
W www.a1vox.com

ABBEY ROAD STUDIOS
3 Abbey Road, St John's Wood, London NW8 9AY
F 020 7266 7250   T 020 7266 7000
E bookings@abbeyroad.com
W www.abbeyroad.com

ABSOLUTE WORKS LTD
Danson House, Manor Farm Lane
Ledburn, Bucks LU7 0UG
M 07778 934307   T 01525 385400
E absoluteworks@btinternet.com
W www.absoluteworks.com

ACTOR CARDS
Offices in London & Manchester   T 0800 1123434
E hello@actorcards.co.uk
W www.actorcards.co.uk

ACTOR SHOWREELS
Showreel Service
97B Central Hill, London SE19 1BY
M 07939 241377   M 07835 637965
E post@actorshowreels.co.uk
W www.actorshowreels.co.uk

ACTORS CENTRE
Showreels for Actors & Presenters
1A Tower Street, London WC2H 9NP   T 020 7240 3940
E film@actorscentre.co.uk
W www.actorscentre.co.uk

ACTORS INTERACTIVE
Web Design
10 Frobisher Street, London SE10 9XB   T 020 8465 5457
E office@actorsinteractive.com
W www.actorsinteractive.com

ACTOR'S ONE-STOP SHOP THE
*CVs, Photography, Showreels & Websites for
Performing Artists*
First Floor, Above The Gate Pub
Station Road, London N22 7SS   T 020 8888 7006
E info@actorsonestopshop.com
W www.actorsonestopshop.com

ACTORS-SHOWREELS.CO.UK
241 Crystal Palace Road
London SE22 9JQ   M 07915 662767
E info@actors-showreels.co.uk

ACTORSHOP
93 Grove Lane, Headingley
Leeds, West Yorkshire LS6 4AL   M 07970 381944
E info@actorshop.co.uk
W www.actorshop.co.uk

ACTORSILLUMINATED.COM
*Contact: Kosha Engler. Websites for People
in the Performing Arts*
E mail@actorsilluminated.com   M 07769 626074
W www.actorsilluminated.com

ACTUALLYACTORS.COM
Websites
3 Milestone Road, London SE19 2LL   T 020 8325 1946
E mail@actuallyactors.co.uk
W www.actuallyactors.com

AIR-EDEL RECORDING STUDIOS LTD
18 Rodmarton Street, London W1U 8BJ
F 020 7224 0344   T 020 7486 6466
E bethan.barron@air-edel.co.uk
W www.air-edelstudios.co.uk

ANGEL RECORDING STUDIOS LTD
311 Upper Street, London N1 2TU
F 020 7226 9624   T 020 7354 2525
E bookings@angelstudio.co.uk

ANT FARM STUDIOS VOICE-OVERS
Southend Farm, Southend Lane
Waltham Abbey EN9 3SE   T 01992 714664
E antfarmstudio@yahoo.co.uk
W www.antfarmstudios.com

APPLE VIDEO FACILITIES
The Studio, 821 Chorley Old Road
Bolton, Lancs BL1 5SL
F 01204 495020   T 01204 847974
E info@applevideo.co.uk
W www.applevideo.co.uk

ARTS HOSTING
46 Glenmore Drive, Birmingham
West Midlands B38 8YR   T 0845 2508688
E hosting@artshosting.co.uk
W www.artshosting.co.uk

ARTUS William GRAPHIC DESIGN
20 Crowswood Drive, Stalybridge
Cheshire SK15 3RJ   T 0161 303 8192
E williamartus4art@mac.com
W http://gallery.me.com/williamartus4art

ASCENT MEDIA LTD
Film House, 142 Wardour Street
London W1F 8DD
F 020 7878 7800   T 020 7878 0000
W www.ascentmedia.co.uk

BEWILDERING PICTURES
Contact: Graeme Kennedy. Showreel Service & Duplication
West London   M 07974 916258
E gk@bewildering.co.uk
W www.bewildering.co.uk

BLUE CHECKBOX
Website Design
13 Portman House
136 High Road, London N22 6DF   T 0843 2894414
E contact@bluecheckbox.com
W www.bluecheckbox.com

CHANNEL 2020 LTD
2020 House
26-28 Talbot Lane
Leicester LE1 4LR
F 0116 222 1113   T 0844 8402020
E info@channel2020.co.uk
W www.channel2020.co.uk

The Clerkenwell Workshops
27-31 Clerkenwell Close
London EC1R 0AT

CHASE Stephan PRODUCTIONS LTD
Producer of Voice Overs & Showreels
The Studio, 22 York Avenue
London SW14 7LG   T 020 8878 9112
E stephan@stephanchase.com
W www.stephanchase.com

CLAW FILMS LTD
11-15 Betterton Street, London WC2H 9BP
F 020 7470 8810   T 020 7470 8809
E info@clawfilms.com
W www.clawfilms.com

CLICKS MEDIA STUDIOS
Grove Road, Rochester
Kent ME2 4BX
F 01634 726000   T 01634 723838
E info@clicksmediastudios.com
W www.clicksmediastudios.com

CONCEPT
PO Box 192, Liverpool L69 1JA   T 0151 737 1794
E info@soundconcept.co.uk
W www.soundconcept.co.uk

COURTWOOD PHOTOGRAPHIC LTD
Photographic Reproduction
Profile Prints, Freepost TO55, Penzance, Cornwall TR20 8DU
F 01736 741255   T 01736 741222
E images@courtwood.co.uk
W www.courtwood.co.uk

CROWE Ben
Voice Clip Recording
25 Holmes Avenue, Hove BN3 7LA   M 07952 784911
E bencrowe@hotmail.co.uk

CRYING OUT LOUD PRODUCTIONS
Voice-over Specialists. Demo CDs. Radio Ad Production. Voice Training. Studio based in Soho, London
M 07809 549887   T 020 3262 3076
E simon@cryingoutloud.co.uk   W www.cryingoutloud.co.uk

CRYSTAL MEDIA
28 Castle Street, Edinburgh EH2 3HT
F 0131 240 0989   T 0131 240 0988
E hello@crystal-media.co.uk
W www.crystal-media.co.uk

CTS/LANSDOWNE RECORDING STUDIOS LTD
PO Box 47189, London W6 6DA
F 056 0115 5009   T 020 8846 9444
E info@cts-lansdowne.co.uk
W www.cts-lansdowne.co.uk

CUT GLASS PRODUCTIONS
Voice-over Showreels & Production
169-175 Queens Crescent
Camden, London NW5 4DS   T 020 7267 2339
E info@cutglassproductions.com
W www.cutglassproductions.com

infopage

What are promotional services?

This section contains listings for companies who provide practical services to help performers promote themselves. You might need to improve or create your CV; record a showreel or voicereel; design your own website; duplicate CDs; or print photographic repros, CVs or Z-cards: all essential ways to create a good impression with those that count in the industry.

Why do I need to promote myself?

Performers need to invest in marketing and promotion as much as any other self-employed businessperson. Even if you have trained at a leading drama school, have a well-known agent, or have just finished work on a popular TV series, you should never sit back and wait for your phone to ring or for the next job opportunity just to knock on your door. In such a competitive industry, successful performers are usually the ones who market themselves pro-actively and treat their careers as a 'business'.

Having up-to-date and well-produced promotional material makes a performer look professional and serious about their career: and hence a desirable person for a director or agent to work with.

Why is my CV important?

Poor presentation, punctuation and grammar create a bad first impression and you risk your CV being dismissed before it is even read. Make sure that you continually update your CV - you don't want it to look as if you haven't been working recently when you have, and you don't want to miss out on an audition because you haven't included skills you have put time and effort into achieving. Your CV should be kept to a maximum of one page and printed on good-quality paper.

Why is my covering letter important?

Always include a covering letter to introduce your CV and persuade casting professionals that it is worth reading. Remember that they receive hundreds each week. Keep your communication concise and be professional at all times. We also recommend that your letter has some kind of focus: perhaps you can tell them about your next showcase, or where they can see you currently appearing on stage. Ideally this should be addressed to an individual, not "Dear Sir or Madam".

Why is my headshot important?

Your CV should feature, or be accompanied by, a recent headshot which is an accurate current likeness. See the 'Photographers' section for more information about promotional photography. You may need to print copies of your headshot through a repro company, some of whom are listed over the following pages.

Why do I need a voicereel?

If you are interested in voice-over and/or radio work, you will need a professional-sounding voicereel to show agents, casting directors and potential employers what your voice is capable of. For commercial and corporate voice-over work this should be no more than two minutes long with a number of short clips demonstrating your range, but showcase the strengths of your natural voice as much as possible. It should contain a mixture of commercials and narrations.

A radio voicereel should be around eight minutes long, with four clips no longer than two minutes each, and read in your natural voice. To achieve a good balance of material, one clip should be 'classical', one 'contemporary', one 'comic' and one a poem. This is designed to give an overview of your suitability to various areas of radio work.

Record your voicereel in a professional studio to ensure a high-quality result, otherwise you are unlikely to be considered in this competitive industry. For further information please see the 'Agents - Voice-over' and 'Radio' sections.

Why do I need a showreel?

Some casting directors nowadays will only consider a performer for an audition if they have first seen them demonstrating their skills in a showreel. A CV and headshot give some indication of their potential, but can only provide a basic summary.

What should I do if I don't currently have anything on film?

Showreels are expensive to produce if you don't currently have any broadcasted material to use, but it is advisable to get one professionally recorded and edited if at all possible. Showreels help you to promote yourself, but a casting director may be put off by a poor quality one. You might want to consider a *Spotlight Intro* as a temporary alternative to a full showreel (see below). It may also be worth considering working on a student film. Students are usually willing to let you keep a copy of their film and casting professionals would consider this an acceptable alternative. See 'Film & Television Schools' for further advice and listings.

How long should my showreel be?

We would recommend no more than three or four minutes. Casting professionals receive thousands of CVs and showreels and do not have time to watch every actor for ten minutes each. This is why we suggest you do not send your showreel out with your CV, but instead mention in your covering letter that one is available.

What should I use in my showreel?

Rather than one long excerpt, it is more beneficial to demonstrate your versatility with a number of different clips. Focus on your strongest characters to enable the casting director to picture you in the roles you play best.

The first 30 seconds are the most important in your showreel, and can be the only part a busy casting director or agent has time to look at. You may wish to start with a brief montage summarising the clips that are to follow, or with a headshot of yourself so that they know who to watch out for.

The focus should be on you, not on the other actors, so close-up shots ought to be included. You should be speaking most if not all of the time. A visual contrast is good, whether this means filming in a different location or setting, or changing your outfit. You should avoid well-known scripts in order to prevent drawing comparisons between yourself and previous successful interpretations.

What is a *Spotlight Intro?*

If you are a Spotlight member, a *Spotlight Intro* is your opportunity to give casting professionals a quick introduction to you, your character and your voice with a one or two minute video as part of your Spotlight CV. Think of it as a video version of a covering letter you might enclose with a paper CV. It could also be used as a temporary alternative to a showreel, although ideally you should include both. Please visit www.spotlight.com/spotlightintro for further information.

How should I use these listings?

If you are looking for a company to help you with any of these promotional items, browse through this section carefully and get quotes from a number of places to compare. If you are a Spotlight member, some companies offer a discount on their services. Always ask to see samples of a company's work, and ask friends in the industry for their own recommendations.

infopage

Martin Fisher is the producer at SonicPond Studio in Islington. An actor himself for 20 years, he specialises in voiceover reels, having produced his first in 1998, as well as video showreels, websites and musical theatre demos.

As an actor, you rarely have enough spare money to spend on promotional material without thinking of the cost. Yet it is almost always a false economy to cut corners. Photographers, voicereel studios and showreel companies all have expertise, experience and ultimately a value to you that goes way beyond the quality of their equipment. All companies are different, so do your research, trust your instincts, choose carefully, and if you can't afford to do it properly now, wait until you can.

People can be quick to tell you how hard the voiceover industry is to get into. Impossible, according to some. This simply isn't true. The voiceover industry is growing with every passing day, as are the opportunities for voiceover artists. Animations, iphone apps, the internet, new cable channels, gaming, info loops in banks and stores: the list is ever growing.

Your voicereel should concentrate on your natural voice; don't get wrapped up in accents unless you have genuine stand-out ability or a background in them. Five minutes spent looking at voiceover agencies' websites will illustrate this very clearly. They want you to specialise (people are rarely cast because they do fifteen things well). It will also teach you most of what you need to know about how to sell yourself to satisfy their needs. Some agencies will describe clients in just three adjectives on their site, so try to focus your reel.

When looking for a studio, don't let price be the deciding factor. Listen to the reels each company produces, and choose the one whose output seems most in touch with modern trends and *holds your attention*. Or go on recommendation. The most important thing in getting a reel right is the suitability of the material, the quality of the direction, and the time spent to get it right. Don't think that an hour on a mate's fancy microphone will cut it – it won't. A good studio will help you find suitable pieces. Some will even include a consultation to get you up to speed before the recording day. But don't get too hung up on the pieces themselves or worry about being inexperienced or having a little fear. Everyone starts at the same level. The studio knows all this and is there to make everything easy for you.

When it comes to the finished product, some agencies prefer just an mp3 of the final 'montage' attached to an e-mail. If you do send out hard copies, make sure they look professional and have all the information printed on them that the agent will need. Don't let yourself down at this very last stage by cutting corners. The studio should provide you with a list of agencies and contacts, as well as some advice on how to approach them. All agencies vary in this respect, but remember a polite and respectful phone call allows them to hear your voice from the minute they answer the phone, and that's half the battle!

It's easy to make the mistake of waiting for the 'perfect' balance of material, or for good TV scenes, before getting your first video showreel done. Some of the most interesting showreels are made from student films. Most people convince themselves they don't have enough material, but a three minute reel can be a thing of beauty. More importantly, a showreel is an organic, growing organism that will develop throughout your career. Don't wait to get it started. Casting directors have the option on Spotlight to only list actors with an online showreel, so don't be left out.

If you're not having much success getting TV work, be proactive and chase down student film opportunities, or use a company that can shoot you a scene or two especially for your showreel. If you get your reel edited by a company that archives your material, you can return to it at a later date and easily add new material. The studio should offer you special rates to do this.

Finally, be ruthless when choosing material to include. Don't throw the kitchen sink at it and overstay your welcome. Use 3-5 scenes, ideally around 45 seconds maximum each. Perhaps include a short montage at the start. Don't get caught up in fancy effects, and avoid using stage production photos or anything irrelevant to a screen casting director to flesh your reel out. You can then feature digital versions of this reel on Spotlight, YouTube, Shooting People, and of course your own website, to get your work out there.

Please visit www.sonicpond.co.uk for further information and advice.

DARKSIDE PHOTOGRAPHIC
Photographic Repro Service
4 Helmet Row, London EC1V 3QJ
F 020 7250 1771   T 020 7250 1200
E info@darksidephoto.co.uk
W www.darksidephoto.co.uk

DE LANE LEA SOUND
Post-Production. Re-Recording Studios
75 Dean Street, London W1D 3PU
F 020 7432 3838   T 020 7432 3800
E solutions@delanelea.com
W www.delanelea.com

DENBRY REPROS LTD
Photographic Reproduction
57 High Street, Hemel Hempstead
Herts HP1 3AF   T 01442 242411
E info@denbryrepros.com
W www.denbryrepros.com

DV2BROADCAST
3 Carolina Way, Salford M50 2ZY   T 0161 736 5300
E info@dv2broadcast.co.uk
W www.dv2broadcast.co.uk

DYNAMIC ISLE STUDIO
58 Selhurst New Road
South Norwood
London SE25 5PU   M 07956 951090
E olympicrecords@tiscali.co.uk
W www.olympicrecordsuk.com

EDGAR Richard STUDIOS
6 Millan Court, Lumphanan
Aberdeenshire AB31 4QF   T 05602 625262
E richard.edgar@vcstudios.co.uk
W www.vcstudios.co.uk

ELMS STUDIOS
Contact: Phil Lawrence. Composing/Scoring for Film &
Television. Intel Power Mac. Live Studio
10 Empress Avenue
London E12 5ES   T 020 8518 8629
E info@elmsstudios.com
W www.elmsstudios.com

ESSENTIAL MUSIC
20 Great Chapel Street, London W1F 8FW
F 020 7287 3597   T 020 7439 7113
E info@essentialmusic.co.uk

EXECUTIVE AUDIO VISUAL
DVD Duplication Service. Showreels for Actors & Presenters
E chris.jarvis60@gmail.com   T/F 020 7723 4488

FIREFLY PRODUCTIONS
Twin Oaks, Hale Purlieu
Fordingbridge SP6 2NN   M 07956 675276
E theonlyfirefly@aol.com
W www.fireflyproductions.info

FLIXELS LTD
Unit 7 Rutland Studios
Cumberland Park
Scrubs Lane, London NW10 6RE   T 020 8960 2577
E info@flixels.co.uk
W www.flixels.co.uk

FLOURISH NEW BIZ LTD
Learn How to Market Yourself
13 Temple Close, London E11 1JN   T 020 8539 5400
E simone@flourishnewbiz.co.uk
W www.flourishnewbiz.co.uk

FREEDALE PRESS LTD
Printing
36 Hedley Street
Maidstone, Kent ME14 5AD
F 01622 200131   T 01622 200123
E michael@freedale.co.uk

GENESIS TEE SHIRTS & HOODIES
18 Pendre Enterprise Park
Tywyn, Gwynedd LL36 9LW
F 01654 712461   T 01654 710137
E info@genesis-uk.com
W www.genesis-uk.com

GLITTERGAL WEBS
E info@glittergalwebs.com   M 07931 318021
W www.glittergalwebs.com

GYROSCOPE STUDIOS
Contact: Frank Sanderson
Hökmossevägen 34, SE12638 Hägersten
Sweden   T 00 46 86 45 92 23
E frank@gyroscope-studios.com
W www.gyroscope-studios.com

HARVEY HOUSE FILMS LTD
Animation. Showreels. Video Production
71 Shouthfield Road, London W4 1BB   M 07968 830536
E chris@harveyhousefilms.co.uk
W www.harveyhousefilms.co.uk

HEAVY ENTERTAINMENT LTD
111 Wardour Street, London W1F 0UH
F 020 7494 1100   T 020 7494 1000
E info@heavy-entertainment.com
W www.heavy-entertainment.com

HORIZON STUDIO
Musical Demos. Voice Tapes
12 Rutford Road, London SW16 2DH   M 07961 100006
E guyholden@post.com
W www.sound2picture.com

HOTQS CREATIVE
Showreels
63 Redchurch Street, London E2 7DJ   M 07903 017819
E pat@houseofthequietstorm.com
W www.houseofthequietstorm.com

HOTREELS
Voice & Showreels
M 07793 394951   T 020 7952 4362
E info@hotreels.co.uk
W www.hotreels.co.uk

IMAGE PHOTOGRAPHIC
Photographic Reproduction
54 Shepherds Bush Road
London W6 7PH   T 020 7602 1190
E digital@imagephotographic.com
W www.imagephotographic.com

JMS GROUP LTD THE
Park Farm Studios, Norwich Road
Hethersett, Norfolk NR9 3DL
F 01603 812255   T 01603 811855
E info@jms-group.com
W www.jms-group.com

KONK STUDIOS
84-86 Tottenham Lane, London N8 7EE
F 020 8348 3952   T 020 8340 7873
E linda@konkstudios.com

LONDON SHOWREELS
PO Box 55278, London N22 9FZ
E sales@londonshowreels.co.uk   T 020 8144 6750
W www.londonshowreels.co.uk

LUMEN STUDIO
103 Islingword Road, Brighton
East Sussex BN2 9SG   T/F 01273 690149
E info@lumenstudio.co.uk
W www.lumenstudio.co.uk

MEDIAWEBS
Graphic & Web Design
20 Parker Road, Millbank Place
Colchester CO4 5BE   M 07887 480241
E jon@mediawebs.co.uk
W www.mediawebs.co.uk

MINAMON FILM
Specialist in Showreels
117 Downton Avenue
London SW2 3TX   T 020 8674 3957
E studio@minamonfilm.co.uk
W www.minamonfilm.co.uk

MOTIVATION SOUND STUDIOS
35A Broadhurst Gardens
London NW6 3QT
F 020 7624 4879   T 020 7328 8305
E info@motivationsound.co.uk
W www.motivationsound.co.uk

MUSIC IN MOTION LTD
4 Ravenshaw Street, London NW6 1NN   M 07813 070961
E neil@neilmyers.com
W www.neilmyers.com

NOHO STUDIOS LTD
Contact: Michael Hobdell
31 Harley Street, London W1G 9QS M 07889 895510
E michael@nohostudios.co.uk
W www.nohostudios.co.uk

PROFESSIONAL SHOWREELS OF MANCHESTER
10 Old Hall Court, Old Hall Lane, Manchester M45 7JW
M 07738 819880 T 0161 272 1029
E showreels@btinternet.com

PROFILE PRINTS
Photographic Reproduction
Unit 2, Plot 1A, Rospeath Industrial Estate, Crowlas TR20 8DU
F 01736 741255 T 01736 741222
E sales@courtwood.co.uk
W www.courtwood.co.uk

RED FACILITIES
61 Timber Bush, Leith, Edinburgh EH6 6QH
F 0131 555 0088 T 0131 555 2288
E doit@redfacilities.com
W www.redfacilities.com

REEL DEAL SHOWREEL CO THE
6 Charlotte Road, Wallington
Surrey SM6 9AX T 020 8647 1235
E info@thereel-deal.co.uk
W www.thereel-deal.co.uk

REEL GEEKS.COM THE
West Kensington, London W14 0DU M 07951 757024
E thereelgeeks@hotmail.com
W www.thereelgeeks.com

REEL McCOY THE
Showreel Editing Service
Flat 2A, Crampton Road, London SE20 7AT M 07708 626477
E reelmccoyservice@aol.com
W www.jameshyland.co.uk/reelmccoy

REMOTE LIVE RECORDINGS
244A Kingston Road, Leatherhead
Surrey KT22 7QA M 07968 100557
E info@remoteliverecordings.co.uk
W www.remoteliverecordings.co.uk

REPLAY LTD
Showreels & Performance Recording
Museum House, 25 Museum Street
London WC1A 1JT T 020 7637 0473
E sales@replayfilms.co.uk
W www.replayfilms.co.uk

RESOLUTION LONDON
Photography. Web Design
The Diary House
Rickett Street, London SW6 1RU
M 07962 471118 T 0800 4488675
E info@resolutionlondon.co.uk
W www.resolutionlondon.co.uk

RETRO REELS
Showreels. Voicereels. Websites. Shoots From Scratch
Flat 1, 29 Park Avenue
London NW2 5AN M 07896 299932
E mail@retroreels.co.uk
W www.retroreels.co.uk

ROUND ISLAND SHOWREELS & VOICEREELS
Contact: Ben Warren, Guy Michaels
E mail@roundisland.net M 07701 093183
W www.roundisland.net

SCARLET INTERNET
Suite 4, 15 Market Square
Bishop's Stortford, Herts CM23 3UT
F 0870 2241418 T 0870 7771820
E info@scarletinternet.com
W www.scarletinternet.com

SETTLE THE SCORE
157 Grove Road, London E17 9BZ M 07853 643346
E toby@settlethescore.co.uk
W www.settlethescore.co.uk

SHOWREEL THE
Demo Production Services. Voice-over Workshops
Knightsbridge House, 229 Acton Lane
Chiswick, London W4 5DD T 020 7043 8660 (Bookings)
E info@theshowreel.com
W www.theshowreel.com

SHOWREELS 1
45-46 Poland Street, London W1F 7NA
F 020 7437 2830   M 07932 021232
E showreels1@aol.com
W www.ukscreen.com/company/showreels1

SHOWREELZ
28 Eastbury Grove, Chiswick
London W4 2JZ   M 07885 253477
E brad@showreelz.com
W www.showreelz.com

SILVER-TONGUED PRODUCTIONS
Specialising in the Recording and Production of Voicereels
Greater London   T 020 8309 0659
E contactus@silver-tongued.co.uk
W www.silver-tongued.co.uk

SMALL SCREEN SHOWREELS
The Production Office, 17 Knole Road
Crayford, London   T 020 8816 8896
E info@smallscreenshowreels.co.uk
W www.smallscreenshowreels.co.uk

SOHO SHOWREELS
101 Wardour Street, London W1F 0UG   T 0844 5040731
E info@sohoshowreels.co.uk
W www.sohoshowreels.co.uk

SOHO THIRTY THREE
8 Wimbledon Village Business Centre, Thornton Road
Wimbledon SW19 4NG   T 020 8123 6085
E info@sohothirtythree.co.uk
W www.sohothirtythree.co.uk

SONICPOND STUDIO
Specialising in Voicereels. Showreels. Websites
70 Mildmay Grove South, Islington
London N1 4PJ   T 020 7690 8561
E info@sonicpond.co.uk
W www.sonicpond.co.uk

SOUND
4 St Paul's Road, Clifton, Bristol BS8 1LT   T 0117 973 4595
E kenwheeler@mac.com
W www.soundat4.com

SOUND COMPANY LTD
23 Gosfield Street, London W1W 6HG
F 020 7580 6454   T 020 7580 5880
E bookings@sound.co.uk
W www.sound.co.uk

SOUND HOUSE POST PRODUCTION LTD THE
4th Floor, South Central, 11 Peter Street, Manchester M2 5QR
F 0161 832 7266   T 0161 832 7299
E mail@thesoundhouse.tv
W www.thesoundhouse.tv

SOUND MARKETING
Strattons House, Strattons Walk
Melksham, Wiltshire SN12 6JL
F 01225 701601   T 01225 701600
E nicki@soundm.com
W www.soundm.com

STAGES CAPTURE THE MOMENT
Showreels
31 Evensyde, Croxley Green
Watford, Herts WD18 8WN   T 020 7193 8519
E info@stagescapturethemoment.com
W www.stagescapturethemoment.com/videopages/showreels.php

STAMP PRODUCTIONS
10 Margaret Street, London W1W 8RL   T 020 3178 2367
E ben@stamp-productions.co.uk

SYNCREDIBLE A
26-28 Hammersmith Grove, London W6 7BA   T 020 7117 6776
E contact@syncredible.com
W www.syncredible.com

TAKE FIVE CASTING STUDIO
Showreels
37 Beak Street, London W1F 9RZ
F 020 7287 3035   T 020 7287 2120
E info@takefivestudio.com
W www.takefivestudio.com

TM DESIGN LTD
Actors CVs. Headshots. Model Cards. Web Design
Suites 14-15, Marlborough Business Centre
96 George Lane, South Woodford
London E18 1AD   T 020 8530 4382
E info@tmphotography.co.uk
W www.tmphotography.co.uk

TOP TV ACADEMY
Showreels
Elstree Film & TV Studios, Shenley Road, Herts WD6 1JG
F 020 7485 7536   M 07971 284958
E liz@toptvacademy.co.uk
W www.toptvacademy.co.uk

TOUCHWOOD AUDIO PRODUCTIONS
6 Hyde Park Terrace, Leeds, West Yorkshire LS6 1BJ
M 07745 377772   T 0113 278 7180
E bruce@touchwoodaudio.com
W www.touchwoodaudio.com

TV PRESENTER TRAINING - ASPIRE
3 Mills Studios, Three Mill Lane
London E3 3DU   T 0800 0305471
E info@aspirepresenting.com
W www.aspirepresenting.com

TWITCH FILMS
Showreels
22 Grove End Gardens, 18 Abbey Road
London NW8 9LL   T 020 7266 0946
E post@twitchfilms.co.uk
W www.twitchfilms.co.uk

UNIVERSAL SOUND (JUST PLAY) LTD
Old Farm Lane, London Road East
Amersham, Buckinghamshire HP7 9DH
F 01494 723500   T 01494 723400
E foley@universalsound.co.uk
W www.universalsound.co.uk

www.Flixels.co.uk

VISUALEYES PHOTOREPRO SERVICES
Photographic Reproduction
95 Mortimer Street, London W1W 7ST
F 020 7323 7438   T 020 7323 7430
E imaging@visualeyes.co.uk
W www.visualeyes.co.uk

VOICE MASTER
Creators of the Hudson Voice Technique, the only Technique
in the World for Voice-overs
88 Erskine Hill, London NW11 6HR   T 020 8455 2211
E stevehudson@voicemaster.co.uk
W www.voicemaster.co.uk

VOICE TAPE SERVICES INTERNATIONAL
Professional Management Voice-over Direction & CDs
80 Netherlands Road, New Barnet, Herts EN5 1BS
F 020 8441 4828   T 020 8440 4848
E info@vtsint.co.uk
W www.vtsint.co.uk

VOICEREELS.CO.UK
43 Fallsbrook Road, London SW16 6DU   M 07989 602880
E rob@voicereels.co.uk
W www.voicereels.co.uk

VSI - VOICE & SCRIPT INTERNATIONAL
Foreign Language Specialists. Casting. Dubbing. Editing
Recording Studios. Subtitling. Translation
132 Cleveland Street, London W1T 6AB
F 020 7692 7711   T 020 7692 7700
E info@vsi.tv   W www.vsi.tv

WARWICK HALL OF SOUND
Warwick Hall
Off Banastre Avenue, Heath
Cardiff CF14 3NR   T/F 029 2069 4455
E promotions@cardiffrecordingstudios.co.uk
W www.cardiffrecordingstudios.co.uk

WARWICK SOUND
Sound Transfer/Optical & Magnetic
Warwick Sound
111A Wardour Street
London W1F 0UJ
F 020 7439 0372   T 020 7437 5532
E studio@warwicksound.com
W www.warwicksound.com

WORLDWIDE PICTURES LTD
Unit 30, 10-50 Willow Street
London EC2A 4BH
F 020 7613 6581   T 020 7613 6580
E anthead@worldwidepictures.tv
W www.worldwidepictures.tv

WOW FACTOR THE
Unit 39
Cornmill Shopping Centre
Darlington
Durham DL3 6EN
F 01325 253468   T 01325 241680
E wowfactor@hotmail.co.uk
W www.wowfactorautographs.co.uk

07000 BIG TOP
Big Top. Circus. Seating
The Arts Exchange, Congleton
Cheshire CW12 1JG
F 01260 270777   T 01260 276627
E info@arts-exchange.com
W www.arts-exchange.com

10 OUT OF 10 PRODUCTIONS LTD
Design. Hire. Installation. Lighting. Sales. Sound
5 Orchard Business Centre
Kangley Bridge Road
London SE26 5AQ   T 0845 1235664
E sales@10outof10.co.uk
W www.10outof10.co.uk

147RESEARCH
Will find anything needed for period or modern productions
Chaucers, Oare
Hermitage, Thatcham RG18 9SD
M 07778 002147   T 01635 200147
E jenniferdalton@147research.com
W www.147research.com

3D CREATIONS
Production Design. Prop Makers. Scenery Contractors
Scenic Artists
9A Bells Road, Gorleston-on-Sea
Great Yarmouth, Norfolk NR31 6BB
F 01493 443124   T 01493 652055
E info@3dcreations.co.uk
W www.3dcreations.co.uk

AC FLUTES
Handmade Native American-style Flutes
Handmade Wood & Leather Crafts
E info@acflutes.co.uk   T 020 8123 5925
W www.acflutes.co.uk

ACROBAT PRODUCTIONS
Advisors. Artistes
12 Oaklands Court, Hempstead Road
Watford WD17 4LF   T 01923 224938
E info@acrobatproductions.com
W www.acrobatproductions.com

ACTION CARS LTD
Contact: Steven Royffe
Room 586, East Side Complex, Pinewood Studios
Pinewood Road, Iver Heath, Bucks SL0 0NH
F 01753 652027   T 01753 785690
E info@actioncars.co.uk
W www.actioncars.co.uk

ADAMS ENGRAVING
Unit G1A, The Mayford Centre, Mayford Green
Woking GU22 0PP
F 01483 751787   T 01483 725792
E adamsengraving@pncl.co.uk
W www.adamsengraving.co.uk

AIRBOURNE SYSTEMS INTERNATIONAL
All Skydiving Requirements Arranged. Parachute Hire
(Period & Modern)
8 Burns Crescent, Chelmsford
Essex CM2 0TS   T 01245 268772

ALCHEMICAL LABORATORIES ETC
Medieval Science & Technology Recreated for Museums &
Films
2 Stapleford Lane, Coddington
Newark, Nottinghamshire NG24 2QZ   T 01636 707836
W www.jackgreene.co.uk

ALL SCENE ALL PROPS
Props, Masks, Painting & Scenery Makers
Units 2 & 3, Spelmonden Farm
Goudhurst, Kent TN17 1HE
F 01580 211131   T 01580 211121
E info@allscene.net
W www.allscene.net

ALL STARS
Fieldgate, Station Road
Northiam, Rye TN31 6QT   T 01797 252528
E dazwills@aol.com
W www.limo-hire-sussex-kent.co.uk

AMERICAN DREAMS
Vehicle Supply
47 Wilsons Lane, Mark's Tey
Essex CO6 1HP   T 0800 8488032
E tphj47@aol.com
W www.americandreams.co.uk

ANELLO & DAVIDE
Handmade Shoes
15 St Albans Grove, London W8 5BP   T 020 7938 2255
W www.handmadeshoes.co.uk

ANNUAL CLOWNS DIRECTORY THE
Contact: Salvo The Clown
13 Second Avenue
Kingsleigh Park
Thundersley, Essex SS7 3QD   T 01268 745791
E salvo@annualclownsdirectory.com
W www.annualclownsdirectory.com

AQUARIUS
Film & Television Stills Library
PO Box 5, Hastings TN34 1HR   T 01424 721196
E aquarius.lib@clara.net
W www.aquariuscollection.com

AQUATECH
Camera Boats
2 Cobbies Rock, Epney
Gloucestershire GL2 7LN
F 01452 741958   T 01452 740559
E office@aquatech-uk.com
W www.aquatech-uk.com

ARCHERY CENTRE THE
Tuition
PO Box 39, Battle
East Sussex TN33 0ZT   T 01424 777183
E sales@archerycentre.co.uk
W www.archerycentre.co.uk

ARMS & ARCHERY
Armour. Chainmail. Longbows. Tents. Weaponry. X-bows
Thrift Lane, Off London Road
Ware, Herts SG12 9QS   T 01920 460335
E armsandarchery@btconnect.com

ART *
Art Consultant. Supplier of Paintings & Sculpture
E h@art8star.co.uk
W www.art8star.co.uk

ART DIRECTORS & TRIP PHOTO LIBRARY
Digital Scans, Colour Slides (All Subjects)
57 Burdon Lane, Cheam
Surrey SM2 7BY
F 020 8395 7230   T 020 8642 3593
E images@artdirectors.co.uk
W www.artdirectors.co.uk

A. S. DESIGNS
Theatrical Designer
Costumes, Heads, Masks, Puppets, Sets etc
E maryannscadding@btinternet.com　　T 01279 722416
W www.astheatricaldesign.co.uk

ASH Riky
Equity Registered Stunt Performer/Co-ordinator
M 07850 471227　　　　　　　　　T 01476 407383
E stuntmanriky@fallingforyou.tv
W www.fallingforyou.tv

AUTOMOTIVE ACTION
Suppliers of Replica Humvees/H1 Hummers & Prototypes
Constructor of Specialist Vehicles
E carstunts@hotmail.co.uk　　　　　M 07974 919589
W www.carstunts.co.uk

AWESOME
Bespoke Custom Upholstery Specialists
The Stables
Grange Farm, Green End
Great Stukeley, Huntingdon
Cambridgeshire PE28 4AE
F 01480 464879　　　　　　　　　T 01480 457007
E glenn@awesome.eu.com
W www.awesome.eu.com

BAPTY 2000 LTD
Dressing, Props, Weapons etc
1A Witley Gardens
Norwood Green
Middlesex UB2 4ES
F 020 8571 5700　　　　　　　　　T 020 8574 7700
E hire@bapty.demon.co.uk

BARNES CATERERS LTD
9 Ripley Drive, Normanton
Wakefield, West Yorkshire WF6 1QT
F 01924 223730　　　　　　　　　T 01924 896148

BARTON Joe
Puppeteer. Model & Prop Maker
7 Brands Hill Avenue, High Wycombe
Buckinghamshire　　　　　　　　　T 01494 439056

BEAT ABOUT THE BUSH LTD
Musical Instrument Hire
Unit 23, Enterprise Way
Triangle Business Centre
Salter Street (Off Hythe Road)
London NW10 6UG
F 020 8969 2281　　　　　　　　　T 020 8960 2087
E info@beataboutthebush.com
W www.beataboutthebush.com

BIANCHI AVIATION FILM SERVICES
Historic & Other Aircraft
Wycombe Air Park
Booker Marlow
Buckinghamshire SL7 3DP
F 01494 461236　　　　　　　　　T 01494 449810
E info@bianchiaviation.com
W www.bianchiaviation.com

BIG BREAK CARDS
Theatrical greetings cards featuring Hamlet the pig, drawn
by Harry Venning, as seen in The Stage
Made by actors for actors
E info@bigbreakcards.co.uk　　　　T 01386 438952
W www.bigbreakcards.co.uk

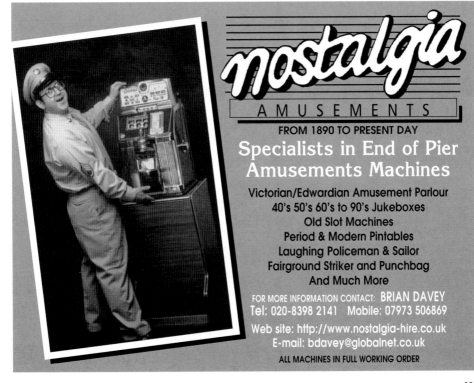

BLUE MILL LTD
Dyers. Finishers
84 Halstead Street, Leicester LE5 3RD
F 0116 253 7633   T 0116 248 8130
E info@bluemill.co.uk
W www.bluemill.co.uk

BLUEBELL RAILWAY PLC
*Period Stations. Pullman Coaches. Steam Locomotives. Much
Film Experience*
Sheffield Park Station
East Sussex TN22 3QL
F 01825 720804   T 01825 720800
E info@bluebell-railway.co.uk
W www.bluebell-railway.co.uk

BOLDGATE COMMERCIAL SERVICES LTD
The Crossbow Centre, 40 Liverpool Road
Slough, Berkshire SL1 4QZ
F 01753 610587   T 01753 610525
E info@boldgate.co.uk
W www.boldgate.co.uk

BOSCO LIGHTING
Design/Technical Consultancy
47 Woodbourne Avenue
London SW16 1UX   T 020 8769 3470
E boscolx@lineone.net

BOUNCY CASTLES BY P. A. LEISURE
Specialists in Amusements & Fairground Equipment
Delph House, Park Bridge Road
Towneley Park, Burnley, Lancs BB10 4SD
M 07968 399053   T 01282 453939
E paleisure@btconnect.com
W www.paleisure.com

BRISTOL (UK) LTD
Scenic Paint & StageFloor Duo Suppliers. VFX Solutions
Unit 3, Sutherland Court
Tolpits Lane, Watford WD18 9SP
F 01923 779666   T 01923 779333
E tech.sales@bristolpaint.com
W www.bristolpaint.com

BRODIE & MIDDLETON LTD
Theatrical Suppliers. Glitter, Paints, Powders etc
68 Drury Lane, London WC2B 5SP
F 020 7497 0554   T 020 7836 3289
E info@brodies.net
W www.brodies.net

BRUNEL'S THEATRICAL SERVICES
Removal Services
20A Walnut Lane, Kingswood
Bristol BS15 5JG   T 0117 907 7855
E enquiries@brunelsremovalservices.co.uk
W www.brunelsremovalservices.co.uk

CAMDEN ATTIC
Period Prop Hire & Making
Location House, 5 Dove Lane, Bristol BS2 9HP
F 0117 955 2480   T 0117 941 1969
E genie@camdenattic.co.uk
W www.camdenattic.co.uk

CANDLE MAKERS SUPPLIES
Rear of 102-104 Shepherds Bush Road
London W6 7PD
F 020 7602 2796   T 020 7602 1812
E candles@candlemakers.co.uk
W www.candlemakers.co.uk

CARLINE & CREW TRANSPORTATION
Celebrity Services
12A Bridge Industrial Estate, Balcombe Road
West Sussex RH6 9HU
F 01293 430432   T 01293 430430
E carlinehire@btconnect.com
W www.carlineprivatehire.co.uk

CAULFIELD TWINS THE
Technical & Production Services
71 Turner Road, Walthamstow
London E17 3JG   T 020 8925 0140
E admin@thecaulfieldtwins.co.uk
W www.thecaulfieldtwins.co.uk

CHASE 55
Prop Hire Specialist. Victorian to Present Day
55 Chase Road, London NW10 6LU
F 020 8965 8107   T 0871 2310900
E trez.evans@chase55.com
W www.chase55.com

CHRISANNE LTD
Specialist Fabrics & Accessories for Theatre & Dance
Chrisanne House, 110-112 Morden Road
Mitcham, Surrey CR4 4XB
F 020 8640 2106   T 020 8640 5921
E sales@chrisanne.com
W www.chrisanne.com

CIRCUS MANIACS
Circus Equipment, Rigging & Training
Unit 62, Basepoint Business Centre
Oakfield Close, Tewkesbury Business Park
Tewkesbury, Gloucestershire GL20 8SD
M 07977 247287   T 01684 854412
E info@circusmaniacs.com
W www.circusmaniacs.com

CIRCUS PROMOTIONS
Entertainers
36 St Lukes Road, Tunbridge Wells
Kent TN4 9JH   T 01892 537964
E mike@heypresto.orangehome.co.uk
W www.heyprestoentertainment.co.uk

CLASSIC CAR AGENCY THE
Advertising. Film. Promotional. Publicity
PO Box 427, Dorking, Surrey RH5 6WP
M 07788 977655   T 01306 731052
E theclassiccaragency@btopenworld.com
W www.theclassiccaragency.com

CLASSIC CAR HIRE
Over 30 Classic and Vintage Vehicles
Unit 2 Hampton Court Estate, Summer Road
Thames Ditton KT7 0RG
F 020 8939 3987   T 020 8398 8304
E info@classic-hire.co.uk
W www.classic-hire.com

CLASSIC COLLECTION THE
Bespoke Wedding Cars
43 Dunstan Close, Chester Le Street DH2 3HX   T 0191 388 2387
E info@the-classic-collection.co.uk
W www.the-classic-collection.co.uk

CLASSIC OMNIBUS
Vintage Open-Top Buses & Coaches
44 Welson Road, Folkestone
Kent CT20 2NP   T 01303 248999
W www.opentopbus.co.uk

COBO MEDIA LTD
Performing Arts, Entertainment & Leisure Marketing
43A Garthorne Road, London SE23 1EP
F 020 8291 4969   T 020 8291 7079
E admin@cobomedia.com
W www.cobomedia.com

COMPTON Mike & Rosi
Costumes. Models. Props
11 Woodstock Road, Croydon, Surrey CR0 1JS
F 020 8681 3126   T 020 8680 4364
E mikeandrosicompton@btopenworld.com

CONCEPT ENGINEERING LTD
Smoke, Fog, Snow etc
7 Woodlands Business Park, Woodlands Park Avenue
Maidenhead, Berkshire SL6 3UA
F 01628 826261   T 01628 825555
E info@conceptsmoke.com
W www.concept-smoke.co.uk

COOK Sheila TEXTILES
Textiles, Costumes & Accessories for Hire/Sale
26 Addison Place, London W11 4RJ   T 020 7603 3003
E sheilacook@sheilacook.co.uk
W www.sheilacook.co.uk

COSTUMES & SHOWS UNLIMITED
Costume Rental & Design. Ice Rink Rental. Show Production
PO Box 57, Poulton-le-Fylde, Lancs FY6 8GN
M 07881 970398   T 01253 827092
E iceshowpro@aol.com
W www.ice-shows-and-costumes-unlimited.co.uk

CREATIVE WORKS
Floral Design
Unit 1, The Stable Block
Brewer Street, Bletchingley, Surrey RH1 4QP   T 01883 742999
E info@ckworks.net
W www.ckworks.net

CRESTA BLINDS LTD
Supplier of Vertical Blinds
Crown Works, Tetnall Street, Dudley DY2 8SA
F 01384 457675   T 01384 255523
E info@crestablindsltd.co.uk
W www.crestablindsltd.co.uk

CROFTS Andrew
Book Writing Services
Westlands Grange, West Grinstead
Horsham, West Sussex RH13 8LZ   T/F 01403 864518
E croftsa@aol.com
W www.andrewcrofts.com

CUE ACTION POOL PROMOTIONS
Advice for UK & US Pool, Snooker, Trick Shots
PO Box 3941, Colchester
Essex CO2 8HN
F 01206 729480   T 07000 868689
E sales@cueaction.com
W www.stevedaking.com

CURTAIN TRACKS & DRAPES
28 The Street, Brettenham
Ipswich, Suffolk IP7 7QP   T 01449 736305
E piehatch@aol.com
W www.suffolkscenery.info

DAVEY Brian
See NOSTALGIA AMUSEMENTS

DESIGN PROJECTS
Perrysfield Farm, Broadham Green
Old Oxted, Surrey RH8 9PG
F 01883 723707   T 01883 730262
W www.designprojects.co.uk

DEVEREUX DEVELOPMENTS LTD
Haulage. Removals. Trucking
Daimler Drive, Cowpen Industrial Estate
Billingham, Cleveland TS23 4JD
F 01642 566664   T 01642 560854
E mikebell@britdev.com

DORANS PROPMAKERS/SET BUILDERS
53 Derby Road, Ashbourne
Derbyshire DE6 1BH   T/F 01335 300064
E info@doransprops.com
W www.doransprops.com

DURRENT Peter
Audition & Rehearsal Pianist. Cocktail Pianist. Composer
Vocalist
Blacksmiths Cottage
Bures Road, Little Cornard
Sudbury, Suffolk CO10 0NR   T 01787 373483

EAT TO THE BEAT
Production & Location Caterers
Studio 4-5, Garnett Close
Watford, Herts WD24 7GN
F 01923 211704   T 01923 211702
E enquiries@eattothebeat.com
W www.globalinfusiongroup.com

ELECTRO SIGNS LTD
97 Vallentin Road, London E17 3JJ
F 020 8520 8127   T 020 8521 8066
E info@electrosigns.co.uk

GREENPROPS Foliage * Flowers * Fruit & Veg
Importers of Raffia Grass Matting

The Artificial STAGE SUPPLIERS, serving The West End, The UK and Europe
T: 01398 361531   trevor@greenprops.org   www.greenprops.org

ELMS LESTERS PAINTING ROOMS
Scenic Painting
1-3-5 Flitcroft Street, London WC2H 8DH
F 020 7379 0789   T 020 7836 6747
E info@elmslesters.co.uk

ES GROUP LTD
Project Management. Staging. Temporary Structures
Trucking
Bell Lane, North Woolwich Road
London E16 2AB
F 020 7055 7201   T 020 7055 7200
E info@esgroup-uk.com
W www.esgroup-uk.com

ESCORT GUNLEATHER
Custom Leathercraft
602 High Road, Benfleet
Essex SS7 5RW
F 01268 566775   T 01268 792769
E info@escortgunleather.com
W www.escortgunleather.com

EVANS Peter STUDIOS LTD
Scenic Embellishment. Vacuum Forming
12-14 Tavistock Street, Dunstable
Bedfordshire LU6 1NE
F 01582 481329   T 01582 725730
E sales@peterevansstudios.co.uk
W www.peterevansstudios.co.uk

FACADE
Musical Production Services
43A Garthorne Road, London SE23 1EP
F 020 8291 4969   T 020 8291 7079
E facade@cobomedia.com

FAIRGROUND ARTWORK
Halstead, Fovant
Salisbury, Wiltshire SP3 5NL
M 07710 287251   T 01722 714786
E sv@pozzy.co.uk
W www.pozzy.co.uk

FELLOWES Mark TRANSPORT SERVICES
Transport. Storage
59 Sherbrooke Road, London SW6 7QL
M 07850 332818   T 020 7386 7005
W www.fellowesproductions.com

FILM MEDICAL SERVICES
Units 5 & 7, Commercial Way
Park Royal, London NW10 7XF
F 020 8961 7427   T 020 8961 3222
E filmmed@aol.com
W www.filmmedical.co.uk

FINAL CREATION
Unit 19, The Loft Studio
Hill Lane Industrial Estate, Markfield, Leicestershire LE67 9PN
F 01530 249400   T 01530 249100
E gemma@finalcreation.co.uk
W www.finalcreation.co.uk

FIREBRAND
Flambeaux Hire & Sales
Leac Na Ban, Tayvallich
By Lochgilphead, Argyll PA31 8PF   T 01546 870310
E firebrand.props@btinternet.com

FIRST NIGHT DESIGN
Greeting Cards & Gifts
E info@firstnightdesign.co.uk   M 07773 770781
W www.firstnightdesign.co.uk

FLAME RETARDING LTD
Grove Farm, Grove Farm Road
Tolleshunt Major, Maldon, Essex CM9 8LR
F 07092 036931   T 01621 818477
E email@flameretarding.co.uk
W www.flameretarding.co.uk

FLAMENCO PRODUCTIONS
Entertainers
Sevilla 4 Cormorant Rise, Lower Wick
Worcester WR2 4BA   T 01905 424083

FLINT HIRE & SUPPLY LTD
Queen's Row, London SE17 2PX
F 020 7708 4189   T 020 7703 9786
E sales@flints.co.uk
W www.flints.co.uk

FLYING BY FOY
Flying Effects for Theatre, TV, Corporate Events etc
Unit 4, Borehamwood Enterprise Centre
Theobald Street
Borehamwood, Herts WD6 4RQ
F 020 8236 0235   T 020 8236 0234
E mail@flyingbyfoy.co.uk
W www.flyingbyfoy.co.uk

FRANCO THE MAGICIAN
Flat 1, 79 Brent Street, London NW4 2EA   T/F 020 8202 4940
E franco@francomagic.co.uk
W www.francomagic.co.uk

FRANKIE'S YANKEES
Classic 1950s American Cars, Memorabilia, New Superstretch
Limos & Action Vehicles
283 Old Birmingham Road, Bromsgrove B60 1HQ
M 07970 062142   T 0121 445 5522
E wow@frankiesyankees.com

FREEDALE PRESS LTD
Printing
36 Hedley Street, Maidstone
Kent ME14 5AD
F 01622 200131   T 01622 200123
E michael@freedale.co.uk

FROST John NEWSPAPERS
Historical Newspaper Service
22B Rosemary Avenue, Enfield
Middlesex EN2 0SS   T 020 8366 1392
E andrew@johnfrostnewspapers.com
W www.johnfrostnewspapers.com

GARRATT Jonathan FRSA
Suppliers of Traditional & Unusual Garden Pots &
Installations. Glazed Tableware
Hare Lane Farmhouse
Cranborne
Dorset BH21 5QT   T 01725 517700
E jonathan.garratt@talk21.com
W www.jonathangarratt.com

GAV NICOLA THEATRICAL SHOES
E gavnicola@yahoo.com   M 07961 974278
W www.theatricalshoes.com

GET STUFFED
Taxidermy
105 Essex Road, London N1 2SL
M 07831 260062   T 020 7226 1364
E taxidermy@thegetstuffed.co.uk
W www.thegetstuffed.co.uk

GHOSTWRITER/AUTHOR
Contact: John Parker
Dove Cottage, The Street
Ickham CT3 1QP   T 01227 721071
E parkerwrite@aol.com
W www.ghostwriteruk.info

GORGEOUS GOURMETS LTD
Caterers. Equipment Hire
Gresham Way, Wimbledon SW19 8ED
F 020 8946 1639   T 020 8944 7771
E hire@gorgeousgourmets.co.uk
W www.gorgeousgourmets.co.uk

GOULD Gillian ANTIQUES
Scientific & Marine Antiques & Collectables
38 Denman Drive South, London NW11 6RH
M 07831 150060   T 020 8458 7675
E gillgould@dealwith.com
W www.gilliangouldantiques.co.uk

GRADAV HIRE & SALES LTD
Lighting & Sound Hire/Sales
Units C6 & C9 Hastingwood Trading Estate
Harbet Road, Edmonton, London N18 3HU
F 020 8803 5060   T 020 8803 7400
E office@gradav.co.uk

GRAY Robin COMMENTARIES
Bridles. Hunting Attire. Racing Colours. Saddles
Comptons, Isington
Alton, Hampshire GU34 4PL
M 07831 828424   T 01420 23347
E gray@isington.fsnet.co.uk

GREENPROPS
Prop Suppliers. Artificial Flowers, Fruit, Grass, Plants,
Trees etc
E trevor@greenprops.org   T 01398 361531
W www.greenprops.org

GREENSOURCE SOLUTIONS LTD
Providers of Mobile Phone Props
14 Kingsland Trading Estate, St Phillips Road
Bristol BS2 0JZ
F 0117 304 2391   T 0845 3100200
E props@greensource.co.uk
W www.greensource.co.uk

HAMPTON COURT HOUSE
Hampton Court Road, East Molesey KT8 9BS
F 020 8977 5357   T 020 8943 0889
W www.hamptoncourthouse.co.uk

HANDS UP PUPPETS
7 Cavendish Vale, Nottingham
Nottinghamshire NG5 4DS   M 07909 824630
E marcus@handsuppuppets.com
W www.handsuppuppets.com

HARLEQUIN (BRITISH HARLEQUIN PLC)
Floors for Stage, Opera, Dance, Concert, Shows & Events
Festival House, Chapman Way
Tunbridge Wells, Kent TN2 3EF
F 01892 514222   T 01892 514888
E enquiries@harlequinfloors.com
W www.harlequinfloors.com

HERON & DRIVER
Scenic Furniture & Prop Makers
Unit 7, Dockley Road Industrial Estate
Rotherhithe, London SE16 3SF
F 020 7394 8680   T 020 7394 8688
E mail@herondriver.co.uk
W www.herondriver.co.uk

HI-FLI (Flying Effects)
2 Boland Drive, Manchester M14 6DS   T/F 0161 224 6082
E mikefrost@hi-fli.co.uk

HISTORICAL INTERPRETER & ROLE PLAYING
Contact: Donald Clarke
80 Warden Avenue
Rayners Lane
Harrow, Middlesex HA2 9LW
M 07811 606285   T 020 8866 2997
E info@historicalinterpretations.co.uk
W www.historicalinterpretations.co.uk

HISTORY IN THE MAKING LTD
Weapon & Costume Hire
4A Aysgarth Road, Waterlooville
Hampshire PO7 7UG   T 023 9225 3175
E enquiries@history-making.com
W www.history-making.com

HOME JAMES CHAUFFEUR SERVICE
Moor Lane, Witton
Birmingham B6 7HH   T 0121 323 4717
E enquiries@homejamescars.com
W www.homejamescars.com

HOMESITE ESTATE AGENTS
16 Lambton Place, London W11 2SH
F 020 7243 5794   T 020 7243 3535
E info@homesite.co.uk
W www.homesite.co.uk

HOTCHPOTCHPROPS
21 Silvan Drive, Braunton
Devon EX33 2EQ   M 07734 685254
E jo@hotchpotchprops.com
W www.hotchpotchprops.com

HOWARD Rex DRAPES
Trading division of Hawthorns
Unit F, Western Trading Estate
London NW10 7LU   T 020 8740 5881
E hire@hawthorns.uk.com

IMPACT
Private & Contract Hire of Coaches
1 Leighton Road, Ealing
London W13 9EL
F 020 8840 4880   T 020 8579 9922
E sales@impactgroup.co.uk
W www.impactgroup.co.uk

IMPACT PERCUSSION
Percussion Instruments for Sale
Unit 7 Goose Green Trading Estate
47 East Dulwich Road
London SE22 9BN
F 020 8299 6704   T 020 8299 6700
E sales@impactpercussion.com

IMPACT PRINT DISPLAY
Leaflet & Poster Distribution & Display
Tuscany Wharf, 4B Orsman Road, London N1 5QJ
F 020 7729 5994   T 020 7729 5978
E contactus@impactprintdisplay.com
W www.impactprintdisplay.com

IMPACT SCHOOL OF MOTORING
Expert Driving Instructors on All Vehicles
248A Columbia Road, Bournemouth BH10 4DS
M 07775 713780   T 01202 666001
E andyd@mail2world.com

JAPAN PROMOTIONS
Japanese Costumes & Props
200 Russell Court, 3 Woburn Place
London WC1H 0ND   T/F 020 7278 4099
E info@japan-promotions.co.uk
W www.japan-promotions.co.uk

JASON'S
Daily Scheduled Trips to Camden Lock
Opposite 42 Blomfield Road
Little Venice, London W9 2PD
E info@jasons.co.uk
W www.jasons.co.uk

JULIETTE DESIGNS
Diamante Jewellery Manufacturer: Necklaces, Crowns etc
90 Yerbury Road, London N19 4RS
F 020 7281 7326   T 020 7263 7878
E juliettedesigns@hotmail.com
W www.stagejewellery.com

KEIGHLEY & WORTH VALLEY LIGHT RAILWAY LTD
Crew. Props. Carriages, Engines & Stations
The Railway Station, Haworth
Keighley, West Yorkshire BD22 8NJ
F 01535 647317   T 01535 645214
E admin@kwvr.co.uk
W www.kwvr.co.uk

KENSINGTON EYE CENTRE LTD
Special Eye Effects
37 Kensington Church Street
London W8 4LL   T/F 020 7937 8282

KEW BRIDGE STEAM MUSEUM
Green Dragon Lane, Brentford
Middlesex TW8 0EN
F 020 8569 9978   T 020 8568 4757
E jo@kbsm.org
W www.kbsm.org

KIRBY'S AFX LTD
8 Greenford Avenue, Hanwell
London W7 3QP
M 07958 285608   T/F 020 8723 8552
E mail@afxuk.com
W www.kirbysflying.co.uk

KNEBWORTH HOUSE, GARDENS & PARK
Knebworth
Herts SG3 6PY   T 01438 812661
E info@knebworthhouse.com
W www.knebworthhouse.com

LAREDO Alex
Expert with Ropes, Bullwhips, Shooting, Riding
29 Lincoln Road, Dorking
Surrey RH4 1TE
M 07906 271766   T 01306 889423

LAREDO WILD WEST TOWN
Wild West Entertainment
1 Bower Walk, Staplehurst
Tonbridge, Kent TN12 0LU
M 07947 652771   T 01580 891790
E enquiries@laredo.org.uk
W www.laredo.org.uk

LEES-NEWSOME LTD
Manufacturers of Flame Retardant Fabrics
Ashley Works, Unit 2
Rule Business Park
Grimshaw Lane, Middleton
Manchester M24 2AE
F 0845 0708006   T 0845 0708005
E info@leesnewsome.co.uk
W www.leesnewsome.co.uk

LEIGHTON HALL
Historic House
Carnforth, Lancashire LA5 9ST
F 01524 720357   T 01524 734474
E info@leightonhall.co.uk
W www.leightonhall.co.uk

LEVRANT Stephen - HERITAGE ARCHITECTURE LTD
Architects. Historic Building Consultants
62 British Grove, Chiswick
London W4 2NL
F 020 8748 4992   T 020 8748 5501
E info@heritagearchitecture.co.uk

LIMELIGHT ENTERTAINMENT
Theatre Merchandise
Unit 13, The io Centre
The Royal Arsenal, Seymour Street
London SE18 6SS
F 020 8853 0979   T 020 8853 9570
E enquiries@thelimelightgroup.co.uk

LONDON BUSINESS EQUIPMENT
Authorised Canon Dealer
527-529 High Road, Leytonstone
London E11 4PB
F 020 8556 4865   T 020 8558 0024
E sales@londonbusinessequipment.com
W www.londonbusinessequipment.com

LONDON QUALITY DRY CLEANERS LTD
Dry Cleaners. Dyers. Launderers. Costumes & Stage Curtains
222 Baker Street,
London NW1 5RT   T 020 7935 7316

LONO DRINKS CO
23/24 Failsworth Industrial Estate
Greenhalgh Street
Failsworth, Manchester M35 0BN   T 0800 8250035
E info@lono.co.uk
W www.lono.co.uk

LOS KAOS
Animatronics. Puppetry. Street Theatre
Quay House, Quayside
Brockweir, Gloucestershire NP16 7NQ   T/F 01291 680074
E kaos@loskaos.co.uk
W www.loskaos.co.uk

LUCKINGS
Stage Hands. Storage. Transporters
Boston House
69/75 Boston Manor Road
Brentford, Middlesex TW8 9JJ
F 020 8332 3000   T 020 8332 2000
E info@luckings.co.uk
W www.luckings.co.uk

LUCKINGS SCREEN SERVICES
Artists' Trailers/Splits/2-3 Ways
Boston House
69/75 Boston Manor Road
Brentford, Middlesex TW8 9JJ
F 020 8332 3000   T 020 8332 2000
E info@luckings.co.uk
W www.luckings.co.uk

LYON EQUIPMENT
*Petzl & Beal Rope Access Equipment (PPE)
for Industrial & Theatrical Work*
Junction 38, M6, Tebay
Cumbria CA10 3SS
F 01539 626250   T 01539 624857
E work.rescue@lyon.co.uk
W www.lyon.co.uk

M A C
Sound Hire
1-2 Attenburys Park, Park Road
Altrincham, Cheshire WA14 5QE
F 0161 962 9423   T 0161 969 8311
E hire@macsound.co.uk
W www.macsound.co.uk

MACKIE Sally LOCATIONS
Location Finding & Management
Cownham Farm
Broadwell
Moreton-in-Marsh
Gloucestershire GL56 0TT   T 01451 830294
E sally@mackie.biz
W www.sallymackie-locations.com

MAGICAL MART
*Magic. Punch & Judy. Ventriloquists' Dolls. Hire & Advising
Callers by Appointment*
42 Christchurch Road, Sidcup
Kent DA15 7HQ   T/F 020 8300 3579
W www.johnstylesentertainer.co.uk

MAINSTREAM LEISURE GROUP
Riverboat/Canal Boat Hire
5 The Mews
6 Putney Common
London SW15 1HL
F 020 8788 0073   T 020 8788 2669
W www.mainstreamleisure.co.uk

MARCUS HALL PROPS
Unit 2B/C Vanguard Court
Rear of 36-38 Peckham Road
London SE5 8QT   T 020 7252 6291
E chris@marcushallprops.com
W www.marcushallprops.com

MARKSON PIANOS
8 Chester Court, Albany Street
London NW1 4BU
F 020 7224 0957   T 020 7935 8682
E info@marksonpianos.com
W www.marksonpianos.com

MATT-LX
Lighting. Technical Production
Gunnery House
9 Gunnery Terrace
London SE18 6SW
F 020 8301 8149   T 020 8301 8692
E intray@mattlx.com
W www.mattlx.com

McNEILL Brian
Vintage Truck & Coaches
Hawk Mount, Kebcote
Todmorden, Lancashire OL14 8SB   T 01706 812291
E autotrans@uk2.net
W www.rollingpast.com

MIDNIGHT ELECTRONICS
Sound Hire
Off Quay Building, Foundry Lane
Newcastle upon Tyne NE6 1LH
F 0191 224 0080   T 0191 224 0088
E info@midnightelectronics.co.uk
W www.midnightelectronics.co.uk

MILITARY, MODELS & MINATURES
Model Figures
38A Horsell Road, London N5 1XP
F 020 7700 4624   T 020 7700 7036
E minaturesmodels@aol.com

MODDED MOTORS AGENCY
Suppliers of Modified Cars
38 Williamson Way, Rickmansworth
Hertfordshire WD3 8GL   M 07989 128131
E daniellechristie@hotmail.com
W www.moddedmotorsagency.com

MODEL BOX
Computer Aided Design. Design Services
35 Mill Road, Okehampton
Devon EX20 1PS   T 01837 54342
E info@modelbox.co.uk
W www.modelboxplans.com

MOORFIELDS PHOTOGRAPHIC LTD
2 Old Hall Street, Liverpool L3 9RQ   T 0151 236 1611
E info@moorfieldsphoto.com
W www.moorfieldsphoto.com

MORTON G & L
Farming. Horses
Hashome Carr, Holme-on-Spalding Moor
Yorkshire YO43 4BD   T 01430 860393

MOTORHOUSE HIRE LTD
Contact: Michael Geary. Action Vehicles
Oatleys Hall, Turweston
Northants NN13 5JX
F 01280 704944   T 020 7495 1618
E michael@motorhouseltd.co.uk

MPG BOOKS GROUP
Quality Book Manufacturers
Victoria Square, Bodmin
Cornwall PL31 1EB
F 01208 73603   T 01208 73266
E print@mpg-books.co.uk
W www.mpg-booksgroup.com

M V DIXIE QUEEN
Thames Luxury Charters
5 The Mews, 6 Putney Common
London SW15 1HL
F 020 8788 0072   T 020 8780 1562
E sales@thamesluxurycharters.co.uk
W www.thamesluxurycharters.co.uk

NATIONAL MOTOR MUSEUM
John Montagu Building, Beaulieu
Brockenhurst, Hampshire SO42 7ZN
F 01590 612624   T 01590 612345
E info@beaulieu.co.uk
W www.beaulieu.co.uk

NEWMAN HIRE COMPANY
Lighting Hire
16 The Vale, Acton
London W3 7SB   T 020 8743 0741
E info@newmanhire.co.uk

NINE-NINE CARS LTD
Hyde Meadow Farm, Hyde Lane
Hemel Hempstead HP3 8SA   T 01923 266373
E david@nineninecars.com
W www.nineninecars.com

NORTHERN LIGHT
Assembly Street, Leith
Edinburgh EH6 7RG
F 0131 622 9101   T 0131 622 9100
E enquiries@northernlight.co.uk
W www.northernlight.co.uk

NOSTALGIA AMUSEMENTS
Contact: Brian Davey
22 Greenwood Close, Thames Ditton
Surrey KT7 0BG
M 07973 506869   T 020 8398 2141

**NOTTINGHAM JOUSTING ASSOCIATION SCHOOL OF
NATIONAL EQUITATION LTD**
*Jousting & Medieval Tournaments. Horses & Riders
for Films & TV*
Bunny Hill Top, Costock
Loughborough, Leicestershire LE12 6XN   T 01509 852366
E info@bunnyhill.co.uk
W www.bunnyhill.co.uk

OCEAN LEISURE
Scuba Diving. Watersports Retail
11-14 Northumberland Avenue
London WC2N 5AQ
F 020 7930 3032   T 020 7930 5050
E info@oceanleisure.co.uk
W www.oceanleisure.co.uk

OFFSTAGE
Theatre & Film Book
BlackGull Bookshop, 121 High Road
London N2 8AG   T 020 8444 4717
E offstagebookshop@aol.com

PAPERFLOW PLC
Office Equipment. Stationery
Units 5 & 6, Meridian Trading Estate
20 Bugsbys Way, Charlton, London SE7 7SJ
F 020 8331 2001   T 020 8331 2000
E info@paperflowgroup.com

PAPERPROPMAKER
*Paper Props Created for Theatre, Film & Television. Letters
Notebooks, Paper Ephemera etc. Handwritten or Printed
Any Style or Period Reproduced*
Based in London
E sianwillis@live.co.uk   M 07545 281486

PATCHETTS EQUESTRIAN CENTRE
Location
Hillfield Lane, Aldenham
Watford, Herts WD25 8PE
F 01923 859289   T 01923 852255
E info@patchetts.co.uk
W www.patchetts.co.uk

PATERSON Helen
Typing Services
40 Whitelands House, London SW3 4QY   T 020 7730 6428
E pater@waitrose.com

PERIOD PETROL PUMP COLLECTION
c/o Diss Ironworks, 7 St Nicholas Street
Diss, Norfolk IP22 4LB   T 01379 643978
W www.periodpetrolpump.co.uk

PHOSPHENE
Lighting & Sound. Design. Hire. Sales
Milton Road South, Stowmarket
Suffolk IP14 1EZ   T 01449 770011
E phosphene@btconnect.com
W www.phosphene.co.uk

PIANO PEOPLE THE
Piano Hire & Transport
74 Playford Road, London N4 3PH   T 0845 6076713
E info@pianopeople.co.uk
W www.pianopeople.co.uk

PICKFORDS MOVING & STORAGE
Laxcon Close, London NW10 0TG   T 020 3188 2100
E enquiries@pickfords.com
W www.pickfords.com

PICTURES PROPS CO LTD
Film, Stage & Television Hire
12-16 Brunel Road, London W3 7XR
F 020 8740 5846   T 020 8749 2433
E picturesprops@tiscali.co.uk

PINK POINTES DANCEWEAR
1A Suttons Lane, Hornchurch
Essex RM12 6RD   T/F 01708 438584
E pink.pointes@btconnect.com

PLUNGE PRODUCTIONS
Creative Services. Graphic Design. Props
Unit 10, 18A Arthur Street
Hove BN3 5FD   T/F 01273 557550
E info@plungeproductions.com
W www.plungeproductions.com

PLUS FILM LTD
All Periods Vehicle Hire
1 Mill House Cottages
Winchester Road
Bishop's Waltham SO32 1AH   T 01489 895559
E stephen.lamonby@googlemail.com

POLAND Anna: SCULPTOR AND MODELMAKER
Sculpture, Models, Puppets, Masks etc
Salterns, Old Bursledon
Southampton, Hampshire SO31 8DH   T 023 8040 5166
E polandanna@hotmail.com

POLLEX PROPS / FIREBRAND
Prop Makers
Leac Na Ban, Tayvallich
Lochgilphead, Argyll PA31 8PF   T/F 01546 870310
E firebrand.props@btinternet.com

**PRAETORIAN ASSOCIATES/PROCUREMENT
SERVICES - SA**
*Personal Safety & Anti-Stalking Consultancy. Services for
Film/TV Industry within South Africa*
Tintagel, 1 St Clairs Road
St Osyth, Essex CO16 8QG
M 07973 505981   T 020 7096 1827
E martin.beale@praetorianasc.com
W www.praetorianasc.com

PREMIER CHAUFFEUR SERVICES
164 Haydock Street, Newton-le-Willows
Merseyside WA12 9DH
M 07890 661050   T 01925 299112
E mike.vizard@hotmail.co.uk

PRINTMEDIA GROUP
E info@printmediagroup.eu
W www.printmediagroup.eu

PROBLOOD
11 Mount Pleasant, Framlingham
Suffolk IP13 9HQ   T/F 01728 723865

PROFESSOR PATTEN'S PUNCH & JUDY
Hire & Performances. Advice on Traditional Show
14 The Crest, Goffs Oak
Hertfordshire EN7 5NP   T 01707 873262
W www.dennispatten.co.uk

PROP FARM LTD
Contact: Pat Ward
Grange Farm, Elmton
Nr Creswell, North Derbyshire S80 4LX
F 01909 721465   T 01909 723100
E pat/les@propfarm.co.uk

PROP STUDIOS LTD
Unit 3 Old Kiln Works, Ditchling Common Industrial Estate
Hassocks BN6 8SG
F 01444 250089   T 01444 250088
E info@propstudios.co.uk
W www.propstudios.co.uk

PROPS GALORE
Period Textiles/Jewellery
15 Brunel Road, London W3 7XR
F 020 8354 1866   T 020 8746 1222
E propsgalore@farley.co.uk

PUNCH & JUDY PUPPETS & BOOTHS
Hire & Advisory Service. Callers by Appointment
42 Christchurch Road, Sidcup
Kent DA15 7HQ   T/F 020 8300 3579
W www.johnstylesentertainer.co.uk

Q2Q GROUP
Technical Resources
187 Drury Lane, Covent Garden
London WC2B 5QD
F 020 7430 2777   T 020 7269 9730
E solutions@q2qgroup.com
W www.q2qgroup.com

RAINBOW PRODUCTIONS LTD
Creation & Appearances of Costume Characters/Stage Shows
Unit 3, Greenlea Park
Prince George's Road, London SW19 2JD
F 020 8254 5306   T 020 8254 5300
E info@rainbowproductions.co.uk
W www.rainbowproductions.co.uk

RENT-A-CLOWN
Contact: Mattie Faint
37 Sekeforde Street, Clerkenwell
London EC1R 0HA   T/F 020 7608 0312
E mattiefaint@gmail.com

REPLAY LTD
Showreels. TV Facilities Hire
Museum House, 25 Museum Street
London WC1A 1JT   T 020 7637 0473
E sales@replayfilms.co.uk
W www.replayfilms.co.uk

ROBERTS Chris INTERIORS
Specialist Painters & Decorators to the Film Industry
117 Colebrook Lane
Loughton IG10 2HP   M 07956 512074

ROOTSTEIN Adel LTD
Mannequin Manufacturer
9 Beaumont Avenue, London W14 9LP
F 020 7381 3263   T 020 7381 1447
W www.rootstein.com

ROYAL HORTICULTURAL HALLS & CONFERENCE CENTRE THE
Film Location: Art Deco & Edwardian Buildings
80 Vincent Square, London SW1P 2PE
F 020 7834 2072   T 0845 3704606
E horthalls@rhs.org.uk
W www.rhhonline.co.uk

RUDKIN DESIGN
Design Consultants. Advertising, Brochures, Corporate etc
10 Cottesbrooke Park, Heartlands Business Park
Daventry, Northamptonshire NN11 8YL
F 01327 311715   T 01327 301770
E arudkin@rudkindesign.co.uk
W www.rudkindesign.com

RUMBLE Jane
Props to Order. No Hire
121 Elmstead Avenue, Wembley
Middlesex HA9 8NT   T 020 8904 6462

SABAH STYLIST
Props. Sets. Wardrobe
2841 N. Ocean Blvd, Apt 501
Fort Lauderdale, Florida 33308 USA
M (954) 383 2179   T/F (954) 566 6219
E sabah561@aol.com

SALVO THE CLOWN
13 Second Avenue, Kingsleigh Park
Thundersley, Essex SS7 3QD   T 01268 745791
E salvo@annualclownsdirectory.com
W www.annualclownsdirectory.com

SAPEX SCRIPTS
The Maxwell Building, Elstree Film Studios
Shenley Road, Borehamwood
Herts WD6 1JG
F 020 8324 2771   T 020 8236 1600
E scripts@sapex.co.uk
W www.sapex.co.uk

SCHULTZ & WIREMU FABRIC EFFECTS LTD
Distressing. Dyeing. Printing
Unit B202 Faircharm Studios, 8-12 Creekside
London SE8 3DX   T/F 020 8469 0151
E swfabricfx@london.com
W www.schultz-wiremufabricfx.co.uk

SCRIPTRIGHT
Contact: S.C. Hill. Script/Manuscript Typing Services
Script Reading Services
6 Valetta Road, London W3 7TN   T 020 8740 7303
E samc.hill@virgin.net

SCRIPTS BY ARGYLE
Play, Film & Book. Binding. Copying. Editing. Word Processing. London Collection of Manuscript on Request
43 Clappers Lane, Fulking
West Sussex BN5 9ND   M 07905 293319
E argyle.associates@me.com
W www.scriptsbyargyle.co.uk

SFD
Ground Floor, Sunningdale, The Belfry
Colonial Way, Watford, Herts WD24 4WH
F 01923 232326   T 01923 232425
E sales@sfd.co.uk
W www.sfd.co.uk

SHAOLIN WAY
Martial Arts Supplies. Lion Dance & Kung Fu Instruction
10 Little Newport Street
London WC2H 7JJ   T 020 7734 6391
E shaolinway@btconnect.com
W www.shaolinway.com

SHIRLEY LEAF & PETAL COMPANY
Flower Makers Museum & Manufacturers
58A High Street, Old Town
Hastings, East Sussex TN34 3EN   T/F 01424 427793

SIDE EFFECTS
FX. Models. Props
92 Fentiman Road, London SW8 1LA
F 020 7207 0062   T 020 7587 1116
E sfx@lineone.net

SNOW BUSINESS
Snow/Winter Effects on Any Scale
The Snow Mill, Bridge Road
Ebley, Stroud, Gloucestershire GL5 4TR   T/F 01453 840077
E snow@snowbusiness.com
W www.snowbusiness.com

SOFT PROPS
Costume & Modelmakers
92 Fentiman Road, London SW8 1LA
F 020 7207 0062   T 020 7587 1116
E jackie@softprops.co.uk

SPUR CREATIVE WORKSHOP
Unit 1A, North Yard, Pennybridge Lane
Mayfield, East Sussex TN20 6QB
M 07970 805871   T 01435 873755
E info@spurcreative.co.uk
W www.spurcreative.co.uk

STANSTED AIRPORT TAXIS & CHAUFFEURS
55 Croasdaile Road, Stansted Airport
Essex CM24 8DW　　　　　　　T 0845 6436705
E enquiries@stanstedtaxiservice.co.uk
W www.stanstedtaxiservice.co.uk

STEELDECK RENTALS/SALES LTD
Modular Staging. Stage Equipment Hire
Unit 58, T Marchant Trading Estate
42-72 Verney Road, London SE16 3DH
F 020 7232 1780　　　　　　　T 020 7833 2031
E rentals@steeldeck.co.uk
W www.steeldeck.co.uk

STEVENSON Scott
Prop Maker
60 Ripley Road, Sawmills
Belper, Derbyshire DE56 2JQ　　M 07739 378579
E scott@bodymechprops.co.uk
W www.bodymechprops.co.uk

STOKE BRUERNE BOAT COMPANY LTD
Passenger & Day Boat Operator
Wharf Cottage, Stoke Bruerne
Northants NN12 7SE　　　　　　M 07966 503609
W www.stokebruerneboats.co.uk

SUFFOLK SCENERY
Curtain Tracks & Drapes only
Pie Hatch Farm, Brettenham Road
Buxall, Stowmarket, Suffolk IP14 3DZ
M 07787 548744　　　　　　　T 01449 736305
E piehatch@aol.com
W www.suffolkscenery.info

SUPERSCRIPTS
51 Buckingham Gardens, West Moseley
Surrey KT8 1TJ
M 07793 160138　　　　　　　T 020 8979 8048
E super_scripts@sky.com

SUPERSCRIPTS
Audio Typing. Post-Prod Scripts. Rushes
56 New Road, Hanworth
Middlesex TW13 6TQ
M 07971 671011　　　　　　　T 020 8898 7933
E jackie@superscripts.fsnet.co.uk

TALK TO THE HAND PUPPETS
Custom Puppets for Film, Stage & Television
Studio 277, Wimbledon Art Studios, Riverside Yard
Earlsfield, London SW17 0BB
M 07813 682293　　　　　　M 07855 421454
E info@talktothehandpuppets.com
W www.talktothehandpuppets.com

TAYLOR Charlotte
Props Buyer. Stylist
18 Eleanor Grove, Barnes
London SW13 0JN
M 07836 708904　　　　　　T/F 020 8876 9085
E charlottetaylor1@blueyonder.co.uk

THAMES LUXURY CHARTERS LTD
5 The Mews, 6 Putney Common
London SW15 1HL
F 020 8788 0072　　　　　　　T 020 8780 1562
E sales@thamesluxurycharters.co.uk
W www.thamesluxurycharters.co.uk

THEATRESEARCH
Theatre Consultants
Dacre Hall, Dacre
North Yorkshire HG3 4ET
F 01423 781957　　　　　　　T 01423 780497
E info@theatresearch.co.uk
W www.theatresearch.co.uk

THEATRICAL SHOEMAKERS LTD
Footwear
Unit 7A, Thames Road Industrial Estate
Thames Road, Silvertown, London E16 2EZ
F 020 7476 5220　　　　　　　T 020 7474 0500
E ts@shoemaking.co.uk
W www.shoemaking.co.uk

THEME TRADERS LTD
Props
The Stadium, Oaklands Road
London NW2 6DL
F 020 8450 7322　　　　　　　T 020 8452 8518
E mailroom@themetraders.com
W www.themetraders.com

TOP SHOW
Props. Scenery. Conference Specialists
North Lane, Huntington
Yorks YO32 9SU　　　　　　　T/F 01904 750022

TRACK THAT
Tracking Vehicle/Camera Car Supplier
Wandsworth, London SW18　　M 07941 234254
E info@trackthat.co.uk
W www.trackthat.co.uk

TRANSCRIPTS
Conferences. Interviews. Post-production Scripts. Videos
Formats: CD/DVD, Downloads & Tapes
#2, 6 Cornwall Gardens, London SW7 4AL
M 07973 200197　　　　　　　T 020 7584 9758
E lucy@transcripts.demon.co.uk

TRAPEZE & AERIAL COACH/CHOREOGRAPHER
Contact: Jacqueline Welbourne
c/o Circus Maniacs, Unit 62, Basepoint Business Centre
Oakfield Close, Tewkesbury Business Park
Tewkesbury, Gloucestershire GL20 8SD
M 07977 247287　　　　　　T 01684 854412
E jackie@circusmaniacs.com
W www.circusmaniacs.com

TRISTAR WORLDWIDE CHAUFFEUR SERVICES
Unit 1-2, Horton Road
West Drayton UB7 8BQ　　　　T 01895 432000
E reservations@tristarworldwide.com
W www.tristarworldwide.com

TRYFONOS Mary MASKS
Mask, Headdress & Puppet Specialist
59 Shaftesbury Road
London N19 4QW
M 07764 587433   T 020 7561 9880
E marytryfonos@aol.com

TURN ON LIGHTING
Antique Lighting c1850-1950
11 Camden Passage, London N1 8EA   T/F 020 7359 7616

UK SAME DAY DELIVERY SERVICE
Contact: Philip Collings
18 Billingshurst Road
Broadbridge Heath
West Sussex RH12 3LW
F 01403 266059   M 07785 717179
E philcollings60@hotmail.com

UPBEAT EVENT DESIGN
Corporate Hospitality Caterers
Studio 4-5, Garnett Close
Watford, Herts WD24 7GN
F 01923 211704   T 01923 211703
E enquiries@upbeateventdesign.com
W www.upbeateventdesign.com

UPSTAGE
Live Communications Agency
Studio A
7 Maidstone Buildings Mews
72-76 Borough High Street
London SE1 1GD
F 020 7403 6511   T 020 7403 6510
E post@upstagelivecom.co.uk
W www.upstagelivecom.co.uk

VELOCITY SUPPLY CHAIN LOGISTICS
Unit 1, 42 Hanworth Road
Sunbury, Middlesex TW16 5LN
F 01932 733009   T 01932 733000
E jstrutt@vscl.co.uk
W www.vscl.co.uk

VENTRILOQUIST DOLLS HOME
Hire & Helpful Hints. Callers by Appointment
42 Christchurch Road, Sidcup
Kent DA15 7HQ   T/F 020 8300 3579
W www.johnstylesentertainer.co.uk

VENTRILOQUIST DUMMY HIRE
Contact: Dennis Patten. Hire & Advice
14 The Crest, Goffs Oak
Herts EN7 5NP   T 01707 873262
W www.dennispatten.co.uk

VINMAG ARCHIVE LTD
84-90 Digby Road, London E9 6HX
F 020 8525 9209   T 020 8533 7588
E piclib@vinmagarchive.com
W www.vinmagarchive.com

VINTAGE CARRIAGES TRUST
*Owners of the Museum of Rail Travel at Ingrow Railway
Centre*
Keighley, West Yorkshire BD21 5AX
F 01535 610796   T 01535 680425
E admin@vintagecarriagestrust.org
W www.vintagecarriagestrust.org

VOCALEYES
Providers of Audio Description for Theatrical Performance
1st Floor, 54 Commercial Street
London E1 6LT
F 020 7247 5622   T 020 7375 1043
E enquiries@vocaleyes.co.uk
W www.vocaleyes.co.uk

WALKING YOUR DOG
Dog Walking & Pet Services for South East London
92 Wricklemarsh Road
London SE3 8DS
M 07867 502333   T/F 020 8319 1806
E info@walkingyourdog.net
W www.walkingyourdog.net

WEB AND PRINT
Suite 14, Space House
Space Business Park
Abbey Road, Park Royal
London NW10 7SU   T 020 8838 3555
E info@webandprint.co.uk
W www.webandprint.co.uk

WEBBER Peter HIRE/RITZ STUDIOS
Music Equipment Hire. Rehearsal Studios
110-112 Disraeli Road, London SW15 2DX   T 020 8870 1335
E ben@peterwebberhire.com

WESTED LEATHERS COMPANY
Suede & Leather Suppliers/Manufacturers
Little Wested House, Wested Lane
Swanley, Kent BR8 8EF
F 01322 667039   T 01322 660654
E wested@wested.com

WESTWARD Lynn BLINDS
Window Blind Specialist
458 Chiswick High Road, London W4 5TT
F 020 8742 8444   T 020 8742 8333
E info@lynnwestward.com
W www.lynnwestward.com

WHITE ROOM STUDIO
Unit 03, 45 Morrish Road
London SW2 4EE   T 020 8678 1199
E info@whiteroomstudio.co.uk
W www.whiteroomstudio.co.uk

WILLIAMS Frank
*Beers, Bottles, Flagons, Footwarmers, Inks, Jars, Milk,
Poisons & Spitoons 1870-1940*
33 Enstone Road, Ickenham
Uxbridge, Middlesex   T 01895 672495
E frankwilliams33@talktalk.net

WILTSHIRE A. F. LLP
Agricultural Vehicle Engineers, Repairs etc
The Agricultural Centre, Alfold Road
Dunsfold, Surrey GU4 4NP
F 01483 200491   T 01483 200516
E team@afwiltshire.co.uk

WORBEY Darryl STUDIOS
Specialist Puppet Design
Ground Floor, 33 York Grove
London SE15 2NY
F 020 7635 6397   T 020 7639 8090
E info@darrylworbeystudios.com

ACADEMY PLAYERS DIRECTORY
See PLAYERS DIRECTORY

A C I D PUBLICATIONS
The Basement, Minus One House
Lyttelton Road, London E10 5NQ   T/F 07050 205206
E acidnews@aol.com

ACTING: A DRAMA STUDIO SOURCE BOOK
Peter Owen Publishers
73 Kenway Road, London SW5 0RE   T 020 7373 5628
E admin@peterowen.com
W www.peterowen.com

ACTIONS: THE ACTORS' THESAURUS
By Marina Caldarone & Maggie Lloyd-Williams
Nick Hern Books, The Glasshouse
49A Goldhawk Road, London W12 8QP
F 020 8735 0250   T 020 8749 4953
E info@nickhernbooks.demon.co.uk
W www.nickhernbooks.co.uk

ACTORS' YEARBOOK 2011
Methuen Drama, 36 Soho Square
London W1D 3QY
F 020 7758 0222   T 020 7758 0200
E methuendrama@acblack.com
W www.methuendrama.com

AMATEUR STAGE MAGAZINE & COMMUNITY ARTS DIRECTORY
Next Phase Media Ltd
Suite 404, Albany House
324-326 Regent Street, London W1B 3HH   T 020 7622 6670
E editor@asmagazine.co.uk
W www.asmagazine.co.uk

ANNUAIRE DU CINEMA BELLEFAYE
French Actors' Directory, Production, Technicians & All Technical Industries & Suppliers
30 rue Saint Marc, 75002 Paris
F 00 331 42 96 33 03   T 00 331 32 33 52 52
E contact@bellefaye.com
W www.bellefaye.com

ARTISTES & AGENTS
Richmond House Publishing Co Ltd
70-76 Bell Street, Marylebone, London NW1 6SP
F 020 7224 9688   T 020 7224 9666
E sales@rhpco.co.uk
W www.rhpco.co.uk

AUDITIONS: A PRACTICAL GUIDE
W www.auditionsapracticalguide.com

AUDITIONS UNDRESSED
By Dan Bowling
c/o Global Artists, 23 Haymarket
London SW1Y 4DG   T 020 7839 4888
E nikiwinterson@globalartists.co.uk

AURORA METRO PRESS (1989)
Biography, Drama, Fiction, Humour, Reference & International Literature in English Translation
67 Grove Avenue, Twickenham TW1 4HX
F 020 8898 0735   T 020 3261 0000
E info@aurorametro.com
W www.aurorametro.com

BIRTH OF THEATRE THE - STAGE BY STAGE
Drama. History. Reference. Theatre Studies
Peter Owen Publishers
73 Kenway Road, London SW5 0RE
F 020 7373 6760   T 020 7373 5628
E admin@peterowen.com
W www.peterowen.com

BOOKTHEACT.COM
The Entertainment Booking Site & Directory from The Stage
47 Bermondsey Street, London SE1 3XT
F 020 7939 8479   T 020 7939 8489
E info@booktheact.com
W www.booktheact.com

BRITISH PERFORMING ARTS YEARBOOK
Rhinegold Publishing
241 Shaftesbury Avenue
London WC2H 8TF   T 020 7333 1720
E bpay@rhinegold.co.uk
W www.rhinegold.co.uk

BRITISH THEATRE DIRECTORY
Richmond House Publishing Co Ltd
70-76 Bell Street, Marylebone
London NW1 6SP
F 020 7224 9688   T 020 7224 9666
E sales@rhpco.co.uk
W www.rhpco.co.uk

BROADCAST
Greater London House
Hampstead Road
London NW1 7EJ
F 020 7728 5555   T 020 7728 5542
W www.broadcastnow.co.uk

CASTCALL
Casting Information Services. Incorporating Castfax
106 Wilsden Avenue, Luton LU1 5HR
F 01582 480736   T 01582 456213
E admin@castcall.co.uk
W www.castcall.co.uk

CASTWEB
7 St Luke's Avenue, London SW4 7LG   T 020 7720 9002
E info@castweb.co.uk
W www.castweb.co.uk

CELEBRITY BULLETIN THE
10 Wiseton Road, London SW17 7EE
F 020 8672 2282   T 020 8672 3191
E enquiries@celebrity-bulletin.co.uk

CHAPPELL OF BOND STREET
Sheet Music. Musical Instruments. Pianos Synthesizers. Keyboards
152-160 Wardour Street, London W1F 8YA
F 020 7432 4410   T 020 7432 4400
W www.chappellofbondstreet.co.uk

CONFERENCE & INCENTIVE TRAVEL MAGAZINE
174 Hammersmith Road, London W6 7JP
F 020 8267 4192   T 020 8267 4307
E cit@haymarket.com
W www.citmagazine.com

CREATIVE HANDBOOK
Centaur Media PLC
50 Poland Street, London W1F 7AX   T 020 7970 6455
W www.creativehandbook.co.uk

DANCE DYNAMIC
A. E. Morgan Publications Ltd
Resource House, 8A High Street
Epsom, Surrey KT19 8AD   T 01372 741411
E sue@aemorgan.co.uk
W www.danceexpression.co.uk

DANCERS SPOTLIGHT
7 Leicester Place, London WC2H 7RJ
F 020 7437 5881   T 020 7437 7631
E questions@spotlight.com
W www.spotlight.com

DIRECTING DRAMA
Peter Owen Publishers
73 Kenway Road, London SW5 0RE   T 020 7373 5628
E admin@peterowen.com
W www.peterowen.com

EQUITY MAGAZINE
Guild House, Upper St Martin's Lane
London WC2H 9EG
F 020 7379 6074   T 020 7670 0211
E ppemberton@equity.org.uk
W www.equity.org.uk

FILMLOG
Subscriptions
Marketing Department, 6-14 Underwood Street
London N1 7JQ   T 020 7549 2578
W www.pcrnewsletter.com

FORESIGHT-NEWS
The Profile Group (UK) Ltd, The Johnson Building
77 Hatton Garden, London EC1N 8JS
F 020 7900 3684   T 020 7190 7777
E info@foresightnews.co.uk
W www.foresightnews.co.uk

FOURTH WALL MAGAZINE
Incorporating The Drama Student Magazine
Top Floor 3, 66 Wansey Street
London SE17 1JP
F 07092 846523   T 020 7701 4536
E editor@fourthwallmaagzine.co.uk
W www.fourthwallmaagzine.co.uk

HERN Nick BOOKS
Plays. Theatrebooks. Screenplays. Performing Rights
The Glasshouse, 49A Goldhawk Road
London W12 8QP
F 020 8735 0250   T 020 8749 4953
E info@nickhernbooks.demon.co.uk
W www.nickhernbooks.co.uk

HOLLYWOOD REPORTER THE
5th Floor, Endeavour House
189 Shaftesbury Avenue, London WC2H 8TJ
F 020 7420 6014   T 020 7420 6000
E london_one@eu.hollywoodreporter.com
W www.thr.com

HOW TO BECOME FAMOUS - A GUIDE FOR ACTORS IN THE UK
5 Blanche Street, Canning Town
London E16 4JP   M 07932 594312
E info@howtobecomefamous.co.uk
W www.howtobecomefamous.co.uk

KAY'S UK & EUROPEAN PRODUCTION MANUALS
Pinewood Studios, Pinewood Road
Iver Heath, Bucks SL0 0NH
F 020 8960 6700   T 020 8960 6900
E info@kays.co.uk
W www.kays.co.uk

KEMPS GLOBAL
Reed Business Information
East Grinstead House, East Grinstead
West Sussex RH19 1XA
F 01342 336113   T 01342 335779
E kemps.marketing@rbi.co.uk
W www.kftv.com

KNOWLEDGE THE
6-14 Underwood Street, London N1 7JQ
F 020 7549 8668   T 020 7549 8666
E knowledge@wilmington.co.uk
W www.theknowledgeonline.com

LIMELIGHT THE
Limelight Publications, Contacts & Casting Directory
PO Box 760, Randpark Ridge
2156, Gauteng, South Africa
F 00 27 86 545 7231   T 00 27 11 793 7231
E info@limelight.co.za
W www.limelight.co.za

MAKING OF THE PROFESSIONAL ACTOR THE
Peter Owen Publishers
73 Kenway Road, London SW5 0RE   T 020 7373 5628
E admin@peterowen.com
W www.peterowen.com

METHUEN DRAMA
36 Soho Square, London W1D 3QY
F 020 7758 0222   T 020 7758 0200
E methuendrama@acblack.com
W www.methuendrama.com

MOVIE MEMORIES MAGAZINE
Devoted to Films & Stars of the 40s, 50s & 60s
10 Russet Close, Scunthorpe
N. Lincs DN15 8YJ
E crob.mvm@ntlworld.com

MUSIC WEEK DIRECTORY/MUSIC WEEK
UBM
3rd Floor, Ludgate House
245 Blackfriars Road, London SE1 9UY   T 020 7921 8320
E enquiries@musicweek.com
W www.musicweek.com

MUSICAL STAGES
Musical Theatre Magazine
PO Box 8365, London W14 0GL   T/F 020 7603 2227
E editor@musicalstages.co.uk
W www.musicalstages.co.uk

OFFICIAL LONDON SEATING PLAN GUIDE THE
Richmond House Publishing Co Ltd, 70-76 Bell Street
Marylebone, London NW1 6SP
F 020 7224 9668   T 020 7224 9666
E sales@rhpco.co.uk
W www.rhpco.co.uk

PA ENTERTAINMENT
292 Vauxhall Bridge Road, Victoria
London SW1V 1AE
F 0870 1203201   T 0870 1203200
E events@pressassociation.com
W www.pressassociation.com

PANTOMIME BOOK THE
Peter Owen Publishers
73 Kenway Road, London SW5 0RE   T 020 7373 5628
E admin@peterowen.com
W www.peterowen.com

PCR
See PRODUCTION & CASTING REPORT

PLAYERS DIRECTORY
2210 W. Olive Avenue, Suite 320
Burbank, California 91506   T (310) 247 3058
E info@playersdirectory.com
W www.playersdirectory.com

PLAYS INTERNATIONAL
33A Lurline Gardens, London SW11 4DD   T 020 7720 1950
W www.playsinternational.org.uk

PRESENTERS CLUB THE
Presenter Promotions
123 Corporation Road
Gillingham, Kent ME7 1RG   M/F 07782 224207
E info@presenterpromotions.com
W www.presenterpromotions.com

PRESENTERS SPOTLIGHT
7 Leicester Place, London WC2H 7RJ
F 020 7437 5881　　　　　　　　T 020 7437 7631
E questions@spotlight.com
W www.spotlight.com

PRODUCTION & CASTING REPORT
Editorial
PO Box 11, London N1 7JZ
F 020 7566 8284　　　　　　　　T 020 7566 8282
E info@pcrnewsletter.com
W www.pcrnewsletter.com

Subscriptions
Marketing Department, 6-14 Underwood Street
London N1 7JQ　　　　　　　　　T 020 7549 2578

RADIO TIMES
201 Wood Lane, London W12 7TQ
F 020 8433 3923　　　　　　　　T 020 8433 3999
E radio.times@bbc.co.uk
W www.radiotimes.com

RICHMOND HOUSE PUBLISHING COMPANY LTD
70-76 Bell Street, Marylebone, London NW1 6SP
F 020 7224 9688　　　　　　　　T 020 7224 9666
E sales@rhpco.co.uk
W www.rhpco.co.uk

ROUTLEDGE PUBLISHING
2 Park Square, Milton Park
Abington, Oxon OX14 4RN
F 020 7017 6336　　　　　　　　T 020 7017 6000
E book.orders@tandf.co.uk
W www.routledge.com

SBS LTD
Suite 204, 254 Belsize Road, London NW6 4BT
F 020 7372 1992　　　　　　　　T 020 7372 6337
E office@sbscasting.co.uk

SCREEN INTERNATIONAL
Greater London House
Hampstead Road, London NW1 7EJ
F 020 7728 5555　　　　　　　　T 020 7728 5605
E mai.le@emap.com
W www.screendaily.com

SHOWBIZ FRIENDS
Community Website for Showbiz People
W www.showbizfriends.com

SHOWCAST
PO Box 2001, Leumeah
NSW 2560 Australia
F 02 4647 4167　　　　　　　　T 02 4647 4166
E danelle@showcast.com.au
W www.showcast.com.au

SHOWDIGS.CO.UK
E info@showdigs.co.uk　　　　　M 07984 422353
W www.showdigs.co.uk

SIGHT & SOUND
British Film Institute
21 Stephen Street, London W1T 1LN
F 020 7436 2327　　　　　　　　T 020 7255 1444
E s&s@bfi.org.uk
W www.bfi.org.uk/sightandsound

SO YOU WANT TO BE AN ACTOR?
By Timothy West & Prunella Scales
Nick Hern Books, The Glasshouse
49A Goldhawk Road, London W12 8QP
F 020 8735 0250　　　　　　　　T 020 8749 4953
E info@nickhernbooks.demon.co.uk
W www.nickhernbooks.co.uk

SO YOU WANT TO BE A THEATRE DIRECTOR?
By Stephen Unwin
Nick Hern Books, The Glasshouse
49A Goldhawk Road, London W12 8QP
F 020 8735 0250　　　　　　　　T 020 8749 4953
E info@nickhernbooks.demon.co.uk
W www.nickhernbooks.co.uk

SO YOU WANT TO BE A THEATRE PRODUCER?
By James Seabright
Nick Hern Books, The Glasshouse
49A Goldhawk Road, London W12 8QP
F 020 8735 0250　　　　　　　　T 020 8749 4953
E info@nickhernbooks.demon.co.uk
W www.nickhernbooks.co.uk

SO YOU WANT TO BE A TV PRESENTER?
By Kathryn Wolfe
Nick Hern Books, The Glasshouse
49A Goldhawk Road, London W12 8QP
F 020 8735 0250　　　　　　　　T 020 8749 4953
E info@nickhernbooks.demon.co.uk
W www.nickhernbooks.co.uk

SPEECH FOR THE SPEAKER
Peter Owen Publishers
73 Kenway Road, London SW5 0RE　T 020 7373 5628
E admin@peterowen.com
W www.peterowen.com

SPOTLIGHT
7 Leicester Place, London WC2H 7RJ
F 020 7437 5881　　　　　　　　T 020 7437 7631
E questions@spotlight.com
W www.spotlight.com

STAGE NEWSPAPER LTD THE
47 Bermondsey Street, London SE1 3XT
F 020 7939 8478　　　　　　　　T 020 7939 8483
E editor@thestage.co.uk
W www.thestage.co.uk

TELEVISUAL MEDIA UK LTD
48 Charlotte Street, London W1T 2NS
F 020 3008 5784　　　　　　　　T 020 3008 5750
E advertising@televisual.com
W www.televisual.com

THEATRE LIST THE
Society of London Theatre
32 Rose Street, London WC2E 9ET　T 020 7557 6700
E gemma@solttma.co.uk

THEATRE RECORD
131 Sherringham Avenue, London N17 9RU　T/F 01243 539437
E editor@theatrerecord.com
W www.theatrerecord.com

TIME OUT GROUP LTD
Universal House, 251 Tottenham Court Road, London W1T 7AB
F 020 7813 6001　　　　　　　　T 020 7813 3000
W www.timeout.com

TV TIMES
IPC Media
Blue Fin Building, 110 Southwark Street, London SE1 0SU
F 020 3148 8115　　　　　　　　T 020 3148 5615

VARIETY NEWSPAPER
Procter House, Procter Street, London WC1V 6EU
F 020 7911 1922　　　　　　　　T 020 7911 1701
W www.variety.com

WHITE BOOK THE
One Canada Square, Canary Wharf
London E14 5AP　　　　　　　　T 020 7772 8300
E admin@whitebook.co.uk
W www.whitebook.co.uk

ARTHUR Leone PR
The Ground Floor
3 Charlotte Mews, London W1T 4DZ
F 020 7637 2984   T 020 7637 2994
E info@arthurleone.com
W www.arthurleone.com

AVALON PUBLIC RELATIONS
Arts. Marketing
4A Exmoor Street, London W10 6BD
F 020 7598 7223   T 020 7598 8000
E markj@avalonuk.com
W www.avalonuk.com

BARLOW Tony ASSOCIATES
Press & Marketing for Music, Dance & Theatre
13 Burns Court, Park Hill Road
Wallington SM6 0SF
M 07711 929170   T 020 8773 1919
E artspublicity@hotmail.com

BOLTON Erica & QUINN Jane LTD
6 Addison Avenue, London W11 4QR
F 020 7221 8100   T 020 7221 5000
E name@boltonquinn.com
W www.boltonquinn.com

BORKOWSKI
65 Clerkenwell Road, London EC1R 5BL
F 020 7404 5000   T 020 7404 3000
E suresh@borkowski.co.uk
W www.borkowski.co.uk

CENTRESTAGE PUBLIC RELATIONS
1 Barricane, St Johns, Woking GU21 7RB
F 0870 2882398   M 07838 995736
E mail@centrestagepr.com
W www.centrestage.com

CHESTON Judith PUBLICITY
30 Telegraph Street, Shipston-on-Stour
Warwickshire CV36 4DA
F 01608 663772   T 01608 661198
E jacheston@tiscali.co.uk

CLARKE Duncan PR
24 Severus Street, York
North Yorkshire YO24 4NL   M 07880 893750
E duncanclarkepr@yahoo.co.uk
W www.duncanclarkepr.wordpress.com

CLOUT COMMUNICATIONS LTD
79 Wardour Street, London W1D 6QD   T 020 7851 8625
E info@cloutcom.co.uk
W www.cloutcom.co.uk

DAVEY Christine ASSOCIATES
29 Victoria Road, Eton Wick
Windsor, Berkshire SL4 6LY
F 01753 851123   T 01753 852619

DDA PUBLIC RELATIONS LTD
192-198 Vauxhall Bridge Road
London SW1V 1DX
F 020 7932 4950   T 020 7932 9800
E info@ddapr.com
W www.ddapr.com

DS MANAGEMENT
St Martin's Theatre, West Street, London WC2N 9NH
M 07711 245848   T 020 8743 7777
E ds@denisesilvey.com

ELSON Howard PROMOTIONS
Management. Marketing. PR
16 Penn Avenue, Chesham, Buckinghamshire HP5 2HS
F 01494 784760   T 01494 785873
E helson1029@aol.com

EMPICA LTD
1 Lyons Court, Long Ashton Business Park
Yanley Lane, Bristol BS41 9LB
F 01275 393933   T 01275 394400
E info@empica.com
W www.empica.com

GADABOUTS LTD
Theatre Marketing & Promotions
54 Friary Road, London N12 9PB
F 0870 7059140   T 020 8445 5450
E info@gadabouts.co.uk
W www.gadabouts.co.uk

GAYNOR Avril ASSOCIATES
126 Brudenell Road, London SW17 8DE M 07958 623013
E gaynorama@aol.com

GENERATE PR
Contact: Fran Walker
9 Winchester Way
Peterborough PE3 6HL   M 07545 499254
E fran@generatepr.co.uk

GOODMAN Deborah PUBLICITY (DGPR)
25 Glenmere Avenue, London NW7 2LT
F 020 8959 7875   T 020 8959 9980
E publicity@dgpr.co.uk
W www.dgpr.co.uk

HYMAN Sue ASSOCIATES LTD
St Martin's House, 59 St Martin's Lane
London WC2N 4JS
M 07976 514449   T 020 7379 8420
E sue.hyman@btinternet.com
W www.suehyman.com

IMPACT AGENCY THE
3 Bloomsbury Place, London WC1A 2QL
F 020 7580 7200   T 020 7580 1770
E mail@impactagency.co.uk
W www.theimpactagency.com

KEAN LANYON LTD
Contact: Sharon Kean
Rose Cottage, The Aberdeen Centre
22 Highbury Grove, London N5 2EA
M 07973 843133   T 020 7354 3574
E sharon@keanlanyon.com
W www.keanlanyon.com

KELLER Don ARTS MARKETING
65 Glenwood Road, Harringay
London N15 3JS   T 020 8800 4882
E info@dakam.org.uk

LAKE-SMITH GRIFFIN ASSOCIATES
Walter House, 418 Strand
London WC2R 0PT
F 020 7836 1040   T 020 7836 1020
E info@lakesmithgriffin.co.uk

LEEP MARKETING & PR
Marketing. Press. Publicity
5 Nassau House, 122 Shaftesbury Avenue
London W1D 5ER
F 020 7439 8833   T 020 7439 9777
E philip@leep.biz

MATTHEWS Liz PR
2 Sutton Lane, London EC1M 5PU   T 020 7253 1639
E liz@lizmatthewspr.com
W www.lizmatthewspr.com

MAYER Anne PR
82 Mortimer Road, London N1 4LH
M 07764 192842   T 020 7254 7391
E annemayer@btopenworld.com

McAULEY ARTS MARKETING LTD
118 Broxholm Road, London SE27 0BT   T 020 8676 4773
E sam@mcauleyartsmarketing.co.uk
W www.mcauleyartsmarketing.co.uk

MITCHELL Jackie
JM Communications
4 Sims Cottages, The Green, Claygate, Surrey KT10 0JH
F 01372 471073   T 01372 465041
E pr@jackiem.com
W www.jackiem.com

MOBIUS
The Crypt, St Georges Church
6-7 Little Russell Street, London WC1A 2HR   T 020 7269 9929
E info@mobiusindustries.com
W www.mobiusindustries.com

MORGAN Jane ASSOCIATES (JMA)
Marketing. Media
8 Heathville Road, London N19 3AJ   T 020 7263 9867
E jma@janemorganassociates.com
W www.janemorganassociates.com

NELSON BOSTOCK COMMUNICATIONS
Compass House, 22 Redan Place, London W2 4SA
F 020 7727 2025   T 020 7229 4400
E info@nelsonbostock.com
W www.nelsonbostock.com

PARKER James ASSOCIATES
29 Edinburgh Gardens, Windsor SL4 2AN
M 07947 430759   T 01753 855931
E jimparkerjpa@hotmail.com

PR OFFICE THE
720 Highgate Studios, 53-79 Highgate Road, London NW5 1TL
F 020 7485 0345   T 020 7284 6969
E kphillips@theproffice.com
W www.theproffice.com

PR PEOPLE THE
1 St James Drive, Sale, Cheshire M33 7QX   T 0161 976 2729
E graham@pr-people.uk.com
W www.pr-people.uk.com

PREMIER PR
91 Berwick Street, London W1F 0NE
F 020 7734 2024   T 020 7292 8330
W www.premierpr.com

PRESS COMPLAINTS COMMISSION
Halton House, 20/23 Holborn
London EC1N 2JD   T 020 7831 0022
E complaints@pcc.org.uk
W www.pcc.org.uk

PUBLIC EYE COMMUNICATIONS LTD
Suite 313, Plaza, 535 Kings Road, London SW10 0SZ
F 020 7351 1010   T 020 7351 1555
E ciara@publiceye.co.uk

PURPLE REIGN PUBLIC RELATIONS
28 Undercliff Road, Lewisham
London SE13 7TT   M 07809 110982
E info@purplereignpr.co.uk
W www.purplereignpr.co.uk

RAW-PHOTOS.COM
5 Clos y Berllan, Newbridge-on-Wye
Llandrindod Wells LD1 6LZ   T 01597 860124
E studio@raw-photos.com
W www.raw-photos.com

RICHMOND TOWERS COMMUNICATIONS LTD
26 Fitzroy Square, London W1T 6BT
F 020 7388 7761   T 020 7388 7421
W www.rt-com.com

RKM COMMUNICATIONS LTD
London & Los Angeles
5th Floor, 4 New Burlington Street, London W1S 2JG
F 020 7287 1704   T 020 3130 7090
E info@rkmcom.com
W www.rkmcom.com

S & X MEDIA
Contact: Roulla Xenides
The Gatehouse, 2B Victoria Works
Vittoria Street, Birmingham B1 3PE
F 0121 694 6494   T 0121 604 6366
E roulla@sx-media.com
W www.sx-media.com

SAVIDENT Paul
Marketing. Press Management
The Office, 27 St Dunstan's Road, London W7 2EY
F 0870 0516418   T 020 8567 2089
E info@savident.com
W www.savident.com

SHIPPEN Martin MARKETING & MEDIA
88 Purves Road, London NW10 5TB
M 07956 879165   T 020 8968 1943
E m.shippen@virgin.net

SNELL Helen LTD
4th Floor, 80-81 St Martin's Lane, London WC2N 4AA
F 020 7240 2947   T 020 7240 5537
E info@helensnell.com

SOCIETY OF LONDON THEATRE
32 Rose Street, London WC2E 9ET   T 020 7557 6727
E alison@solttma.co.uk

STOTT Barbara
20 Sunbury Lane, London SW11 3NP   T 020 7350 1159
E b-stott@talktalk.net

TARGET LIVE LTD
Design. Marketing. Media. Press
45-51 Whitfield Street, London W1T 4HB
F 020 3372 0951   T 020 3372 0950
E info@target-live.co.uk
W www.target-live.co.uk

TAYLOR HERRING PUBLIC RELATIONS
11 Westway Centre, 69 St Marks Road, London W10 6JG
F 020 8206 5155   T 020 8206 5151
E james.herring@taylorherring.com
W www.taylorherring.com

THOMPSON Peter ASSOCIATES
Flat One, 12 Bourchier Street, London W1V 5HN
F 020 7439 1202   T 020 7439 1210

TRE-VETT Eddie
Brink House, Avon Castle
Ringwood, Hampshire BH24 2BL   T 01425 475544

WILLIAMS Tei PRESS & ARTS MARKETING
Post Office Cottage, Clifton, Oxon OX15 0PD
M 07957 664116   T 01869 337940
E artsmarketing@btconnect.com

WILSON Stella PUBLICITY & PERSONAL MANAGEMENT
293 Faversham Road, Seasalter
Whitstable, Kent CT5 4BN   M 07860 174301
E stella@stellawilson.com

WINGHAM Maureen PRESS & PUBLIC RELATIONS
PO Box 125, Stowmarket, Suffolk IP14 1PB   T 01449 771200
E maureen.wingham@mwmedia.uk.com

WORKS PR THE
11 Marshalsea Road, London SE1 1EN   T 020 7940 4686
E nick@theworkspr.com
W www.theworkspr.com

R

Radio
BBC Radio
BBC Local Radio Stations
Independent Local Radio

Rehearsal Rooms & Casting Suites
Role Play Companies / Theatre Skills
in Business

BBC RADIO, Broadcasting House
London W1A 1AA
T 020 7580 4468 (Main Switchboard)

The BBC plans to relocate a number of its departments to a new site in Salford Quays from 2011. These departments include children's, sport, Radio 5 Live, learning and parts of future media and technology. While these relocations are taking place, please contact the BBC's main London switchboard.

• DRAMA
BBC Radio Drama
Bush House
The Aldwych, London WC2B 4PH
T 020 7580 4468 (Main Switchboard)

Production

Head	Alison Hindell
Production Executive	Rebecca Wilmshurst
Administrator Radio Drama Company	Cynthia Fagan

Executive Producers

World Service	Marion Nancarrow
London	Sally Avens
	David Hunter
	Jeremy Mortimer
	Di Speirs
Manchester	Sue Roberts
Birmingham	Vanessa Whitburn

Producers - London

Elizabeth Allard	Duncan Minshull
Marc Beeby	Tracey Neale
Jessica Dromgoole	Jonquil Panting
Claire Grove	Mary Peate
Emma Harding	Justin Willett
Gemma Jenkins	Sasha Yevtushenko
Peter Kavanagh	

Producers - Manchester

Gary Brown	Nadia Molinari
Pauline Harris	

Producers - Birmingham

Naylah Ahmed	Rosemary Watts (Archers)
Kim Greengrass (Silver Street)	Peter Wild

Development Producers

Charlotte Riches (Birmingham)
Fiona Kelcher (Manchester)
Abigail Le Fleming

[CONTACTS 2011]

Why should I work in radio?

To make a smooth transition from stage or camera to radio acting, everything that would otherwise be conveyed through body language and facial expressions must all be focused into the tone and pitch of the actor's voice.

If you have only ever considered visual acting work before, pursuing radio work would certainly enable you to expand your horizons and add additional skills to your CV. It is an opportunity to work in a different way and meet new requirements. Rehearsal and recording time is reduced in radio, which may allow you to pursue visual and radio acting alongside each other. Time constraints can be a pressure, and you have to get used to working without props (just sound effects), but this 'back to basics' existence is appealing to a lot of actors.

How can I become a radio presenter?

Presenting work in any medium comes under a different category as this is not classed as acting. It is a skill in its own right. Please refer to the 'Agents – Presenters' section for more information.

Do I need a voicereel?

This has to be your first and most important step into getting work as a radio actor. Your CV is not enough to get you a job without a professional-sounding voicereel. Voice-over work in commercial and corporate sectors requires a different type of reel. Please see the 'Promotional Services' section for more detailed voicereel advice.

Do I need an agent?

It is not strictly necessary to have an agent for radio work. The BBC is by far the main producer of radio drama and welcomes applications directly from actors, but some independent radio stations prefer using agents to put actors forward. It might be worth doing some research on your local radio stations and finding out their preferred method of contact and making a decision from there. If you are looking for a new agent and are interested in radio work as well as straight acting work, find out whether they deal with this area of the industry before signing up. If you only want to pursue radio and/or voice-over work, or are looking for a specialist agent in addition to your main agent, please see the 'Agents – Voice-over' section for further advice and listings.

How do I find work in radio?

You can send your CV and voicereel directly out to producers of radio drama, but make sure you target your search. Listen to radio plays and make a note of any producers whose work you particularly liked. This may also help you to identify what types of dramas you feel your voice would be most suited to. Once you have done your research and made a shortlist, send your voicereel with a personalised letter. Mention the plays you liked and explain that you feel he or she will be able to use your voice in productions like these. This method is likely to be much more effective than sending out a generic covering letter en masse, and will make you stand out. You don't need to send a headshot with your CV, but you could incorporate your photo in the body of your CV. It would be a good idea to have your name and contact details professionally printed onto your voicereel CD in case it becomes separated from your CV - see 'Promotional Services' for listings of companies that can do this for you.

infopage

Di Speirs is the Editor of Readings, BBC Radio, London. After five years in professional theatre, Di worked for ABC Australia before joining Woman's Hour on BBC Radio 4. She edited the Woman's Hour serial reading for five years and edited two collections of Woman's Hour short stories. Since 1997 she has produced readings and drama across Radio 4 and 3, particularly Book at Bedtime. She runs and judges the BBC National Short Story Award and was Chair of the Orange Award for New Writers in 2010.

The world of audio can be an overlooked one for actors, especially those starting out or who have perhaps come up through a screen route. And yet, on BBC Radio alone, there are hours of readings and radio drama every week and the commercial audiobook market is now taking advantage of the rapid growth of new media, from downloads to apps. For those whose voice is a strong part of their acting armoury there are opportunities, be they the most established of names and or at the beginning of their careers. And audio, particularly radio, is exciting and empowering for actors. It's a medium where they can take on roles they could never realistically hope to play in more visual mediums, stage or screen. The shortest actress can play that 'painted maypole', Helena, and in readings in particular, there's an unrivalled opportunity to not only give voice to both genders and all age ranges, but to people a whole cast.

As with anything in life, knowing the market is key to starting to work in it. In my area of radio readings, the bulk of the output is on BBC Radio 4, though Radio 3 also has proms and twenty minute interval slots, which are often stories, as well as The Essay. On Radio 4 there are three main strands: Book of the Week, 9.45am Monday to Friday, which is non-fiction; the Afternoon Reading, a mix of contemporary and classic commissioned and published stories and non-fiction; and Book at Bedtime, the original reading slot, which goes out at 10.45pm Monday to Friday and is usually a ten part abridgement of a new or classic novel.

Beyond this lie the riches of radio drama - with the Woman's Hour drama serial, the Afternoon Play at 2.45pm, the Saturday Play, and the Classic Serial on Sunday afternoons (repeated on Saturday evenings), not to mention The Archers. And then there are the plays on Radio 3 and occasional originations, often of science fiction, on Radio 7.

For many actors, radio has a special appeal, despite the smaller fees on offer. It is swift and frequently very convenient – a reading or a role in a radio drama can often be fitted in around the demands of a filming or a rehearsal schedule, or can be an ideal job once a play is running. BBC Radio has a devoted, loyal and large audience – often of over a million listeners – so you, and your talent, reaches many ears and may prompt other work. The variety of the work is enormous. Casting can be counter-intuitive and certainly allows a performer to explore areas they might not reach otherwise. If you still sound younger than your advancing years, you may yet get a coveted romantic lead; similarly the most able and versatile voice artists are able to adopt nationalities at will. Over two decades I have directed the same actress creating characters who were Welsh-Maltese, Ukrainian, Italian and Danish in different Book at Bedtimes.

The quality of the writing is, by and large, also extremely high. Radio is an unforgiving medium in that sense and poor writing shows. Given the wealth of literature on offer and the comparatively few slots available, the books that are chosen for broadcast are amongst the best of contemporary and classic writing and hopefully a pleasure to work on. Similarly the cost of dramatising a great classic, whilst still high in radio budget terms, remains feasible. And radio's ability to paint the best pictures through sound, part of which is of course through the performances, make it a challenging and satisfying environment to work in.

Beyond that, there is a magic about the intimacy of radio which is something actors, producers and directors relish. Listen out and you will hear the greatest British acting talent on our airwaves. It is always a small team – with readings a very small one – but that also means that there is a real sense of collaboration when working, and a real sense of connection, on a one-to-one basis, with that great unseen audience.

Getting your voice heard in the first place is the next question. I cast largely from theatre (which has some affinity) rather than film - and from other radio productions. BBC Radio maintains a unique theatrical institution – The Radio Drama Company - which began in the midst of the Blitz to keep a small company of actors safe and at hand for productions during the war. These days, while no longer 50 strong, the RDC consists of a group of actors on contract for a matter of months who appear in numerous dramas across the networks. Through its Soundstart programme, BBC Audio Drama also runs two major awards – The Carleton Hobbs and the Norman Beaton awards. For details on these and advice on how to get started in radio do look at the Soundstart webpages at www.bbc.co.uk/soundstart. There are many independent companies making productions for the audio market and for the BBC. It is worth sending demo tapes to them too.

If you are particularly interested in readings I would suggest including fairly long passages in any demo, which demonstrate not only the ability to create a host of characters (please don't over-characterise though – shading is usually more successful) but also that more elusive element – the narrator. Also take advantage of the useful facility on Spotlight to upload voice clips and include narration on the audio content. It's impossible to judge the ability of a potential reader or actor from an advertising voice-over. And if you are good at dialects, include a couple on your Spotlight page, as well as listing them. Listen to the output and get a sense of the tone of the network or outlet as well as the book. If sent the original book as well as the abridgement, try to read at least some of it. They tend to be sent because the background information will inform your performance. And prepare your scripts before either an audition or a job. There is nothing more disheartening than actors who clearly hope to sight read!

Great actors are not necessarily good readers – as we've all discovered. An empathy for storytelling and for literature, and an intelligence and interest in language does matter. It is quite an exposed place if you are used to working with a larger cast and there is nowhere to hide. It is tiring spending a day alone in a studio, often going over the same material for small nuances. But please don't let that put you off. I hope it's also one of the great unsung pleasures of a broad acting career.

Please visit www.bbc.co.uk/soundstart for further information and advice.

Writersroom

Director   Kate Rowland

BROADCAST

Radio Drama - BBC Scotland

Editor, Radio Drama   Bruce Young
Management Assistant   Sue Meek

Producers

Gaynor Macfarlane   Kirsty Williams
David Ian Neville

Radio Drama - BBC Wales

Ka te McAll

Radio Drama - BBC Northern Ireland

All enquiries to Anne Simpson

• RADIO COMEDY/RADIO PRODUCTION

Head, Radio Comedy   Jane Berthoud
Executive Producers   Steven Canny
                                       Alison Vernon-Smith

Producers

Colin Anderson   Simon Mayhew-Archer
Sam Bryant   Julia McKenzie
Leanne Coop   Sam Michell
Tilusha Ghelani   Ed Morrish
Claire Jones   Katie Tyrrell
Victoria Lloyd   Ben Walker

Production Executive   Sophie Butler

Production Manager   Mel Almond

• NEWS AND CURRENT AFFAIRS

BBC News (Television & Radio)
Television Centre
Wood Lane, London W12 7RJ
T 020 8743 8000 (Main Switchboard)

Director, News   Helen Boaden
Deputy Director, BBC News & Head
  of Multimedia Programmes   Stephen Mitchell
Head of BBC Newsroom   Mary Hockaday
Head of Newsgathering   Fran Unsworth
Controller of BBC News Channel
  (incl. News at One) & Deputy Head of BBC Newsroom
                                       Kevin Bakhurst
Head of Editorial Development   Sam Taylor
Controller of Operations & Technology   Peter Coles
Head of Political Programmes,
  Analysis & Research   Sue Inglish
Executive Editor & Commissioning
  Editor for Current Affairs   Clive Edwards

Executive Editor, Radio
  Current Affairs   Nicola Meyrick
Head of Editorial Development,
  Multimedia   Peter Clifton
Director of MC & A, BBC Journalism   Sanjay Nazerali
Editor, Six & Ten o'clock News   James Stephenson
Editor, Newsnight   Peter Rippon
Editor, Breakfast   Alison Ford
Editor, Panorama   Tom Giles

Radio Programmes

Editor, Today   Ceri Thomas
Editor, PM/Broadcasting House
  The World This Weekend/The World at One   Joanna Carr
Editor, Newsbeat, Radio 1   Rod McKenzie

• RADIO SPORT

Head of Sport   Gordon Turnbull
Commissioning Editor   Jonathan Wall

• CONTROLLERS

Director of Audio & Music   Tim Davie

RADIO 1

Controller   Andy Parfitt

RADIO 2

Controller   Bob Shennan

RADIO 3

Controller   Roger Wright

RADIO 4 & RADIO 7

Controller   Gwyneth Williams

RADIO 5 LIVE

Controller   Adrian Van Klaveren

• BBC NEW WRITING

BBC Writersroom
Grafton House
379-381 Euston Road
London NW1 3AU   **T 020 7765 2703**
e-mail: writersroom@bbc.co.uk
Website: www.bbc.co.uk/writersroom

Creative Director   Kate Rowland
Development Manager   Paul Ashton

BBC BEDFORDSHIRE, HERTFORDSHIRE & BUCKINGHAMSHIRE THREE COUNTIES RADIO
Contact: Mark Norman (Managing Editor)
1 Hastings Street, Luton LU1 5XL
F 01582 401467   T 01582 637400
E 3cr@bbc.co.uk
W www.bbc.co.uk/threecounties

BBC RADIO BRISTOL
Contact: Tim Pemberton (Managing Editor), Angela Frain (News Editor)
PO Box 194, Bristol BS99 7QT
F 0117 923 8323   T 0117 974 1111
E radio.bristol@bbc.co.uk
W www.bbc.co.uk/bristol

BBC RADIO CAMBRIDGESHIRE
Contact: Dave Harvey (Managing Editor)
Cambridge Business Park
Cowley Road
Cambridge CB4 0WZ   T 01223 259696
E cambs@bbc.co.uk
W www.bbc.co.uk/cambridgeshire

BBC TEES
Contact: Matthew Barraclough (Managing Editor)
Broadcasting House
Newport Road
Middlesbrough TS1 5DG
F 01642 211356   T 01642 225211
E tees.studios@bbc.co.uk
W www.bbc.co.uk/tees

BBC RADIO CORNWALL
Contact: Pauline Causey (Managing Editor)
Phoenix Wharf, Truro
Cornwall TR1 1UA
F 01872 240679   T 01872 275421
W www.bbc.co.uk/cornwall

BBC COVENTRY & WARWICKSHIRE
Contact: Sue Curtis (Senior Broadcast Journalist)
Priory Place, Coventry CV1 5SQ
F 024 7655 2000   T 024 7655 1000
E coventry.warwickshire@bbc.co.uk
W www.bbc.co.uk/coventry

BBC RADIO CUMBRIA
Contact: Nigel Dyson (Managing Editor)
Annetwell Street, Carlisle
Cumbria CA3 8BB
F 01228 511195   T 01228 592444
E radio.cumbria@bbc.co.uk
W www.bbc.co.uk/radiocumbria

BBC RADIO DERBY
Contact: Simon Cornes (Managing Editor)
PO Box 104.5, Derby DE1 3HL   T 01332 361111
E radio.derby@bbc.co.uk
W www.bbc.co.uk/derby

BBC RADIO DEVON
Contact: Mark Grinnell (Managing Editor)
PO Box 1034
Plymouth PL3 5BD
F 01752 234595   T 01752 260323
E radio.devon@bbc.co.uk
W www.bbc.co.uk/devon

BBC ESSEX
Contact: Gerald Main (Managing Editor)
PO Box 765, Chelmsford
Essex CM2 9AB
F 01245 492983   T 01245 616000
E essex@bbc.co.uk
W www.bbc.co.uk/essex

BBC RADIO GLOUCESTERSHIRE
Contact: Mark Hurrell (Managing Editor)
London Road, Gloucester GL1 1SW   T 01452 308585
E radio.gloucestershire@bbc.co.uk
W www.bbc.co.uk/gloucestershire

BBC GUERNSEY
Contact: Robert Wallace (Managing Editor), Kay Langlois (Assistant Editor), David Earl (Senior Broadcast Journalist)
Broadcasting House
Bulwer Avenue
St Sampsons, Guernsey GY2 4LA
F 01481 200361   T 01481 200600
E bbcguernsey@bbc.co.uk
W www.bbc.co.uk/guernsey

BBC HEREFORD & WORCESTER
Contact: James Coghill (Managing Editor)
Hylton Road, Worcester WR2 5WW   T 01905 748485
W www.bbc.co.uk/herefordandworcester

BBC RADIO HUMBERSIDE
Contact: Simon Pattern (Editor)
Queens Court, Queens Gardens
Hull HU1 3RH
F 01482 226409   T 01482 323232
E radio.humberside@bbc.co.uk
W www.bbc.co.uk/humberside

BBC RADIO JERSEY
Contact: Denzil Dudley (Editor)
Matthew Price (Assistant Editor)
18 & 21 Parade Road, St Helier
Jersey JE2 3PL
F 01534 732569   T 01534 870000
E radiojersey@bbc.co.uk
W www.bbc.co.uk/jersey

BBC RADIO KENT
Contact: Paul Leaper (Managing Editor)
The Great Hall
Mount Pleasant Road
Tunbridge Wells, Kent TN1 1QQ   T 01892 670000
E radio.kent@bbc.co.uk
W www.bbc.co.uk/kent

BBC RADIO LANCASHIRE
Contact: John Clayton (Editor)
20-26 Darwen Street, Blackburn
Lancashire BB2 2EA   T 01254 262411
E radio.lancashire@bbc.co.uk
W www.bbc.co.uk/lancashire

BBC RADIO LEEDS
Contact: Rozina Breen (Managing Editor)
BBC Broadcasting Centre, 2 St Peter's Square
Leeds LS9 8AH
F 0113 224 7316   T 0113 244 2131
E radioleeds@bbc.co.uk
W www.bbc.co.uk/leeds

BBC RADIO LEICESTER
Contact: Kate Squire (Managing Editor)
9 St Nicholas Place, Leicester LE1 5LB
F 0116 251 1463   T 0116 251 6688
E leicester@bbc.co.uk
W www.bbc.co.uk/leicester

BBC LINCOLNSHIRE
Contact: Charlie Partridge (Managing Editor)
Newport, Lincoln LN1 3XY
F 01522 511058   T 01522 511411
W www.bbc.co.uk/lincolnshire

BBC LONDON 94.9 FM
Contact: David Robey (Managing Editor)
Egton House, Portland Place
London W1A 1AA   T 020 7224 2424
W www.bbc.co.uk/london

BBC RADIO MANCHESTER
Contact: John Ryan (Managing Editor)
PO Box 951, Oxford Road
Manchester M60 1SD   T 0161 200 2000
W www.bbc.co.uk/manchester

BBC RADIO MERSEYSIDE
Contact: Mick Ord (Managing Editor)
PO Box 95.8, Liverpool L69 1ZJ   T 0151 708 5500
E radio.merseyside@bbc.co.uk
W www.bbc.co.uk/liverpool

BBC RADIO NEWCASTLE
Contact: Andrew Robson (Editor)
Broadcasting Centre, Barrack Road
Newcastle upon Tyne NE99 1RN
F 0191 232 5082   T 0191 232 4141
E bbcnewcastle.news@bbc.co.uk
W www.bbc.co.uk/tyne

BBC RADIO NORFOLK
Contact: David Clayton (Managing Editor)
The Forum, Millennium Plain
Norwich NR2 1BH
F 01603 284488   T 01603 617411
E norfolk@bbc.co.uk
W www.bbc.co.uk/norfolk

BBC NORTHAMPTON
Contact: Laura Moss (Manager)
Broadcasting House, Abington Street
Northampton NN1 2BH
F 01604 230709   T 01604 239100
E northampton@bbc.co.uk
W www.bbc.co.uk/northamptonshire

BBC RADIO NOTTINGHAM
Contact: Mike Bettison (Editor)
London Road, Nottingham NG2 4UU
F 0115 902 1984   T 0115 955 0500
E radio.notthingham@bbc.co.uk
W www.bbc.co.uk/nottingham

BBC RADIO SHEFFIELD
Contact: Gary Keown (Managing Editor)
54 Shoreham Street, Sheffield S1 4RS
F 0114 267 5454   T 0114 273 1177
E radio.sheffield@bbc.co.uk
W www.bbc.co.uk/sheffield

BBC RADIO SHROPSHIRE
Contact: Tim Beech (Editor), Tracey Higgins
(Senior Broadcast Journalist News)
2-4 Boscobel Drive
Shrewsbury
Shropshire SY1 3TT
F 01743 271702   T 01743 248484
E radio.shropshire@bbc.co.uk
W www.bbc.co.uk/shropshire

BBC RADIO SOLENT
Contact: Chris Carnegy (Managing Editor)
Broadcasting House
10 Havelock Road
Southampton SO14 7PW
F 023 8033 9648   T 023 8063 1311
E radio.solent@bbc.co.uk
W www.bbc.co.uk/hampshire

BBC RADIO STOKE
Contact: Sue Owen (Managing Editor)
Cheapside, Hanley
Stoke-on-Trent
Staffordshire ST1 1JJ
F 01782 289115   T 01782 208080
E radio.stoke@bbc.co.uk
W www.bbc.co.uk/stoke

BBC RADIO SUFFOLK
Contact: Peter Cook (Editor)
Broadcasting House
St Matthews Street
Ipswich IP1 3EP
F 01473 210887   T 01473 250000
E radiosuffolk@bbc.co.uk
W www.bbc.co.uk/suffolk

BBC SUSSEX & SURREY
Contact: Nicci Holliday (Managing Editor)
Sara David (Assistant Editor)
Broadcasting Centre, Guildford
Surrey GU2 7AP
F 01483 304952   T 01273 320400
E sussex@bbc.co.uk
W www.bbc.co.uk/sussex

BBC WILTSHIRE
Contact: Tony Worgan (Manager)
Broadcasting House
56-58 Prospect Place
Swindon SN1 3RW   T 01793 513626
E wiltshire@bbc.co.uk
W www.bbc.co.uk/wiltshire

BBC WEST MIDLANDS
Contact: Keith Beech (Editor Local Services)
The Mailbox
Birmingham B1 1RF   T 0121 567 6767
E bbcwm@bbc.co.uk
W www.bbc.co.uk/westmidlands

BBC RADIO YORK
Contact: Sarah Drummond (Managing Editor)
20 Bootham Row, York YO30 7BR   T 01904 641351
E radio.york@bbc.co.uk
W www.bbc.co.uk/york

ABERDEEN
Northsound Radio
Abbotswell Road, West Tullos
Aberdeen AB12 3AJ
F 01224 400003   T 01224 337000
W www.northsound.com

AYR
West Sound Radio
Incorporating West Sound 1035 AM & West 96.7 FM
Radio House, 54A Holmston Road
Ayr KA7 3BE   T 01292 283662
E carolyn.mcallister@westsound.co.uk
W www.westsound.co.uk

BELFAST
City Beat 96.7 FM & 102.5 FM
2nd Floor, Arena Building
85 Ormeau Road, Belfast BT7 1SH
F 028 9089 0100   T 028 9023 4967
E newsdesk@citybeat.co.uk
W www.citybeat.co.uk

BELFAST
Cool FM
Kiltonga Industrial Estate, Newtownards
Co Down BT23 4ES   T 028 9181 7181
E info@coolfm.co.uk
W www.coolfm.co.uk

BELFAST
Downtown Radio
Kiltonga Industrial Estate, Newtownards
Co Down BT23 4ES   T 028 9181 5555
E info@downtown.co.uk
W www.downtown.co.uk

BERKSHIRE & NORTH HAMPSHIRE
Heart
PO Box 2020, Reading
Berkshire RG31 7FG   T 0118 945 4400
E news1029@heart.co.uk
W www.heart.co.uk

BIRMINGHAM
BRMB 96.4 & Gold
Nine Brindley Place, 4 Oozells Square
Birmingham B1 2DJ   T 0121 566 5200
W www.brmb.co.uk

BORDERS THE
Radio Borders Ltd
Tweedside Park, Galashiels TD1 3TD
F 0845 3457080   T 01896 759444
E info@radioborders.com
W www.radioborders.com

BRADFORD
Sunrise Radio
55 Leeds Road, Bradford BD1 5AF
F 01274 728534   T 01274 735043
W www.sunriseradio.fm

BRADFORD, HUDDERSFIELD, HALIFAX, KEIGHLEY & DEWSBURY
Pulse 2
Forster Square, Bradford BD1 5NE T 01274 203040
E general@pulse.co.uk
W www.pulse2.net

BRIGHTON, EASTBOURNE & HASTINGS
Heart
Radio House, Franklin Road, PO Box 2000, Brighton BN41 2SS
F 01273 316909   T 01273 430111
W www.southernfm.co.uk

BRISTOL
Heart
1 Passage Street, PO Box 2000
Bristol BS99 7SN
F 0117 984 3202   T 0117 984 3200
W www.heartbristol.co.uk

CAMBRIDGE & NEWMARKET
Heart
Enterprise House, The Vision Park
Chivers Way, Histon
Cambridge CB24 9ZR   T 01223 235255
E cambridge.news@heart.co.uk
W www.heart.co.uk

CARDIFF & NEWPORT
Red Dragon FM & Gold
Atlantic Wharf, Cardiff Bay
Cardiff CF10 4DJ   T 029 2066 2066
W www.reddragonfm.co.uk

CHESTER, NORTH WALES & WIRRAL
Heart
Contact: Clive Douthwaite (Programme Controller)
The Studios, Mold Road
Wrexham LL11 4AF   T 01978 752202
E news.wrexham@heart.co.uk
W www.heart.co.uk

COVENTRY
Mercia
Hertford Place, Coventry CV1 3TT
F 024 7686 8209   T 024 7686 8200
W www.mercia.co.uk

DERBY
Ram FM
35-36 Irongate, Derby DE1 3GA   T 01332 324000
W www.ramfm.co.uk

DUMFRIES
South West Sound FM
Unit 40, The Loreburn Centre
High Street, Dumfries DG1 2BD
F 01387 265629   T 01387 250999
W www.southwestsound.co.uk

DUNDEE & PERTH
Radio Tay AM
PO Box 123, 6 North Isla Street
Dundee DD3 7JQ   T 01382 200800
E tayam@radiotay.co.uk
W www.radiotay.co.uk

DUNDEE & PERTH
Radio Tay FM
PO Box 123, 6 North Isla Street
Dundee DD3 7JQ   T 01382 200800
E tayfm@radiotay.co.uk
W www.radiotay.co.uk

EDINBURGH
Radio Forth Ltd
Forth House, Forth Street
Edinburgh EH1 3LE   T 0131 556 9255
E info@radioforth.com
W www.radioforth.com

EXETER & TORBAY
Heart
Hawthorn House
Exeter Business Park
Exeter EX1 3QS
F 01392 354249   T 01392 444444
W www.heart.co.uk

FALKIRK
Central FM
201-203 High Street, Falkirk FK1 1DU
F 01324 611168　　　　　　　　T 01324 611164
W www.centralfm.co.uk

GLASGOW
Radio Clyde 1
3 South Avenue, Clydebank Business Park
Glasgow G81 2RX
F 0141 565 2265　　　　　　　　T 0141 565 2200
W www.clyde1.com

GLASGOW
Radio Clyde 2
3 South Avenue, Clydebank Business Park
Glasgow G81 2RX
F 0141 565 2265　　　　　　　　T 0141 565 2200
W www.clyde2.com

GLOUCESTER & CHELTENHAM
Heart 102.4
Bridge Studios
Eastgate Centre, Gloucester GL1 1SS
F 01452 572409　　　　　　　　T 01452 572400
W www.heart.co.uk

GREAT YARMOUTH & NORWICH
Heart
St Georges Plain, 47-49 Colegate, Norwich NR3 1DB
F 01603 671189　　　　　　　　T 01603 630621
W www.heart.co.uk

GUILDFORD
Eagle Radio 96.4
Eagle Radio Ltd, Dolphin House, 3 North Street
Guildford, Surrey GU1 4AA
F 01483 454443　　　　　　　　T 01483 300964
E onair@964eagle.co.uk
W www.964eagle.co.uk

HEREFORD & WORCESTER
Wyvern FM
1st Floor, Kirkham House
John Comyn Drive, Worcester WR3 7NS　　　T 01905 545500
W www.wyvernfm.co.uk

INVERNESS
Moray Firth Radio
PO Box 271, Scorguie Place, Inverness IV3 8UJ
F 01463 227714　　　　　　　　T 01463 224433
E mfr@mfr.co.uk
W www.mfr.co.uk

IPSWICH
Heart 97.1 & 96.4 FM
Radio House, Alpha Business Park
Whitehouse Road, Ipswich IP1 5LT
F 01473 467549　　　　　　　　T 01473 461000
W www.heart.co.uk

ISLE OF WIGHT
Isle of Wight Radio
Dodnor Park, Newport, Isle of Wight PO30 5XE
F 01983 822109　　　　　　　　T 01983 822557
E admin@iwradio.co.uk
W www.iwradio.co.uk

KENT
Heart 103.1/102.8 & Gold Kent
Radio House, John Wilson Business Park
Whitstable, Kent CT5 3QX　　　　　T 01227 772004
E neil.webster@thisisglobal.com
W www.heart.co.uk

LEEDS
Radio Aire 96.3 & Magic 828
51 Burley Road, Leeds LS3 1LR
F 0113 283 5501　　　　　　　　T 0113 283 5500
W www.radioaire.com

LEICESTER
Leicester Sound
6 Dominus Way
Meridian Way Business Park, Leicester LE19 1RP
F 0116 256 1309　　　　　　　　T 0116 256 1300
W www.leicestersound.co.uk

LIVERPOOL
Radio City
St Johns Beacon, 1 Houghton Street
Liverpool L1 1RL　　　　　　　　T 0151 472 6800
W www.radiocity.co.uk

LONDON
Absolute Radio
1 Golden Square, London W1F 9DJ
F 020 7434 1197　　　　　　　　T 020 7434 1215
W www.absoluteradio.co.uk

LONDON
Choice FM
Global
30 Leicester Square, London WC2H 7LA
F 020 7766 6100　　　　　　　　T 020 7766 6810
W www.choicefm.com

LONDON
Classic FM
Global
30 Leicester Square, London WC2H 7LA
F 020 7054 8019　　　　　　　　T 020 7054 8000
W www.classicfm.com

LONDON
Gold
Global
30 Leicester Square, London WC2H 7LA
F 020 7054 8019　　　　　　　　T 020 7054 8000
W www.mygoldmusic.co.uk

LONDON
Independent Radio News
Mappin House, 4 Winsley Street
London W1W 8HF　　　　　　　　T 020 7182 8591
E radio@bskyb.com
W www.irn.co.uk

LONDON
London Greek Radio
437 High Road, Finchley, London N12 0AP　T 020 8349 6950
W www.lgr.co.uk

LONDON
Magic 105.4 FM
Mappin House, 4 Winsley Street
London W1W 8HF　　　　　　　　T 020 7182 8233
W www.magic.co.uk

LONDON
Smooth Radio 102.2
26-27 Castlereagh Street, London W1H 5DL　T 020 7706 4100
E info@smoothradio.com
W www.smoothradio.com

LUTON & BEDFORD
Heart
Broadcast Centre, Chiltern Road, Dunstable LU6 1HQ
F 01582 676209　　　　　　　　T 01582 676200
W www.heart.co.uk

MANCHESTER
Key 103 FM & Magic 1152
Piccadilly Radio Ltd, Castle Quay
Castle Field, Manchester M15 4PR
F 0161 288 5151   T 0161 288 5000
W www.key103.co.uk

MILTON KEYNES
Heart
14 Vincent Avenue
Milton Keynes Broadcast Centre
Crownhill, Milton Keynes MK8 0AB   T 01908 269111
W www.heart.co.uk

NORTHAMPTON
Heart & Gold
19-21 St Edmunds Road
Northampton NN1 5DY   T 01604 795600
E northantsnews@heart.co.uk
W www.heart.co.uk

NORTHAMPTONSHIRE
Connect FM 97.2 & 107.4 FM
2nd Floor, 5 Church Street
Peterborough PE1 1XB
F 01733 898107   T 0844 8001769
W www.connectfm.com

NOTTINGHAM
Trent 96 FM
Chapel Quarter, Maid Marion Way
Nottingham NG1 6JR
F 0115 873 1569   T 0115 873 1500
W www.trentfm.co.uk

OXFORD & BANBURY
Heart
Radio House, Pony Road, Oxford OX4 2XR   T 01865 871000
W www.heart.co.uk

PETERBOROUGH
Heart
PO Box 225, Queensgate Centre
Peterborough PE1 1XJ   T 01733 460460
W www.heart.co.uk

PLYMOUTH
Heart & Gold
Earl's Acre, Alma Road, Plymouth PL3 4HX   T 01752 275600
W www.heart.co.uk

PORTSMOUTH & SOUTHAMPTON
Galaxy South Coast
Global
Radio House, Whittle Avenue
Segensworth West
Fareham, Hampshire PO15 5SX   T 01489 589911
W www.galaxysouthcoast.co.uk

PORTSMOUTH & SOUTHAMPTON
Gold
Global
Radio House, Whittle Avenue
Segensworth West, Fareham
Hampshire PO15 5SX   T 01489 589911
W www.thisisglobal.com

PORTSMOUTH & SOUTHAMPTON
Heart
Global
Radio House, Whittle Avenue
Segensworth West, Fareham
Hampshire PO15 5SX   T 01489 589911
W www.heart.co.uk

SOMERSET
Heart
Haygrove House
Shoreditch Road
Taunton TA3 7BT   T 01823 338448
W www.heart.co.uk

SOUTH MANCHESTER
Imagine 104.9 FM
Waterloo Place
Watson Square
Stockport, Cheshire SK1 3AZ   T 0161 609 1400
E sales@imaginefm.net
W www.imaginefm.net

STOKE-ON-TRENT & STAFFORD
Signal Radio
Stoke Road, Stoke-on-Trent
Staffordshire ST4 2SR   T 01782 441300
E info@signalradio.com
W www.signalone.co.uk

SWANSEA
The Wave 96.4 FM
Victoria Road, Gowerton
Swansea SA4 3AB   T 01792 511964
W www.thewave.co.uk

TEESSIDE
Magic 1170
Yale Crescent, Teesdale
Thornaby, Stockton on Tees TS17 6AA   T 01642 888222
W www.magic1170.co.uk

TEESSIDE
TFM Radio
Yale Crescent, Teesdale
Thornaby
Stockton on Tees TS17 6AA   T 01642 888222
W www.tfmradio.com

TYNE & WEAR, NORTHUMBERLAND & DURHAM
Magic 1152
55 Degrees North
Pilgrim Street
Newcastle upon Tyne NE1 6BF   T 0191 230 6100
W www.magic1152.co.uk

TYNE & WEAR, NORTHUMBERLAND & DURHAM
Metro Radio
55 Degrees North
Pilgrim Street
Newcastle upon Tyne NE1 6BF   T 0191 230 6100
W www.metroradio.co.uk

**WOLVERHAMPTON & BLACK COUNTRY/SHREWSBURY
& TELFORD**
West Midlands Beacon Radio
267 Tettenhall Road
Wolverhampton WV6 0DE   T 01902 461200
W www.beaconradio.co.uk

YORKSHIRE
Hallam FM & Magic AM
Radio House, 900 Herries Road
Hillsborough
Sheffield S6 1RH   T 0114 209 1000
W www.hallamfm.co.uk

YORKSHIRE & LINCOLNSHIRE
Viking 96.9 FM & Magic 1161 AM
Commercial Road
Hull HU1 2SG   T 01482 325141
W www.vikingfm.co.uk

infopage

How should I prepare for an audition?

When you are called to a casting you should make sure you are fully prepared with accurate information about the audition time, venue and format. Research the casting director too: look on his or her website and pay attention to media news. What productions have they worked on previously? What do they seem to look for and expect from the actors they cast?

For most auditions you will be given a script to learn, but you could be provided with a brief in advance and asked to find something suitable yourself. It would be advisable to have about five or six pieces ready to choose from that demonstrate your range before you are even called to a casting. You should select two relevant but contrasting pieces of about two to three minutes each for your audition, with the others as backups. If you can, read the whole play in addition to your speech.

It is generally best not to use 'popular' or very well-known pieces and instead to use original modern speeches, as this prevents the likelihood of the casting director comparing you, perhaps unfavourably, with anyone else. Having said this, however, you should still rehearse at least one Shakespeare piece. To find suitable speeches you should read widely for inspiration, or you could search online. If you are still struggling, think about who your favourite playwrights are and find out if they have written anything that is not too well-known.

What should I expect when I arrive at the audition?

Arrive early for your audition, but be prepared to wait! Time slots are allocated but auditions can overrun for various reasons. Be presentable and think about how your character might choose to dress, but overall you will feel more comfortable and confident if you don't differ too much from what you would normally wear. Don't come in costume unless specifically asked.

When you enter the audition room, you may have just the casting director in the room, or you could be confronted with a panel including the director and/or producer, and an editor and cameraman if you are being filmed. Don't let this disconcert you. Nerves are to be expected, but try to be positive and enjoy yourself. Remember, the casting director doesn't want to spend several days auditioning – they want you to get the job!

Take a few moments to work out where you should stand and where everything is. Don't ask too many questions as this can be irritating but you could ask whether to address your monologue to the casting director/camera, or whether to speak into the 'middle distance'. Make sure that your face, and in particular your eyes, can be seen as much as possible.

Once you have performed your monologue, pause and wait for the casting director to speak to you. Don't ask if they want to see a second speech. If they want another one, and if there's time, they will ask you. You may be asked your opinion on the speech so be prepared with possible answers. Never criticise previous productions you have worked on. At the end of the casting, remember to take your script away unless you are asked to leave it, otherwise it can look as if you're not interested.

Auditions are never a waste of time, even if you don't get the part. You may have performed well but you might not have been quite right for that particular role. Every audition is great practice and experience, and the casting director may very well keep you in mind for future productions.

Should I attend a casting in a house or flat?

Professional auditions are rarely held anywhere other than an official casting studio or venue. Be very wary if you are asked to go elsewhere. Trust your instincts. If something doesn't seem right to you, it probably isn't. Always take someone with you if you are in any doubt.

101 IDENTITY REHEARSAL & PERFORMANCE STUDIOS
73-75 Arcola Stree
London E8 2EB   T 020 3119 0058
E info@theidentitystudios.com
W www.theidentitystudios.com

3 MILLS STUDIOS
Three Mill Lane, London E3 3DU
F 0871 5944028   T 020 7363 3336
E info@3mills.com
W www.3mills.com

ACTORS CENTRE (LONDON) THE
Auditioning. Casting. Rehearsals. Room Hire
1A Tower Street
London WC2H 9NP   T 020 7632 8012
E operations@actorscentre.co.uk
W www.actorscentre.co.uk

ACTORS STUDIO REHEARSAL & CASTING SPACE
Pinewood Studios
Pinewood Road
Iver Heath, Bucks SLO 0NH   T 01753 650951
E info@actorsstudio.co.uk
W www.actorsstudio.co.uk

Unit 10, 21 Wren Street
London WC1 0HX

ACTOR'S TEMPLE THE
13-14 Warren Street, London W1T 5LG
M 07771 734670   T 020 3004 4537
E info@actorstemple.com
W www.actorstemple.com

AIRCRAFT CIRCUS
Unit 7A, Mellish House
Harrington Way, London SE18 5NR   M 07951 896945
E moira@aircraftcircus.com
W www.aircraftcircus.com

ALBANY THE
Contact: Lilly Hannell
Douglas Way, Deptford
London SE8 4AG
F 020 8469 2253   T 020 8692 0231
E hires@thealbany.org.uk
W www.thealbany.org.uk

ALFORD HOUSE
Aveline Street, London SE11 5DQ   T 020 7735 1519
E tim@alfordhouse.org.uk
W www.alfordhouse.org.uk

ALL TALENT, THE SONIA SCOTT AGENCY
Unit 325, 95 Morrison Street
Glasgow G5 8BE
M 07971 337074   T 0141 418 1074
E enquiries@alltalentuk.co.uk
W www.alltalentuk.co.uk

ALRA (Academy of Live and Recorded Arts)
The Royal Victoria Patriotic Building
John Archer Way
London SW18 3SX
F 020 8875 0789   T 020 8870 6475
E info@alra.co.uk
W www.alra.co.uk

AMERICAN CHURCH IN LONDON THE
Whitefield Memorial Church
79A Tottenham Court Road, London W1T 4TD
F 020 7580 5013   T 020 7580 2791
E latchcourt@amchurch.co.uk
W www.latchcourt.com

ARCH 468 THEATRE STUDIO
Arch 468, 209A Coldharbour Lane
London SW9 8RU   M 07973 302908
E rebecca@arch468.com
W www.arch468.com

ARTEMIS STUDIOS LTD
30 Charles Square, Bracknell, Berkshire RG12 1AY
E info@artemis-studios.co.uk   T 01344 429403
W www.agency.artemis-studios.co.uk

ARTS THEATRE THE
6-7 Great Newport Street
London WC2E 7NX   T 020 7395 1409
E info@theartstheatrelondon.co.uk

ARTSADMIN
Toynbee Studios, 28 Commercial Street
London E1 6AB
F 020 7247 5103   T 020 7247 5102
E admin@artsadmin.co.uk
W www.artsadmin.co.uk

AVIV DANCE STUDIOS
Watford Boys Grammar School
Rickmansworth Road
Watford WD18 7JF   T/F 01923 250000
E info@avivdance.com
W www.avivdance.com

BAC (Battersea Arts Centre)
Lavender Hill, London SW11 5TN
F 020 7978 5207   T 020 7326 8211
E venues@bac.org.uk
W www.bac.org.uk/hires

BELSIZE MUSIC ROOMS
Auditioning. Casting. Filming. Piano Hire
67 Belsize Lane, Hampstead
London NW3 5AX   T 020 7916 0111
E info@belsize-music-rooms.co.uk
W www.belsize-music-rooms.co.uk

BEYOND
21 StoneHouse, 199 Eade Road, London N4 1DN
M 07921 950704   T 020 8809 6946
E mirian@beyond-centre.com
W www.beyond-centre.com

BIG CITY STUDIOS
Montgomery House, 159-161 Balls Pond Road
Islington, London N1 4BG
F 020 7241 3006   T 020 7241 6655
W www.pineappleagency.com

BLACK BOX CREATIVE COMMUNITIES CIC LTD
The Black Box, 21 Hutchinson Walk
Liverpool L6 1JW
F 0151 260 3001   T 0151 260 3000
E admin@blackboxmerseyside.co.uk
W www.blackboxmerseyside.co.uk

BLOOMSBURY THEATRE THE
15 Gordon Street, London WC1H 0AH   T 020 7679 2777
E admin@thebloomsbury.com
W www.thebloomsbury.com

BRIXTON COMMUNITY BASE
Formerly Brixton St Vincent's Community Centre
Talma Road, London SW2 1AS T 020 7326 4417
E carofunnell@bsvcc.org
W www.bsvcc.org

CARAVANSERAI PRODUCTIONS & ACTING STUDIO
Unit 30, Grand Union Centre
West Row, London W10 5AS T 020 8968 3769
E info@caravanseraiproductions.com
W www.caravanseraiproductions.com

CARDINBROOK LTD
32 Barkston Gardens, London SW5 0EN T 020 7373 1665
E info@ycbc.co.uk
W www.ycbc.co.uk/roomhire.htm

CAST IN SPACE
Lupus House, 2nd Floor, 11-13 Macklin Street
Covent Garden, London WC2B 5NH T 020 7404 9637
E castinspace@btconnect.com
W www.castinspace.tv

CASTING AT SWEET
Sweet Venues Ltd, 42 Theobalds Road, London WC1X 8NW
F 07092 863782 T 020 7404 6411
E info@sweet-uk.net

CECIL SHARP HOUSE
2 Regent's Park Road, London NW1 7AY
F 020 7284 0534 T 020 7485 2206
E hire@efdss.org
W www.efdss.org

BRIXTON COMMUNITY BASE

* FORMERLY BRIXTON ST VINCENT'S COMMUNITY CENTRE *

◄ **REHEARSAL STUDIO** 16 x 7.5 metres ►

SECOND SPACE AVAILABLE

Piano / keyboards / showers / facility for aerial work / WiFi

Full Disabled Access

TEL – 020 7326 4417

Brixton Tube – Victoria line   **www.bsvcc.org**   Talma Road SW2 1AS

CENTRAL LONDON GOLF CENTRE
Burntwood Lane, London SW17 0AT
F 020 8874 7447   T 020 8871 2468
E golf@clgc.co.uk
W www.clgc.co.uk

CENTRAL STUDIOS
470 Bromley Road, Bromley, Kent BR1 4PN
F 020 8697 8100   T 020 8698 8880
E bonnie@dandbmanagement.com
W www.dandbperformingarts.co.uk

CENTRE THE
20 Cavendish Square, London W9 2JA
F 020 7266 1225   T 020 7286 1680
E amadeus@amadeuscentre.co.uk
W www.centreca.co.uk

CHATS PALACE
42-44 Brooksby's Walk, Hackney
London E9 6DF   T 020 8533 0227
E info@chatspalace.com
W www.chatspalace.com

CHELSEA THEATRE
Contact: Francis Alexander
World's End Place, King's Road
London SW10 0DR
F 020 7352 2024   T 020 7349 7811
E admin@chelseatheatre.org.uk
W www.chelseatheatre.org.uk

CIRCUS MANIACS SCHOOL OF CIRCUS ARTS
Casting Facilities. Circus Skills Rehearsal
Unit 62, Basepoint Business Centre
Oakfield Close, Tewkesbury Business Park
Tewkesbury, Gloucestershire GL20 8SD
M 07977 247287   T 01684 854412
E info@circusmaniacs.com
W www.circusmaniacs.com

CLAPHAM COMMUNITY PROJECT
St Anne's Hall, 31-33 Bromells Road
London SW4 0BN   T/F 020 7720 8731
E admin@claphamcommunityproject.org.uk
W www.rehearseatccp.co.uk

CLEAN BREAK
2 Patshull Road, London NW5 2LB
F 020 7482 8611   T 020 7482 8600
E general@cleanbreak.org.uk
W www.cleanbreak.org.uk

CLUB FOR ACTS & ACTORS
Incorporating Concert Artistes Association
20 Bedford Street, London WC2E 9HP   T 020 7836 3172
E office@thecaa.org
W www.thecaa.org

COLOMBO CENTRE THE
Audition & Rehearsal Space
34-68 Colombo Street, London SE1 8DP   T 020 7261 1658
E colombodm@jubileehalltrust.org
W www.colombo-centre.org

COPTIC STREET STUDIO LTD
9 Coptic Street, London WC1A 1NH   T 020 7636 2030
E studio@copticstreet.com

COVENT GARDEN DRAGON HALL TRUST
17 Stukeley Street, London WC2B 5LT   T 020 7404 7274
E director@dragonhall.org.uk
W www.dragonhall.org.uk

CUSTARD FACTORY THE
Gibb Street, Digbeth, Birmingham B9 4AA
F 0121 604 8888   T 0121 224 7777
E info@custardfactory.co.uk
W www.custardfactory.co.uk

DANCE ATTIC STUDIOS
368 North End Road, London SW6   T 020 7610 2055
E danceattic@hotmail.com

DANCE COMPANY STUDIOS
76 High Street, Beckenham BR3 1ED   T 020 8402 2424
E hire@dancecompanystudios.co.uk
W www.dancecompanystudios.co.uk

DANCEWORKS
16 Balderton Street, London W1K 6TN
F 020 7629 2909   T 020 7318 4100
E info@danceworks.net
W www.danceworks.net

DAVIES Siobhan STUDIOS
85 St George's Road, London SE1 6ER
F 020 7091 9669   T 020 7091 9650
E info@siobhandavies.com
W www.siobhandavies.com

DRILL HALL THE
16 Chenies Street, London WC1E 7EX
F 020 7307 5062   T 020 7307 5060
E box.office@drillhall.co.uk
W www.drillhall.co.uk

EALING STUDIOS
Ealing Green, London W5 5EP
F 020 8758 8658   T 020 8567 6655
E bookings@ealingstudios.com
W www.ealingstudios.com

ELMS LESTERS PAINTING ROOMS
1-3-5 Flitcroft Street, London WC2H 8DH
F 020 7379 0789   T 020 7836 6747
E info@elmslesters.co.uk
W www.elmslesters.co.uk

ENGLISH FOLK DANCE & SONG SOCIETY
Cecil Sharp House
2 Regent's Park Road
London NW1 7AY
F 020 7284 0534   T 020 7485 2206
E hire@efdss.org
W www.efdss.org

ENGLISH NATIONAL OPERA
Lilian Baylis House, 165 Broadhurst Gardens
London NW6 3AX
F 020 7625 3398   T 020 7624 7711
E receptionlbh@eno.org
W www.eno.org

ENGLISH TOURING THEATRE
25 Short Street, Waterloo
London SE1 8LJ
F 020 7633 0188   T 020 7450 1990
E admin@ett.org.uk
W www.ett.org.uk

ETCETERA THEATRE
(Above the Oxford Arms)
265 Camden High Street
London NW1 7BU
F 020 7482 0378   T 020 7482 4857
E etc@etceteratheatre.com
W www.etceteratheatre.com

EUROKIDS & EKA CASTING STUDIOS
The Warehouse Studios
Glaziers Lane
Culcheth, Warrington, Cheshire WA3 4AQ
F 01925 767563   T 01925 761088
E castings@eka-agency.com
W www.eka-agency.com

EXCHANGE THE
Old Market Hill
Sturminster Newton DT10 1FH   T 01258 475137
E info@stur-exchange.co.uk
W www.stur-exchange.co.uk

EXPRESSIONS STUDIOS
Linton House, 39-51 Highgate Road
London NW5 1RT
F 020 7813 1582   T 020 7813 1580
E info@expressionsstudios.com
W www.expressionsstudios.com

FACTORY FITNESS & DANCE CENTRE THE
407 Hornsey Road, London N19 4DX   T 020 7272 1122
E info@factorylondon.com
W www.factorylondon.com

FSU LONDON STUDY CENTRE
99 Great Russell Street
London WC1B 3LA
F 020 7813 3270   T 020 7813 3223

GRAEAE THEATRE COMPANY
Bradbury Studios, 138 Kinsland Road
London E2 8DY   T 020 7613 6900
E info@graeae.org
W www.graeae.org

GREAT EASTERN DINING ROOM
54-56 Great Eastern Street, Shoreditch
London EC2A 3QR   T 020 7613 4545
E greateastern@rickerrestaurants.com
W www.rickerrestaurants.com

HAMPSTEAD THEATRE
Eton Avenue, Swiss Cottage
London NW3 3EU
F 020 7449 4201   T 020 7449 4200
E info@hampsteadtheatre.com
W www.hampsteadtheatre.com

HANGAR ARTS TRUST
Unit 7A, Mellish House
Harrington Way, London SE18 5NR   T 020 8317 8401
E a.frith@hangarartstrust.org
W www.hangaruk.com

HEYTHROP COLLEGE
University of London
23 Kensington Square
London W8 5HN   T 020 7795 6600
E conferences@heythrop.ac.uk
W www.heythrop.ac.uk

HOLY INNOCENTS CHURCH
Paddenswick Road, London W6 0UB
F 020 8563 8735   T 020 8748 2286
E administrator@hisj.co.uk
W www.hisj.co.uk

HOLY TRINITY W6
Holy Trinity Parish Centre
41 Brook Green
London W6 7BL   T 020 7603 3832
E brookgreen@rcdow.org.uk
W www.holytrinityw6.org

HOMES FOR ISLINGTON
Highbury House, 5 Highbury Crescent
London N5 1RN   T 020 7527 8632
E service.development@homesforislington.org.uk
W www.homesforislington.org.uk

HOPE STREET LTD
13A Hope Street, Liverpool L1 9BQ
F 0151 709 3242   T 0151 708 8007
E peter@hope-street.org
W www.hope-street.org

HOXTON HALL THEATRE & YOUTH ARTS CENTRE
130 Hoxton Street, London N1 6SH   T 020 7684 0060
E office@hoxtonhall.co.uk
W www.hoxtonhall.co.uk

HUB THE @ TOOTING & MITCHAM
Imperial Fields
Bishops Ford Road
Morden, Surrey SM4 6BF
F 020 8685 6190   T 020 8685 6193
E reception@thehubattmufc.co.uk
W www.thehubattmufc.co.uk

IMT SPACE LTD
Unit 2
210 Cambridge Heath Road
London E2 9NQ   T 020 8980 5475
E mail@imagemusictext.com
W www.imagemusictext.com

INC SPACE
9-13 Grape Street, Covent Garden
London WC2H 8ED
F 020 7557 6656   T 020 7557 6650
E studiohire@inc-space.com
W www.inc-space.com

ISLINGTON ARTS FACTORY
2 Parkhurst Road, London N7 0SF
F 020 7700 7229   T 020 7607 0561
E info@islingtonartsfactory.org
W www.islingtonartsfactory.org

JACKSONS LANE
Various Spaces incl Rehearsal Rooms & Theatre Hire
269A Archway Road
London N6 5AA
T 020 8340 5226   T 020 8340 8902
E reception@jacksonslane.org.uk
W www.jacksonslane.org.uk

JERWOOD SPACE
171 Union Street, London SE1 0LN
F 020 7654 0172   T 020 7654 0171
E space@jerwoodspace.co.uk
W www.jerwoodspace.co.uk

LIVE THEATRE
Broad Chare, Quayside
Newcastle upon Tyne NE1 3DQ   T 0191 261 2694
E info@live.org.uk
W www.live.org.uk

LONDON BUBBLE THEATRE COMPANY LTD
5 Elephant Lane, London SE16 4JD
F 020 7231 2366   T 020 7237 4434
E admin@londonbubble.org.uk
W www.londonbubble.org.uk

LONDON SCHOOL OF CAPOEIRA
Units 1 & 2 Leeds Place
Tollington Park
London N4 3RF   T 020 7281 2020
E info@londonschoolofcapoeira.co.uk
W www.londonschoolofcapoeira.co.uk

The Playground Studio
2,500sq.ft beautiful rehearsal space
London W10

Sprung Floor
Mirrored Wall
Natural Day Light

www.the-playground.co.uk
info@the-playground.co.uk
T: 020 8960 0110

LONDON STUDIO CENTRE
42-50 York Way, London N1 9AB
F 020 7837 3248   T 020 7837 7741
E info@london-studio-centre.co.uk
W www.london-studio-centre.co.uk

LONDON WELSH TRUST LTD
157-163 Gray's Inn Road, London WC1X 8UE   T 020 7837 3722
E administrator@wcentre.demon.co.uk
W www.londonwelsh.org

LYRIC HAMMERSMITH
King Street, London W6 0QL
F 020 8741 5965   T 0871 2211722
E enquiries@lyric.co.uk
W www.lyric.co.uk

MACKINTOSH Cameron REHEARSAL STUDIO
The Tricycle, 269 Kilburn High Road, London NW6 7JR
F 020 7328 0795   T 020 7372 6611
E admin@tricycle.co.uk
W www.tricycle.co.uk

MADDERMARKET THEATRE
St John's Alley, Norwich, Norfolk NR2 1DR   T 01603 626560
E mmtheatre@btconnect.com
W www.maddermarket.com

MENIER CHOCOLATE FACTORY
53 Southwark Street, London SE1 1RU
F 020 7378 1713   T 020 7378 1712
E office@menierchocolatefactory.com
W www.menierchocolatefactory.com

CENTRAL LONDON REHEARSAL ROOMS

four large rooms
with pianos

photos and dimensions:
www.drillhall.co.uk

facilities: **reception** | **production office** | **bar** | **free wi-fi access**
also for hire: two **theatres** | four **meeting rooms**
just off **Tottenham Court Road** | two minutes' walk: ⊖ **Goodge Street**

16 Chenies Street
London WC1E 7EX

www.drillhall.co.uk
020 7307 5060

the **drillhall**

MHI STUDIO
Burwarton
Near Bridgnorth
Shropshire WV16 6QJ   T 01746 787574
E meghawkins@btinternet.com
W www.meghawkins.com

MOBERLY SPORTS & EDUCATION CENTRE
Kilburn Lane, Kensal Rise
London W10 4AE
F 020 7641 5878   T 020 7641 4807

MOVING EAST STUDIO
Harlequin Sprung Floor
Quadrophonic Sound System
St Matthias Church Hall
Wordsworth Road
London N16 8DD   T 020 7503 3101
E admin@movingeast.co.uk
W www.movingeast.co.uk

MUSIC ROOM AT COLE KITCHENN
212 Strand, London WC2R 1AP   T 020 7427 5680
E info@colekitchenn.com

NATIONAL YOUTH THEATRE OF GREAT BRITAIN
443-445 Holloway Road
London N7 6LW   T 020 7281 3863
E info@nyt.org.uk
W www.nyt.org.uk

NEALS YARD MEETING ROOMS
14 Neals Yard, Covent Garden
London WC2H 9DP   T/F 020 7436 9875
E info@walkinbackrub.co.uk
W www.meetingrooms.org.uk

NETTLEFOLD THE
Theatre Hire only. No Casting Enquiries
West Norwood Library Centre
1 Norwood High Street
London SE27 9JX   T 020 7926 8070
E thenettlefold@lambeth.gov.uk

NEW DIORAMA THEATRE THE
80 Seat Blackbox Theatre
15-16 Triton Street
Regents Park
London NW1 3BF   T 020 7916 5467
W www.newdiorama.com

NEW PLAYERS THEATRE
The Arches, Off Villiers Street
London WC2N 6NL
F 0845 6382102   T 020 7930 5868
E info@newplayerstheatre.com
W www.newplayerstheatre.com

NLPAC PERFORMING ARTS
Casting & Production Office Facilities
76 St James Lane, Muswell Hill
London N10 3DF
F 020 8444 4040   T 020 8444 4544
E nlpac@aol.com
W www.nlpac.co.uk

OBSERVATORY STUDIOS THE
45-46 Poland Street, London W1F 7NA
F 020 7437 2830   T 020 7437 2823
E info@theobservatorystudios.com
W www.theobservatorystudios.com

OCTOBER GALLERY
24 Old Gloucester Street, London WC1N 3AL
F 020 7405 1851   T 020 7831 1618
E rentals@octobergallery.co.uk
W www.octobergallery.co.uk

OLD VIC THEATRE THE
The Cut, London SE1 8NB   T 020 7928 2651
E hires@oldvictheatre.com
W www.oldvictheatre.com

ONLY CONNECT UK
32 Cubitt Street
London WC1X 0LR   T 0845 3707990
E info@oclondon.org
W www.oclondon.org

OPEN DOOR COMMUNITY CENTRE
Beaumont Road
Wimbledon SW19 6TF   T/F 020 8871 8172
E dconstantinou@wandsworth.gov.uk
W www.wandsworth.gov.uk

OUT OF JOINT
7 Thane Works, Thane Villas
London N7 7NU
F 020 7609 0203   T 020 7609 0207
E ojo@outofjoint.co.uk
W www.outofjoint.co.uk

Graeae Theatre Company

Rehearsal Space with vinyl sprung floor. 10.7m x 8.5m. A light and airy space offering natural light with near blackout if required

State of the art lighting rig and mixing desk

Sound system, wireless microphones and mixing desk

Audio description system and induction loop

7m x4m, air conditioned Meeting Room with Plasma screen

Access to changing rooms, toilets, showers, kitchen and breakout area

Free WiFi access

Competitive rates

Event co-ordination

www.graeae.org

GRAEae
THEATRE COMPANY

OVAL HOUSE
52-54 Kennington Oval, London SE11 5SW   T 020 7582 0080
E info@ovalhouse.com
W www.ovalhouse.com

PAINES PLOUGH REHEARSAL & AUDITION SPACE
4th Floor, 43 Aldwych, London WC2B 4DN
F 020 7240 4534   T 020 7240 4533
E office@painesplough.com
W www.painesplough.com

PEOPLE SHOW
3 Rehearsal Rooms. Casting Suites. Set Building Workshop
Sound & Lighting Equipment for Hire
People Show Studios, Pollard Row, London E2 6NB
F 020 7739 0203   T 020 7729 1841
E people@peopleshow.co.uk   W www.peopleshow.co.uk

PHA CASTING SUITE
Tanzaro House, Ardwick Green North, Manchester M12 6FZ
F 0161 273 4567   T 0161 273 4444
E info@pha-agency.co.uk
W www.pha-agency.co.uk

PINEAPPLE DANCE STUDIOS
7 Langley Street, Covent Garden, London WC2H 9JA
F 020 7836 0803   T 020 7836 4004
E studios@pineapple.uk.com
W www.pineapple.uk.com

PLACE THE
Robin Howard Dance Theatre, 17 Duke's Road
London WC1H 9PY
F 020 7121 1142   T 020 7121 1100
E info@theplace.org.uk   W www.theplace.org.uk

PLAYGROUND STUDIO THE
Unit 8, Latimer Road
London W10 6RQ   T/F 020 8960 0110
E info@the-playground.co.uk
W www.the-playground.co.uk

POOR SCHOOL THE
242 Pentonville Road, London N1 9JY   T 020 7837 6030
E acting@thepoorschool.com
W www.thepoorschool.com

PRECINCT THEATRE THE
Units 2/3 The Precinct, Packington Square
London N1 7UP
F 020 7359 3660   T 020 7359 3594
E agency@breakalegman.com
W www.breakalegman.com

PRETZEL FILMS
11-12 Tottenham Mews, London W1T 4AG
F 020 7580 2232   T 020 7580 9595
E mark@pretzelfilms.com
W www.pretzelfilms.com

QUESTORS THEATRE EALING THE
12 Mattock Lane, London W5 5BQ
F 020 8567 2275   T 020 8567 0011
E alice@questors.org.uk
W www.questors.org.uk

RAG FACTORY THE
16-18 Heneage Street, London E1 5LJ   T 020 7650 8749
E hello@ragfactory.org.uk
W www.ragfactory.org.uk

RAMBERT DANCE COMPANY
94 Chiswick High Road, London W4 1SH
F 020 8747 8323   T 020 8630 0600
E rdc@rambert.org.uk
W www.rambert.org.uk

REALLY USEFUL GROUP THEATRES
Contact: Michael Townsend
22 Tower Street, London WC2H 9TW
F 020 7240 1292   T 020 7240 0880
E mike.townsend@reallyuseful.co.uk
W www.reallyuseful.com

REELTHINGPRODUCTIONS
MeadHaze, Lower Cookham Road
Maidenhead, Berkshire SL6 8JL   M 07990 543290
E mbradley@reelthingproductions.co.uk
W www.reelthingproductions.co.uk

RIDGEWAY STUDIOS
Fairley House, Andrews Lane
Cheshunt, Herts EN7 6LB
F 01992 633844   T 01992 633775
E info@ridgewaystudios.co.uk

RITZ STUDIOS
Provides Backline Hire for Musicians
110-112 Disraeli Road, London SW15 2DX   T 020 8870 1335
E lee@ritzstudios.com
W www.ritzstudios.com

RIVERSIDE STUDIOS
Crisp Road, Hammersmith
London W6 9RL
T 020 8237 1007   T 020 8237 1000
E lornapaterson@riversidestudios.co.uk
W www.riversidestudios.co.uk

ROOFTOP STUDIO THEATRE
Rooftop Studio, High Street Arcade
Stone, Staffordshire ST15 8AU
F 01785 818176   T 01785 761233
E elaine@pssa.co.uk
W www.rooftopstudio.co.uk

ROOMS ABOVE THE
Westheath Yard
(Opposite The Emmanuel School)
174 Mill Lane, West Hampstead
London NW6 1TB
F 020 8201 9464   T 0845 6860802
E info@theroomsabove.org.uk
W www.theroomsabove.org.uk

SPOTLIGHT ROOMS & STUDIOS

Spacious, air-conditioned meeting rooms and casting studios in the heart of Central London

Large waiting rooms with free receptionist service

DVD-quality audition clips posted online within minutes

Ideal for TV, film and commercial castings, plus read-throughs, production meetings or theatre projects

www.spotlight.com/spaces
T: 020 7440 5041
E: studios@spotlight.com

7 Leicester Place
London WC2H 7RJ

ROSE STUDIO & GALLERY
Rose Theatre, Kingston
24-26 High Street
Kingston upon Thames
Surrey KT1 1HL
F 020 8546 8783
E hiresandevents@rosetheatrekingston.org
W www.rosetheatrekingston.org
T 020 8546 6983

ROTHERHITHE STUDIOS
82 St Marychurch Street
London SE16 4HZ
F 020 7231 2119
E ostockman@sandsfilms.co.uk
W www.sandsfilms.co.uk
T 020 7231 2209

ROYAL ACADEMY OF DANCE
36 Battersea Square
London SW11 3RA
F 020 7924 3129
E info@rad.org.uk
W www.rad.org.uk
T 020 7326 8000

ROYAL ACADEMY OF DRAMATIC ART
62-64 Gower Street
London WC1E 6ED
E bookings@rada.ac.uk
T 020 7908 4754

ROYAL SHAKESPEARE COMPANY
35 Clapham High Street, London SW4 7TW
F 020 7845 0505
E london@rsc.org.uk
W www.rsc.org.uk
T 020 7845 0500

RTM STUDIOS
Central Chambers
93 Hope Street, Glasgow G2 6LD
F 0141 221 8622
E kay@resolutiontalentmanagement.com
W www.rtmstudios.co.uk
T 0141 221 2258

RUDEYE STUDIOS
73 St John Street, Farringdon
London EC1M 4NJ
E info@rudeye.com
W www.rudeye.com
T 020 7014 3023

SADLER'S WELLS THEATRE
Rosebery Avenue, London EC1R 4TN
F 020 7863 8061
E events@sadlerswells.com
W www.sadlerswells.com
T 020 7863 8065

SMA CENTRE
Vicarage Gate, Kensington
London W8 4HN
F 020 7368 6505
E manager@smacentre.com
W www.smacentre.com
T 020 7937 8885

SOHO GYMS
Borough Gym
Empire Square
Long Lane, London SE1 4NA
F 020 7234 9397
W www.sohogyms.com
T 0845 6778890

Camden Town Gym
193-199 Camden High Street
London NW1 7BT
F 020 7267 0500
T 020 7482 4524

Clapham Common Gym
95-97 Clapham High Street
London SW4 7TB
F 020 7720 6510
T 020 7720 0321

Covent Garden Gym
12 Macklin Street
London WC2B 5NF
F 020 7242 0899
T 020 7242 1290

Earl's Court Gym
254 Earl's Court Road
London SW5 9AD
F 020 7244 6893
T 020 7370 1402

Waterloo Gym
11-15 Brad Street
London SE1 8TG
F 020 7928 8623
T 020 7261 9798

SOHO THEATRE
21 Dean Street
London W1D 3NE
F 020 7287 5061
E hires@sohotheatre.com
W www.sohotheatre.com
T 020 7478 0117

SOUTH LONDON DANCE STUDIOS
130 Herne Hill
London SE24 9QL
E info@southlondondancestudios.co.uk
W www.southlondondancestudios.co.uk
T 020 7978 8624

SPACE @ CLARENCE MEWS
40 Clarence Mews
London E5 8HL   T 020 8986 5260
E frith.salem@virgin.net
W www.movingarchitecture.com

SPACE ARTS CENTRE THE
269 Westferry Road
London E14 3RS   T 020 7515 7799
E info@space.org.uk
W www.space.org.uk

SPACE CITY STUDIOS
79 Blythe Road, London W14 0HP
F 020 7371 4001   T 020 7371 4000
E info@spacecity.co.uk
W www.spacecitystudios.co.uk

SPOTLIGHT
Casting Studios. Room Hire
7 Leicester Place
London WC2H 7RJ
F 020 7287 1201   T 020 7440 5041
E rooms@spotlight.com
W www.spotlight.com/rooms

ST ANDREW'S CHURCH
Short Street, Southbank
London SE1 8LJ   T 020 7633 9819
W www.stjohnswaterloo.co.uk

ST GEORGE'S CHURCH BLOOMSBURY
Vestry Hall
6 Little Russell Street
London WC1A 2HR   T 020 7242 1979
E hiring@stgeorgesbloomsbury.org.uk
W www.stgeorgesbloomsbury.org.uk

ST JAMES'S CHURCH PICCADILLY
197 Piccadilly, London W1J 9LL   T 020 7292 4860
E secretary@st-james-piccadilly.org
W www.st-james-piccadilly.org

ST MARTINS-IN-THE-FIELDS
6 St Martins Place
London WC2N 4JJ   T 020 7766 1130
E jennifer.lang@smitf.org
W www.smitf.org

ST MARY NEWINGTON CHURCH HALL
The Parish Office
57 Kennington Park Road
London SE11 4JQ   T 020 7735 1894

ST MARY'S CHURCH HALL PADDINGTON
c/o Bill Kenwright Ltd
1 Venice Walk
London W2 1RR
F 020 7446 6222   T 020 7446 6200
E lindsey.milligan@kenwright.com

ST SWITHUN'S CHURCH
Meetings. Workshops
Hither Green Lane
Lewisham SE13 6QE   T 020 8318 9226
W www.saintswithuns.org.uk

STUDIO THE
4 Great Queen Street
London WC2B 5DG   T 020 7831 7899
E will@studiocoventgarden.com
W www.studiocoventgarden.com

The Old Finsbury Town Hall, Rosebery Avenue, EC1, the Central London home of **The Urdang Academy**, offers studios for castings, rehearsals and auditions. Sprung Harlequin floors, mirrors, pianos, sound system and WIFI.
T: 020 7713 7710 ext 2222 E: studiohire@theurdangacademy.com

STUDIO THE
Burwarton, Nr Bridgnorth
Shropshire WV16 6QJ   T 01746 787574
E meghawkins@btinternet.com
W www.meghawkins.com

SUMMERS Mark CASTING STUDIOS
1 Beaumont Avenue, West Kensington
London W14 9LP   T 020 7229 8413
E info@marksummers.com
W www.marksummers.com

SUMMIT STUDIOS
2-4 Spring Bridge Mews, Spring Bridge Road
Ealing, London W5 2AB
F 020 8840 2446   T 020 8840 2200
E info@summitstudios.co.uk
W www.summitstudios.co.uk

TAKE FIVE CASTING STUDIO
Casting Suite
37 Beak Street, London W1F 9RZ
F 020 7287 3035   T 020 7287 2120
E info@takefivestudio.com
W www.takefivestudio.com

TREADWELL'S
34 Tavistock Street, Covent Garden
London WC2E 7PB   T 020 7240 8906
E info@treadwells-london.com
W www.castingspacecoventgarden.co.uk

TRESTLE ARTS BASE
Home of Trestle Theatre Company
Russet Drive, St Albans, Herts AL4 0JQ
F 01727 855558   T 01727 850950
E admin@trestle.org.uk
W www.trestle.org.uk

TRICYCLE THE
269 Kilburn High Road, London NW6 7JR
F 020 7328 0795   T 020 7372 6611
E trish@tricycle.co.uk
W www.tricycle.co.uk

TT DANCE STUDIO
Parkwood Health & Fitness Centre, Darkes Lane
Potters Bar, Herts EN6 1AA
M 07930 400647   M 07904 771980
E ttdancestudio@aol.com
W www.talenttimetheatre.com

UNICORN THEATRE
147 Tooley Street
London SE1 2HZ   T 020 7645 0500
E admin@unicorntheatre.com
W www.unicorntheatre.com

UNION CHAPEL PROJECT
Compton Avenue, London N1 2XD
F 020 7354 8343   T 020 7266 3750
E spacehire@unionchapel.org.uk
W www.unionchapel.org.uk

URDANG ACADEMY THE
The Old Finsbury Town Hall
Rosebery Avenue
London EC1R 4RP
F 020 7278 6727   T 020 7713 7710
E studiohire@theurdangacademy.com
W www.theurdangacademy.com

WALKING FORWARD LTD
Studio 6, The Aberdeen Centre
22-24 Highbury Grove
London N5 2EA   T/F 020 7359 5249
E info@walkingforward.co.uk
W www.walkingforward.co.uk

WATERMANS
40 High Street
Brentford TW8 0DS
F 020 8232 1030   T 020 8232 1020
E info@watermans.org.uk
W www.watermans.org.uk

YOUNG Sylvia THEATRE SCHOOL
1 Nutford Place, London W1H 5YZ
F 020 7258 3915   T 020 7258 2330
E syoung@syts.co.uk
W www.syts.co.uk

YOUNG ACTORS THEATRE
70-72 Barnsbury Road, London N1 0ES
F 020 7833 9467   T 020 7278 2101
E info@yati.org.uk
W www.yati.org.uk

Y TOURING THEATRE COMPANY
One KX, 120 Cromer Street
London WC1H 8BS   T 020 7520 3090
E info@ytouring.org.uk
W www.ytouring.org.uk

ACTIVATION
Riverside House
Feltham Avenue
Hampton Court
Surrey KT8 9BJ
F 020 8783 9345   T 020 8783 9494
E info@activation.co.uk
W www.activation.co.uk

ACT UP
Unit 88, 99-109 Lavender Hill
London SW11 5QL
F 020 7924 6606   T 020 7924 7701
E info@act-up.co.uk
W www.act-up.co.uk

APROPOS PRODUCTIONS LTD
2nd Floor
91A Rivington Street
London EC2A 3AY
F 020 7739 3852   T 020 7739 2857
E info@aproposltd.com
W www.aproposltd.com

BROWNE Michael ASSOCIATES LTD
The Cloisters
168C Station Road
Lower Stondon
Bedfordshire SG16 6JQ   T/F 01462 812483
E enquiries@mba-roleplay.co.uk
W www.mba-roleplay.co.uk

CRAGRATS
Lawster House
140 South Street
Dorking
Surrey RH4 2EU   T 0844 8111184
E enquiries@cragrats.com
W www.cragrats.com

DRAMANON LLP
Langtons House
Templewood Lane
Farnham Common
Buckinghamshire SL2 3HD
F 01753 647783   T 01753 647795
E info@dramanon.co.uk
W www.dramanon.co.uk

FRANK PARTNERS
14 Brynland Avenue
Bishopston
Bristol BS7 9DT   T 0117 908 5384
E neil@frankpartners.co.uk
W www.frankpartners.co.uk

GLOBAL7
PO Box 56232
London N4 4XP
M 07956 956652   T/F 020 7281 7679
E global7castings@gmail.com
W www.global7casting.com

IMPACT UNIVERSAL
Hope Bank House, Woodhead Road
Honley, Huddersfield HD9 6PF
F 01484 660088 · T 01484 668881
E jill.beckwith@impactuniversal.com
W www.impactuniversal.com

INTERACT
138 Southwark Bridge Road
London SE1 0DG
F 020 7793 7755 · T 020 7793 7744
E info@interact.eu.com
W www.interact.eu.com

LADA PRODUCTIONS
Sparkhouse Studios
Ropewalk, Lincoln, Lincs LN6 7DQ
F 01522 837201 · T 01522 837242
E productions@lada.org.uk
W www.lada.org.uk

NV MANAGEMENT LTD
E hello@nvmanagement.co.uk
W www.nvmanagement.co.uk

PERFORMANCE BUSINESS THE
The Coach House, 78 Oatlands Drive
Weybridge, Surrey KT13 9HT · T 01932 888885
E lucy@theperformance.biz
W www.theperformance.biz

ROLEPLAY UK
2 St Mary's Hill
Stamford PE9 2DW
F 01780 764436 · T 01780 761960
W www.roleplayuk.com

STEPS DRAMA LEARNING DEVELOPMENT
Unit 4.1.1
The Leathermarket
Weston Street
London SE1 3ER
F 020 7403 0909 · T 020 7403 9000
E mail@stepsdrama.com
W www.stepsdrama.com

THEATRE& LTD
Church Hall
St James Road
Marsh
Huddersfield HD1 4QA
F 01484 532962 · T 01484 532967
E cmitchell@theatreand.com
W www.theatreand.com

WEST END WORKSHOPS
Arts Workshops
Audition Coaching
E info@westendworkshops.co.uk · T 01202 526667
W www.westendworkshops.co.uk

S

Set Construction, Lighting, Sound & Scenery

3D SET COMPANY LTD
Construction. Exhibition Stands. Scenery Design. Sets
Unit 8 Temperance Street
Manchester M12 6HR
F 0161 273 6786   T 0161 273 8831
E twalsh@3dsetco.com
W www.3dsetco.com

ALBEMARLE SCENIC STUDIOS
Suppliers of Scenery & Costumes Construction/Hire
Admin: PO Box 240
Rotherfield TN6 9BN   T 0845 6447021
E albemarle.productions@virgin.net
W www.albemarleproductions.com

ALL SCENE ALL PROPS
Painting Contractors. Props. Scenery
Units 2 & 3, Spelmonden Farm
Goudhurst, Kent TN17 1HE
F 01580 211131   T 01580 211121
E info@allscene.net
W www.allscene.net

BRISTOL (UK) LTD
Scenic Paint
Unit 3, Southerland Court
Tolpits Lane, Watford WD18 9SP
F 01923 779666   T 01923 779333
E tech.sales@bristolpaint.com
W www.bristolpaint.com

CAP PRODUCTION SOLUTIONS
116 Wigmore Road, Carshalton
Surrey SM5 1RQ   M 07973 432576
E leigh@leighporter.com

CCT LIGHTING UK LTD
Lighting. Dimmers. Sound & Stage Machinery
Unit 3, Ellesmere Business Park
Haydn Road, Sherwood
Nottingham NG5 1DX
F 0115 985 7091   T 0115 985 8919
E office@cctlighting.co.uk
W www.cctlighting.com

COD STEAKS
*Costume. Design. Exhibitions. Model Making.
Set Construction*
2 Cole Road, Bristol BS2 0UG   T 0117 980 3910
E mail@codsteaks.com
W www.codsteaks.com

CREW CO
Stage & Technical Crew for London & Midlands
55 Main Street, Long Compton
Warwickshire CV36 5JS
F 0845 4589411   T 0845 4589400
E contactus@crewco.net
W www.crewco.net

DAP STUDIO
55 Longdown Lane North, Epsom
Surrey KT17 3JB   T/F 01892 730897
E info@dapstudio.co.uk
W www.dapstudio.co.uk

DISPLAY MAINTENANCE LTD
Unit 1, Calder Trading Estate
Lower Quarry Road
Bradley, Huddersfield HD5 0RR   T 0844 8711801
E enquiries@dmnsolutions.co.uk
W www.dmnsolutions.co.uk

[CONTACTS 2011]

35 years of specialist construction
large & small scale installation for theatre, opera, dance, events & display
TMS International Ltd
306 St James's Road London SE1 5JX
+44 (0)20 7394 9519
email: production@tmsi.co.uk
www.tmsinternational.co.uk

DOBSON SOUND PRODUCTION LTD
Design. Installation. Sound Hire
66 Windsor Avenue, Merton
London SW19 2RR
F 020 8543 3636   T 020 8545 0202
E enquiries@dobsonsound.co.uk

DOVETAIL SPECIALIST SCENERY
Furniture, Prop & Scenery Builders
42-50 York Way, London N1 9AB   T/F 020 7278 7379
E dovetail.ss@btopenworld.com

FULL EFFECT THE
Live Event Producers including Choreographers
Exchange Building
16 St Cuthbert's Street
Bedford MK40 3JG
F 01234 214445   T 01234 269099
E mark.harrison@tfe.co.uk
W www.thefulleffect.co.uk

FUTURIST SOUND & LIGHT LTD
Unit 15, Carlton Trading Estate
Pickering Street, Leeds LS12 2QG
F 0113 279 0066   T 0113 279 0033
E info@futurist.co.uk
W www.futurist.co.uk

GILL Perry
Installation. Production Management. Set Construction
E perry_gill100@hotmail.com   M 07815 048164

HALL STAGE LTD
Unit 4, Cosgrove Way
Luton, Beds LU1 1XL
F 0845 3454256   T 0845 3454255
E sales@hallstage.com
W www.hallstage.com

HAND & LOCK
Embroidery for Costumes & Interiors
86 Margaret Street
London W1W 8TE
F 020 7580 7499   T 020 7580 7488
E enquiries@handembroidery.com
W www.handembroidery.com

HARLEQUIN (British Harlequin Plc)
Festival House
Chapman Way
Tunbridge Wells, Kent TN2 3EF
F 01892 514222   T 01892 514888
E sales@harlequinfloors.com
W www.harlequinfloors.com

HENSHALL John
Director of Lighting & Photography
68 High Street
Stanford in the Vale
Oxfordshire SN7 8NL   T 01367 710191
E john@epi-centre.com

HERON & DRIVER
Scenic Furniture & Structural Prop Makers
Unit 7, Dockley Road Industrial Estate
Rotherhithe, London SE16 3SF
F 020 7394 8680   T 020 7394 8688
E mail@herondriver.co.uk
W www.herondriver.co.uk

LIGHT WORKS LTD
2A Greenwood Road, London E8 1AB
F 020 7254 0306   T 020 7249 3627

MALTBURY STAGING
Portable Staging Sales & Consultancy
Unit 9, Level 5 South
New England House
New England Street, Brighton BN1 4GH
F 0333 8008882   T 0333 8008881
E info@maltbury.com
W www.maltbury.com

MASSEY Bob ASSOCIATES
Electrical & Mechanical Stage Consultants
9 Worrall Avenue, Arnold
Nottinghamshire NG5 7GN   T/F 0115 967 3969
E bm.associates@virgin.net

MATT-LX
Lighting & Technical Production
Gunnery House, 9 Gunnery Terrace
London SE18 6SW
F 020 8301 8149   T 020 8301 8692
E intray@mattlx.com
W www.mattlx.com

MODELBOX
Computer Aided Design. Design Services
35 Mill Road, Okehampton
Devon EX20 1PS   T 01837 54342
E info@modelbox.co.uk
W www.modelboxplans.com

MODERNEON LONDON LTD
Lighting. Signs
Cromwell House, 27 Brabourne Rise
Park Langley, Beckenham, Kent BR3 6SQ
F 020 8658 2770   T 020 8650 9690
E info@moderneon.co.uk
W www.moderneon.co.uk

MOUNSEY Matthew
E matthewmounsey@hotmail.com   M 07941 355450

NEED Paul J
Lighting Designer
c/o 10 out of 10 Productions
5 Orchard Business Centre
Kangley Bridge Road, London SE26 5AQ
F 020 8778 9217   T 020 8659 2558
E paul@10outof10.co.uk
W www.pauljneed.co.uk

NORTHERN LIGHT
Communications, Lighting, Sound & Stage Equipment
Assembly Street, Leith
Edinburgh EH6 7RG
F 0131 622 9101   T 0131 622 9100
E info@northernlight.co.uk
W www.northernlight.co.uk

ORBITAL
Sound Hire & Design
57 Acre Lane, Brixton
London SW2 5TN
F 020 7501 6869   T 020 7501 6868
E hire@orbitalsound.co.uk
W www.orbitalsound.co.uk

PANALUX
12 Waxlow Road, London NW10 7NU
F 020 8233 7001   T 020 8233 7000
E info@panalux.biz
W www.panalux.biz

PMB THEATRE & EXHIBITION SERVICES LTD
The Barn, Kingston Wood Manor
Arrington, Royston, Herts SG8 0AP
F 01954 718032   T 01954 718227
E pmb@creatingtheimpossible.co.uk
W www.creatingtheimpossible.co.uk

PRODUCTION STORE
Matt-lx Ltd, Gunnery House
9 Gunnery Terrace, London SE18 6SW   T 020 8301 8692
E sales@mattlx.com
W www.productionstore.net

PROPS2ORDER LTD
E swoozen@hotmail.com
W www.props2order.co.uk

REVOLVING STAGE COMPANY LTD THE
Unit F5
Little Heath Industrial Estate
Old Church Road, Coventry
Warwickshire CV6 7ND
F 024 7668 9355   T 024 7668 7055
E enquiries@therevolvingstagecompany.co.uk
W www.therevolvingstagecompany.co.uk

RK RESOURCE
2 Wyvern Way, Henwood
Ashford, Kent TN24 8DW
F 01233 750133   T 01233 750180
E rkresource2007@aol.co.uk

RWS ELECTRICAL & AUDIO CONTRACTORS LTD
*All Aspects of Electrical Services including Installation
Design & Consultancy*
1 Spinners Close, Biddenden
Kent TN27 8AY   T 01580 291764
E dick@rwselectrical.com
W www.rwselectrical.com

S + H TECHNICAL SUPPORT LTD
Starcloths. Drapes
Starcloth Way
Mullacott Industrial Estate
Ilfracombe, Devon EX34 8PL
F 01271 865423   T 01271 866832
E shtsg@aol.com
W www.starcloth.co.uk

S2 EVENTS
*Design, Equipment Hire, Production, Scenery, Set
Construction & Technical Services for Creative Live Events*
3-5 Valentine Place, London SE1 8QH
F 020 7928 6082   T 020 7928 5474
E info@s2events.co.uk
W www.s2events.co.uk

SCENA PRODUCTIONS LTD
Set Construction
240 Camberwell Road, London SE5 0DP
F 020 7703 7012   T 020 7703 4444
E info@scenapro.com
W www.scenapro.com

SCENIC WORKSHOPS LTD
Baltic Road, Bootle, Liverpool L20 1AW
F 0151 933 6699   T 0151 933 6677
E info@scenicworkshops.co.uk
W www.scenicworkshops.co.uk

SCOTT FLEARY PRODUCTIONS LTD
Unit 1-4 Block A
Vale Industrial Park
170 Rowan Road, London SW16 5BN
F 0870 4448322   T 0870 4441787
E info@scottflearyltd.com

SETS IN THE CITY
Location House, 5 Dove Lane, Bristol BS2 9HP
F 0117 955 2480   T 0117 955 5538
E info@setsinthecity.co.uk
W www.setsinthecity.co.uk

SHOWSTORM LTD
24 The Poplars, Littlehampton BN17 6GZ
F 0871 8575062   T 020 8123 3453
E mark@showstorm.tv
W www.showstorm.tv

SMITH Paul Don
Graffiti Mural Artist. Graphics. Scenery
11A Cadogan Road, Surbiton
Surrey KT6 4DQ   M 07949 710306
E firedon_1@hotmail.com

STAGE MANAGEMENT COMPANY
Unit 1 Accent Business Park
Barkerend Road
Bradford, West Yorkshire BD3 9BD   M 07731 429544
E info@stagemanagementcompany.co.uk
W www.stagemanagementcompany.co.uk

STAGE SYSTEMS
*Designers & Suppliers of Modular Staging, Tiering &
Auditorium Seating*
Stage House, Prince William Road
Loughborough LE11 5GU
F 01509 233146   T 01509 611021
E info@stagesystems.co.uk
W www.stagesystems.co.uk

STAGECRAFT TECHNICAL SERVICES LTD
*Hire & Sales of Audio Visual, Lighting, Sound & Staging for
Conference & Live Events*
Porton Business Centre
Porton, Wiltshire SP4 0ND
F 0845 8382016   T 0845 8382015
E hire@stagecraft.co.uk
W www.stagecraft.co.uk

STAGEWORKS WORLDWIDE PRODUCTIONS
Lighting. Props. Scenery. Sound
525 Ocean Boulevard
Blackpool FY4 1EZ
F 01253 342702   T 01253 342426
E info@stageworkswwp.com
W www.stageworkswwp.com

STEWART Helen
Theatre Designer
29C Hornsey Rise Gardens
London N19 3PP   M 07887 682186
E helen@helenstewart.co.uk
W www.helenstewart.co.uk

STORM LIGHTING LTD
Warwick House
Monument Way West
Woking, Surrey GU21 5EN
F 01483 757710   T 01483 757211
E hire@stormlighting.co.uk
W www.stormlighting.co.uk

SVIDSMYNDIR SCENIC STUDIOS
Steinhella 17B
221 Hafnarfjordur
Iceland
F 00 35 45 88 93 95   T 00 35 45 88 93 93
E smynd@svidsmyndir.is
W www.svidsmyndir.is

TITAN TOUR PRODUCTIONS
55 Hereford Road
Eccles
Greater Manchester M30 9BX   M 07894 868750
E charlotte@titantourproductions.com
W www.titantourproductions.com

TMS INTERNATIONAL LTD (Terry Murphy Scenery)
Set Construction & Painting
306 St James's Road
London SE1 5JX
F 020 7232 2347   T 020 7394 9519
E production@tmsi.co.uk
W www.terrymurphy.co.uk

TOP SHOW
Props. Scenery. Conference Specialists
North Lane
Huntington
York YO32 9SU   T 01904 750022

WEST John
Art Director. Production Designer
103 Abbotswood Close
Winyates Green
Redditch
Worcestershire B98 0QF
M 07753 637451   T/F 01527 516771
E johnwest@blueyonder.co.uk
W www.johnwestartist.co.uk

WHITE LIGHT LTD
20 Merton Industrial Park
Jubilee Way
Wimbledon, London SW19 3WL
F 020 8254 4801   T 020 8254 4800
E info@whitelight.ltd.uk
W www.whitelight.ltd.uk

BBC Television
Wood Lane, London W12 7RJ
T 020 8743 8000

The BBC plans to relocate a number of its departments to a new site in Salford Quays from 2011. These departments include children's, sport, Radio 5 Live, learning and parts of future media and technology. While these relocations are taking place, please contact the BBC's main London switchboard, where you can request further advice.

• TALENT & RIGHTS NEGOTIATION GROUP

Room 3400, 201 Wood Lane
White City , London W12 7TS

Head of Talent Rights & Negotiation	Roger Leatham
Head of Copyright Contracting	Rob Kirkham
Head of Performance Contracting	Annie Thomas

LITERARY COPYRIGHT
Room 395 Drama Building
BBC Television Centre
London W12 7RJ

Manager	Neil Hunt

Senior Executives

Sue Dickson	Julieann May
Julie Gallagher	Sally Millwood
David Knight	Hilary Sagar

MUSIC COPYRIGHT & MUSIC ENTERTAINMENT PERFORMANCE

Room 201 EBX Building
BBC Television Centre, London W12 7RJ

Manager	Nicky Bignell

Executives

Laura Amphlett	Celine Palavioux
Sally Dunsford	Debbie Rogerson
Catherine Grimes	Vicki Willis
Madeline Hennessy	

BBC JOURNALISM
Room 5200
BBC Television Centre
London W12 7RJ

Rights Manager	Tessa Beckett
Rights Executive	Gary Casey

LONDON FACTUAL
Room 401, MC4 DI Media Centre
201 Wood Lane, London W12 7TQ

Rights Manager	Chris Dabbs

Executives

Alice Brandon	Stuart Krelle
Selena Harvey	Shelagh Morrison
Matthew Hickling	

Classical Music Rights Manager	Simon Brown

T

Television
Television (BBC London)
BBC Television & Sound (Regional)
Independent

Theatre Producers
Theatre
Alternative & Community
Children's, Young People's & TIE
English Speaking in Europe
London
Outer London, Fringe & Venues
Provincial/Touring
Puppet Theatre Companies
Repertory (Regional)

(For further details of TIE/YPT see Theatre - Children's, Young People's & TIE)

[CONTACTS 2011]

LONDON FICTION
Rooms 341-344/350-253
Drama Building
BBC Television Centre
London W12 7RJ

Rights Manager
Nicola Hill

Executives (TV)
Mike Bickerdike	Candice Nichols
Lorraine Clark	Annie Pollard
Teresa Cordall	Colette Robertson
Jemma McGee	

Executives (Radio)
Stephanie Beynon	Emma Luffingham

BRISTOL

Executives
Jane Armstrong	Sophie Clark

BIRMINGHAM

Executives
Rachel Amos	Jill Ridley
Andrea Coles	

MANCHESTER

Executives
Colleen Burrows	Collette Tanner
Sarah McHugh	

• DRAMA
Room 265, Drama Room
Wood Lane, London W12 7RJ
T 020 8743 8000 (Main Switchboard)

Controller, Drama Production & New Talent	John Yorke
Director, Drama Production	Nicolas Brown
Controller, Series & Serials	Kate Harwood
Executive Producer, EastEnders	Bryan Kirkwood
Creative Director	Manda Levin
Head of Production	Susy Liddell
Development Executive	Phil Temple

Executive Producers, Drama Production
Ruth Caleb	Sue Hogg
Belinda Campbell	Hilary Salmon
Phillippa Giles	Jessica Pope
Kate Harwood	Diederick Santer
	Will Trotter

Producers, Drama Production
Sarah Brown	George Ormond
Ben Evans	Sally Stokes
Mike Hobson	Annie Tricklebank
Kate Lewis	Pier Wilkie
Peter Lloyd	Colin Wratten

• COMMISSIONING
Controller, BBC Knowledge	George Entwistle
Commissioning Editors, Drama	Sarah Brandist
	Polly Hill
Commissioning Editor, Independent Drama	Lucy Richer
Controller, Drama Production Studios	John Yorke
Controller, BBC Four	Richard Klein
Head of Knowledge Commissioning	Emma Swain
Controller, Series & Serials	Kate Harwood
Controller, Drama Commissioning	Ben Stephenson

• NEWS AND CURRENT AFFAIRS
BBC News (Television & Radio)
Television Centre, Wood Lane, London W12 7RJ
T 020 8743 8000 (Main Switchboard)

Director, News	Helen Boaden
Deputy Director, News & Head of Multimedia Programmes, News	Stephen Mitchell
Head of Newsgathering	Fran Unsworth
Head of Newsroom	Mary Hockaday
Head of Political Programmes, Research & Analysis	Sue Inglish
Controller of Production, News	Jenny Baxter
Controller, English Regions	David Holdsworth

London Factual Executive Producers
T 020 8743 8000 (Main Switchboard)
All based in the Media Centre at White City Media Village.

Arts	Basil Comely
	Jonty Claypole
Documentaries & Features	Tina Fletcher
	Eamon Hardy
	Gary Hunter
	Nick Mirsky
	Clare Sillery
Consumer	Lisa Ausden
Science	Andrew Cohen
	Tina Fletcher
	Michael Mosley
	Jonathan Renouf

Horizon Editor	Aidan Laverty
Business & History	Dominic Crossley-Holland
	Eamon Hardy
Editor, The Culture Show	Janet Lee
Editor, The One Show	Sandy Smith

• CHILDREN

Director	Joe Godwin
Controller, CBBC	Damian Kavanagh
Controller, CBeebies	Kay Benbow
Head of In-house Production	Steven Andrew
Head of Children's Programmes, Scotland	Simon Parsons

• MUSIC

Head of Television, Classical Music & Performance	Peter Maniura
Managing Editor, Classical Music, Television	Caroline Speed
Editor Music Programmes, Television, Classical Music & Performance	Oliver Macfarlane
Talent Producer/Programme Development Manager	Victoria Jones

Executive Producer   Celina Parker

Producers/Directors

Dominic Best	Andy King-Dabbs
Jonathan Haswell	Helen Mansfield
Francesca Kemp	

Production Executive   Ian Taitt

• SPORT

Director of Sport	Barbara Slater
Head of Major Events	Dave Gordon
Head of TV Sport	Philip Bernie
Head of Radio Sport	Gordon Turnbull
Head of Interactive & Formula 1	Ben Gallop
Head of Sports News	Richard Burgess
Head of Production	Jackie Myburgh
Head of HR Development	Pam Sikora
Head of Sports Rights	David Murray
Head of Marketing & Communications, Sports & Events	Louise Fyans
Finance Partner, Journalism, Sports	Richard Jones

• NEW WRITING

BBC Writersroom
Grafton House, 379-381 Euston Road
London NW1 3AU   **T 020 7765 2703**
E writersroom@bbc.co.uk
W www.bbc.co.uk/writersroom

Creative Director	Kate Rowland
Development Manager	Paul Ashton

• BBC BRISTOL

Broadcasting House
Whiteladies Road
Bristol BS8 2LR   T 0117 973 2211

NETWORK TELEVISION FEATURES AND DOCUMENTARIES

Head of Bristol Factual   Ben Gale

Executive Producers

Robi Dutta	Julian Mercer
Simon Knight	Michael Poole
Pete Lawrence	Simon Shaw

Series Producers

Lynn Barlow	Alastair Laurence
Kate Broome	Kimberley Littlemore
Michele Burgess	Peter Smith
Chris Hutchins	Ben Southwell

Producers/Directors

Robert Bayley	David Olusoga
Louise Hibbins	Tuppence Stone
Colin Napthine	

BBC AUDIO & MUSICAL PRODUCTION BRISTOL
(BBC RADIO 4)

Managing Editor	Clare McGinn
Production Manager	Kate Chaney

Producers

John Byrne	Chris Ledgard
Sara Davies	Mark Smalley
Tim Dee	Mary Ward-Lowery
Jolyon Jenkins	Miles Warde

NATURAL HISTORY UNIT

Contact: Siobhan Lane (Assistant to Head of Natural History Unit)

Head of Natural History Unit   Andrew Jackson

Executive Producers

Wendy Darke	Brian Leith
Sara Ford	Tim Martin
Alastair Fothergill	Fiona Pitcher
Mike Gunton	Tim Scoones
Julian Hector	

• BBC WEST

Broadcasting House
Whiteladies Road
Bristol BS8 2LR   T 0117 973 2211

Head of Regional & Local Programmes, including BBC West, Radio Bristol, BBC Somerset, BBC Gloucestershire, BBC Wiltshire	Lucio Mesquita
Editor, Output	Stephanie Marshall
News Gathering	Neil Bennett

• BBC SOUTH WEST

Seymour Road
Mannamead
Plymouth PL3 5BD   T 01752 229201

Head of BBC South West	Jane McCloskey
Editor TV Current Affairs	Simon Willis
Output Editor	Simon Read

• BBC SOUTH

Havelock Road
Southampton SO14 7PU   T 023 8022 6201

Head of Regional & Local Programmes	Jason Horton
TV News Editor	Lee Desty
Executive Editor, BBC Oxford	Steve Taschini
Managing Editor, BBC Solent	Chris Carnegy
Managing Editor, Berkshire	Marianne Bell

• BBC LONDON

35C Marylebone High Street
London W1M 4AA   T 020 7224 2424

BBC London News:
TV: The Politics Show
Radio: BBC London Radio 94.9FM
Online: BBC London online

Head of BBC London	Michael MacFarlane
TV Editor	Antony Dore
Editor, Inside Out	Dippy Chaudhary
Managing Editor, BBC Radio London 94.9FM	David Robey
Political Editor	Tim Donovan
Editor, BBC London Online	Claire Timms

• BBC SOUTH EAST

The Great Hall Arcade
Mount Pleasant Road
Tunbridge Wells
Kent TN1 1QQ   **T 01892 670000**

Head of Regional & Local	
Programmes BBC South East	Michael Rawsthorne
Managing Editor BBC Radio Kent	Paul Leaper
Managing Editor BBC Southern Counties	Nicki Holliday
Editor BBC South East Today	Quentin Smith
Editor Inside Out	Linda Bell
Editor Politics Show	Dan Fineman

• BBC NORTH WEST

New Broadcasting House
Oxford Road
Manchester M60 1SJ   **T 0161 200 2020**
W www.bbc.co.uk/manchester
W www.bbc.co.uk/liverpool
W www.bbc.co.uk/lancashire

Entertainment & Features

Editor, Entertainment & Features	Helen Bullough

Religion & Ethics

Head of Religion & Ethics &	
Commissioning Editor for Religion TV	Aaqil Ahmed
Executive Editor &	
Head of Religion Radio	Christine Morgan

Network News & Current Affairs

Executive Producer, Network News	
& Current Affairs	Sinead Rocks

Regional & Local Programmes

Head of Regional & Local	
Programmes, North West	Aziz Rashid
Head of Regional & Local Programmes,	
North East & Cumbria	Phil Roberts

• BBC BIRMINGHAM

BBC Birmingham
The Mailbox
Birmingham B1 1RF
F 0121 567 6875   **T 0121 567 6767**

English Regions

Controller, English Regions	David Holdsworth
Head of New Services, English Regions	Laura Ellis
Chief Operating Officer, English Regions	Ian Hughes
Senior Officer, Press & PR	Caroline Boots
Secretary, BBC Trust	Louise Hall
Head of Regional & Local	
Programmes, West Midlands	Cath Hearne

Vision Productions

Head of Birmingham & Manchester Factual	Nick Patten
Head of Production Talent,	
Birmingham & Manchester	Manjit Ahluwalia

Audio & Music

Executive Editor	Andrew Thorman
Deputy Editor	Fran Barnes
Executive Producer, Radio 2	Bob McDowell

Drama

BBC Birmingham TV Drama Village
Archibald House
1059 Bristol Road, Selly Oak
Birmingham B29 6LT   **T 0121 567 7417**

Executive Producer	Will Trotter

• BBC SCOTLAND

40 Pacific Quay
Glasgow G51 1DA   **T 0141 422 6000**
W www.bbc.co.uk/scotland

Scottish Executive Board

Director, Scotland	Ken MacQuarrie
Head of Programmes & Services	Donalda MacKinnon
Head of Public Policy	Ian Small
Chief Operating Officer	Bruce Malcolm
Head of Talent Division	Donald-Iain Brown
Head of HR & Development	Wendy Aslett
Head of Marketing, Communications	
& Audiences	Mairead Ferguson
Head of Strategy	Catherine Smith

• BBC SCOTLAND cont'd

Genre Heads

Commissioning Editor, Television & Head of Sport	Ewan Angus
Head of News & Current Affairs	Atholl Duncan
Head of Radio	Jeff Zycinski
Head of Service, BBC Alba	Margaret Mary Murray
Service Editor, BBC Alba	Marion MacKinnon
Head of Factual	Andrea Miller
Head of Drama, Television	Anne Mensah
Head of Drama, Radio	Bruce Young
Head of Children's	Simon Parsons
Executive Editor for CBBC Scotland	Sue Morgan
Editor for Cbeebies Scotland	Sara Harkins
Head of Entertainment & Events	Eileen Herlihy
Executive Editor, Comedy	Jemma Rodgers
Head of Learning	Nick Simons
Executive Editor, Cross Media	Matthew Lee
Director, BBC Scottish Symphony Orchestra	Gavin Reid
Executive Editor, Entertainment Commissioning	Alan Tyler
Commissioning Executive, BBC Daytime, Scotland & Northern Ireland	Jo Street
Executive Producer, Scotland, Knowledge Commissioning	Sam Anthony

BBC Scotland provides television and radio programmes for Scotland and the UK networks as well as online and interactive content. Based in the new digital headquarters in Glasgow since 2007, there are also centres throughout Scotland which includes City Halls, the home of the BBC Scottish Symphony Orchestra.

Aberdeen
Broadcasting House
Beechgrove Terrace
Aberdeen AB15 5ZT   T 01224 625233

Dumbarton
Strathleven Bottling Plant
Dumbarton
Dunbartonshire G82 2AP   T 01389 736666

Dumfries
Elmbank, Lover's Walk
Dumfries DG1 1NZ   T 01387 268008

Dundee
Nethergate Centre
4th Floor, 66 Nethergate
Dundee DD1 4ER   T 01382 202481

Edinburgh
The Tun, 4 Jackson's Entry
111 Holyrood Road
Edinburgh EH8 8PJ   T 0131-557 5888

Glasgow
Glasgow City Halls
(BBC Scottish Symphony Orchestra)
87 Albion Street
Glasgow G1 1NQ   T 0141 552 0909

Inverness
7 Culduthel Road
Inverness IV2 4AD   T 01463 720720

Orkney
Castle Street, Kirkwall
Orkney KW15 1DF   T 01856 873939

Portree
Clydesdale Bank Buildings
Somerled Square
Portree
Isle of Skye IV51 9BT   T 01478 612005

Selkirk
Unit 1, Ettrick Riverside
Dunsdale Road
Selkirk TD7 5EB   T 01750 724567

Shetland
Pitt Lane, Lerwick
Shetland ZE1 0DW   T 01595 694747

Stornoway
Radio nan Gaidheal
Rosebank
52 Church Street
Stornoway
Isle of Lewis HS1 2LS   T 01851 705000

• BBC WALES

Broadcasting House
Llandaff, Cardiff CF5 2YQ   **T 029 2032 2000**

Director	Menna Richards
Head of Programmes (Welsh)	Keith Jones
Head of Programmes (English)	Clare Hudson
Head of Strategy & Communications	Rhodri Talfan Davies
Head of News & Current Affairs	Mark O'Callaghan
Head of HR & Development	Jude Gray
Chief Operating Officer	Gareth Powell
Head of Drama	Piers Wenger
Head of Broadcast Development	Cathryn Allen
Head of Sport	Geoff Williams
Head of Factual & Music	Adrian Davies
Editor Radio Wales	Steve Austins
Editor Radio Cymru	Sian Gwynedd
Editor New Media	Iain Tweedale

• BBC NORTHERN IRELAND

Belfast
BBC Broadcasting House
Ormeau Avenue, Belfast BT2 8HQ   **T 028 9033 8000**
W www.bbc.co.uk/ni

Director, BBC Northern Ireland	Peter Johnston
Head of Programmes	Ailsa Orr
Head of News & Current Affairs	Andrew Coleman
Chief Operating Officer	Mark Taylor
Head of Public Policy, Corporate & Community Affairs	Mark Adair
Head of Marketing, Communications & Audiences	Kathy Martin
Head of HR & Development	Lawrence Jackson
Head of TV Current Affairs	Jeremy Adams
Head of Entertainment & Events	Mike Edgar
Head of Factual	Paul McGuigan
Editor of Sport	Shane Glynn
Head of Multi-platform Commissioning	Fergus Keeling
Managing Editor, Learning, Language & Social Action	Jane Cassidy
Head of Radio Ulster	Susan Lovell
Editor of Radio Foyle	Michael Tumelty

BBC Radio Ulster
BBC Broadcasting House
Ormeau Avenue
Belfast BT2 8HQ   **T 028 9033 8000**
W www.bbc.co.uk/radioulster

BBC Radio Foyle
8 Northland Road
Londonderry BT48 7JD   **T 028-7126 2244**

100th

SPOTLIGHT

{STAGE
{TELEVISION
{FILM
{RADIO
{+ADVICE

[CONTACTS] 100th Edition
www.contactshandbook.com

 **Anglia**

ITV ANGLIA

Head Office

Anglia House, Norwich NR1 3JG

F 0844 5563931   T 0844 8816900

e-mail: anglianews@itv.com

East of England: Weekday & Weekend

Regional News Centres

Cambridge

Link House, Station Road, Great Shelford

Cambridge CB22 5LT   News 0844 8816985

Northampton

Portfolio Innovation Centre

University of Northampton

St George's Avenue

Northampton NN2 6JD   T 0844 8816974

Ipswich

Hubbard House

Civic Drive, Ipswich IP1 2QA   T 0844 8816999

 Channel Television

CHANNEL TELEVISION LTD

Registered Office

The Television Centre, La Pouquelaye, St Helier

Jersey JE1 3ZD, Channel Islands

F 01534 816817   T 01534 816816

W www.channelonline.tv

Channel Islands: Weekday and Weekend

Managing Director (Broadcast)	Karen Rankine
Programme Producer	Laura Holgate
Managing Director (Commercial)	Mike Elsey
Director of Resource & Transmission	Kevin Banner
Programme Editor	Eric Blakeley

CHANNEL FOUR TELEVISION CORPORATION

London Office

124 Horseferry Road, London SW1P 2TX

Textphone 020 7396 8691   T 020 7396 4444

Members of the Board

Chairman	Lord Terry Burns
Deputy Chairman	Lord David Puttnam
Chief Executive	David Abraham
Director of Television	Kevin Lygo
Group Finance Director	Anne Bulford
Sales Director	Andy Barnes
Director of Future Media Techology	Jon Gibby

Non-Executive Directors

Karren Brady	Martha Lane Fox
Tony Hall	Andy Mollett
Stephen Hill	

Heads of Department

Head of Features & Factual Entertainment	Sue Murphy
Head of E4	Angela Jain
Head of Specialist Factual	Ralph Lee
Controller of Broadcasting	Rosemary Newell
Head of Scheduling & T4	Julie Oldroyd
Head of Documentaries & More 4	Hamish Mykura
Head of News & Current Affairs	Dorothy Byrne
Head of Entertainment	Justin Gorman
Head of Drama & FilmFour	Tessa Ross
Head of Education	
& Managing Editor Commissioning	Janey Walker
Director of Nations & Regions	Stuart Cosgrove
Director of Corporate Relations	Nick Toon
Controller of Research & Insight	Claire Grimmond
Director of Human Resources	Diane Herbert
Head of Facilities Management	Julie Kortens
Head of Media Planning & Presentations	Greg Smith
Controller of Press & Publicity	Matt Baker
Network Creative Director	Brett Foraker
Head of Marketing	Rufus Radcliffe
Head of Sponsorship	David Charlesworth
Head of Airtime Management	Merlin Inkley
Head of Online Sales	Errol Baran
Head of Strategic Sales	Mike Parker
Head of Channel 4	Julian Bellamy

five

CHANNEL FIVE BROADCASTING

22 Long Acre, London WC2E 9LY

F 020 7550 5554   T 020 7550 5555

W www.five.tv

Managing Director	Mark White
Controller	Richard Woolfe
Director of Strategy	Charles Constable
Director of Finance	David Hockley
Director of Legal	Paul Chinnery
Head of Scheduling	Richard Brent
Head of News & Current Affairs	Chris Shaw
Head of Factual	Andrew O'Connell
Controller of Sport	Robert Charles
Controller of Children's	Nick Wilson
Managing Director of Digital Channels	
& Acquisitions	Jeff Ford

GMTV

London Television Centre
Upper Ground, London SE1 9TT
F 020 7827 7001   **T 020 7827 7000**
W www.gm.tv

Editor	Sue Walton
Managing Editor	Neil Thompson
Head of Futures	Annemarie Leahy
Deputy Head of Futures	Caroline Sigley
Head of Entertainment	Corinne Bishop
Finance Director	Andy Whitaker

INDEPENDENT TELEVISION NEWS

200 Gray's Inn Road
London WC1X 8XZ   **T 020 7833 3000**

Chief Executive	John Hardie
Editor-in-Chief, ITV News	David Mannion
Editor, ITV News	Deborah Turness
Editor, Channel 4 News	Jim Gray

ITV PLC

Registered Office
The London Television Centre
London SE1 9LT
F 020 7849 9344   **T 020 7157 3000**
W www.itv.com

Management Board

Chairman	Archie Norman
Chief Executive	Adam Crozier
Director of Television, Channels & Online	Peter Fincham
Director of Strategy & Development	Carolyn Fairbairn
Group Director of Communications	Ruth Settle
Group Finance Director	Ian Griffiths
Managing Director, ITV Studios	Lee Bartlett
HR Director	Andy Doyle
Group Legal Director	
& Company Secretary	Andrew Garard

ITV PLC *cont'd*

Managing Director, ITV Brand	
& Commercial	Rupert Howell

Casting Directors at ITV Studios

Manchester
Gennie Radcliffe, Coronation Street
June West, Casting Director
Rick Laxton, Casting Assistant (to Gennie Radcliffe)
Katy Belshaw, Casting Assistant (to June West)

Leeds
Faye Styring, Emmerdale
Louise Bennett, Casting Assistant

If you would like one of the casting teams to cover your performance in a stage production, please e-mail casting@itv.com including your name, the theatre and the dates.

ITV MERIDIAN

ITV Meridian is part of ITV Plc
Forum One
Solent Business Park
Whiteley, Hants PO15 7PA
F 0844 8812074   **T 0844 8812000**

Meridian Board

Director of Regional Sales	David Croft
Regional Director, ITV Meridian,	
ITV London & ITV Anglia	Mark Southgate

Executives

Finance Manager	Natasha Coxhead
Head of News	Robin Britton

 Wales

ITV WALES

Television Centre
Culverhouse Cross
Cardiff CF5 6XJ   **T 0844 8810100**
E news@itvwales.com
W www.itv.com/wales

Wales: All week

Director, ITV Wales	Mike Blair

West    Westcountry

ITV WEST & ITV WESTCOUNTRY

Bath Road, Bristol BS4 3HG T 0844 8812345

Director, ITV West Mark Southgate

S4C - THE WELSH FOURTH CHANNEL AUTHORITY

Parc Tŷ Glas
Llanishen
Cardiff CF14 5DU
F 029 2075 4444 T 029 2074 7444
e s4c@s4c.co.uk
W www.s4c.co.uk

The Welsh Fourth Channel Authority

Chair John Walter Jones OBE

Authority Members

Bill Davies Dr Glenda Jones
John Davies Sir Roger Jones OBE
Cenwyn Edwards Winston Roddick CB QC
Dyfrig Jones Rheon Tomos

Senior Staff

Chief Executive Iona Jones
Director of Commissioning Rhian Gibson
Director of Communications Garffild Lloyd Lewis
Director of Finance & Human Resources Kathryn Morris
Director of Broadcast & Distribution Arshad Rasul
Director of Business Affairs Delyth Wynne Griffiths
Director of Commercial & Corporate Policy Elin Morris

STV

Glasgow Office

Pacific Quay, Glasgow G51 1PQ
F 0141 300 3030 T 0141 300 3000
W www.stv.tv

Aberdeen Office

Television Centre, Craigshaw Business Park
West Tullos, Aberdeen AB12 3QH T 01224 848848
W www.stv.tv

London Office

2nd Floor, Garfield House
86-88 Edgware Road
London W2 2EA T 020 7535 7250
W www.stv.tv

Managing Director Bobby Hain
Head of News & Current Affairs Gordon MacMillan
Chief Executive Rob Woodward
Director of Content Alan Clements
Head of Drama Margaret Enefer
Head of Factual & Factual Entertainment Paul Murray

 Tyne Tees    Border

ITV TYNE TEES & ITV BORDER

Television House, The Watermark
Gateshead NE11 9SZ T 0844 8815000

Teesside News Gathering

20 Manor Way
Belasis Hall Technology Park
Billingham, Cleveland TS23 4HN
E tttvnews@itv.com T 0844 8815000

North East and North Yorkshire: Weekday and Weekend

Executive Chair ITV Adam Crozier
Head of News Lucy West
Managing Director, SignPost Malcolm Wright

UTV PLC

Ormeau Road, Belfast BT7 1EB
F 028 9024 6695 T 028 9032 8122
E info@u.tv
W www.u.tv

Northern Ireland: Weekday and Weekend

Chairman J B McGuckian BSc (Econ)
Group Chief Executive J McCann BSc, FCA
Group Financial Director Jim Downey
Managing Director, Television Michael Wilson
Head of Communications Orla McKibbin
Head of News & Current Affairs Rob Morrison
Sales Director Paul Hutchinson

itv Yorkshire

ITV YORKSHIRE

The Television Centre, Leeds LS3 1JS
F 0113 244 5107   T 0113 222 7000
W www.itv.com

London Office
London Television Centre
Upperground, London SE1 9LT   T 020 7620 1620

Executives

Head of News	Will Venters
Controller of Comedy Drama	
& Drama Features	Michelle Buck
Creative Director ITV Studios	John Whiston

sky

SKY SATELLITE TELEVISION
BRITISH SKY BROADCASTING LTD (BSkyB)

Grant Way, Isleworth
Middlesex TW7 5QD
F 0870 2403060   T 0870 2403000
W www.sky.com/corporate

Chief Executive	Jeremy Darroch
Chief Financial Officer	Andrew Griffith
Managing Director,	
Entertainment & News	Sophie Turner Laing
Director for People	Deborah Baker
Chief Operating Officer	Mike Darcey
Group Director of Corporate Affairs	Graham McWilliam
General Counsel	James Conyers
Managing Director, Sky Sports	Barney Francis
Group Director of Engineering	
& Platform Technology	Alun Webber
Chief Technology Officer	Didier Lebrat
Group Director, Business Performance	William Mellis
Managing Director, Enterprise	David Rowe
Managing Director, Customer Group	Andrea Zappia

10TH PLANET PRODUCTIONS
75 Woodland Gardens, London N10 3UD   T/F 020 8442 2659
E admin@10thplanetproductions.com
W www.10thplanetproductions.com

30 BIRD PRODUCTIONS
Citylife, 182-190 Newmarket Road
Cambridge CB5 8HE   M 07970 960995
E info@30birdproductions.org
W www.30birdproductions.org

A STAGE KINDLY
7 Northiam, Cromer Street
London WC1H 8LB   M 07947 074887
E astagekindly@aol.com
W www.astagekindly.com

ACORN ENTERTAINMENTS LTD
PO Box 64, Cirencester
Glos GL7 5YD
F 01285 642291   T 01285 644622
E info@acornents.co.uk
W www.acornents.co.uk

ACT PRODUCTIONS LTD
20-22 Stukeley Street, 3rd Floor, London WC2B 5LR
F 020 7242 3568   T 020 3077 8900
E info@actproductions.co.uk
W www.actproductions.co.uk

ACT 1 PRODUCTIONS
25 Falkland Road, Kentish Town
London NW5 2PU   M 07814 171929
E info@act1productions.co.uk
W www.act1productions.co.uk

ACTOR'S TEMPLE THE
13-14 Warren Street, London W1T 5LG
M 07771 734670   T 020 3004 4537
E info@actorstemple.com
W www.actorstemple.com

ACTORS PLATFORM LTD
Showcase for Professional Actors. Central London. Monthly
7 Brookfield Road, West Kirby
Wirral CH48 4EJ   M 07849 999035
E melissa@actorsplatform.com
W www.actorsplatform.com

AJTC THEATRE COMPANY
28 Rydes Hill Crescent, Guildford
Surrey GU2 9UH   T/F 01483 232795
W www.ajtctheatre.co.uk

ALGERNON LTD
24 Cleveleys Road, London E5 9JN
F 0870 1388516   T 07092 805026
E info@algernonproductions.com
W www.algernonproductions.com

AMBASSADOR THEATRE GROUP
39-41 Charing Cross Road, London WC2H 0AR
F 020 7534 6109   T 020 7534 6100
E atglondon@theambassadors.com
W www.ambassadortickets.com

ANTIC DISPOSITION
4A Oval Road, London NW1 7EB   T 020 7284 0760
E info@anticdisposition.co.uk
W www.anticdisposition.co.uk

AOD (ACTORS OF DIONYSUS)
14 Cuthbert Road, Brighton BN2 0EN   T/F 01273 692604
E info@actorsofdionysus.com
W www.actorsofdionysus.com

ARDEN ENTERTAINMENT
17-19 Bedford Street, Covent Garden
London WC2E 9HP   T 020 7868 5535
E info@arden-entertainment.co.uk
W www.arden-entertainment.co.uk

ARTS MANAGEMENT (Redroofs Associates)
Contact: By Post
Novello Theatre, High Street
Sunninghill, Ascot SL5 9NE

ASHTON GROUP THEATRE THE
The Old Fire Station, Abbey Road
Barrow-in-Furness, Cumbria LA14 1XH   T 01229 430636
E theashtongroup@btconnect.com
W www.ashtongroup.co.uk

ATC
The Tab Centre, 3 Godfrey Place
London E2 7NT
F 020 7033 7360   T 020 7739 8298
E atc@atctheatre.com
W www.atctheatre.com

ATTIC THEATRE COMPANY (LONDON) LTD
Mitcham Library, 157 London Road
Mitcham CR4 2YR   T 020 8640 6800
E info@attictheatrecompany.com
W www.attictheatrecompany.com

BARNES Andy PRODUCTIONS
5A Irving Street, London WC2H 7AT   T 020 7839 9003
E andy@andybarnesproductions.com
W www.andybarnesproductions.com

BEE & BUSTLE ENTERPRISES
32 Exeter Road, London NW2 4SB
F 020 8450 1057   T 020 8450 0371
E info@beeandbustle.co.uk
W www.beeandbustle.co.uk

BIRMINGHAM STAGE COMPANY THE
Suite 228, The Linen Hall, 162 Regent Street
London W1B 5TB
F 020 7437 3395   T 020 7437 3391
E info@birminghamstage.com
W www.birminghamstage.com

BLUE BOX ENTERTAINMENT LTD
Top Floor, 80-81 St Martin's Lane
London WC2N 4AA
F 020 3292 1699   T 020 7395 7520
E info@newbluebox.com
W www.newbluebox.com

BLUE STAR PRODUCTIONS
Contact: Barrie Stacey, Keith Hopkins
7-8 Shaldon Mansions, 132 Charing Cross Road
London WC2H 0LA
F 020 7836 2949   T 020 7836 6220
E hopkinstacey@aol.com
W www.barriestacey.com

BORDER CROSSINGS
13 Bankside, Enfield EN2 8BN
F 020 8366 5239   T 020 8829 8928
E info@bordercrossings.org.uk
W www.bordercrossings.org.uk

BOTELLO Catalina
48 New Cavendish Street, London W1G 8TG
M 07939 060434   T 020 7935 1360
E contact@catalinabotello.com
W www.outoftheboxproductions.org

BRIT-POL THEATRE LTD
10 Bristol Gardens, London W9 2JG   T 020 7266 0323
E admin@britpoltheatre.com
W www.britpoltheatre.com

BRITISH THEATRE SEASON IN MONACO
1 Hogarth Hill, London NW11 6AY   T 020 8455 3278
E mail@montecarlotheatre.co.uk
W www.montecarlotheatre.co.uk

BROADHOUSE PRODUCTIONS LTD
Lodge Rocks House, Bilbrook
Minehead, Somerset TA24 6RD
F 01984 641027   T 01984 640773
E admin@broadhouse.co.uk

BROOKE Nick LTD
2nd Floor, 80-81 St Martin's Lane
London WC2N 4AA
F 020 7240 2947   T 020 7240 3901
E nick@nickbrooke.com
W www.nickbrooke.com

BUDDY WORLDWIDE LTD
PO Box 293, Letchworth Garden City
Herts SG6 9EU
F 01462 684851   T 020 7240 9941
E info@buddyshow.com
W www.buddythemusical.com

BUSH THEATRE
Shepherd's Bush Green, London W12 8QD   T 020 8743 3584
E info@bushtheatre.co.uk
W www.bushtheatre.co.uk

CAHOOTS THEATRE COMPANY
Contact: Denise Silvey
St Martin's Theatre, West Street
London WC2N 9NH   T 020 8743 7777
E ds@denisesilvey.com

CAP PRODUCTION SOLUTIONS LTD
116 Wigmore Road, Carshalton
Surrey SM5 1RQ
F 07970 763480   M 07973 432576
E leigh@leighporter.com

CAPRICORN STAGE (& SCREEN) DIRECTIONS
9 Spencer House, Vale of Health
Hampstead, London NW3 1AS   T 020 7794 5843

CENTRELINE PRODUCTIONS
293 Lea Bridge Road, London E10 7NE   M 07710 522438
E jenny@centrelinenet.com
W www.centrelinenet.com

CHAIN REACTION THEATRE COMPANY
Three Mills Studios, Sugar House Yard
Sugar House Lane, London E15 2QS   T/F 020 8534 0007
E mail@chainreactiontheatre.co.uk
W www.chainreactiontheatre.co.uk

CHANNEL THEATRE PRODUCTIONS LTD
Penistone House, 58 High Street
St Lawrence, Ramsgate, Kent CT11 0QH   T 01843 587950
E info@channel-theatre.co.uk
W www.channel-theatre.co.uk

CHAPMAN Duggie ASSOCIATES
Concerts. Musicals. Pantomime
The Old Coach House, 202 Common Edge Road
Blackpool FY4 5DG   T/F 01253 691823
E duggie@chapmanassociates.fsnet.co.uk
W www.duggiechapman.co.uk

CHEEK BY JOWL
Contact: Declan Donnellan, Nick Ormerod
Stage Door, Barbican Centre
Silk Street, London EC2Y 8DS   T 020 7382 7281
E info@cheekbyjowl.com
W www.cheekbyjowl.com

CHICHESTER FESTIVAL THEATRE
Oaklands Park, Chichester, West Sussex PO19 6AP
F 01243 787288   T 01243 784437
E admin@cft.org.uk
W www.cft.org.uk

CHICKENSHED
Chase Side, Southgate
London N14 4PE   T 020 8351 6161
E susanj@chickenshed.org.uk
W www.chickenshed.org.uk

CHOL THEATRE
Contact: Andrew Loretto (Director, Theatre & International),
Susan Burns (Director, Education & Community)
Lawrence Batley Theatre, 8 Queen Street
Huddersfield, West Yorkshire HD1 2SP
F 01484 425336   T 01484 536008
E info@choltheatre.co.uk
W www.choltheatre.co.uk

CHURCHILL THEATRE BROMLEY LTD
Producing Theatre
The Churchill, High Street
Bromley, Kent BR1 1HA
F 020 8290 6968   T 020 8464 7131
W www.ambassadortickets.com/churchill

CLEAN BREAK
Theatre Education. New Writing
2 Patshull Road, London NW5 2LB
F 020 7482 8611   T 020 7482 8600
E general@cleanbreak.org.uk
W www.cleanbreak.org.uk

CODRON Michael PLAYS LTD
Aldwych Theatre Offices, London WC2B 4DF
F 020 7240 8467   T 020 7240 8291

COLE KITCHENN LTD
212 Strand, London WC2R 1AP
F 020 7353 9639   T 020 7427 5682
E info@colekitchenn.com
W www.colekitchenn.com

COMPLICITE
14 Anglers Lane, London NW5 3DG
F 020 7485 7701   T 020 7485 7700
E email@complicite.org
W www.complicite.org

CONCORDANCE
Contact: Neil McPherson
Finborough Theatre, 118 Finborough Road
London SW10 9ED   T 020 7244 7439
E admin@concordance.org.uk
W www.concordance.org.uk

CONTEMPORARY STAGE COMPANY
9 Finchley Way, London N3 1AG
E contemp.stage@hotmail.co.uk
W www.contemporarystage.co.uk

CONWAY Clive CELEBRITY PRODUCTIONS LTD
32 Grove Street, Oxford OX2 7JT
F 01865 514409   T 01865 514830
E info@celebrityproductions.org

infopage

What is a theatre producer?

A theatre producer is someone who oversees and organises a theatre show. He or she will find, or arrange for other professionals to find, a suitable script, design, director and cast for each production, while also managing all finances and marketing.

How should I use these listings?

Theatre producers tend to use casting directors to put forward suitable actors for the parts in forthcoming productions, but you could also try approaching them yourself. Rather than sending your CV and headshot to every producer listed, it would be best to do some research first in order to target your search. You need to decide what type of work you want to do first, as there is no need to waste your time and the producer's time sending your CV to unsuitable companies. Then find out what each company has produced in the past, what they are currently working on, and if possible what they are considering producing in the future, and only send your CV to those most relevant to the roles you want to play. Don't forget to include a covering letter which states why you are contacting this producer in particular: this could be because you feel you are perfect for a particular role in their next production, for example. Personalising and targeting your correspondence in this way gives you the best chance of your CV being considered in a favourable light.

How should I approach theatre producers?

You should contact theatre producers by post or e-mail only. We would advise against calling them, especially when approaching them for the first time. Address your correspondence to an individual within the company, as this demonstrates that you have done your research. If you are unsure as to the best method of applying to theatre producers, as with other casting professionals it is safest to post your CV and headshot in the traditional way rather than e-mailing it. Remember to put your name and telephone number on the back of the photo in case it gets separated from your CV. It would be a good idea to include a SAE big enough to contain your 10 x 8 photo and with sufficient postage to increase your chances of getting a reply. Do not enclose your showreel but you can mention that you have one available in your covering letter, and if the producer is interested in viewing it they will contact you.

When should I approach theatre producers?

Listen to industry news and have a look at theatre producers' websites for forthcoming production details. The casting process usually takes place around three months prior to rehearsals, so bear this in mind when you are writing your covering letter.

How do I become a theatre producer?

The best way to learn about producing is to work in producing. Internships are a good way to get to grips with the industry; research the theatre producers listed over the following pages by checking their websites' jobs sections for vacancies. Remember to make sure they actually work in the area you are interested in before making contact. You should also try to build up a good general knowledge of the industry by going to see as many theatrical productions as you can and keeping track of which producers work on which types of shows.

Richard Jordan is an award-winning theatre producer who has produced over 130 productions in 16 different countries, enjoying associations with many of the world's leading producing theatres and organisations. In 2000 he became the first recipient of the TIF/Society of London Theatre Producers Bursary and has been listed in The Stage's Top 100 British Professionals for five years. In 2008 Richard was nominated for the TMA/Stage Award for Outstanding Achievement in UK Regional Theatre.

Alan Ayckbourn once said: "Keep in with a commercial producer and you will never starve!" For the most part those days are behind us and today's theatre industry is certainly not fuelled by expensive lunches. It is an industry where we all need each other, whether onstage, backstage, or in the audience, if the industry is to have a future.

So, what makes a good producer? I believe it's a combination of passion, business sense, and a large dollop of optimism! Over the following pages you will read a range of different producer and company names representing theatre production across its many mediums. We are quite an eclectic bunch so whether you're interested in physical theatre, musicals, new writing, dance, puppetry, or classical drama, you're sure to find someone creating exactly that.

The producer is the person who helms the production, and whilst the director may be the person you first come into contact with, it is ultimately the producer who will hold the final say and who will engage the company. A key thing I look for is someone who can both serve the production well and also will be a good company member. Good theatre is about team work and collaboration that ultimately results in serving the work well when it's finally presented before an audience.

The most important element when approaching a producer is research. So much time and expense can be wasted on sending out CVs, photographs, or scripts if the person you are writing to does not produce the work that interests you. Being theatrically aware is important for anyone working in the constantly evolving theatre industry. Some companies have their own casting directors and it is always good to check first before sending in resumes. Whilst many producers welcome resumes being sent in, speculative enquiries without any knowledge of forthcoming productions are usually less successful. The Society of London Theatre (SOLT) publishes a comprehensive index of forthcoming productions. The Stage newspaper also provides news from across the industry and is a valuable source for developments within the industry.

A while back I was told the story of a colleague who was casting a show and called an agent to make an availability check on an actor, to be told by the agent that she "no longer represented them". He asked, "Could you tell me where he went?" and after a few moments and some scrabbling of papers the agent returned and said, "Actually I do still represent him!" Ultimately you are your own machine and what you put in is what you get back. Whilst many actors have agents, it is important to also keep yourself abreast of opportunities. Often if you spot something which you think you may be suitable for, it's good to draw your agent's attention to it just in case they've missed it or even forgotten about you – there's that element of team work again!

One way of attracting a producer's attention would be to invite them to your upcoming show. Ensuring you get your invitations out in good time is very important. Producers tend to get booked up, and once into rehearsal and performance actors often become distracted, meaning that so often an invite arrives with a matter of days left to see the production. Often the reason for doing a job for little remuneration is to increase your exposure. It's therefore heartbreaking if you've slogged your guts out only to have not got your invitations out in sufficient time.

To keep their business alive producers need actors, directors, and designers but above all they need work to produce. Some producers accept unsolicited scripts, while others only use literary agents, so it is advisable to check first and again to be aware of the work they produce.

Finally, it's sometimes easy to forget that we all work in 'show *business*' and ultimately your own decisions drive forward your own career ambitions. It's important to understand the logic behind the choices you make – even if only you understand them! As a producer this is particularly important; it keeps me motivated and passionate for the work I produce and the collaborations that I enjoy both now and in the future. Ultimately for all of us working in the theatre industry, the relationships we forge, whether over the lunch table or within the rehearsal room, can form the basis of many long runs, hopefully with our own careers being part of them!

CREATIVE MANAGEMENT & PRODUCTIONS (CMP) LTD
1st Floor, 26-28 Neal Street
London WC2H 9QQ
F 020 7240 3037   T 020 7240 3033
E mail@cmplimited.com
W www.cmplimited.com

CRO18 PRODUCTIONS
Town Hall Theatre, Galway
Co. Galway, Ireland   T 00 353 851420683
E croiproductions@yahoo.co.uk

DEAD EARNEST THEATRE
Sheffield Design Studio, 40 Ball Street
Sheffield S3 8DB   T 0114 321 0450
E info@deadearnest.co.uk
W www.deadearnest.co.uk

DEAN Lee
PO Box 10703, London WC2H 9ED
F 020 7836 6968   T 020 7497 5111
E admin@leedean.co.uk

DEBUT PRODUCTIONS
Actor Showcases in London's West End & Manchester
65 Norton Way North, Letchworth
Herts SG6 1BH   M 07505 677994
E submissions@debutproductions.co.uk
W www.debutproductions.co.uk

DISNEY THEATRICAL PRODUCTIONS (UK)
Lyceum Theatre
21 Wellington Street
London WC2E 7RQ
F 020 7845 0999   T 020 7845 0900

DONEGAN David LTD
PO Box LB689, London W1A 9LB   M 07957 358909
E daviddonegan@hotmail.co.uk

DRAMATIS PERSONAE LTD
Contact: Nathan Silver, Nicolas Kent
19 Regency Street, London SW1P 4BY   T 020 7834 9300
E ns@nathansilver.com

DU FER Paul TOUR BOOKING SERVICES
39 Ludford Close, Warrington Road
Croydon, Surrey CRO 4BY   T 020 8941 8122
E info@pauldufer.com
W www.pauldufer.com

EASTERN ANGLES THEATRE COMPANY
Touring
Sir John Mills Theatre, Gatacre Road
Ipswich, Suffolk IP1 2LQ
F 01473 384999   T 01473 218202
E admin@easternangles.co.uk
W www.easternangles.co.uk

EASY TIGER PRODUCTIONS LTD
7 Caroline House, London W6 9RG   T/F 020 7371 8656
E anything@easytigerproductions.com
W www.easytigerproductions.com

ELLIOTT Paul
16 Westbourne Park Road
London W2 5PH   T 020 7379 4870
E pre@paulelliott.ltd.uk

ENGLISH NATIONAL OPERA
London Coliseum, St Martin's Lane
London WC2N 4ES
F 020 7845 9277   T 020 7836 0111
W www.eno.org

ENGLISH STAGE COMPANY LTD
Royal Court Theatre, Sloane Square
London SW1W 8AS
F 020 7565 5001   T 020 7565 5050
E info@royalcourttheatre.com
W www.royalcourttheatre.com

ENGLISH TOURING THEATRE (ETT)
25 Short Street, London SE1 8LJ
F 020 7633 0188   T 020 7450 1990
E admin@ett.org.uk
W www.ett.org.uk

ENTERTAINMENT BUSINESS LTD THE
Cameo House, 11 Bear Street
London WC2H 7AS
F 020 7766 5275   T 020 7766 5274
E info@entbiz.co.uk
W www.entbiz.co.uk

EUROPEAN THEATRE COMPANY THE
15 Beverley Avenue, London SW20 0RL   T 020 8946 3400
E admin@europeantheatre.co.uk
W www.europeantheatre.co.uk

FACADE
Musicals
43A Garthorne Road, London SE23 1EP
F 020 8291 4969   T 020 8291 7079
E facade@cobomedia.com

FAIRBANK PRODUCTIONS
Contact: Gerald Armin
27 Harcourt Road, London E15 3DX   T/F 020 8555 3085
E info@fairbankproductions.co.uk
W www.fairbankproductions.co.uk

FEATHER PRODUCTIONS LTD
Unit 3, Blade House
77 Petersham Road, Richmond   T 020 8940 2335
E anna@featherproductions.com
W www.featherproductions.com

FELL Andrew LTD
4 Ching Court, 49-51 Monmouth Street
London WC2H 9EY
F 020 7240 2499   T 020 7240 2420
E hq@andrewfell.co.uk

FERGUSON Jason LTD
5 The Gallery, 6 North Road
Richmond, London TW9 4HA
F 020 8711 5662   T 020 8876 2707
E info@fergusonlive.com
W www.fergusonlive.com

FIELD Anthony ASSOCIATES LTD
Top Floor, 80-81 St Martin's Lane
London WC2N 4AA
F 020 7240 2947   T 020 7240 5453
E info@anthonyfieldassociates.com
W www.anthonyfieldassociates.com

FIELDER Simon PRODUCTIONS
The Leatherhead Theatre, 7 Church Street
Leatherhead, Surrey KT22 8DN
F 01372 365135   T 01372 365134
E enquiries@simonfielder.com

FIERY ANGEL LTD
22-24 Torrington Place, London WC1E 7HJ
F 020 7436 6287   T 020 7907 7012
E mail@fiery-angel.com
W www.fiery-angel.com

FORBIDDEN THEATRE COMPANY
20 Rupert Street, London W1D 6DF T 0845 0093084
E info@forbidden.org.uk
W www.forbidden.org.uk

FORD Vanessa PRODUCTIONS LTD
Upper House Farm, Upper House Lane
Shamley Green, Surrey GU5 0SX T 01483 278203
E vanessa@vanessafordproductions.co.uk
W www.thehobbittour.co.uk

FOX Robert LTD
6 Beauchamp Place, London SW3 1NG
F 020 7225 1638 T 020 7584 6855
E info@robertfoxltd.com
W www.robertfoxltd.com

FRANK Lina B. / AUSFORM
Circus. Live Arts. Theatre. London & Scandinavia
90 York Road, Montpelier BS6 5QF
M 07951 596078 T +46 07 61 38 28 29
E lina@ausform.co.uk
W www.ausform.co.uk

FRANKLIN Neil PRODUCTIONS LTD
187 Drury Lane, London WC2B 5QD M 07736 931654
E neil@franklinproductions.co.uk

FREEDMAN Bill LTD
Colebrooke House, 10-12 Gaskin Street
London N1 2RY T 020 7226 5554

FRESH GLORY PRODUCTIONS
59 St Martin's Lane, London WC2N 4JS T 020 7240 1941
E info@freshglory.com
W www.freshglory.com

FRICKER Ian (THEATRE) LTD
3rd Floor, 146 Strand
London WC2R 1JD
F 020 7836 3078 T 020 7836 3090
E mail@ianfricker.com
W www.ianfricker.com

FRIEDMAN Sonia PRODUCTIONS
Duke of York's Theatre
104 St Martin's Lane
London WC2N 4BG
F 020 7845 8759 T 020 7845 8750
E office@soniafriedman.com
W www.soniafriedman.com

GALLEON THEATRE COMPANY LTD
Contact: Alice De Sousa
Greenwich Playhouse
Greenwich BR Station Forecourt
189 Greenwich High Road, London SE10 8JA
F 020 8310 7276 T 020 8858 9256
E boxoffice@galleontheatre.co.uk
W www.galleontheatre.co.uk

GBM PRODUCTIONS LTD
Bidlake Toft, Roadford Lake
Germansweek, Devon EX21 5BD
F 01837 871123 T 01837 871522
E gbm@bidlaketoft.com
W www.musicaltheatrecreations.com

GIANT STEPS LTD
41 Parfrey Street, London W6 9EW
M 07808 742307 T/F 020 8741 2446
E giantstepstheatre@googlemail.com
W www.rolandjaquarello.com

GINGERBEE PRODUCTIONS LTD
Sparkhouse Studios, Ropewalk
Lincoln, Lincs LN6 7DQ
F 01522 837201 T 01522 730356
E info@gingerbee.co.uk
W www.gingerbee.co.uk

GODOT COMPANY
51 The Cut, London SE1 8LF T 020 7633 0599
E godot@calderpublications.com

GOODNIGHTS ENTERTAINMENT LTD
74 Pannier Place
Milton Keynes MK14 7QP T 01908 672077
E goodnights@talk21.com
W www.goodnights.org

GOUCHER Mark LTD
3rd Floor, 20-22 Stukeley Street
London WC2B 5LR
F 020 7438 9577 T 020 7438 9570
E jess@markgoucher.com

GRAEAE THEATRE COMPANY
Bradbury Studios, 138 Kingsland Road
London E2 8DY T 020 7613 6900
E info@graeae.org
W www.graeae.org

GRAHAM David ENTERTAINMENT LTD
72 New Bond Street, London W1S 1RR
F 0870 3211700 T 0870 3211600
E info@davidgraham.co.uk
W www.davidgrahamentertainment.com

HAMPSTEAD THEATRE PRODUCTIONS LTD
Eton Avenue, Swiss Cottage
London NW3 3EU
F 020 7449 4201 T 020 7449 4200
E info@hampsteadtheatre.com
W www.hampsteadtheatre.com

HANDSTAND PRODUCTIONS
13 Hope Street, Liverpool L1 9BH
F 0151 709 3515 T 0151 708 7441
E info@handstand-uk.com
W www.handstand-uk.com

HARLEY PRODUCTIONS
68 New Cavendish Street
London W1G 8TE
F 020 8202 8863 T 020 7580 3247
E harleyprods@aol.com

HAYDEN SCOTT PRODUCTIONS
Contact: Daniel Sparrow, Mike Walsh
44B Floral Street, London WC2E 9DA M 07879 897900
E info@danielsparrowproductions.com
W www.danielsparrowproductions.com

HAYMARKET THE
c/o The Anvil Trust, Wote Street
Basingstoke, Hampshire RG21 7NW
F 01256 814845 T 01256 819797
E christine.bradwell@anvilarts.org.uk
W www.anvilarts.org.uk

HEADLONG THEATRE LTD
3rd Floor, 34-35 Berwick Street
London W1F 8RP
F 020 7438 1749 T 020 7478 0270
E info@headlongtheatre.co.uk
W www.headlongtheatre.co.uk

HENDERSON Glynis PRODUCTIONS LTD
69 Charlotte Street, London W1T 4PJ
F 020 7436 1489   T 020 7580 9644
E info@ghmp.co.uk
W www.ghmp.co.uk

HENDRY Jamie PRODUCTIONS LTD
Amadeus House, Floral Street
London WC2E 9DP
F 020 7812 6495   T 020 7812 7296
E office@jamiehendryproductions.com
W www.jamiehendryproductions.com

HENNEGAN Nicholas LTD
33A Prebend Mansions, Chiswick High Road
London W4 2LU   T 020 8582 7506
E info@nicholashennegan.com
W www.nicholashennegan.com

HESTER John PRODUCTIONS (Intimate Mysteries Theatre Company)
105 Stoneleigh Park Road, Epsom
Surrey KT19 0RF   T/F 020 8393 5705
E hjohnhester@aol.com

HISS & BOO COMPANY LTD THE
Contact: Ian Liston. By Post (SAE). No unsolicited scripts
Nyes Hill, Wineham Lane
Bolney, West Sussex RH17 5SD
F 01444 882057   T 01444 881707
E email@hissboo.co.uk
W www.hissboo.co.uk

HISTORIA THEATRE COMPANY
8 Cloudesley Square, London N1 0HT
M 07811 892079   T 020 7837 8008
E kateprice@lineone.net
W www.historiatheatre.com

HOIPOLLOI
Office F, Dale's Brewery
Gwydir Street, Cambridge CB1 2LJ   T 01223 322748
E info@hoipolloi.org.uk
W www.hoipolloi.org.uk

HOLLOW CROWN PRODUCTIONS
2 Norfolk Road, London E17 5QS   M 07930 530948
E enquiries@hollowcrown.co.uk
W www.hollowcrown.co.uk

HOLMAN Paul ASSOCIATES LTD
Morritt House, 58 Station Approach
South Ruislip, Middlesex HA4 6SA
F 020 8839 3124   T 020 8845 9408
E enquiries@paulholmanassociates.co.uk
W www.paulholmanassociates.co.uk

HOLT Thelma LTD
Noel Coward Theatre, 85 St Martin's Lane
London WC2N 4AU
F 020 7812 7550   T 020 7812 7455
E thelma@dircon.co.uk
W www.thelmaholt.co.uk

HOUSE OF GULLIVER
Contact: By Post
60 Beaconsfield Road, Tring
Herts HP23 4DW

HUGHES Steve
Oakwood, 4 Armitage Road
Armitage Bridge HD4 7PG   M 07816 844024
E steve@hughes-productions.co.uk
W www.hughes-productions.co.uk

HULL TRUCK THEATRE
50 Ferensway, Hull HU2 8LB
F 01482 581182   T 01482 224800
E admin@hulltruck.co.uk
W www.hulltruck.co.uk

HUMBLE THEATRE COMPANY LTD THE
1 Broadwater Avenue
Letchworth SG6 3HE   T 0844 7400715
E info@humbletheatre.com
W www.humbletheatre.com

IAN David PRODUCTIONS
Third Floor, 33 Henrietta Street
London WC2E 8NA
F 020 7257 6381   T 020 7257 6380
W www.davidianproductions.com

IBSEN STAGE COMPANY
Flat 1, 1 Thurleigh Road
London SW12 8UB   M 07958 566274
E ask@ibsenstage.com
W www.ibsenstage.com

ICARUS THEATRE COLLECTIVE
32 Portland Place, London W1B 1NA   T 020 7998 1562
E info@icarustheatre.co.uk
W www.icarustheatre.co.uk

IMAGE MUSICAL THEATRE
23 Sedgeford Road, Shepherd's Bush
London W12 0NA
F 020 8749 9294   T 020 8743 9380
E brian@imagemusicaltheatre.co.uk
W www.imagemusicaltheatre.co.uk

INCISOR
41 Edith Avenue, Peacehaven
East Sussex BN10 8JB
F 020 8830 4992   M 07979 498450
E sarahmann7@hotmail.co.uk
W www.theatre-company-incisor.com

INDIGO ENTERTAINMENTS
Tynymynydd, Bryneglwys
Corwen, Denbighshire LL21 9NP   T 01978 790211
E info@indigoentertainments.com
W www.indigoentertainments.com

INGRAM Colin LTD
Suite 526, Linen Hall
162-168 Regent Street
London W1B 5TE
F 020 7038 3907   T 020 7038 3906
E info@coliningramltd.com
W www.coliningramltd.com

INSIDE INTELLIGENCE
Theatre. Contemporary Opera. Music Theatre
13 Athlone Close
London E5 8HD
F 020 8985 7211   T 020 8986 8013
E admin@inside-intelligence.org.uk
W www.inside-intelligence.org.uk

INSTANT WIT
Comedy Improvisation Theatre Show. Corporate/Conference Entertainment Show. Drama Based Training
6 Worrall Place, Worrall Road
Clifton, Bristol BS8 2WP
M 07711 644094   T 0117 974 5734
E info@instantwit.co.uk
W www.instantwit.co.uk

Richard Jordan Productions Ltd

- **Producing**
- **General Management**
  UK and International Productions,
  and International Festivals
- **Consultancy**
- **Richard Jordan Productions Ltd**
  Mews Studios, 16 Vernon Yard
  London W11 2DX

  Tel: 020 7243 9001
  Fax: 020 7313 9667
  e-mail: richard.jordan@virgin.net

INTERNATIONAL THEATRE & MUSIC LTD
Contact: Piers Chater Robinson
Garden Studios, 11-15 Betterton Street
Covent Garden, London WC2H 9BP
F 020 7379 0801   T 020 7470 8786
E info@it-m.co.uk
W www.it-m.co.uk

JAM THEATRE COMPANY
21 Beechtree Avenue, Marlow
Bucks SL7 3NH   T 01628 487773
E office@jamtheatre.co.uk
W www.jamtheatre.co.uk

JAMES Bruce PRODUCTIONS LTD
68 St Georges Park Avenue
Westcliff-on-Sea, Essex SS0 9UD
M 07850 369018   T/F 01702 335970
E info@brucejamesproductions.co.uk
W www.brucejamesproductions.co.uk

JENKINS Andrew LTD
63 Kidbrooke Park Road, London SE3 0EE
F 020 8856 7106   T 020 8319 3657
E info@andrewjenkinsltd.com
W www.andrewjenkinsltd.com

JOHNSON David
85B Torriano Avenue, London NW5 2RX   T 020 7284 3733
E david@johnsontemple.co.uk

JOHNSON Gareth LTD
Plas Hafren, Eglwyswrw
Crymych, Pembrokeshire SA41 3UL
M 07770 225227   T 01239 891368
E gjltd@mac.com

JORDAN Andy PRODUCTIONS LTD
Studio D, 413-419 Harrow Road
Maida Vale, London W9 3QJ   M 07775 615205
E andy@andyjordanproductions.co.uk

JORDAN Richard PRODUCTIONS LTD
Mews Studios, 16 Vernon Yard
London W11 2DX
F 020 7313 9667   T 020 7243 9001
E richard.jordan@virgin.net

JORDAN PRODUCTIONS LTD
Phoenix Auction Rooms, 142 Langney Road
Eastbourne, East Sussex BN22 8AQ
F 01323 417766   T 01323 417745
E info@jordanproductionsltd.co.uk

KELLY Robert C. LTD
The Alhambra Suite
82 Mitchell Street
Glasgow G1 3NA
F 0141 229 1441   T 0141 229 1444
E robert@robertckelly.co.uk
W www.robertckelly.co.uk

KENWRIGHT Bill LTD
BKL House, 1 Venice Walk, London W2 1RR
F 020 7446 6222   T 020 7446 6200
E info@kenwright.com
W www.kenwright.com

KING'S HEAD THEATRE PRODUCTIONS LTD
115 Upper Street, London N1 1QN   T 020 7226 8561
W www.kingsheadtheatre.org

LATCHMERE THEATRE
Contact: Chris Fisher
Unit 5A, Spaces Business Centre
Ingate Place, London SW8 3NS
F 020 7978 2631   T 020 7978 2620
E latchmere@fishers.org.uk

LHP LTD
PO Box 60231, London EC1P 1FL   M 07973 938634
E lhpltd@msn.com

LIMELIGHT PRODUCTIONS
Unit 13, The io Centre, The Royal Arsenal
Seymour Street, London SE18 6SX
F 020 8853 9579   T 020 8853 9570
E enquiries@thelimelightgroup.co.uk

LINNIT PRODUCTIONS LTD
123A King's Road, London SW3 4PL
F 020 7352 3450   T 020 7352 7722

LIVE THEATRE
Broad Chare, Quayside
Newcastle upon Tyne NE1 3DQ   T 0191 261 2694
E info@live.org.uk
W www.live.org.uk

LONDON BUBBLE THEATRE COMPANY LTD
5 Elephant Lane, London SE16 4JD
F 020 7231 2366   T 020 7237 4434
E admin@londonbubble.org.uk
W www.londonbubble.org.uk

LONDON CLASSIC THEATRE
The Production Office
63 Shirley Avenue
Sutton, Surrey SM1 3QT   T 020 8395 2095
E admin@londonclassictheatre.co.uk
W www.londonclassictheatre.co.uk

LONDON PRODUCTIONS LTD
PO Box 10703, London WC2H 9ED
F 020 7836 6968   T 020 7497 5111
E admin@leedean.co.uk

LONDON REPERTORY COMPANY
27 Old Gloucester Street
London WC1N 3XX   T/F 020 7258 1944
E info@londonrepertorycompany.com
W www.londonrepertorycompany.com

MACKINTOSH Cameron LTD
Contact: Paul Wooler (Casting Assistant)
1 Bedford Square, London WC1B 3RB
F 020 7436 2683   T 020 7637 8866
E paul@camack.co.uk

MACNAGHTEN PRODUCTIONS
19 Grange Court, Grange Road
Cambridge CB3 9BD　　　　　T 01223 577974

MALCOLM Christopher PRODUCTIONS LTD
11 Claremont Walk, Bath BA1 6HB
F 01225 480077　　　　　T 01225 445459
E cm@christophermalcolm.co.uk
W www.christophermalcolm.co.uk

MANS Johnny PRODUCTIONS LTD
PO Box 196, Hoddesdon, Herts EN10 7WG
F 01992 470516　　　　　T 01992 470907
E johnnymansagent@aol.com
W www.johnnymansproductions.co.uk

MASTERSON Guy PRODUCTIONS
The Hawthorne Auditorium
Campus West, The Campus
Welwyn Garden City, Herts AL8 6BX　　T/F 01707 330360
E admin@theatretoursinternational.com
W www.theatretoursinternational.com

MEADOW Jeremy LTD
73 Great Titchfield Street, London W1W 6RD
F 0870 7627882　　　　　T 020 7436 2244
E info@jeremymeadow.com

MENZIES Lee LTD
118-120 Wardour Street, London W1F 0TU
F 020 7734 4224　　　　　T 020 7734 9559
E leemenzies@leemenzies.co.uk
W www.leemenzies.co.uk

MIDDLE GROUND THEATRE CO LTD
3 Gordon Terrace, Malvern Wells
Malvern, Worcestershire WR14 4ER
F 01684 574472　　　　　T 01684 577231
E middleground@middlegroundtheatre.co.uk
W www.middlegroundtheatre.co.uk

MILLIONTH MUSE PRODUCTIONS
1st & 2nd Floors, 20 Stansfield Road
Stockwell, London SW9 9RZ　　T/F 020 7737 5300
E paul@millionthmuse.com
W www.millionthmuse.com

MITCHELL Matthew LTD
New Barn Farm, London Road
Hassocks, West Sussex BN6 9ND　　T/F 01273 842572
E info@matthewmitchell.org

MJE PRODUCTIONS LTD
Contact: Carole Winter, Michael Edwards
First Floor, 18 Exeter Street, London WC2E 7DU
F 020 7395 0261　　　　　T 020 7395 0260
E info@mjeproductions.com
W www.mjeproductions.com

MMP
4 D'Arblay Street, Soho
London W1F 8DJ　　　　　T 020 7494 4007
E mailbox@michaelmccabe.net
W www.michaelmccabe.net

MOKITAGRIT
6 Addington Road, London N4 4RP　　M 07980 564849
E mail@mokitagrit.com
W www.mokitagrit.com

MONSTER THEATRE PRODUCTIONS
c/o 17 Prince Road, Wallsend, Tyne & Wear NE28 8DN
F 0191 240 4016　　　　　T 0191 240 4011
E info@monsterproductions.co.uk
W www.monsterproductions.co.uk

MOVING THEATRE
16 Laughton Lodge
Nr Lewes, East Sussex BN8 6BY
F 01323 815736　　　　　T 01323 815726
E info@movingtheatre.com
W www.movingtheatre.com

MUSIC THEATRE LONDON
c/o Capriol Films, The Old Reading Room
The Street, Brinton, Melton Constable
Norfolk NR24 2QF　　　　　M 07831 243942
E info@capriolfilms.co.uk
W www.capriolfilms.co.uk

NADINE'S WINDOW
Showcase Theatre Company
E nadineswindow@yahoo.co.uk
W www.nadineswindow.com

NATIONAL ANGELS
123A Kings Road, London SW3 4PL
F 020 7352 3450　　　　　T 020 7376 4878
E admin@nationalangels.com

NATIONAL THEATRE
South Bank, London SE1 9PX
F 020 7452 3344　　　　　T 020 7452 3333
W www.nationaltheatre.org.uk

NEAL STREET PRODUCTIONS LTD
1st Floor
26-28 Neal Street, London WC2H 9QQ
F 020 7240 7099　　　　　T 020 7240 8890
E post@nealstreetproductions.com

NEWPALM PRODUCTIONS
26 Cavendish Avenue, London N3 3QN
F 020 8346 8257　　　　　T 020 8349 0802
E newpalm@btopenworld.com
W www.newpalm.co.uk

NEW PERSPECTIVES THEATRE COMPANY
Regional/National New Writing Touring Theatre
Park Lane Business Centre, Park Lane
Basford, Nottinghamshire NG6 0DW　　T 0115 927 2334
E info@newperspectives.co.uk
W www.newperspectives.co.uk

NICHOLAS Paul & IAN David ASSOCIATES LTD
c/o Third Floor, 33 Henrietta Street
London WC2E 8NA
F 020 7257 6381　　　　　T 020 7257 6380

NITRO
Formerly Black Theatre Co-operative
6 Brewery Road, London N7 9NH
F 020 7609 1221　　　　　T 020 7609 1331
E info@nitro.co.uk
W www.nitro.co.uk

NORDIC NOMAD PRODUCTIONS
Contact: Tanja Raaste (Creative Producer). Specialising in New Writing, Site Specific & Interactive Work, and Tango & Dance Events. Training & Workshops: Business Skills for Performers
64 Tulse Hill, London SW2 2PT　　M 07980 619165
E info@nordicnomad.com
W www.nordicnomad.com

NORTHERN BROADSIDES THEATRE COMPANY
Dean Clough
Halifax HX3 5AX　　　　　T 01422 369704
E sue@northern-broadsides.co.uk
W www.northern-broadsides.co.uk

NORTHERN STAGE (THEATRICAL PRODUCTIONS) LTD
Barras Bridge
Newcastle upon Tyne NE1 7RH
F 0191 242 7257   T 0191 232 3366
E info@northernstage.co.uk
W www.northernstage.co.uk

NORTHUMBERLAND THEATRE COMPANY (NTC)
The Playhouse, Bondgate Without
Alnwick, Northumberland NE66 1PQ
F 01665 605837   T 01665 602586
E admin@northumberlandtheatre.co.uk
W www.northumberlandtheatre.co.uk

OFF THE CUFF THEATRE COMPANY
2nd Floor, 91A Rivington Street
London EC2A 3AY
F 020 7739 3852   T 020 7739 2857
E otctheatre@aol.com
W www.otctheatre.co.uk

OLD VIC PRODUCTIONS PLC
The Old Vic Theatre, The Cut
Waterloo, London SE1 8NB
F 020 7981 0991   T 020 7928 2651
E becky.barber@oldvictheatre.com

ONE NIGHT BOOKING COMPANY THE
1 Hogarth Hill, London NW11 6AY   T 020 8455 3278
E mail@onenightbooking.com
W www.onenightbooking.com

OPERATING THEATRE COMPANY
22 Burghley Road, London NW5 1UE   T 020 7419 2476
E info@operating-theatre.co.uk
W www.operating-theatre.co.uk

OUT OF JOINT
7 Thane Works, Thane Villas, London N7 7NU
F 020 7609 0203   T 020 7609 0207
E ojo@outofjoint.co.uk
W www.outofjoint.co.uk

OVATION
Upstairs at The Gatehouse
The Gatehouse
Highgate Village, London N6 4BD
F 020 8340 3466   T 020 8340 4256
E events@ovationproductions.com
W www.ovationtheatres.com

PAINES PLOUGH
Fourth Floor, 43 Aldwych
London WC2B 4DN
F 020 7240 4534   T 020 7240 4533
E office@painesplough.com
W www.painesplough.com

PAPATANGO THEATRE COMPANY
184A Tressillian Road
London SE4 1XY   M 07834 958804
E papatango.theatre@gmail.com
W www.papatango.co.uk

PAPER MOON THEATRE COMPANY
6 Thames Meadow, West Molesey
Surrey KT8 1TQ   T/F 020 8873 1901
E jan@papermoontheatre.co.uk

PASSWORD PRODUCTIONS LTD
Contact: John Mackay
85B Torriano Avenue, London NW5 2RX   T 020 7284 3733
E johnmackay2001@aol.com

PENDLE PRODUCTIONS
Bridge Farm, 249 Hawes Side Lane
Blackpool FY4 4AA
F 01253 792930   T 01253 839375
E admin@pendleproductions.co.uk
W www.pendleproductions.co.uk

PENTABUS THEATRE
National Touring Company for New Writing
Bromfield, Ludlow
Shropshire SY8 2JU   T 01584 856564
E john@pentabus.co.uk
W www.pentabus.co.uk

PEOPLE SHOW
People Show Studios, Pollard Row
London E2 6NB
F 020 7739 0203   T 020 7729 1841
E people@peopleshow.co.uk
W www.peopleshow.co.uk

PERFECT PITCH MUSICALS LTD
5A Irving Street, London WC2H 7AT   T 020 7839 9003
E wendy@perfectpitchmusicals.com
W www.perfectpitchmusicals.com

PERFORMANCE BUSINESS THE
78 Oatlands Drive, Weybridge
Surrey KT13 9HT   T 01932 888885
E info@theperformance.biz
W www.theperformance.biz

PILOT THEATRE
New Writing & Multimedia YPT
York Theatre Royal, St Leonard's Place, York YO1 7HD
F 01904 656378   T 01904 635755
E info@pilot-theatre.com
W www.pilot-theatre.com

PLANTAGENET PRODUCTIONS
Drawing Room Recitals
Westridge Open Centre, Star Lane
Highclere, Nr Newbury RG20 9PJ   T 01635 253322

PLAYFUL PRODUCTIONS
Haymarket House, 1 Oxenden Street
London SW1Y 4EE
F 020 7811 4622   T 020 7811 4600
E aboutus@playfuluk.com

PLAYHOUSE ENTERTAINMENT GROUP THE
Playhouse Studios, First Floor, 104 Cavendish Place
Eastbourne, East Sussex BN21 3TZ   T/F 01323 638980
E enquiries@playhousecostumes.co.uk
W www.playhousecostumes.co.uk

PLUTO PRODUCTIONS LTD
New End Theatre, 27 New End
Hampstead, London NW3 1JD
F 020 7794 4044   T 020 7472 5800
E briandaniels@newendtheatre.co.uk
W www.newendtheatre.co.uk

POLKA THEATRE
240 The Broadway, Wimbledon SW19 1SB
F 020 8545 8365   T 020 8543 4888
E admin@polkatheatre.com
W www.polkatheatre.com

POPULAR PRODUCTIONS LTD
8A High Street, London N8 7PD   T 020 8347 0221
E info@popularproductions.com
W www.popularproductions.com

PORTER Richard LTD
214 Grange Road, London SE1 3AA
E office@richardporterltd.com
W www.richardporterltd.com
M 07884 183404

POSTER Kim
4th Floor, 80-81 St Martin's Lane
London WC2N 4AA
F 020 7504 8656
E admin@stanhopeprod.com
T 020 7240 3098

PROMENADE PRODUCTIONS
71 Endell Street, London WC2H 9AT
E natalie@promenadeproductions.com
W www.promenadeproductions.com
T 020 7240 3407

PUGH David & ROGERS Dafydd
Wyndhams Theatre, Charing Cross Road
London WC2H 0DA
F 020 7292 0399
E dpl@davidpughltd.com
T 020 7292 0390

PURSUED BY A BEAR PRODUCTIONS
Farnham Maltings, Bridge Square
Farnham GU9 7QR
E pursuedbyabear@yahoo.co.uk
W www.pursuedbyabear.co.uk
T 01252 745445

PW PRODUCTIONS LTD
2nd Floor, 80-81 St Martin's Lane
London WC2N 4AA
F 020 7240 2947
E info@pwprods.co.uk
W www.pwprods.co.uk
T 020 7395 7580

QDOS ENTERTAINMENT
Qdos House, Queen Margaret's Road
Scarborough, North Yorkshire YO11 2YH
F 01723 361958
E info@qdosentertainment.co.uk
W www.qdosentertainment.com
T 01723 500038

QUANTUM THEATRE
The Old Button Factory, 1-11 Bannockburn Road
Plumstead, London SE18 1ET
E office@quantumtheatre.co.uk
W www.quantumtheatre.co.uk
T 020 8317 9000

RAGS & FEATHERS THEATRE COMPANY
80 Summer Road, Thames Ditton
Surrey KT7 0QP
M 07958 724374
E jill@ragsandfeathers.freeserve.co.uk
T 020 8224 2203

RAIN OR SHINE THEATRE COMPANY
25 Paddock Gardens, Longlevens
Gloucester GL2 0ED
E theatre@rainorshine.co.uk
W www.rainorshine.co.uk
T/F 01452 521575

RATTLING TONGUE THEATRE COMPANY
44 Fairfield South, Kingston Upon Thames
Surrey KT1 2UW
E info@rattlingtongue.com
W www.rattlingtongue.com
M 07817 697510

REAL CIRCUMSTANCE THEATRE COMPANY
100 Lexden Road, West Bergholt
Colchester CO6 3BW
E info@realcircumstance.com
W www.realcircumstance.com

REALLY USEFUL THEATRE COMPANY THE
22 Tower Street, London WC2H 9TW
F 020 7240 1293
T 020 7240 0880

RED ROOM THE
11-15 Betterton Street, Covent Garden
London WC2H 9BP
E info@theredroom.org.uk
W www.theredroom.org.uk
T 020 7470 8790

RED ROSE CHAIN
Gippeswyk Hall, Gippeswyk Avenue
Ipswich, Suffolk IP2 9AF
E info@redrosechain.co.uk
W www.redrosechain.co.uk
T 01473 288886

RED SHIFT THEATRE COMPANY
PO Box 60151, London SW19 2TB
E jane@redshifttheatreco.co.uk
W www.redshifttheatreco.co.uk
T/F 020 8540 1271

REGENT'S PARK THEATRE LTD
The Iron Works, Inner Circle
Regent's Park, London NW1 4NR
F 020 7487 0776
W www.openairtheatre.com
T 0844 3753460

REVEAL THEATRE COMPANY LTD
The Creative Village
Staffordshire, University Business Village
72 Leek Road, Stoke on Trent ST4 2AR
E enquiries@revealtheatre.co.uk
W www.revealtheatre.co.uk
T 01782 294871

RGC PRODUCTIONS
260 Kings Road, Kingston
Surrey KT2 5HX
E info@rgcproductions.com
W www.rgcproductions.com
M 07740 286727

RHO DELTA LTD
Contact: Greg Ripley-Duggan
26 Goodge Street, London W1T 2QG
E info@ripleyduggan.com
T 020 7436 1392

ROCKET THEATRE
32 Baxter Road, Sale, Manchester M33 3AL
M 07788 723570
E martin@rockettheatre.co.uk
W www.rockettheatre.co.uk
T 0161 969 1444

ROGERS Nick LTD
212 Strand, London WC2R 1AP
E info@nickrogerslimited.com
W www.nickrogerslimited.com
T 020 7100 1123

ROSE Michael LTD
The Old Dairy, Throop Road
Holdenhurst, Bournemouth, Dorset BH8 0DL
F 01202 522311
E firstname@michaelroseltd.com
T 01202 522711

ROSENTHAL Suzanna LTD
PO Box 40001, London N6 4YA
E admin@suzannarosenthal.com
T/F 020 8340 4421

ROYAL COURT THEATRE PRODUCTIONS LTD
Sloane Square, London SW1W 8AS
F 020 7565 5001
E info@royalcourttheatre.com
W www.royalcourttheatre.com
T 020 7565 5050

ROYAL EXCHANGE THEATRE
St Ann's Square, Manchester M2 7DH
W www.royalexchange.co.uk
T 0161 833 9333

ROYAL SHAKESPEARE COMPANY
1 Earlham Street, London WC2H 9LL
F 020 7845 0505
W www.rsc.org.uk
T 020 7845 0500

ROYAL SHAKESPEARE COMPANY
The Courtyard Theatre
Southern Lane
Stratford-upon-Avon CV37 6BB
F 01789 272509   T 01789 296655
W www.rsc.org.uk

RUBINSTEIN Mark LTD
25 Short Street, London SE1 8LJ
F 0870 7059731   T 020 7021 0787
E info@mrluk.com

SALBERG & STEPHENSON LTD
18 Soho Square, London W1D 3QL   M 07960 999374
E soholondon@aol.com

SCAMP
Sutherland Callow Arts Management & Production
44 Church Lane, Arlesey, Beds SG15 6UX
M 07710 491111   T 01462 734843
E admin@scamptheatre.com
W www.scamptheatre.com

SCARLET THEATRE
Studio 4, The Bull, 68 High Street
Barnet, Herts EN5 5SJ   T 020 8441 9779
E admin@scarlettheatre.co.uk
W www.scarlettheatre.co.uk

SEABRIGHT PRODUCTIONS LTD
3rd Floor, 118-120 Wardour Street
London W1F 0TU
F 0870 1255706   T 020 7439 1173
E office@seabrightproductions.co.uk
W www.seabrightproductions.co.uk

SHAKESPEARE'S MEN
10 Dee Close, Upminster
Essex RM14 1QD   T 01708 222938
E terence@terencemustoo.com
W www.terencemustoo.com

SHARED EXPERIENCE
National & International Touring
13 Riverside House
27-29 Vauxhall Grove
London SW8 1SY   T 020 7587 1596
E admin@sharedexperience.org.uk
W www.sharedexperience.org.uk

SHOW OF STRENGTH
74 Chessel Street, Bedminster
Bristol BS3 3DN   T 0117 902 0235
E info@showofstrength.org.uk
W www.showofstrength.org.uk

SHOWCASE ENTERTAINMENTS LTD
Contact: Geoffrey J.L. Hindmarch (Executive Producer)
2 Lumley Close, Newton Aycliffe
Co Durham DL5 5PA   T 01325 316224
E gjl@showcaseproductions.co.uk
W www.showcaseproductions.co.uk

SIMPLY THEATRE
Chemin des Couleuvres 8B
1295 Tannay
Switzerland 1295   T 00 41 22 8600518
E info@simplytheatre.com
W www.simplytheatre.com

SINDEN Marc PRODUCTIONS
1 Hogarth Hill, London NW11 6AY   T 020 8455 3278
E mail@sindenproductions.com
W www.sindenproductions.com

SIXTEENFEET PRODUCTIONS
25 Rattray Road, London SW2 1AZ
M 07958 448690   T 020 7326 4417
E info@sixteenfeet.co.uk
W www.sixteenfeet.co.uk

SOHO THEATRE COMPANY
21 Dean Street, London W1D 3NE
F 020 7287 5061   T 020 7287 5060
W www.sohotheatre.com

SPARROW Daniel & WALSH Mike PRODUCTIONS
1A Neal's Yard, London WC2H 9AW
M 07879 897900   T 020 7240 2720
E info@danielsparrowproductions.com
W www.danielsparrowproductions.com

SPHINX THEATRE COMPANY
13 Riverside House, 27-29 Vauxhall Grove
London SW8 1SY   T 020 7587 1596
E info@sphinxtheatre.co.uk
W www.sphinxtheatre.co.uk

SPINNING WHEEL THEATRE
Contact: By Post/e-mail
5 Haughmond, Woodside Grange Road
Finchley, London N12 8ST
E georgia@spinningwheeltheatre.com
W www.spinningwheeltheatre.com

SPLATS ENTERTAINMENT
5 Denmark Street, London WC2H 8LP   M 07944 283659
E admin@splatsentertainment.co.uk
W www.splatsentertainment.co.uk

SPLITMOON THEATRE
PO Box 58891, London SE15 9DE   T 020 7252 8126
E info@splitmoontheatre.org
W www.splitmoontheatre.org

SQUAREDEAL PRODUCTIONS LTD
Contact: Jenny Topper
24 De Beauvoir Square, London N1 4LE
F 020 7275 7553   T 020 7249 5966
E jenny@jennytopper.com

SQUIRES & JOHNS PRODUCTIONS LTD
Sullon Lodge, Sullon Side Lane
Garstang PR3 1GH
F 01253 407715   T 0871 2003343
E info@squiresjohns.com
W www.squiresjohns.com

STAGE ENTERTAINMENT UK LTD
6th Floor, Swan House, 52 Poland Street
London W1F 7NQ
F 020 7025 6971   T 020 7025 6970
W www.stage-entertainment.co.uk

STAGE FURTHER PRODUCTIONS LTD
Westgate House, Stansted Road
Eastbourne, East Sussex BN22 8LG
F 01323 736127   T 01323 739478
E garthsfp@hotmail.co.uk

STANHOPE PRODUCTIONS LTD
4th Floor, 80-81 St Martin's Lane
London WC2N 4AA
F 020 7504 8656   T 020 7240 3098
E admin@stanhopeprod.com

STRAIGHT LINE PRODUCTIONS
58 Castle Avenue, Epsom, Surrey KT17 2PH
F 020 8393 8079   T 020 8393 4220
E hilary@straightlinemanagement.co.uk

SUPPORT ACT PRODUCTIONS
Contact: Ian McCracken
197 Church Road, Northolt UB5 5BE   T 0845 0940796
E info@supportact.co.uk
W www.supportact.co.uk

TALAWA THEATRE COMPANY
Ground Floor, 53-55 East Road, London N1 6AH
F 020 7251 5969   T 020 7251 6644
E hq@talawa.com
W www.talawa.com

TAMASHA THEATRE COMPANY
Unit 220, Great Guildford Business Square
30 Great Guildford Street, London SE1 OHS
F 020 7021 0421   T 020 7633 2270
E info@tamasha.org.uk
W www.tamasha.org.uk

TBA MUSIC
1 St Gabriels Road, London NW2 4DS
F 0700 607 0808   T 0845 1203722
E peter@tbagroup.co.uk

TEG PRODUCTIONS LTD
73 Great Titchfield Street, London W1W 6RD
F 0870 7627882   T 020 7436 2244
E info@tegproductions.com

THAT'S ENTERTAINMENT PRODUCTIONS
PO Box 4766, Worthing BN11 9NY   T 01903 263454
E info@thatsentertainmentproductions.co.uk
W www.thatsentertainmentproductions.co.uk

THEATRE ABSOLUTE
Insititute for Creative Enterprise, Technology Park
Puma Way, Coventry CV1 2TT   T 024 7615 8340
E info@theatreabsolute.co.uk
W www.theatreabsolute.co.uk

THEATRE ALIVE!
13 St Barnabas Road, London E17 8JZ
E theatrealive@tiscali.co.uk
W www.theatrealive.org.uk

THEATRE NORTH
22 Port Hall Place, Brighton BN1 5PN
M 07837 878732   T 01273 542518
E info@theatrenorth.co.uk
W www.theatrenorth.co.uk

THEATRE OF COMEDY COMPANY LTD
Shaftesbury Theatre, 210 Shaftesbury Avenue
London WC2H 8DP
F 020 7836 8181   T 020 7379 3345
E info@shaftesburytheatre.com

THEATRE ROYAL HAYMARKET PRODUCTIONS
Theatre Royal Haymarket, 18 Suffolk Street
London SW1Y 4HT   T 020 7389 9669
E nigel@trh.co.uk

THEATRE ROYAL STRATFORD EAST
Gerry Raffles Square, Stratford
London E15 1BN
F 020 8534 8381   T 020 8534 7374
E theatreroyal@stratfordeast.com
W www.stratfordeast.com

THEATRE SANS FRONTIERES
Queen's Hall Arts Centre, Beaumont Street
Hexham NE46 3LS
F 01434 607206   T 01434 652484
E info@tsf.org.uk
W www.tsf.org.uk

THEATRE SET-UP
12 Fairlawn Close, Southgate
London N14 4JX   T 020 8886 9572
W www.ts-u.co.uk

THEATRE TOURS INTERNATIONAL
Contact: Guy Masterson
The Hawthorne Auditorium
Campus West, The Campus
Welwyn Garden City, Herts AL8 6BX   T/F 01707 330360
E admin@theatretoursinternational.com
W www.theatretoursinternational.com

THEATRE WORKOUT LTD
13A Stratheden Road
Blackheath
London SE3 7TH   T 020 8144 2290
E enquiries@theatreworkout.co.uk
W www.theatreworkout.com

THEATREWORKS
2 Hanley Road, Malvern Wells
Worcs WR14 4PQ   T 01684 578342
E info@theatreworks.info
W www.theatreworks.info

TIATA FAHODZI
AH 112 Aberdeen Centre
22-24 Highbury Grove
London N5 2EA   T/F 020 7226 3800
E info@tiatafahodzi.com
W www.tiatafahodzi.com

TOLD BY AN IDIOT
Unit LF 1.7 Lafone House
The Leathermarket
11-13 Weston Street, London SE1 3ER
F 020 7407 9002   T 020 7407 4123
E info@toldbyanidiot.org
W www.toldbyanidiot.org

TOPPER Jenny
SquaredDeal Productions Ltd
24 De Beauvoir Square, London N1 4LE
F 020 7275 7553   T 020 7249 5966
E jenny@jennytopper.com

TOWER THEATRE COMPANY
Full-time non-professional
St Bride Foundation, Bride Lane
London EC4Y 8EQ   T/F 020 7353 5700
E info@towertheatre.freeserve.co.uk
W www.towertheatre.org.uk

TREAGUS Andrew ASSOCIATES LTD
5th Floor, 35 Soho Square
London W1D 3QX
F 020 7851 0151   T 020 7851 0150
E admin@at-assoc.co.uk

TRESTLE THEATRE COMPANY
Visual/Physical Theatre. Music. Choreography. New Writing
Trestle Arts Base, Russet Drive
Herts, St Albans AL4 0JQ
F 01727 855558   T 01727 850950
E admin@trestle.org.uk
W www.trestle.org.uk

TRICYCLE LONDON PRODUCTIONS
269 Kilburn High Road, London NW6 7JR
F 020 7328 0795   T 020 7372 6611
E admin@tricycle.co.uk
W www.tricycle.co.uk

TRIUMPH PROSCENIUM PRODUCTIONS LTD
1 Lumley Court, Off 402 The Strand
London WC2R 0NB   T 020 7207 1301

TURTLE KEY ARTS
Ladbroke Hall, 79 Barlby Road
London W10 6AZ
F 020 8964 4080   T 020 8964 5060
E admin@turtlekeyarts.org.uk
W www.turtlekeyarts.org.uk

TWO'S COMPANY
244 Upland Road, London SE22 0DN
F 020 8299 3714   T 020 8299 4593
E graham@2scompanytheatre.co.uk

UK ARTS INTERNATIONAL
First Floor, 6 Shaw Street
Worcester WR1 3QQ
F 01905 22868   T 01905 26424
E janryan@ukarts.com
W www.ukarts.com

UK PRODUCTIONS LTD
Churchmill House, Ockford Road
Godalming, Surrey GU7 1QY
F 01483 418486   T 01483 423600
E mail@ukproductions.co.uk
W www.ukproductions.co.uk

UNRESTRICTED VIEW
Above Hen & Chickens Theatre Bar
109 St Paul's Road
London N1 2NA   T 020 7704 2001
E james@henandchickens.com
W www.henandchickens.com

VANDER ELST Anthony PRODUCTIONS
The Studio, 14 College Road
Bromley, Kent BR1 3NS   T 020 8466 5580

VAYU NAIDU COMPANY
Unit C5, The Old Imperial Laundry
71 Warriner Gardens, Battersea
London SW11 4XW   T 020 7720 0707
E info@vayunaiducompany.org.uk
W www.vayunaiducompany.org.uk

VINTAGE
Opportunities for Maturer Practitioners
Lockles Cottages, 286 Church Road
Kessingland, Suffolk NR33 7SB   T 01502 741796
E info@vintageventures.co.uk

VOLCANO THEATRE COMPANY LTD
Swansea Metropolitan University
Townhill Road
Swansea SA2 0UT   T 01792 281280
E claud@volcanotheatre.co.uk
W www.volcanotheatre.co.uk

WALKING FORWARD LTD
Studio 6, Aberdeen Centre
22-24 Highbury Grove
London N5 2EA   T/F 020 7359 5249
E info@walkingforward.co.uk
W www.walkingforward.co.uk

WALLACE Kevin LTD
10 St Martin's Place
London WC2N 4JL
F 020 7836 9587   T 020 7836 9586
E info@kevinwallace.co.uk

WAREHOUSE THEATRE COMPANY
Dingwall Road, Croydon CR0 2NF
F 020 8688 6699   T 020 8681 1257
E info@warehousetheatre.co.uk
W www.warehousetheatre.co.uk

WAX Kenny LTD
3rd Floor, 25 Lexington Street
London W1F 9AG
F 020 3214 6063   T 020 7437 1736
W www.kennywax.com

WELDON Duncan C. PRODUCTIONS LTD
1 Lumley Court, Off 402 The Strand
London WC2R 0NB   T 020 7207 1301

WEST END PROPERTY PRODUCTIONS
29 Creek Road, Hayling Island
Hampshire PO11 9QZ
F 023 9263 7264   T 023 9263 7067
E directaccounts@btconnect.com
W www.soultraders-themusical.com

WEYLAND Valerie
29 Darby Crescent
Lower Sunbury TW16 5LB   T 01932 886413
E valweyland@hotmail.com

WHITALL Keith
25 Solway, Hailsham
East Sussex BN27 3HB   T 01323 844882

WHITEHALL Michael
10 Lower Common South, London SW15 1BP
F 020 8788 2340   T 020 8785 3737
E mwhitehall@msn.com

WILLS Newton MANAGEMENT
The Studio, 29 Springvale Avenue
Brentford, Middlesex TW8 9QH
F 00 33 468 218685   M 07989 398381
E newtoncttg@aol.com
W www.newtonwills.com

WORD & MUSIC COMPANY THE
Riverside Studios, Crisp Road
London W6 9RL   T 020 8237 1080
E info@associatedstudios.co.uk
W www.wordandmusiccompany.co.uk

WORK THE ROOM
Unit 2, The Wheelwright Building
125 Pomeroy Street, London SE14 5BT   M 07576 354267
E info@worktherooments.co.uk
W www.worktherooments.co.uk

WORTMAN UK / POLESTAR PICTURES
Theatre & Film Productions
48 Chiswick Staithe, London W4 3TP
M 07976 805976   T 020 8994 8886
E neville@speakwell.co.uk
W www.speakwell.co.uk

YELLOW EARTH THEATRE
3rd Floor, 20 Rupert Street
London W1D 6DF   T 020 7734 5988
E admin@yellowearth.org
W www.yellowearth.org

YOUNG VIC THEATRE
66 The Cut, London SE1 8LZ
F 020 7922 2802   T 020 7922 2800
E info@youngvic.org
W www.youngvic.org

1623 THEATRE COMPANY
Shakespeare in Non-traditional Theatre Spaces
61 Haven Baulk Lane, Littleover
Derby DE23 4AD   M 07867 996959
E messages@1623theatre.co.uk
W www.1623theatre.co.uk

ABERYSTWYTH ARTS CENTRE
Penglais Campus, Aberystwyth
Ceredigion SY23 3DE
F 01970 622883   T 01970 621512
E ggo@aber.ac.uk
W www.aber.ac.uk/artscentre

ADMIRATION THEATRE
124 Commercial Road, London E1 1NL   M 07010 041579
E email@admirationtheatre.com
W www.admirationtheatre.com

AGE EXCHANGE THEATRE TRUST
Contact: Suzanne Lockett (Administrator)
The Reminiscence Centre, 11 Blackheath Village
London SE3 9LA
F 020 8318 0060   T 020 8318 9105
E administrator@age-exchange.org.uk
W www.age-exchange.org.uk

ALTERNATIVE ARTS
Top Studio, Montefiore Centre
Hanbury Street, London E1 5HZ
F 020 7375 0484   T 020 7375 0441
E info@alternativearts.co.uk
W www.alternativearts.co.uk

ANGLES THEATRE THE
Alexandra Road, Wisbech
Cambridgeshire PE13 1HQ
F 01945 581967   T 01945 585587
E ratz@anglestheatre.co.uk

ARUNDEL JAILHOUSE
Arundel Town Hall, Arundel
West Sussex BN18 9AP   T/F 01903 889821
E info@arundeljailhouse.co.uk
W www.arundeljailhouse.co.uk

ASHTON GROUP THEATRE THE
The Old Fire Station, Abbey Road
Barrow-in-Furness, Cumbria LA14 1XH   T/F 01229 430636
E theashtongroup@btconnect.com
W www.ashtongroup.co.uk

ATTIC THEATRE COMPANY
Mitcham Library, 157 London Road
Mitcham CR4 2YR   T 020 8640 6800
E info@attictheatrecompany.com
W www.attictheatrecompany.com

BANNER THEATRE
Oaklands New Church Centre
Winleigh Road
Handsworth Wood, Birmingham B20 2HN   T 0845 4581909
E info@bannertheatre.co.uk

BECK THEATRE
Grange Road, Hayes
Middlesex UB3 2UE   T 020 8561 7506
E enquiries@becktheatre.org.uk
W www.becktheatre.org.uk

BENT BACK TULIPS THEATRE COMPANY
59B Crystal Palace Park Road, Crystal Palace
London SE26 6UT   M 07971 159940
E info@bentbacktulips.com
W www.bentbacktulips.com

BISHOPS GREAVES THEATRE
Bishop Grosseteste University College, Newport
Lincoln, Lincolnshire, LN1 3DY   T 01522 583761
E theatre@bishopg.ac.uk
W www.bishopg.ac.uk/theatre

BLUEYED THEATRE PRODUCTIONS
59B Crystal Palace Park Road
London SE26 6UT   M 07799 137487
E info@blueyedtheatreproductions.co.uk
W www.blueyedtheatreproductions.co.uk

BLUNDERBUS THEATRE COMPANY LTD
The Studio, The Palace Theatre
Appletongate, Newark, Notts NG24 1JY   T 01636 678900
E admin@blunderbus.co.uk
W www.blunderbus.co.uk

BRUVVERS THEATRE COMPANY
36 Lime Street, Ouseburn
Newcastle upon Tyne NE1 2PQ   T 0191 261 9230
E mikeofbruvvers@hotmail.com
W www.bruvvers.co.uk

CAPITAL ARTS YOUTH THEATRE
Wyllyotts Centre, Darkes Lane
Potters Bar, Herts EN6 2HN
M 07885 232414   T/F 020 8449 2342
E capitalarts@btconnect.com

CARIB THEATRE COMPANY
73 Lancelot Road, Wembley
Middlesex HA0 2AN   T/F 020 8903 4592
E antoncarib@yahoo.co.uk

CENTRE FOR PERFORMANCE RESEARCH
The Foundry, Parry Williams
Penglais Campus SY23 3AJ
F 01970 622132   T 01970 622133
E cprwww@aber.ac.uk
W www.thecpr.org.uk

CHAIN REACTION THEATRE COMPANY
Three Mills Studios, Sugar House Yard
Sugar House Lane, London E15 2QS   T/F 020 8534 0007
E mail@chainreactiontheatre.co.uk
W www.chainreactiontheatre.co.uk

CHALKFOOT THEATRE ARTS
c/o Channel Theatre Productions Ltd
Penistone House, 5 High Street
St Lawrence, Ramsgate, Kent CT11 0QH
E info@chalkfoot.org.uk
W www.chalkfoot.org.uk

CHATS PALACE ARTS CENTRE
42-44 Brooksby's Walk, Hackney
London E9 6DF   T 020 8533 0227
E info@chatspalace.com
W www.chatspalace.com

CHICKENSHED
Chase Side, Southgate, London N14 4PE
F 020 8292 0202   T 020 8351 6161
E susanj@chickenshed.org.uk
W www.chickenshed.org.uk

CHOL THEATRE
Contact: Andrew Loretto (Director, Theatre & International),
Susan Burns (Director, Education & Community)
Lawrence Batley Theatre, 8 Queen Street
Huddersfield, West Yorkshire HD1 2SP
F 01484 425336   T 01484 536008
E info@choltheatre.co.uk
W www.choltheatre.co.uk

There are hundreds of theatres in the UK, varying dramatically in size and type. The theatre sections are organised under headings which best indicate a theatre's principal area of work. A summary of each of these is below.

Alternative and Community

Many of these companies tour to Arts Centres, small and middle-scale theatres, and non-theatrical venues which do not have a resident company, or they may be commissioned to develop site specific projects. The term 'alternative' is sometimes used to describe work that is more experimental in style and execution.

Children's, Young People's and TIE

The primary focus of these theatre companies is to reach younger audiences. They often tour to smaller theatres, schools and non-theatrical venues. Interactive teaching - through audience participation and workshops - is often a feature of their work.

English Speaking Theatre Companies in Europe

These work principally outside of the UK. Some are based in one venue whilst others are touring companies. Their work varies enormously and includes Young People's Theatre, large scale musicals, revivals of classics and dinner theatre. Actors are employed either for an individual production or a 'season' of several plays.

London Theatres

Larger theatres situated in the West End and Central London. A few are producing houses, but most are leased to Theatre Producers who take responsibility for putting together a company for a run of a single show. In such cases it is they and not the venue who cast productions (often with the help of Casting Directors). Alternatively, a production will open outside London and tour to Provincial Theatres, then subsequently, if successful, transfer to a London venue.

Outer London, Fringe and Venues

Small and middle-scale theatres in Outer London and around the country. Some are producing houses, others are only available for hire. Many of the London venues have provided useful directions on how they may be reached by public transport.

Provincial/Touring

Theatre Producers and other companies sell their ready-made productions to the Provincial/Touring Theatres, a list of larger venues outside London. A run in each theatre varies between a night and several weeks, but a week per venue for tours of plays is usual. Even if a venue is not usually a producing house, most Provincial Theatres and Arts Centres put on a family show at Christmas.

Puppet Theatre Companies

Some Puppet Theatres are one-performer companies who literally create their own work from scratch. The content and style of productions varies enormously. For example, not all are aimed at children, and some are more interactive than others. Although we list a few theatres with Puppet Companies in permanent residence, this kind of work often involves touring. As with all small and middle scale touring, performers who are willing, and have the skills, to involve themselves with all aspects of company life are always more valuable.

Repertory (Regional) Theatres

Theatres situated outside London which employ a resident company of actors (i.e. the 'repertory company') on a play-by-play basis or for a season of several plays. In addition to the main auditorium (usually the largest acting space) these theatres may have a smaller studio theatre attached, which will be home to an additional company whose focus is education or the production of new plays (see Children's, Young People's and TIE). In recent years the length of repertory seasons has become shorter; this means that a number of productions are no longer in-house. It is common for gaps in the performance calendar to be filled by tours mounted by Theatre Producers, other Repertory (Regional) Theatres and non-venue based production companies.

CLOSE FOR COMFORT THEATRE COMPANY
34 Boleyn Walk, Leatherhead
Surrey KT22 7HU
M 07710 258290   T 01372 378613
E close4comf@aol.com
W www.closeforcomforttheatre.co.uk

COLLUSION THEATRE COMPANY
131 Renfrew Street, Glasgow G3 6QZ
F 0141 644 4163   T 0141 332 7001
E admin@collusiontheatre.co.uk
W www.collusiontheatre.co.uk

COMPLETE WORKS CREATIVE COMPANY LTD THE
The Old Truman Brewery, 91 Brick Lane
London E1 6QL
F 020 7247 7405   T 020 7377 0280
E theatre@tcw.org.uk
W www.tcw.org.uk

CORNELIUS & JONES ORIGINAL PRODUCTIONS
49 Carters Close, Sherington
Newport Pagnell
Buckinghamshire MK16 9NW   T/F 01908 612593
E admin@corneliusjones.com
W www.corneliusjones.com

CUT-CLOTH THEATRE
41 Beresford Road, Highbury
London N5 2HR   T 020 7503 4393

EALDFAEDER
12 Carleton Close, Great Yeldham
Essex CO9 4QJ   T 01787 238257
E pete@gippeswic.demon.co.uk
W www.ealdfaeder.org

ELAN WALES
European Live Arts Network
17 Douglas Buildings, Royal Stuart Lane
Cardiff CF10 5EL   T/F 029 2019 0077
E elanwales@ntlbusiness.com
W www.elanwales.org

ELECTRIC CABARET
107 High Street, Brackley
Northants NN13 7BN
M 07714 089763   T 01280 700956
E richard@electriccabaret.co.uk
W www.electricccabaret.co.uk

EUROPEAN THEATRE COMPANY THE
15 Beverley Avenue, London SW20 0RL   T 020 8946 3400
E admin@europeantheatre.co.uk
W www.europeantheatre.co.uk

FEMME FATALE THEATRE COMPANY
30 Creighton Avenue, Muswell Hill
London N10 1NU   M 07779 611414
E dianeleefley@yahoo.com
W www.femmefataletheatrecompany.com

FOREST FORGE THEATRE COMPANY
The Theatre Centre, Endeavour Park, Crow Arch Lane
Ringwood, Hampshire BH24 1SF
F 01425 471158   T 01425 470188
E info@forestforge.co.uk
W www.forestforge.co.uk

FOUND THEATRE
The Byways, Church Street
Monyash, Derbyshire DE45 1JH   T 01629 813083
E found_theatre@yahoo.co.uk
W www.foundtheatre.org.uk

FOURSIGHT THEATRE LTD
Newhampton Arts Centre, Dunkley Street
Wolverhampton WV1 4AN
F 01902 428413   T 01902 714257
E admin@foursighttheatre.co.uk
W www.foursighttheatre.co.uk

FRANTIC THEATRE COMPANY
32 Woodlane, Falmouth TR11 4RF   T/F 0870 1657350
E bookings@frantictheatre.com
W www.frantictheatre.com

GALLEON THEATRE COMPANY LTD
Greenwich Playhouse, Greenwich BR Station Forecourt
189 Greenwich High Road, London SE10 8JA
F 020 8310 7276   T 020 8858 9256
E alice@galleontheatre.co.uk
W www.galleontheatre.co.uk

GOOD NIGHT OUT PRESENTS
Contact: Adam Spreadbury-Maher (Artistic Director)
The Cock Tavern Theatre, 125 Kilburn High Road
London NW6 6JH   T 020 3239 4094
E info@goodnightout.org.uk
W www.goodnightout.org.uk

GRANGE ARTS CENTRE
Rochdale Road, Oldham
Greater Manchester OL9 6EA
F 0161 785 4263   T 0161 785 4239
E grangearts@oldham.ac.uk
W www.grangeartsoldham.co.uk

GREASEPAINT ANONYMOUS
Youth Theatre Company
4 Gallus Close, Winchmore Hill
London N21 1JR
F 020 8882 9189   T 020 8886 2263
E info@greasepaintanonymous.co.uk

GROWING CONCERNS
Outdoor Productions & Events
Lockles Cottages, 286 Church Road
Kessingland, Suffolk NR33 7SB   T 01502 741796
E info@growingconcerns.co.uk

HALL FOR CORNWALL
Contact: Frances Macadam (Projects Administrator)
Back Quay, Truro
Cornwall TR1 2LL
SD 01872 262465   T 01872 321970
E francesm@hallforcornwall.org.uk
W www.hallforcornwall.co.uk

HIJINX THEATRE
Touring Theatre Company. Community. Adults with Learning Disabilities
Wales Millennium Centre
Bute Place, Cardiff CF10 5AL
F 029 2063 5621   T 029 2030 0331
E info@hijinx.org.uk
W www.hijinx.org.uk

HISTORIA THEATRE COMPANY
8 Cloudesley Square, London N1 0HT
M 07811 892079   T 020 7837 8008
E kateprice@lineone.net
W www.historiatheatre.com

ICON THEATRE
The Brook Theatre, Old Town Hall
Chatham, Kent ME4 4SE   T 01634 813179
E nancy@icontheatre.org.uk
W www.icontheatre.org.uk

IMAGE MUSICAL THEATRE
23 Sedgeford Road, Shepherd's Bush
London W12 0NA
F 020 8749 9294   T 020 8743 9380
E brian@imagemusicaltheatre.co.uk
W www.imagemusicaltheatre.co.uk

IMMEDIATE THEATRE
1.2 Hoxton Works, 128 Hoxton Street
London N1 6SH   T 020 7012 1677
E info@immediate-theatre.com
W www.immediate-theatre.com

INOCENTE ART & FILM LTD
Film. Multimedia. Music Videos. Two Rock 'n' Roll Musicals
5 Denmans Lane, Haywards Heath
West Sussex RH16 2LA   M 07973 518132
E tarascas@btopenworld.com

ISOSCELES
7 Amity Grove, Raynes Park
London SW20 0LQ   T 020 8946 3905
E patanddave@isosceles.biz
W www.isosceles.biz

KNUTSFORD CIVIC CENTRE
Toft Road, Knutsford
Cheshire WA16 0PE   T 01565 633005
E alan.cunningham@cheshireeast.gov.uk
W www.cheshireeast.gov.uk/cinemas

KOMEDIA
44-47 Gardner Street, Brighton BN1 1UN
F 01273 647102   T 01273 647101
E info@komedia.co.uk
W www.komedia.co.uk

KORU THEATRE
11 Clovelly Road, London W5 5HF   T 020 8579 1029
E info@korutheatre.co.uk
W www.korutheatre.com

LADDER TO THE MOON ENTERTAINMENT
Unit 105, Battersea Business Centre
99-109 Lavender Hill, London SW11 5QL   T 020 7228 9700
E info@laddertothemoon.co.uk

LIVE THEATRE
New Writing
Broad Chare, Quayside
Newcastle upon Tyne NE1 3DQ
F 0191 232 2224   T 0191 261 2694
E info@live.org.uk
W www.live.org.uk

LONDON ACTORS THEATRE COMPANY
Unit 5A, Imex Business Centre
Ingate Place, London SW8 3NS
F 020 7978 2631   T 020 7978 2620
E latchmere@fishers.org.uk

LONDON BUBBLE THEATRE COMPANY LTD
5 Elephant Lane, London SE16 4JD
F 020 7231 2366   T 020 7237 4434
E admin@londonbubble.org.uk
W www.londonbubble.org.uk

LONG OVERDUE THEATRE COMPANY THE
37 Barnfield Rise, Andover SP10 2UQ   M 07971 277479
E admin@longoverdue.co.uk
W www.longoverdue.co.uk

LSW JUNIOR INTER-ACT
PO Box 31855, London SE17 3XP   T/F 020 7793 9755
E londonswo@hotmail.com
W www.londonshakespeare.org.uk

LSW PRISON PROJECT
PO Box 31855, London SE17 3XP   T/F 020 7793 9755
E londonswo@hotmail.com
W www.lswproductions.co.uk

LSW SENIOR RE-ACTION
PO Box 31855, London SE17 3XP   T/F 020 7793 9755
E londonswo@hotmail.com
W www.lswproductions.co.uk

M6 THEATRE COMPANY
Studio Theatre, Hamer CP School
Albert Royds Street, Rochdale OL16 2SU
F 01706 712601   T 01706 355898
E info@m6theatre.co.uk
W www.m6theatre.co.uk

MADDERMARKET THEATRE
*Resident Community Theatre Company. Small-Scale
Producing & Receiving House*
St John's Alley, Norwich NR2 1DR   T 01603 626560
E mmtheatre@btconnect.com
W www.maddermarket.co.uk

MAGIC HAT PRODUCTIONS
Brookslee, Brookshill Drive
Harrow HA3 6SB   M 07769 560991
E general@magichat-productions.com
W www.magichat-productions.com

MANCHESTER ACTORS COMPANY
PO Box 54, Manchester M60 7AB   T 0161 227 8702
E dramaticnights@aol.com
W www.manactco.org.uk

MAVERICK THEATRE COMPANY LTD
12 Lydney Grove, Northfield
Birmingham, West Midlands B31 1RB
M 07531 138248   T 0121 444 0933
E info@mavericktheatre.co.uk
W www.mavericktheatre.co.uk

MIKRON THEATRE COMPANY LTD
Marsden Mechanics, Peel Street
Marsden, Huddersfield HD7 6BW   T 01484 843701
E admin@mikron.org.uk
W www.mikron.org.uk

MONTAGE THEATRE ARTS
Contact: Judy Gordon (Artistic Director)
The Albany, Douglas Way
London SE8 4AG   T 020 8692 7007
E office@montagetheatre.com
W www.montagetheatre.com

NATURAL THEATRE COMPANY
Street Theatre. Touring. Corporate
Widcombe Institute, Widcombe Hill
Bath BA2 6AA
F 01225 442555   T 01225 469131
E info@naturaltheatre.co.uk
W www.naturaltheatre.co.uk

NET CURTAINS THEATRE COMPANY
Contact: Claire Farrington (Artistic Director)
Scurms, Rye Road
Sandhurst, Kent TN18 5PQ   M 07968 564687
E claire@netcurtains.org
W www.netcurtains.org

NETTLEFOLD THE
West Norwood Library Centre
1 Norwood High Street
London SE27 9JX   T 020 7926 8070
E thenettlefold@lambeth.gov.uk

NEWFOUND THEATRE COMPANY
Contact: By post e-mail
E newfoundtheatre@gmail.com
W www.newfoundtheatre.com

NEW PERSPECTIVES THEATRE COMPANY
Regional/National New Writing Touring Theatre
Park Lane Business Centre, Park Lane
Basford, Nottinghamshire NG6 0DW   T 0115 927 2334
E info@newperspectives.co.uk
W www.newperspectives.co.uk

NORTH COUNTRY THEATRE
3 Rosemary Lane, Richmond
North Yorkshire DL10 4DP   T 01748 825288
E office@northcountrytheatre.com
W www.northcountrytheatre.com

NORTHERN STAGE (THEATRICAL PRODUCTIONS) LTD
Barras Bridge, Newcastle upon Tyne NE1 7RH
F 0191 242 7257   T 0191 232 3366
E info@northernstage.co.uk
W www.northernstage.co.uk

NORTHUMBERLAND THEATRE COMPANY (NTC)
Touring Regionally & Nationally
The Playhouse, Bondgate Without
Alnwick, Northumberland NE66 1PQ
F 01665 605837   T 01665 602586
E admin@northumberlandtheatre.co.uk
W www.northumberlandtheatre.co.uk

NUDGE PRODUCTIONS LTD
32A Stradbroke Road, Pakefield
Lowesloft, Suffolk NR33 7HT   M 07946 731923
E info@nudge-productions.com
W www.nudge-productions.com

NUFFIELD THEATRE
Touring & Projects
University Road, Southampton SO17 1TR
F 023 8031 5511   T 023 8031 5500
E annie.reilly@nuffieldtheatre.co.uk
W www.nuffieldtheatre.co.uk

OLD TYME PLAYERS THEATRE COMPANY
Music Hall. Revues. Locally Based
35 Barton Court Avenue, Barton on Sea
Hants BH25 7EP   T 01425 612830
E oldetymeplayers@tiscali.co.uk
W www.oldetymeplayers.co.uk

OPEN STAGE PRODUCTIONS
49 Springfield Road, Moseley
Birmingham B13 9NN   T/F 0121 777 9086
E info@openstage.co.uk
W www.openstage.co.uk

OXFORDSHIRE THEATRE COMPANY
The Annexe, SS Mary & John School
Meadow Lane, Oxford OX4 1TJ
F 01865 247266   T 01865 249444
E info@oxfordshiretheatrecompany.co.uk
W www.oxfordshiretheatrecompany.co.uk

PASCAL THEATRE COMPANY
35 Flaxman Court, Flaxman Terrace
Bloomsbury, London WC1H 9AR   T 020 7383 0920
E pascaltheatreco@aol.com
W www.pascal-theatre.com

PAUL'S THEATRE COMPANY
Ardleigh House, 42 Ardleigh Green Road
Hornchurch, Essex RM11 2LG   T 01708 447123
E info@paulstheatreschool.com
W www.paulstheatreschool.com

PEOPLE'S THEATRE COMPANY THE
12E High Street, Egham
Surrey TW20 9EA   T 01784 470439
E admin@ptc.org.uk
W www.ptc.org.uk

PHANTOM CAPTAIN THE
618B Finchley Road
London NW11 7RR   T 020 8455 4564
E lambhorn@gmail.com
W www.phantomcaptain.netfirms.com

PLAYTIME THEATRE COMPANY
18 Bennells Avenue
Whitstable, Kent CT5 2HP
F 01227 266648   T 01227 266272
E playtime@dircon.co.uk
W www.playtimetheatre.co.uk

POWERHOUSE THEATRE COMPANY
Castle Arch, Quarry Street
Guildford, Surrey GU1 3SX
M 07949 821567   T 01483 444787
E geoff@powerhousetheatre.co.uk
W www.powerhousetheatre.co.uk

PRIME PRODUCTIONS
54 Hermiston Village
Currie EH14 4AQ   T/F 0131 449 4055
E primeproductions@talktalk.net
W www.primeproductions.co.uk

PROTEUS THEATRE COMPANY
Multimedia & Cross-art Form Work
Queen Mary's College
Cliddesden Road
Basingstoke, Hampshire RG21 3HF   T 01256 354541
E info@proteustheatre.com
W www.proteustheatre.com

PURSUED BY A BEAR PRODUCTIONS
Farnham Maltings, Bridge Square
Farnham GU9 7QR   T 01252 745445
E pursuedbyabear@yahoo.co.uk
W www.pursuedbyabear.co.uk

Q20 THEATRE COMPANY
19 Wellington Crescent, Shipley
West Yorkshire BD18 3PH   T 0845 1260632
E info@q20theatre.co.uk

RIDING LIGHTS THEATRE COMPANY
Friargate Theatre
Lower Friargate
York YO1 9SL
F 01904 651532   T 01904 655317
E info@rltc.org
W www.ridinglights.org

SALTMINE THEATRE COMPANY
61 The Broadway, Dudley DY1 3EB   T 01384 454807
E creative@saltmine.org
W www.saltminetrust.org.uk

SCRATCH PRODUCTIONS
20 Sandpiper Road, Blakespool Park
Bridgwater, Somerset TA6 5QU   T/F 01278 458253
E info@bluemoontheatre.co.uk

SPANNER IN THE WORKS
PO Box 239
Sidcup DA15 0DP
M 07850 313986   T 020 7193 7995
E info@spannerintheworks.org.uk
W www.spannerintheworks.org.uk

SPARE TYRE
Contact: Bonnie Mitchell (General Manager)
Theatre Company Working with Different Communities
Theatre Without Prejudice
Unit 3.22, Canterbury Court, Kennington Park
1-3 Brixton Road, London SW9 6DE   T/F 020 7061 6454
E info@sparetyre.org
W www.sparetyre.org

SPECTACLE THEATRE
Coleg Morgannwg Rhondda, Llwynypia
Tonypandy CF40 2TQ
F 01443 439640   T 01443 430700
E info@spectacletheatre.co.uk
W www.spectacletheatre.co.uk

SPONTANEITY SHOP THE
85-87 Bayham Street, London NW1 0AG   T 020 7788 4080
E info@the-spontaneity-shop.com
W www.the-spontaneity-shop.com

ST JOHN'S CHURCH
Hosts Classical Concerts
Waterloo Road, Southbank
London SE1 8TY   T 020 7633 9819
W www.stjohnswaterloo.co.uk

TAG CITIZENS
Citizens' Theatre, 119 Gorbals Street
Glasgow G5 9DS
F 0141 429 7374   T 0141 429 5561
E info@tag-theatre.co.uk
W www.tag-theatre.co.uk

TAKING FLIGHT THEATRE COMPANY
79 Kings Road, Canton
Cardiff CF11 9DB   T 029 2064 5505
E takingflighttheatre@yahoo.co.uk
W www.takingflighttheatre.com

TARA ARTS GROUP
356 Garratt Lane, London SW18 4ES
F 020 8870 9540   T 020 8333 4457
E tara@tara-arts.com
W www.tara-arts.com

THEATRE& LTD
Church Hall, St James Road
Marsh, Huddersfield HD1 4QA
F 01484 532962   T 01484 532967
E cmitchell@theatreand.com
W www.theatreand.com

THEATRE & FILM WORKSHOP
34 Hamilton Place
Edinburgh EH3 5AX
F 0131 220 0112   T 0131 225 7942
W www.theatre-workshop.com

THEATRE IS...
The Innovation Centre, College Lane
Hatfield AL10 9AB   T 01707 281100
E info@theatreis.org
W www.theatreis.org

THEATRE OF LITERATURE THE
Dramatised Readings
51 The Cut, London SE1 8LF   T 020 7633 0599
E info@calderpublications.com

THEATRE PECKHAM
Havil Street, London SE5 7SD   T 020 7708 5401
E admin@theatrepeckham.co.uk
W www.theatrepeckham.co.uk

THEATR POWYS
The Drama Centre
Tremont Road
Llandrindod Wells
Powys LD1 5EB
F 01597 824381   T 01597 824444
E theatr.powys@powys.gov.uk
W www.theatrpowys.co.uk

TOBACCO FACTORY THEATRE
Raleigh Road, Southville
Bristol BS3 1TF   T 0117 902 0345
E theatre@tobaccofactory.com
W www.tobaccofactorytheatre.com

TRICYCLE THEATRE
269 Kilburn High Road
London NW6 7JR
F 020 7328 0795   T 020 7372 6611
E admin@tricycle.co.uk
W www.tricycle.co.uk

WAREHOUSE THEATRE COMPANY
Dingwall Road
Croydon CRO 2NF
F 020 8688 6699   T 020 8681 1257
E info@warehousetheatre.co.uk
W www.warehousetheatre.co.uk

WINCHESTER HAT FAIR, FESTIVAL OF STREET THEATRE
5A Jewry Street, Winchester
Hampshire SO23 8RZ   T 01962 849841
E info@hatfair.co.uk
W www.hatfair.co.uk

WOMEN & THEATRE BIRMINGHAM LTD
220 Moseley Road, Highgate
Birmingham B12 0DG
F 0121 446 4280   T 0121 440 4203
E info@womenandtheatre.co.uk

Y TOURING THEATRE COMPANY
One KX, 120 Cromer Street
London WC1H 8BS   T 020 7520 3090
E e.lang@ytouring.org.uk
W www.ytouring.org.uk

YELLOW EARTH THEATRE
3rd Floor, 20 Rupert Street
London W1D 6DF   T 020 7734 5988
E admin@yellowearth.org
W www.yellowearth.org

YORICK INTERNATIONALIST THEATRE ENSEMBLE
Yorick Theatre & Film
4 Duval Court
36 Bedfordbury
Covent Garden, London WC2N 4DQ   T/F 020 7836 7637
E yorickx@hotmail.com

YOUNG VIC THEATRE
66 The Cut, London SE1 8LZ
F 020 7922 2801   T 020 7922 2800
E info@youngvic.org
W www.youngvic.org

ZIP THEATRE
Newhampton Arts Centre
Dunkley Street
Wolverhampton WV1 4AN
F 01902 572251   T 01902 572250
E admin@ziptheatre.co.uk
W www.ziptheatre.co.uk

ACTION STATION UK LTD THE
13 Worfield Street, London SW11 4RB   T 0870 7702705
E info@theactionstation.co.uk
W www.theactionstation.co.uk

ACTION TRANSPORT THEATRE
New Writing. Professional Production for, by &
with Young People
Whitby Hall, Stanney Lane
Ellesmere Port, Cheshire CH65 9AE   T 0151 357 2120
E info@actiontransporttheatre.org
W www.actiontransporttheatre.org

ACTIONWORK
Theatre & Film Productions with Young People
PO Box 433, Weston-super-Mare
Somerset BS24 0WY   T 01934 815163
E admin@actionwork.com
W www.actionwork.com

ARTY-FACT THEATRE COMPANY LTD
18 Weston Lane, Crewe
Cheshire CW2 5AN
F 07020 982098   T 07020 962096
W www.arty-fact.co.uk

ASHCROFT YOUTH THEATRE
Ashcroft Academy of Dramatic Art, Malcolm Primary School
Malcolm Road, Penge, London SE20 8RH
M 07799 791586   T 0844 8005328
E geraldi.gillma@btconnect.com
W www.ashcroftacademy.com

BARKING DOG THEATRE COMPANY
14 Leaside Mansions, Fortis Green
London N10 3EB   T 020 8883 0034
E mike@barkingdog.co.uk
W www.barkingdog.co.uk

BECK THEATRE
Grange Road, Hayes
Middlesex UB3 2UE
BO 020 8561 8371   T 020 8561 7506
E enquiries@becktheatre.org.uk
W www.becktheatre.org.uk

BIG ACT THE
Unit 1FA, Gate C, Knorr-Bremse Business Park
Douglas Road, Bristol BS15 8HJ   T 0870 8810367
E info@thebigact.com
W www.thebigact.com

BIG WOODEN HORSE THEATRE COMPANY LTD
30 Northfield Road, West Ealing
London W13 9SY   T 020 8567 8431
E info@bigwoodenhorse.com
W www.bigwoodenhorse.com

BIRMINGHAM STAGE COMPANY THE
Contact: Neal Foster (Actor/Manager), Philip Compton
(Executive Producer)
Suite 228, The Linen Hall, 162 Regent Street
London W1B 5TB
F 020 7437 3395   T 020 7437 3391
E info@birminghamstage.com
W www.birminghamstage.com

BITESIZE THEATRE COMPANY
8 Green Meadows, New Broughton
Wrexham LL11 6SG
F 01978 756308   T 01978 358320
E admin@bitesizetheatre.co.uk
W www.bitesizetheatre.co.uk

BLAH BLAH BLAH THEATRE COMPANY THE
The West Park Centre, Spen Lane
Leeds LS16 5BE   T 0113 274 0030
E admin@blahs.co.uk
W www.blahs.co.uk

BLUE MOON THEATRE COMPANY
20 Sandpiper Road, Blakespool Park
Bridgwater, Somerset TA6 5QU   T/F 01278 458253
E info@bluemoontheatre.co.uk
W www.bluemoontheatre.co.uk

BLUNDERBUS THEATRE COMPANY LTD
The Studio, The Palace Theatre
Appletongate, Newark, Notts NG24 1JY   T 01636 678900
E admin@blunderbus.co.uk
W www.blunderbus.co.uk

BOOSTER CUSHION THEATRE LTD
75 How Wood, Park Street
St Albans, Herts AL2 2RW
F 01727 872597   T 01727 873874
E boostercushion@hotmail.com
W www.booster-cushion.co.uk

BRIDGE HOUSE THEATRE
Professional & School Productions. Visting Companies
Warwick School Site, Myton Road
Warwick CV34 6PP   T 01926 776437
E info@bridgehousetheatre.co.uk
W www.bridgehousetheatre.co.uk

BRIEF CANDLE THEATRE
Chesterfield Studios, 44 Newbold Road
Chesterfield, Derbyshire S41 7PL   T 01246 556161
E office@briefcandle.co.uk
W www.briefcandle.co.uk

CAMBRIDGE TOURING THEATRE
29 Worts Causeway
Cambridge CB1 8RJ   T/F 01223 246533
E info@cambridgetouringtheatre.co.uk
W www.cambridgetouringtheatre.co.uk

CAUGHT IN THE ACT
Conygree House, Church Street
Kingham, Oxfordshire OX7 6YA   T 01608 659555
E cita@caughtintheact.co.uk
W www.caughtintheact.co.uk

CHAIN REACTION THEATRE COMPANY
Three Mills Studios
Sugar House Yard
Sugar House Lane, London E15 2QS   T/F 020 8534 0007
E mail@chainreactiontheatre.co.uk
W www.chainreactiontheatre.co.uk

CHALKFOOT THEATRE ARTS
Contact: Philip Dart (Artistic Director)
c/o Channel Theatre Productions Ltd
Penistone House, 5 High Street
St Lawrence, Ramsgate, Kent CT11 0QH
E info@chalkfoot.org.uk
W www.chalkfoot.org.uk

CHICKENSHED
Contact: Mary Ward MBE (Artistic Director)
Chase Side, Southgate
London N14 4PE
BO 020 8292 9222   T/F 020 8351 6161
E susanj@chickenshed.org.uk
W www.chickenshed.org.uk

CIRCUS MANIACS YOUTH CIRCUS
International Award-Winning Youth Circus Company
Unit 62
Basepoint Business Centre
Oakfield Close, Tewkesbury Business Park
Tewkesbury, Gloucestershire GL20 8SD
M 07977 247287   T 01684 854412
E info@circusmaniacs.com
W www.circusmaniacs.com

CLWYD THEATR CYMRU THEATRE FOR YOUNG PEOPLE
Contact: Education Administrator
Mold, Flintshire CH7 1YA
F 01352 701558   T 01352 701575
E education@clwyd-theatr-cymru.co.uk
W www.ctctyp.co.uk

COMPLETE WORKS CREATIVE COMPANY LTD THE
Contact: Phil Evans (Artistic Director)
The Old Truman Brewery
91 Brick Lane, London E1 6QL
F 020 7247 7405   T 020 7377 0280
E info@tcw.org.uk
W www.tcw.org.uk

CRAGRATS
Lawster House, 140 South Street
Dorking, Surrey RH4 2EU   T 0844 8111184
E enquiries@cragrats.com
W www.cragrats.com

CREATIVE PERFORMANCE LABORATORY
E creativeperformancelab@googlemail.com   M 07902 396618

DAYLIGHT THEATRE
66 Middle Street, Stroud
Gloucestershire GL5 1EA   T 01453 763808

DONNA MARIA COMPANY
16 Bell Meadow, Dulwich
London SE19 1HP   T 020 8670 7814
E info@donnamariasworld.co.uk
W www.donna-marias-world.co.uk

DRAGON DRAMA
Theatre Company. Parties. Tuition. Workshops.
1B Station Road, Hampton Wick
Surrey KT1 4HG   T 020 8617 3141
E askus@dragondrama.co.uk
W www.dragondrama.co.uk

EUROPA CLOWN THEATRE SHOW
36 St Lukes Road
Tunbridge Wells
Kent TN4 9JH   T 01892 537964
E mike@heypresto.orangehome.co.uk
W www.clownseuropa.co.uk

EUROPEAN THEATRE COMPANY THE
15 Beverley Avenue
London SW20 0RL   T 020 8946 3400
E admin@europeantheatre.co.uk
W www.europeantheatre.co.uk

FUSE: NEW THEATRE FOR YOUNG PEOPLE CO LTD
*Contact: Michael Quirke (General Manager), Andrew Raffle
(Artistic Producer)*
13 Hope Street
Liverpool L1 9BH
F 0151 707 9950   T 0151 708 0877
E info@fusetheatre.com
W www.fusetheatre.co.uk

FUTURES THEATRE COMPANY
St John's Crypt, 73 Waterloo Road
London SE1 8UD
F 020 7928 6724   T 020 7928 2832
E info@futurestheatrecompany.co.uk
W www.futurestheatrecompany.co.uk

GAZEBO THEATRE COMPANY
The Town Hall, Church Street
Bilston, West Midlands WV14 0AP
F 01902 497244   T 01902 497222
E admin@gazebotie.org
W www.gazebotie.org

GRANT Derek ORGANISATION LTD
13 Beechwood Road, West Moors
Dorset BH22 0BN   T 01202 855777
E admin@derekgrant.co.uk
W www.derekgrant.co.uk

**GREENWICH & LEWISHAM YOUNG PEOPLE'S THEATRE
(GLYPT)**
The Tramshed, 51-53 Woolwich New Road
London SE18 6ES
F 020 8317 8595   T 020 8854 1316
E postbox@glypt.co.uk
W www.glypt.co.uk

GROUP 64 YOUTH THEATRE
Putney Arts Theatre, Ravenna Road
London SW15 6AW
F 020 8788 6940   T 020 8788 6935
W www.putneyartstheatre.org.uk

GWENT TIE COMPANY
The Drama Centre Pen-y-pound
Abergavenny
Monmouthshire NP7 5UD
F 01873 853910   T 01873 853167
E gwenttie@uwclub.net
W www.gwenttheatre.com

HALF MOON YOUNG PEOPLE'S THEATRE
43 White Horse Road, London E1 0ND
F 020 7709 8914   T 020 7265 8138
E admin@halfmoon.org.uk
W www.halfmoon.org.uk

HOXTON HALL YOUTH ARTS CENTRE
130 Hoxton Street, London N1 6SH   T 020 7684 0060
E getcreative@hoxtonhall.co.uk
W www.hoxtonhall.co.uk

IMAGE MUSICAL THEATRE
23 Sedgeford Road, Shepherd's Bush
London W12 0NA
F 020 8749 9294   T 020 8743 9380
E brian@imagemusicaltheatre.co.uk
W www.imagemusicaltheatre.co.uk

IMPACT UNIVERSAL LTD
Hope Bank House, Woodhead Road
Honley, Huddersfield HD9 6PF
F 01484 660088   T 01484 668881
E jill.beckwith@impactuniversal.com
W www.impactuniversal.com

INDIGO MOON THEATRE
35 Waltham Court, Beverley
East Yorkshire HU17 9JF   M 07855 328552
E info@indigomoontheatre.com
W www.indigomoontheatre.com

INTERPLAY THEATRE
Armley Ridge Road, Leeds LS12 3LE   T 0113 263 8556
E info@interplayleeds.co.uk
W www.interplayleeds.co.uk

KINETIC THEATRE COMPANY LTD
Suite H, The Jubilee Centre
Lombard Road, Wimbledon
London SW19 3TZ
F 020 8286 2645   T 020 8286 2613
E paul@kinetictheatre.co.uk
W www.kinetictheatre.co.uk

KOMEDIA
44-47 Gardner Street, Brighton BN1 1UN
BO 01273 647100   T 01273 647101
E info@komedia.co.uk
W www.komedia.co.uk/brighton

LEIGHTON BUZZARD YOUTH THEATRE
6 Hillside Road
Leighton Buzzard LU7 3BU   T 01525 377222
E sarah.cavender@tesco.net
W www.lbyt.org

LITTLE ACTORS THEATRE COMPANY
16 Hawthorn Road, Parkgate
Cheshire CH64 6SX   T 0151 336 4302
E mail@littleactorstheatre.com

M6 THEATRE COMPANY
Studio Theatre, Hamer CP School
Albert Royds Street, Rochdale OL16 2SU
F 01706 712601   T 01706 355898
E info@m6theatre.co.uk
W www.m6theatre.co.uk

MAGIC CARPET THEATRE
18 Church Street, Sutton-on-Hull HU7 4TS
F 01482 787362   T 01482 709939
E admin@magiccarpettheatre.com
W www.magiccarpettheatre.com

NATIONAL ASSOCIATION OF YOUTH THEATRES (NAYT)
Arts Centre, Vane Terrace
Darlington, County Durham DL3 7AX
F 01325 363313   T 01325 363330
E nayt@btconnect.com
W www.nayt.org.uk

NATIONAL STUDENT DRAMA FESTIVAL
Woolyard, 54 Bermondsey Street
London SE1 3UD
E info@nsdf.org.uk
W www.nsdf.org.uk

NATIONAL YOUTH MUSIC THEATRE THE
2-4 Great Eastern Street, London EC2A 3NW
F 0870 9033785   T 020 7422 8290
E enquiries@nymt.org.uk
W www.nymt.org.uk

NATIONAL YOUTH THEATRE OF GREAT BRITAIN
Woolyard, 52 Bermondsey Street
London SE1 3UD
F 020 7036 9031   T 020 7281 3863
E info@nyt.org.uk
W www.nyt.org.uk

NETTLEFOLD THE
West Norwood Library Centre, 1 Norwood High Street
London SE27 9JX   T 020 7926 8070
E thenettlefold@lambeth.gov.uk

OILY CART
Create work for the under 6's and for young people 3-19
with profound & multiple disabilities (PMLD) or ASD
Smallwood School Annexe, Smallwood Road
London SW17 0TW
F 020 8672 0792   T 020 8672 6329
E oilies@oilycart.org.uk
W www.oilycart.org.uk

ONATTI PRODUCTIONS
Contact: Andrew Bardwell (Artistic Director)
9 Field Close, Warwick
Warwickshire CV34 4QD
F 0870 1643629   T 01926 495220
E info@onatti.co.uk
W www.onatti.co.uk

PANDEMONIUM TOURING PARTNERSHIP
228 Railway Street, Cardiff CF24 2NJ   T 029 2047 2060
E paul@pandemoniumtheatre.com

PANDORA'S BOX THEATRE COMPANY
National Touring Young Children's Theatre
43 Fallsbrook Road, London SW16 6DU   T/F 020 8769 8710
E info@pandorasboxtheatre.co.uk
W www.pandorasboxtheatre.co.uk

PAUL'S THEATRE COMPANY
Ardleigh House
42 Ardleigh Green Road
Hornchurch, Essex RM11 2LG   T 01708 447123
E info@paulstheatreschool.com
W www.paulstheatreschool.com

PIED PIPER COMPANY
1 Lilian Place, Coxcombe Lane
Chiddingfold, Surrey GU8 4QA   T/F 01428 684022
E twpiedpiper@aol.com
W www.piedpipertheatre.co.uk

PILOT THEATRE
York Theatre Royal, St Leonard's Place
York YO1 7HD
F 01904 656378   T 01904 635755
E info@pilot-theatre.com
W www.pilot-theatre.com

PLAY HOUSE THE
Language Alive!/Project
Longmore Street, Birmingham B12 9ED
F 0121 464 5713   T 0121 464 5712
E info@theplayhouse.org.uk
W www.theplayhouse.org.uk

PLAYTIME THEATRE COMPANY
18 Bennells Avenue, Whitstable
Kent CT5 2HP
F 01227 266648   T 01227 266272
E playtime@dircon.co.uk
W www.playtimetheatre.co.uk

POLKA THEATRE
240 The Broadway
Wimbledon SW19 1SB
F 020 8545 8365   T 020 8545 8320
E admin@polkatheatre.com
W www.polkatheatre.com

Q20 THEATRE COMPANY
19 Wellington Crescent, Shipley
West Yorkshire BD18 3PH   T 0845 1260632
E info@q20theatre.co.uk

QUAKER YOUTH THEATRE
Ground Floor, 1 The Lodge
1046 Bristol Road, Birmingham B29 6LJ
F 0121 414 0090   T 0121 414 0099
E qyt@leaveners.org
W www.leaveners.org

QUANTUM THEATRE
*Contact: Michael Whitmore, Jessica Selous
(Artistic Directors)*
The Old Button Factory
1-11 Bannockburn Road
Plumstead, London SE18 1ET   T 020 8317 9000
E office@quantumtheatre.co.uk
W www.quantumtheatre.co.uk

RAINBOW BIGBOTTOM & CO LTD
Parkview 1A, Stanley Avenue
Chesham, Bucks HP5 2JF
M 07778 106552   T 01494 771029
E lorrainebmays@aol.com
W www.mrpanda.co.uk

RAINBOW THEATRE LONDON EAST
56 Sutlej Road, Charlton
London SE7 7DB
F 07092 315384   T 020 8856 5023
E rainbowtheatrelondoneast@yahoo.co.uk
W www.rainbow-theatre.com

REDROOFS THEATRE COMPANY
Contact: By Post
The Novello Theatre, Sunninghill
Nr Ascot, Berkshire SL5 9NE
W www.novellotheatre.co.uk

ROUNDABOUT THEATRE IN EDUCATION
Nottingham Playhouse, Wellington Circus
Nottingham NG1 5AF
F 0115 947 5759   T 0115 947 4361
E roundabout@nottinghamplayhouse.co.uk

ROYAL & DERNGATE
19-21 Guildhall Road
Northampton NN1 1DP   T 01604 626222
E alex.soulsby@royalandderngate.co.uk
W www.royalandderngate.co.uk

ROYAL COURT YOUNG WRITERS PROGRAMME
Playwriting Projects for Young People aged 13-25
Royal Court Theatre
Sloane Square
London SW1W 8AS
F 020 7565 5001   T 020 7565 5050
E ywp@royalcourttheatre.com
W www.royalcourttheatre.com

SCOTTISH YOUTH THEATRE
The Old Sheriff Court
105 Brunswick Street
Glasgow G1 1TF   T 0141 552 3988
E info@scottishyouththeatre.org
W www.scottishyouththeatre.org

SHAKESPEARE 4 KIDZ THEATRE COMPANY THE
Drewshearne Barn
Crowhurst Lane End
Oxted, Surrey RH8 9NT
F 01342 893754   T 01342 894548
E theatre@shakespeare4kidz.com
W www.shakespeare4kidz.com

SHAKESPEAREWORKS
22 Chilswell Road
Oxford OX1 4PJ   T/F 01865 241281
E info@shakespeareworks.co.uk
W www.shakespeareworks.co.uk

SHARED EXPERIENCE YOUTH THEATRE
13 Riverside House
27-29 Vauxhall Grove
London SW8 1SY
F 020 7735 0374   T 020 7587 1596
E admin@sharedexperience.org.uk
W www.sharedexperience.org.uk

SHEFFIELD THEATRES
*Contact: Sue Burley (Education Administrator), Dan Bates
(Chief Executive)*
55 Norfolk Street, Sheffield S1 1DA
F 0114 249 6003   T 0114 249 5999
E info@sheffieldtheatres.co.uk
W www.sheffieldtheatres.co.uk/
creativedevelopmentprogramme

SOLOMON THEATRE COMPANY
Penny Black, High Street
Damerham
Fordingbridge, Hants SP6 3EU   T/F 01725 518760
E office@solomon-theatre.co.uk
W www.solomon-theatre.co.uk

SPECTACLE THEATRE
Coleg Morgannwg
Rhondda, Llwynypia
Tonypandy CF40 2TQ
F 01443 423080   T 01443 430700
E info@spectacletheatre.co.uk
W www.spectacletheatre.co.uk

STOPWATCH THEATRE COMPANY
Unit 318 Solent Business Centre
Millbrook Road West
Southampton SO15 0HW   T 023 8078 3800
E info@stopwatchtheatre.com
W www.stopwatchtheatre.com

STORYTELLERS THEATRE COMPANY THE
Bridge Farm, 249 Hawes Side Lane
Blackpool FY4 4AA
F 01253 792930   T 01253 839375
E admin@pendleproductions.co.uk
W www.pendleproductions.co.uk

SUPPORT ACT PRODUCTIONS
Contact: Ian McCracken
193 Church Road, Northolt UB5 5BE   T 0845 0940796
E info@supportact.co.uk
W www.supportact.co.uk

TALEGATE THEATRE
5 Station Road, Retford
Nottinghamshire DN22 7DE   T 05603 160558
E info@talegatetheatre.co.uk
W www.talegatetheatre.co.uk

THEATR IOLO LTD
The Old School Building
Cefn Road
Mynachdy, Cardiff CF14 3HS
F 029 2052 2225   T 029 2061 3782
E info@theatriolo.com
W www.theatriolo.com

THEATRE ALIBI
Adults & Young People
Northcott Studio Theatre
Emmanuel Road, Exeter EX4 1EJ   T/F 01392 217315
E info@theatrealibi.co.uk
W www.theatrealibi.co.uk

THEATRE CENTRE
National Touring. New Writing for Young Audiences
Shoreditch Town Hall, 380 Old Street
London EC1V 9LT
F 020 7739 9741   T 020 7729 3066
E admin@theatre-centre.co.uk
W www.theatre-centre.co.uk

THEATRE HULLABALOO
Arts Centre, Vane Terrace
Darlington, County Durham DL3 7AX
F 01325 369404   T 01325 352004
E info@theatrehullabaloo.org.uk
W www.theatrehullabaloo.org.uk

THEATRE IS...
The Innovation Centre, College Lane
Hatfield AL10 9AB   T 01707 281100
E info@theatreis.org
W www.theatreis.org

THEATRE NA N'OG
Unit 3, Millands Road Industrial Estate
Neath SA11 1NJ
F 01639 647941   T 01639 641771
E drama@theatr-nanog.co.uk
W www.theatr-nanog.co.uk

THEATRE WORKOUT LTD
13A Stratheden Road, Blackheath
London SE3 7TH   T 020 8144 2290
E enquiries@theatreworkout.co.uk
W www.theatreworkout.com

THEATRE& LTD
Church Hall, St James Road, Marsh, Huddersfield HD1 4QA
F 01484 532962   T 01484 532967
E cmitchell@theatreand.com
W www.theatreand.com

THOUSAND CRANES
48 Brunswick Crescent, London N11 1EB
F 020 8994 7674   M 07801 269772
E kumiko@athousandcranes.org.uk
W www.athousandcranes.org.uk

TICKLISH ALLSORTS SHOW
57 Victoria Road
Wilton
Salisbury, Wiltshire SP2 0DZ   T/F 01722 744949
E garynunn@ntlworld.com
W www.ticklishallsorts.co.uk

TIE ACTION WORK
PO Box 433
Weston-Super-Mare
Somerset BS24 0WY   T 01934 815163
E info@actionwork.com
W www.actionwork.com

TRICYCLE THEATRE
Contact: Gillian Christie (Education Director)
269 Kilburn High Road
London NW6 7JR   T/F 020 7372 6611
E education@tricycle.co.uk
W www.tricycle.co.uk

UNICORN THEATRE
147 Tooley Street
London SE1 2HZ
F 020 7645 0550   T 020 7645 0500
E admin@unicorntheatre.com
W www.unicorntheatre.com

WEST YORKSHIRE PLAYHOUSE
Touring Company
Playhouse Square, Quarry Hill
Leeds LS2 7UP   T 0113 213 7225
E gail.mcintyre@wyp.org.uk

WIZARD THEATRE
*Contact: Leon Hamilton (Director), Emmy Bradbury
(Company Manager)*
175 Royal Crescent
Ruislip
Middlesex HA4 0PN   T 0800 5832373
E admin@wizardtheatre.co.uk
W www.wizardtheatre.co.uk

YOUNG SHAKESPEARE COMPANY
*Contact: Christopher Geelan, Sarah Gordon (Artistic
Directors)*
31 Bellevue Road
Friern Barnet
London N11 3ET
F 020 8368 6713   T 020 8368 4828
E youngshakespeare@mac.com

AUSTRIA
VIENNA
Vienna's English Theatre
Contact: Vanessa Mallatratt (Casting)
See website for casting requirements
UK Representative: VM Theatre Productions Ltd
16 The Street, Ash
Canterbury, Kent CT3 2HJ   T/F 01304 813330
W www.englishtheatre.at

DENMARK
COPENHAGEN
The English Theatre of Copenhagen
Contact: Vivienne McKee (Artistic Director)
Soren Hall (Administrator)
London Toast Theatre
Kochsvej 18
DK-1812 Frb. C, Denmark   T + 45 33 22 8686
E mail@londontoast.dk
W www.londontoast.dk

FRANCE
LYON
Theatre From Oxford (Touring Europe & Beyond)
Contact: Robert Southam. By Post
B.P. 10, F-42750 St-Denis-de-Cabanne, France
E theatre.oxford@virgin.net

FRANCE
PARIS
ACT Company
Contact: Andrew Wilson (Artistic Director), Anne Wilson
(Administrator)
25 Avenue Mal Leclerc, 92240 Malakoff
France   T + 33 1 46 56 20 50
E andrew@actheatre.com
W www.actheatre.com

GERMANY
FRANKFURT AM MAIN
The English Theatre
Contact: Daniel John Nicolai (Artistic Director), Amy Rycroft
(Casting, See RYCROFT CASTING)
Gallusanlage 7, 60329
Frankfurt am Main
Germany
F + 49 9 69 242 316 45   T + 49 69 242 316 20
E mail@english-theatre.org
W www.english-theatre.org

GERMANY
HAMBURG
The English Theatre of Hamburg
Contact: Robert Rumpf, Clifford Dean
Lerchenfeld 14
22081 Hamburg
Germany
F + 49 40 227 7927   T + 49 40 227 7089
W www.englishtheatre.de

GERMANY
TOURING GERMANY
White Horse Theatre
Contact: Peter Griffith, Michael Dray
Boerdenstrasse 17
59494 Soest-Muellingsen
Germany
F + 49 29 21 33 93 36   T + 49 29 21 33 93 39
E theatre@whitehorse.de
W www.whitehorse.de

HUNGARY
BUDAPEST
Merlin International Theatre
Contact: Laszlo Magacs
Gerloczy Utca 4
1052 Budapest
Hungary
F + 36 1 2660904   T + 36 1 3179338
E angol@merlinszinhaz.hu
W www.merlinszinhaz.hu

ICELAND
REYKJAVIK
Light Nights - The Summer Theatre
Contact: Kristine G. Magnus (Artistic Director)
The Travelling Theatre
Baldursgata 37
IS-101 Reykjavik, Iceland   T + 354 551 9181
W www.lightnights.com

ITALY
SANREMO
Theatrino & Melting Pot Theatre - ACLE
Via Roma 54, 18038 Sanremo (IM)
Italy
F + 39 0184 509996   T + 39 0184 506070
E info@acle.org
W www.acle.org

SWITZERLAND
TANNAY
Simply Theatre
Chemin des Couleuvres 8B
1295 Tannay
Switzerland
F + 41 22 8600519   T + 41 22 8600518
E info@simplytheatre.com
W www.simplytheatre.com

UNITED KINGDOM
WARWICK
Onatti Productions
Contact: Andrew Bardwell
9 Field Close, Warwick
Warwickshire CV34 4QD
F 0870 1643629
E info@onatti.co.uk   T 01926 495220
W www.onatti.co.uk

ADELPHI
Strand, London WC2E 7NN
BO 0844 4124651　　　　　　　　　　SD 020 7836 1166

ALDWYCH
Aldwych, London WC2B 4DF
BO 020 7379 3367　　　　　T 020 7836 5537 (Manager/SD)
W www.aldwychtheatre.co.uk

ALMEIDA
Almeida Street, London N1 1TA
BO 020 7359 4404　　　　　　　　Manager 020 7288 4900

AMBASSADORS
West Street, London WC2H 9ND
Manager 020 7395 5410
BO 020 7395 5405　　　　　　　　SD 020 7395 5400
E boxofficemanager@theambassadorstheatre.co.uk
W www.theambassadorstheatre.co.uk

APOLLO
Shaftesbury Avenue, London W1D 7EZ
Manager 020 7494 5834
BO 0844 4124658　　　　　　　　SD 020 7851 2711
E enquiries@nimaxtheatres.com
W www.nimaxtheatres.com

APOLLO VICTORIA
17 Wilton Road
London SW1V 1LG
BO 0870 4000650　　　　T 020 7834 6318 (Manager/SD)
W www.apollovictorialondon.org.uk

ARTS
6-7 Great Newport Street
London WC2H 7JB
BO 0845 0175584　　　　　T 020 7836 8531 (Manager/SD)
E info@artstheatrewestend.com
W www.artstheatrewestend.com

BARBICAN
Barbican, London EC2Y 8DS
BO 0845 1207511　　　　　T 020 7628 3351 (Manager/SD)
W www.barbican.org.uk

BLOOMSBURY
15 Gordon Street, London WC1H 0AH
Manager 020 7679 2777
BO 020 7388 8822　　　　　　　　SD 020 7679 2922
E blooms.theatre@ucl.ac.uk
W www.thebloomsbury.com

BUSH
Shepherds Bush Green
London W12 8QD
BO 020 8743 5050　　　　　　　Manager 020 8743 3584
E info@bushtheatre.co.uk
W www.bushtheatre.co.uk

CAMBRIDGE
Earlham Street
Seven Dials
Covent Garden
London WC2H 9HU
Manager 020 7850 8711
BO 020 7850 8715　　　　　　　　SD 020 7850 8710
W www.cambridgetheatre.co.uk

COLISEUM (English National Opera)
St Martin's Lane, London WC2N 4ES
Manager 020 7836 0111
BO 0870 1450200　　　　　　　　SD 020 7845 9397
W www.eno.org

COMEDY
Panton Street, London SW1Y 4DN
Manager 020 7321 5310
BO 0870 0606637　　　　　　　　SD 020 7321 5300
E comedymanager@theambassadors.com

CRITERION
2 Jermyn Street, Piccadilly
London SW1Y 4XA
BO 0844 8471778　　　　T 020 7839 8811 (Manager/SD)
E admin@criterion-theatre.co.uk
W www.criterion-theatre.co.uk

DOMINION
268-269 Tottenham Court Road
London W1T 7AQ
BO 0870 7490587　　　　　　　　SD 020 7927 0900
W www.dominiontheatrelondon.com

DONMAR WAREHOUSE
41 Earlham Street
London WC2H 9LX
Manager 020 7240 4882
BO 0870 060 6624　　　　　　　　SD 020 7438 9200
E office@donmarwarehouse.com
W www.donmarwarehouse.com

DRURY LANE
Theatre Royal, Catherine Street
London WC2B 5JF
BO 020 7494 5060　　　　　　　　SD 020 7850 8790
W www.rutheatres.com

DUCHESS
Catherine Street, London WC2B 5LA
Manager 020 7632 9601
BO 020 7632 9602　　　　　　　　SD 020 7632 9604
E enquiries@nimaxtheatres.com

DUKE OF YORK'S
St Martin's Lane
London WC2N 4BG
BO 0870 0606623　　　　T 020 7836 4615 (Manager/SD)

FORTUNE
Russell Street, Covent Garden
London WC2B 5HH
BO 0870 0606626　　　　T 020 7010 7901 (Manager/SD)

GARRICK
2 Charing Cross Road
London WC2H 0HH
Manager 020 7520 5692
BO 020 7520 5693　　　　　　　　SD 020 7520 5690
E enquiries@nimaxtheatres.com

GIELGUD
Shaftesbury Avenue
London W1D 6AR
Manager 020 7292 1321
BO 020 7812 7480　　　　　　　　SD 020 7292 1320

HACKNEY EMPIRE
291 Mare Street
London E8 1EJ
BO 020 8985 2424   T 020 8510 4500 (Manager/SD)
E info@hackneyempire.co.uk
W www.hackneyempire.co.uk

HAMMERSMITH APOLLO
Queen Caroline Street
London W6 9QH   BO 0844 8444748
W www.hammersmithapollo.net

HAMPSTEAD
Eton Avenue, Swiss Cottage
London NW3 3EU
BO 020 7722 9301   Manager 020 7449 4200
E info@hampsteadtheatre.com
W www.hampsteadtheatre.com

HER MAJESTY'S
Haymarket, London SW1Y 4QL
BO 0844 4122707   T 020 7850 8750 (Manager/SD)

LONDON PALLADIUM
Argyll Street, London W1F 7TF
Manager 020 7850 8777
BO 0870 8901108   SD 020 7850 8770

LYCEUM
21 Wellington Street
London WC2E 7RQ
BO 0844 8440005   T 020 7420 8100 (Manager/SD)

LYRIC
29 Shaftesbury Avenue
London W1D 7ES
Manager 020 7494 5840
BO 0844 4124661   SD 020 7494 5841
E enquiries@nimaxtheatres.com

LYRIC HAMMERSMITH
King Street, London W6 0QL   BO 0871 2211722
E enquiries@lyric.co.uk
W www.lyric.co.uk

NATIONAL
South Bank, Upper Ground
London SE1 9PX
BO 020 7452 3000   SD 020 7452 3333
W www.nationaltheatre.org.uk

NEW LONDON
Drury Lane, London WC2B 5PW
BO 0870 8900141   T 020 7242 9802 (Manager/SD)
E cuqui.rivera@reallyuseful.co.uk

NEW PLAYERS
The Arches, Off Villiers Street
London WC2N 6NL   Manager 020 7930 5868
E info@newplayerstheatre.com
W www.newplayerstheatre.com

NOEL COWARD (Previously ALBERY)
85 St Martin's Lane
London WC2N 4AU
Manager 020 7759 8011
BO 0844 4825140   SD 020 7759 8010

NOVELLO (Previously STRAND)
5 Aldwych, London WC2B 4LD
BO 0844 4825171   T 020 7759 9611 (Manager/SD)

OLD VIC
The Cut, London SE1 8NB
BO 0844 8717628   T 020 7928 2651 (Manager/SD)
E ovtcadmin@oldvictheatre.com
W www.oldvictheatre.com

PALACE
Shaftesbury Avenue
London W1D 5AY
BO 0844 7550016   T 020 7434 0088 (Manager/SD)
E info@reallyuseful.co.uk
W www.rutheatres.com

PEACOCK
For Administration see SADLER'S WELLS
Portugal Street, Kingsway
London WC2A 2HT
BO 0844 4124322   SD 020 7863 8268
E info@sadlerswells.com
W www.sadlerswells.com

PHOENIX
110 Charing Cross Road
London WC2H 0JP
Manager 020 7438 9610
BO 020 7438 9605   SD 020 7438 9600
E phoenixmanager@theambassadors.com

PICCADILLY
Denman Street
London W1D 7DY
BO 020 7478 8805   T 020 7478 8800 (Manager/SD)
E piccadillymanager@theambassadors.com

PLAYHOUSE
Northumberland Avenue
London WC2N 5DE
BO 0844 8717631   T 020 7839 4292 (Manager/SD)

PRINCE EDWARD
28 Old Compton Street
London W1D 4HS
Manager 020 7440 3021
BO 020 7447 5459   SD 020 7440 3020
W www.delfont-mackintosh.com

PRINCE OF WALES
Coventry Street, London W1D 6AS
Manager 020 7766 2101
BO 0844 4825115   SD 020 7766 2100
W www.delfontmackintosh.co.uk

QUEEN'S
Contact: Nicolas Shaw (Manager)
51 Shaftesbury Avenue, London W1D 6BA
BO 0844 4825160   T 020 7292 1350 (Manager/SD)

REGENT'S PARK OPEN AIR
Inner Circle, Regent's Park
London NW1 4NR
BO 0844 8264242   T 0844 3753460 (Manager/SD)
W www.openairtheatre.com

RIVERSIDE STUDIOS
Crisp Road
Hammersmith
London W6 9RL
BO 020 8237 1111   T 020 8237 1007 (Manager/SD)
E online@riversidestudios.co.uk
W www.riversidestudios.co.uk

ROYAL COURT
Sloane Square
London SW1W 8AS
BO 020 7565 5000   T 020 7565 5050 (Manager/SD)
E info@royalcourttheatre.com
W www.royalcourttheatre.com

ROYAL OPERA HOUSE
Covent Garden
London WC2E 9DD
BO 020 7304 4000   T 020 7240 1200 (Manager/SD)

SADLER'S WELLS
Rosebery Avenue
London EC1R 4TN
Manager 020 7863 8034
BO 0844 4124300   SD 020 7863 8198
E info@sadlerswells.com
W www.sadlerswells.com

SAVOY
Strand
London WC2R 0ET
BO 0870 1648787   SD 020 7845 6050
E savoymanager@theambassadors.com
W www.ambassadortickets.com

SHAFTESBURY
210 Shaftesbury Avenue
London WC2H 8DP
BO 020 7379 5399   T 020 7379 3345 (Manager/SD)
E info@shaftesburytheatre.co.uk

SHAKESPEARE'S GLOBE
21 New Globe Walk
Bankside
London SE1 9DT
BO 020 7401 9919   T 020 7902 1400 (Manager/SD)
E info@shakespearesglobe.com
W www.shakespeares-globe.org

SHAW
100-110 Euston Road
London NW1 2AJ
BO 0844 2091663   T 020 7666 9037 (Artistic Director)
E info@shaw-theatre.com
W www.shaw-theatre.com

SOHO
21 Dean Street, London W1D 3NE
BO 020 7478 0100   T 020 7287 5060
W www.sohotheatre.com

ST MARTIN'S
West Street, London WC2H 9NZ
Manager 020 7497 0578
BO 0844 4991515   SD 020 7836 1086
E enquiries@the-mousetrap.co.uk

THEATRE ROYAL
Haymarket, London SW1Y 4HT
BO 0845 4811870   T 020 7930 8890 (Manager/SD)

TRICYCLE
269 Kilburn High Road, London NW6 7JR
BO 020 7328 1000   T 020 7372 6611 (Manager/SD)
E info@tricycle.co.uk
W www.tricycle.co.uk

VAUDEVILLE
404 Strand, London WC2R 0NH
Manager 020 7836 1820
BO 0870 8900511   SD 020 7836 3191

VICTORIA PALACE
Victoria Street, London SW1E 5EA
Manager 020 7828 0600
BO 0844 2485000   SD 020 7834 2781
E enquiries@victoriapalace.co.uk

WYNDHAM'S
Charing Cross Road, London WC2H 0DA
Manager 020 7759 8077
BO 0870 9500925   SD 020 7759 8070

YOUNG VIC
66 The Cut, London SE1 8LZ
BO 020 7922 2922   T 020 7922 2800 (Manager/SD)
E info@youngvic.org
W www.youngvic.org

ALBANY THE
Douglas Way, Deptford, London SE8 4AG
F 020 8469 2253
BO 020 8692 4446   T 020 8692 0231
E boxoffice@thealbany.org.uk
W www.thealbany.org.uk

ARCH 468 THEATRE STUDIO
Arch 468, 209A Coldharbour Lane
London SW9 8RU   M 07973 302908
E rebecca@arch468.com
W www.arch468.com

ARCOLA THEATRE
Contact: Mehmet Ergen (Artistic Director), Leyla Nazli
(Executive Producer)
27 Arcola Street, Dalston
(Off Kingsland High Street), London E8 2DJ
BO 020 7503 1646   T 020 7503 1645
E info@arcolatheatre.com
W www.arcolatheatre.com
Route: Victoria Line to Highbury & Islington, then North
London Line to Dalston Kingsland (Main Line) - 5 min walk.
Buses: 38 or 242 from West End, 149 from London Bridge or
30, 67, 76, 243

ARTS THEATRE THE
6-7 Great Newport Street
London WC2H 7JB   T 020 7395 1409
E info@theartstheatrelondon.co.uk

ARTSDEPOT
5 Nether Street, Tally Ho Corner
North Finchley, London N12 0GA   BO 020 8369 5454
E info@artsdepot.co.uk
W www.artsdepot.co.uk

BAC (Battersea Arts Centre)
Lavender Hill, London SW11 5TN
F 020 7978 5207
BO 020 7223 2223   T 020 7223 6557
E mailbox@bac.org.uk
W www.bac.org.uk
Route: Victoria or Waterloo (Main Line) to Clapham Junction
then 5 min walk or Northern Line to Clapham Common then
20 min walk

BARONS COURT THEATRE
'The Curtain's Up'
28A Comeragh Road, West Kensington
London W14 9HR   T 020 8932 4747 (Admin/BO)
E londontheatre@gmail.com
W www.offwestend.com
Route: West Kensington or Barons Court tube, Piccadilly &
District Lines

BATES Tristan THEATRE
Contact: Laura Kriefman (Creative Producer)
1A Tower Street, London WC2H 9NP
F 020 7240 3896
BO 020 7240 6283   T 020 7632 8010
E tbt@tristanbatestheatre.co.uk
W www.tristanbatestheatre.co.uk

BECK THEATRE
Grange Road, Hayes
Middlesex UB3 2UE
BO 020 8561 8371   T 020 8561 7506
E enquiries@becktheatre.org.uk
W www.becktheatre.org.uk
Route: Metropolitan Line to Uxbridge then buses 427 or 607
to Theatre or Paddington (Main Line) to Hayes Harlington
then buses 90, H98 or 195 (10 min)

BEDLAM THEATRE
11B Bristo Place, Edinburgh EH1 1EZ
BO 0131 225 9893   T/F 0131 225 9873
E info@bedlamtheatre.co.uk
W www.bedlamtheatre.co.uk

BELLAIRS PLAYHOUSE
Millmead Terrace, Guildford GU2 4YT
BO 01483 444789   T 01483 560701 (Mon-Fri)
E gsaenquiries@gsa.surrey.ac.uk
W www.gsauk.org

BLACKHEATH HALLS
23 Lee Road, Blackheath
London SE3 9RQ
F 020 8852 5154
BO 020 8463 0100   T 020 8318 9758
E programming@blackheathhalls.com
W www.blackheathhalls.com

BLOOMSBURY THEATRE
15 Gordon Street, Bloomsbury
London WC1H 0AH
BO 020 7388 8822   T 020 7679 2777
E admin@thebloomsbury.com
W www.thebloomsbury.com
Route: Tube to Euston, Euston Square or Warren Street

BOOKSHOP THEATRE LTD
51 The Cut, London SE1 8LF   T 020 7620 2900
E info@calderpublications.com

BORLASE THEATRE THE
Sir William Borlase's Grammar School
West Street
Marlow SL7 2BR   T 01628 816500
E mhartley@swbgs.com
W www.swbgs.com

BRENTWOOD THEATRE
Contact: Mark P. Reed (Theatre Administrator)
15 Shenfield Road, Brentwood
Essex CM15 8AG
SD 01277 226658
BO 01277 200305   T/F 01277 230833
E admin@brentwood-theatre.org
W www.brentwood-theatre.org
Route: Liverpool Street (Main Line) to Shenfield,
then 15 min walk

BRIDEWELL THEATRE THE
St Bride Foundation, Bride Lane
Fleet Street, London EC4Y 8EQ
F 020 7353 1547   T 020 7353 3331
E info@stbridefoundation.org
W www.bridewelltheatre.org
Route: Circle Line to St Paul's. City Thameslink Capital
Connect. Fifteen different bus routes

BROADWAY THE
Broadway, Barking IG11 7LS
F 020 8507 5611
BO 020 8507 5607   T 020 8507 5610
E admin@thebroadwaybarking.com
W www.thebroadwaybarking.com

BROADWAY STUDIO THEATRE THE
Contact: Martin Costello (Director)
Catford, London SE6 4RU
BO 020 8690 0002   T 020 8690 1000
E martin@broadwaytheatre.org.uk
W www.broadwaytheatre.org.uk
Route: Charing Cross to Catford Bridge

CAMDEN PEOPLE'S THEATRE
Contact: Matt Ball (Artistic Director)
58-60 Hampstead Road, London NW1 2PY
F 020 7813 3889   T 020 7419 4841
E admin@cptheatre.co.uk
W www.cptheatre.co.uk
Route: Victoria or Northern Line to Euston or Warren Street,
Metropolitan or Circle Line to Euston Square (2 min walk
either way)

CANAL CAFE THEATRE THE
Contact: Emma Taylor (Artistic Director)
The Bridge House, Delamere Terrace
Little Venice, London W2 6ND
BO 020 7289 6054   T 020 7289 6056
E mail@canalcafetheatre.com
W www.canalcafetheatre.com

CHATS PALACE ARTS CENTRE
Contact: Sarah Wickens
42-44 Brooksby's Walk, Hackney
London E9 6DF   T 020 8533 0227
E info@chatspalace.com
W www.chatspalace.com

CHELSEA THEATRE
World's End Place, King's Road
London SW10 0DR
F 020 7352 2024   T 020 7349 7811
E admin@chelseatheatre.org.uk
Route: District or Circle Line to Sloane Square then short bus
ride 11 or 22 down King's Road

CHICKENSHED
Contact: Mary Ward MBE (Artistic Director)
Chase Side, Southgate, London N14 4PE
F 020 8292 0202
BO 020 8292 9222   T 020 8351 6161
E susanj@chickenshed.org.uk
W www.chickenshed.org.uk
Route: Piccadilly Line to Oakwood, turn left outside tube &
walk 8 min down Bramley Road or take 307 bus. Buses 298,
299, 699 or N19. Car parking available & easy access parking
by reservation

CHRIST'S HOSPITAL THEATRE
Contact: Dave Saunders (Director)
Horsham, West Sussex RH13 7LW
BO 01403 247434   T 01403 247435
E dps@christs-hospital.org.uk

CHURCHILL THE
Contact: John Bartliff (Administrator)
High Street, Bromley
Kent BR1 1HA
F 020 8290 6968
BO 0844 8717620   T 020 8290 8210
W www.churchilltheatre.co.uk

CLUB FOR ACTS & ACTORS THE
Contact: Malcolm Knight (Concert Artistes Association)
20 Bedford Street, London WC2E 9HP   T 020 7836 3172
E office@thecaa.org
W www.thecaa.org
Route: Piccadilly or Northern Line to Leicester Square then
few mins walk

COCHRANE THEATRE
Contact: Deirdre Malynn
Southampton Row, London WC1B 4AP
BO 020 7269 1606   T 020 7269 1600
E info@cochranetheatre.co.uk
Route: Central or Piccadilly Line to Holborn then 3 min walk

COCK TAVERN THEATRE THE
Contact: Ben Cooper (Creative Producer)
125 Kilburn High Road, London NW6 6JH   BO 0844 4771000
E info@cocktaverntheatre.com
W www.cocktaverntheatre.com

COCKPIT THEATRE
Gateforth Street, Paddington
London NW8 8EH
F 020 7258 2921
BO 020 7258 2925   T 020 7258 2920
E admin@cockpittheatre.org.uk
W www.cockpittheatre.org.uk
Route: Tube to Marylebone/Edgware Road then short walk
or bus 139 to Lisson Grove & 6, 8 or 16 to Edgware Road

COLOUR HOUSE THEATRE THE
Merton Abbey Mills, Watermill Way
London SW19 2RD   T 020 8542 5511
E info@colourhousetheatre.co.uk
W www.colourhousetheatre.co.uk

CORBETT THEATRE
East 15 Acting School
Hatfields, Rectory Lane, Loughton IG10 3RY
F 020 8508 7521   T 020 8508 5983 (Admin/BO)
E east15@essex.ac.uk
W www.east15.ac.uk
Route: Central Line (Epping Branch) to Debden then 6 min
walk

COURTYARD THEATRE THE
Contact: June Abbott, Tim Gill (Joint Artistic Directors)
Bowling Green Walk, 40 Pitfield Street
London N1 6EU
BO 0844 4771000   T/F 020 7739 6868
E info@thecourtyard.org.uk
W www.thecourtyard.org.uk

CROYDON CLOCKTOWER
Katharine Street
Croydon CR9 1ET   T 020 8253 1030 (Admin/BO)
E arts@croydon.gov.uk
W www.croydonclocktower.org.uk

CUSTARD FACTORY
Gibb Street, Digbeth
Birmingham B9 4AA
F 0121 604 8888   T 0121 224 7777
E info@custardfactory.co.uk
W www.custardfactory.co.uk

DARTFORD ORCHARD THEATRE
Contact: Andy Hill
Home Gardens, Dartford
Kent DA1 1ED
F 01322 227122
BO 01322 220000   T 01322 220099
W www.orchardtheatre.co.uk
Route: Charing Cross (Main Line) to Dartford

DRILL HALL THE
16 Chenies Street, London WC1E 7EX
F 020 7307 5062   BO 020 7307 5060
E box.office@drillhall.co.uk
W www.drillhall.co.uk
Route: Northern Line to Goodge Street then 1 min walk

EDINBURGH FESTIVAL FRINGE
180 High Street, Edinburgh EH1 1QS
F 0131 226 0016   T 0131 226 0026
E admin@edfringe.com
W www.edfringe.com

EDINBURGH UNIVERSITY THEATRE COMPANY
See BEDLAM THEATRE

EMBASSY THEATRE & STUDIOS
The Central School of Speech & Drama
64 Eton Avenue, Swiss Cottage
London NW3 3HY　　　　　　　T 020 7722 8183
E enquiries@cssd.ac.uk
W www.cssd.ac.uk
Route: Jubilee Line to Swiss Cottage then 1 min walk

ETCETERA THEATRE CLUB
Contact: Michelle Flower (Director)
Oxford Arms, 265 Camden High Street
London NW1 7BU
F 020 7482 0378　　　　T 020 7482 4857 (Admin/BO)
E etc@etceteratheatre.com
W www.etceteratheatre.com

FAIRFIELD HALLS
Ashcroft Theatre & Concert Hall, Park Lane
Croydon CR9 1DG
BO 020 8688 9291　　　　T 020 8681 0821 (Admin/SD)
E info@fairfield.co.uk
W www.fairfield.co.uk
Route: Victoria & London Bridge (Main Line) to East Croydon then 5 min walk

FINBOROUGH THEATRE
Contact: Neil McPherson (Artistic Director)
The Finborough, 118 Finborough Road
London SW10 9ED
BO 0844 8471652　　　　　　　T 020 7244 7439
E admin@finboroughtheatre.co.uk
W www.finboroughtheatre.co.uk
Route: District or Piccadilly Line to Earls Court then 5 min walk. Buses 74, 328, C1, C3, 74 then 3 min walk

GATE THEATRE
Contact: Natalie Abrahami, Carrie Cracknell (Artistic Directors)
11 Pembridge Road, Above Prince Albert Pub
Notting Hill, London W11 3HQ
F 020 7221 6055
BO 020 7229 0706　　　　　　　T 020 7229 5387
E gate@gatetheatre.co.uk
W www.gatetheatre.co.uk
Route: Central, Circle or District Line to Notting Hill Gate then 1 min walk. Buses 23, 27, 28, 31, 52, 70, 94, 148, 328, 390, 452

GBS THEATRE (George Bernard Shaw)
Malet Street, London WC1E 7JN
BO 020 7908 4800　　　　　　　T 020 7908 4754
E bookings@rada.ac.uk
W www.radaenterprises.org

GIELGUD John THEATRE
Malet Street, London WC1E 7JN
BO 020 7908 4800　　　　　　　T 020 7908 4754
E bookings@rada.ac.uk
W www.radaenterprises.org

GREENWICH PLAYHOUSE
Contact: Alice de Sousa
Greenwich BR Station Forecourt, 189 Greenwich High Road
London SE10 8JA
F 020 8310 7276　　　　　　　T 020 8858 9256
E alice@galleontheatre.co.uk
W www.galleontheatre.co.uk
Route: Main Line from Charing Cross, Waterloo East or London Bridge, DLR to Greenwich

GREENWICH THEATRE
Contact: James Haddrell (Executive Director)
Crooms Hill, Greenwich
London SE10 8ES
F 020 8858 8042
BO 020 8858 7755　　　　　　　T 020 8858 4447
E info@greenwichtheatre.org.uk
W www.greenwichtheatre.org.uk
Route: Jubilee Line (change Canary Wharf) then DLR to Greenwich Cutty Sark, 3 min walk or Charing Cross (Main Line) to Greenwich, 5 min walk

GUILDHALL SCHOOL OF MUSIC & DRAMA
Silk Street, Barbican
London EC2Y 8DT
F 020 7256 9438　　　　　　　T 020 7628 2571
E info@gsmd.ac.uk
W www.gsmd.ac.uk
Route: Hammersmith & City, Circle or Metropolitan line to Barbican or Moorgate (also served by Northern line) then 5 min walk

HACKNEY EMPIRE THEATRE
291 Mare Street, Hackney
London E8 1EJ
BO 020 8985 2424　　　　T 020 8510 4500 (Admin/Press)
E info@hackneyempire.co.uk
Route: North London Line to Hackney Central

HEN & CHICKENS
Unrestricted View, Above Hen & Chickens Theatre Bar
109 St Paul's Road, Islington, London N1 2NA T 020 7704 2001
E james@henandchickens.com
W www.henandchickens.com
Route: Victoria Line or Main Line to Highbury & Islington directly opposite station

ICA THEATRE
No CVs. Venue only
The Mall, London SW1Y 5AH
F 020 7873 0051
BO 020 7930 3647　　　　　　　T 020 7930 0493
W www.ica.org.uk
Route: Nearest stations Piccadilly & Charing Cross

JACKSONS LANE
269A Archway Road, London N6 5AA　　　T 020 8340 5226
E reception@jacksonslane.org.uk
W www.jacksonslane.org.uk

JERMYN STREET THEATRE
Contact: Gene David Kirk (Artistic Director), Penny Horner (General Manager)
16B Jermyn Street, London SW1Y 6ST
BO 020 7287 2875　　　　　　　T 020 7434 1443
E info@jermynstreettheatre.co.uk
W www.jermynstreettheatre.co.uk

JERWOOD VANBRUGH THEATRE
Malet Street, London WC1E 7JN
BO 020 7908 4800　　　　　　　T 020 7908 4754
E bookings@rada.ac.uk
W www.radaenterprises.org

KING'S HEAD THEATRE
115 Upper Street, Islington
London N1 1QN
BO 0844 2090326　　　　　　　T 020 7226 8561
W www.kingsheadtheatre.org
Route: Northern Line to Angel then 5 min walk. Approx halfway between Angel and Highbury & Islington tube stations

KING'S LYNN CORN EXCHANGE
Tuesday Market Place, King's Lynn
Norfolk PE30 1JW
F 01553 762141
BO 01553 764864   T 01553 765565
E entertainment_admin@west-norfolk.gov.uk
W www.kingslynncornexchange.co.uk

KOMEDIA
Contact: Marina Kobler (Programmer)
44-47 Gardner Street, Brighton BN1 1UN
F 01273 647102
BO 0845 2938480   T 01273 647101
E info@komedia.co.uk
W www.komedia.co.uk

LANDMARK ARTS CENTRE
Ferry Road, Middlesex TW11 9NN
F 020 8977 4830   T 020 8977 7558
E info@landmarkartscentre.org
W www.landmarkartscentre.org

LANDOR THEATRE THE
*Contact: Robert McWhir (Artistic Director), Thomas Hopkins
(Executive Producer)*
70 Landor Road
London SW9 9PH   T 020 7737 7276 (Admin/BO)
E info@landortheatre.co.uk
W www.landortheatre.co.uk
Route: Northern Line Clapham North then 2 min walk

LEICESTER SQUARE THEATRE
6 Leicester Place, London WC2H 7BX
BO 0844 8472475   T 0870 8993335
E info@leicestersquaretheatre.com
W www.leicestersquaretheatre.com

LEIGHTON BUZZARD THEATRE
Lake Street, Leighton Buzzard
Bedfordshire LU7 1RX
BO 0300 3008125   T 0300 3008130
E lbtboxoffice@centralbedfordshire.gov.uk
W www.leightonbuzzardtheatre.co.uk

LILIAN BAYLIS THEATRE
For information see Sadler's Wells Theatre
Rosebery Avenue
London EC1R 4TN
BO 0844 4124300   SD 020 7863 8198
E info@sadlerswells.com
W www.sadlerswells.com

LIVE THEATRE
Broad Chare, Quayside
Newcastle upon Tyne NE1 3DQ
F 0191 232 2224
BO 0191 232 1232   T 0191 261 2694
E info@live.org.uk
W www.live.org.uk

LOST THEATRE
208 Wandsworth Road
London SW8 2JU   T 020 7622 9208
E losttheatre@yahoo.co.uk
W www.losttheatre.co.uk

MACOWAN THEATRE
LAMDA
1-2 Logan Place, London W8 6QN
F 020 7370 1980   T 020 7244 8744
W www.lamda.org.uk
*Route: District or Piccadilly Line to Earl's Court then 6 min
walk*

MADDERMARKET THEATRE
Contact: Michael Lyas (General Manager)
St John's Alley
Norwich NR2 1DR
F 01603 661357
BO 01603 620917   T 01603 626560
E mmtheatre@btconnect.com
W www.maddermarket.co.uk

MENIER CHOCOLATE FACTORY
Menier Chocolate Factory
53 Southwark Street
London SE1 1RU
F 020 7378 1713
BO 020 7907 7060   T 020 7378 1712
E office@menierchocolatefactory.com
W www.menierchocolatefactory.com

MILLFIELD ARTS CENTRE
Silver Street
London N18 1PJ
F 020 8807 3892
BO 020 8807 6680   T 020 8887 7301
E info@millfieldtheatre.co.uk
W www.millfieldtheatre.co.uk
*Route: Liverpool Street (Main Line) to Silver Street or
tube to Turnpike Lane then bus 144 (15 min to Cambridge
Roundabout)*

MYERS STUDIO THEATRE THE
*Contact: Trevor Mitchell (General Manager & Artistic
Director)*
The Epsom Playhouse
Ashley Avenue
Epsom, Surrey KT18 5AL
F 01372 726228
BO 01372 742555   T 01372 742226
E tmitchell@epsom-ewell.gov.uk
W www.epsomplayhouse.co.uk

NETTLEFOLD THE
West Norwood Library Centre
1 Norwood High Street
London SE27 9JX
F 020 7926 8032   T 020 7926 8070 (Admin/BO)
E thenettlefold@lambeth.gov.uk
*Route: Victoria, West Croydon or London Bridge (Main Line)
to West Norwood then 2 min walk, or tube to Brixton then
buses 2, 196, 322, 432, or buses 68, 468*

NEW DIORAMA THEATRE THE
Hire Venue
15-16 Triton Street
Regents Park
London NW1 3BF   T 020 7916 5467
W www.newdiorama.com
*Route: Circle & District Line to Great Portland Street then 5
min walk, or Victoria/Northern line to Warren Street then 1
min walk*

NEW END THEATRE
27 New End
Hampstead
London NW3 1JD
F 020 7794 4044
BO 0870 0332733   T 020 7472 5800
E info@newendtheatre.co.uk
W www.newendtheatre.co.uk
*Route: Northern Line to Hampstead then 2 min walk off
Heath Street*

NEW PLAYERS THEATRE THE
Formerly The Players Theatre
The Arches
Villiers Street
London WC2N 6NL   T 020 7930 5868
E info@newplayerstheatre.com
W www.newplayerstheatre.com

NEW WIMBLEDON THEATRE & STUDIO
The Broadway
Wimbledon
London SW19 1QG
F 020 8543 6637
BO 0844 8717646   T 020 8545 7900
W www.newwimbledontheatre.co.uk
Route: Main Line or District Line to Wimbledon, then 3 min walk. Buses 57, 93, 155

NORTHBROOK THEATRE THE
Contact: Neil Tiplady (Theatre Co-ordinator)
Littlehampton Road
Goring-by-Sea
Worthing, West Sussex BN12 6NU
F 01903 606141   BO 01903 606162
E box.office@nbcol.ac.uk
W www.stacatnorthbrook.com

NORWICH PUPPET THEATRE
St James, Whitefriars
Norwich NR3 1TN
F 01603 617578
BO 01603 629921   T 01603 615564
E info@puppettheatre.co.uk
W www.puppettheatre.co.uk

NOVELLO THEATRE THE
Redroofs Theatre Company
2 High Street, Sunninghill
Nr Ascot, Berkshire   T 01344 620881
Route: Waterloo (Main Line) to Ascot then 1 mile from station

OLD RED LION THEATRE PUB
Contact: Helen Devine (Theatre Manager)
418 St John Street
Islington
London EC1V 4NJ
BO 020 7837 7816   T 020 7833 3053
E info@oldredliontheatre.co.uk
Route: Northern Line to Angel then 1 min walk

ORANGE TREE
Contact: Sam Walters (Artistic Director)
1 Clarence Street
Richmond TW9 2SA
F 020 8332 0369
BO 020 8940 3633   T 020 8940 0141
E admin@orangetreetheatre.co.uk
Route: District Line, Waterloo (Main Line) or North London Line then virtually opposite station

OVAL HOUSE THEATRE
52-54 Kennington Oval
London SE11 5SW
F 020 7820 0990
BO 020 7582 7680   T 020 7582 0080
E info@ovalhouse.com
W www.ovalhouse.com
Route: Northern Line to Oval then 1 min walk, Victoria Line & Main Line to Vauxhall then 10 min walk

PAVILION THEATRE
Marine Road
Dun Laoghaire
County Dublin, Ireland
F 00 353 1 663 6328   T 00 353 1 231 2929
E info@paviliontheatre.ie
W www.paviliontheatre.ie

PENTAMETERS
(Theatre Entrance in Oriel Place)
28 Heath Street
London NW3 6TE   T 020 7435 3648 (Admin/BO)
W www.pentameters.co.uk
Route: Northern Line to Hampstead then 1 min walk. Buses 268, 46

PLACE THE
Main London Venue for Contemporary Dance
17 Duke's Road, London WC1H 9PY
BO 020 7121 1100   T 020 7121 1101
E theatre@theplace.org.uk
W www.theplace.org.uk
Route: Northern or Victoria Line to Euston or King's Cross then 5 min walk (Opposite rear of St Pancras Church)

PLEASANCE ISLINGTON
Contact: Anthony Alderson
Carpenters Mews, North Road
(Off Caledonian Road), London N7 9EF
F 020 7700 7366
BO 020 7609 1800   T 020 7619 6868
E info@pleasance.co.uk
W www.pleasance.co.uk
Route: Piccadilly Line to Caledonian Road, turn left, walk 50 yds, turn left into North Road, 2 min walk. Buses 17, 91, 259, N91, 393

POLKA THEATRE
240 The Broadway
Wimbledon SW19 1SB
F 020 8545 8365
BO 020 8543 4888   T 020 8545 8320
E admin@polkatheatre.com
W www.polkatheatre.com
Route: Waterloo (Main Line) or District Line to Wimbledon then 10 min walk. Northern Line to South Wimbledon then 10 min walk. Tram to Wimbledon, Buses 57, 93, 219, 493

PRINCESS THEATRE HUNSTANTON
The Green, Hunstanton, Norfolk PE36 5AH
F 01485 534463
BO 01485 532252   T 01485 535937
W www.princesstheatrehunstanton.co.uk

PUTNEY ARTS THEATRE
Ravenna Road, Putney SW15 6AW
F 020 8788 6940   T 020 8788 6943
E info@putneyartstheatre.org.uk
W www.putneyartstheatre.org.uk

QUEEN'S THEATRE
Contact: Bob Carlton (Artistic Director)
Billet Lane, Hornchurch, Essex RM11 1QT
F 01708 462363
BO 01708 443333   T 01708 462362 (Admin/SD)
E info@queens-theatre.co.uk
W www.queens-theatre.co.uk
Route: District Line to Hornchurch, Main Line to Romford/Gidea Park. 15 miles from West End take A13, A1306 then A125 or A12 then A127

QUESTORS THEATRE EALING THE
12 Mattock Lane, London W5 5BQ
F 020 8567 2275
BO 020 8567 5184   T 020 8567 0011
E enquiries@questors.org.uk
W www.questors.org.uk
Route: Central or District Line to Ealing Broadway then 5 min walk. Buses 207, 83, 65, 427, 607, E2, E7, E8, E11

RED LADDER THEATRE COMPANY LTD
3 St Peter's Buildings, York Street
Leeds LS9 8AJ
F 0113 245 5351   T 0113 245 5311
E rod@redladder.co.uk
W www.redladder.co.uk

RICHMOND THEATRE
Contact: Karin Gartzke
The Green, Richmond
Surrey TW9 1QJ
F 020 8332 4509
BO 0844 8717651   T 020 8332 4500 (Admin/SD)
E richmondstagedoor@theambassadors.com
W www.ambassadortickets.com/richmond
Route: 20 minutes from Waterloo (South West Trains) or District Line to Richmond then 2 min walk

RIDWARE THEATRE
Contact: Alan & Margaret Williams. Venue only. No resident performing company
Wheelwright's House
Pipe Ridware
Rugeley, Staffs WS15 3QL   T 01889 504380
E al@christmas-time.com
W www.ridwares.co.uk

RIVERSIDE STUDIOS
Crisp Road, London W6 9RL
BO 020 8237 1111   T 020 8237 1000
E info@riversidestudios.co.uk
W www.riversidestudios.co.uk
Route: District, Piccadilly or Hammersmith & City Line to Hammersmith then 5 min walk. Buses 9, 10, 27, 33, 72, 190, 209, 211, 266, 267, 283, 295, 391, 419

ROSE THEATRE
24-26 High Street, Kingston upon Thames
Surrey KT1 1HL
F 020 8546 8783   T 020 8546 6983
E admin@rosetheatrekingston.org
W www.rosetheatrekingston.org

ROSEMARY BRANCH THEATRE
2 Shepperton Road
London N1 3DT   T 020 7704 6665
E cecilia@rosemarybranch.co.uk
W www.rosemarybranch.co.uk
Route: Tube to Bank, Moorgate or Old Street (exit 5), then No 21, 76 or 141 bus to Baring Street, or 271 bus from Highbury and Islington

SCOTTISH STORYTELLING CENTRE
Netherbow Theatre
43-45 High Street
Edinburgh EH1 1SR   T 0131 556 9579
E reception@scottishstorytellingcentre.com
W www.scottishstorytellingcentre.co.uk

SHAW THEATRE @ NOVOTEL LONDON ST PANCRAS
Contact: John-Jackson Almond (Artistic Director)
100-110 Euston Road
London NW1 2AJ
F 020 7666 9025
BO 0844 2091663   T 020 7666 9000
E info@shaw-theatre.com

SOUTH HILL PARK ARTS CENTRE
Bracknell, Berkshire RG12 7PA
BO 01344 484123   T 01344 484858 (Admin/SD)
E admin@southhillpark.org.uk
W www.southhillpark.org.uk
Route: Waterloo (Main Line) to Bracknell then 10 min bus ride or taxi rank at station

SOUTH LONDON THEATRE
Bell Theatre & Prompt Corner
2A Norwood High Street
London SE27 9NS   T 020 8670 3474
E southlondontheatre@yahoo.co.uk
W www.southlondontheatre.co.uk
Route: Victoria or London Bridge (Main Line) to West Norwood then 2 min walk, or Victoria Line to Brixton then buses 2, 68, 196, 322

SOUTHWARK PLAYHOUSE
Contact: Chris Smyrnios (Chief Executive), Ellie Jones (Artistic Director)
Shipwright Yard
Corner of Tooley Street & Bermondsey Street
London SE1 2TF   T 020 7407 0234 (Admin/BO)
E admin@southwarkplayhouse.co.uk
W www.southwarkplayhouse.co.uk
Route: Trains to London Bridge, Jubilee/Northern Line to London Bridge. Buses 47, 381, RV1, N47, N381. River service to London Bridge City

SPACE ARTS CENTRE THE
269 Westferry Road, London E14 3RS   T 020 7515 7799
E info@space.org.uk
W www.space.org.uk

TABARD THEATRE
Contact: Collin Hilton, Fred Perry (Artistic Directors), Simon Reilly (Theatre Manager)
2 Bath Road, London W4 1LW
F 020 8994 6985   T 020 8995 6035
E info@tabardtheatre.co.uk
W www.tabardtheatre.co.uk

THEATRE 503
The Latchmere Pub
503 Battersea Park Road
London SW11 3BW   BO 020 7978 7040
E info@theatre503.com
W www.theatre503.com
Route: Victoria or Waterloo (Main Line) to Clapham Junction then 10 min walk or buses 44, 319, 344, 345 or tube to South Kensington then buses 49 or 345 or tube to Sloane Square then bus 319

THEATRE ALIBI
Northcott Studio Theatre, Emmanuel Road
Exeter EX4 4LS   T 01392 217315
E info@theatrealibi.co.uk
W www.theatrealibi.co.uk

THEATRE ROYAL STRATFORD EAST
Contact: Kerry Michael (Artistic Director)
Gerry Raffles Square
London E15 1BN
F 020 8534 8381
BO 020 8534 0310   T 020 8534 7374
E theatreroyal@stratfordeast.com
W www.stratfordeast.com
Route: Central or Jubilee Lines, DLR, Overground or National Express trains to Stratford then 2 min walk

THEATRO TECHNIS
Contact: George Eugeniou (Artistic Director)
26 Crowndale Road
London NW1 1TT   T 020 7387 6617 (Admin/BO)
E info@theatrotechnis.com
W www.theatrotechnis.com
Route: Northern Line to Mornington Crescent then 3 min walk

TOBACCO FACTORY THEATRE
Raleigh Road, Southville
Bristol BS3 1TF   T 0117 902 0345
E theatre@tobaccofactory.com
W www.tobaccofactorytheatre.com

TRICYCLE THEATRE
Contact: Nicolas Kent (Artistic Director), Mary Lauder (General Manager)
269 Kilburn High Road, London NW6 7JR
F 020 7328 0795
BO 020 7328 1000   T 020 7372 6611
E admin@tricycle.co.uk
W www.tricycle.co.uk
Route: Jubilee Line to Kilburn then 5 min walk or buses 16, 189, 32 pass the door, 98, 31, 206, 316, 332 pass nearby

TRON THEATRE
63 Trongate, Glasgow G1 5HB
F 0141 552 6657
BO 0141 552 4267   T 0141 552 3748
E casting@tron.co.uk
W www.tron.co.uk

UNION THEATRE THE
Contact: Sasha Regan (Artistic Director), Ben De Wynter (Associate Director), Steve Miller (Technical Director), Paul Flynn (All Casting Enquiries)
204 Union Street
Southwark
London SE1 0LX   T/F 020 7261 9876
E sasha@uniontheatre.freeserve.co.uk
W www.uniontheatre.biz
Route: Jubilee Line to Southwark then 2 min walk

UPSTAIRS AT THE GATEHOUSE
Ovation Theatres Ltd
The Gatehouse Pub
Corner of Hampstead Lane/North Road
London N6 4BD
BO 020 8340 3488   T 020 8340 4256
E events@ovationproductions.com
W www.upstairsatthegatehouse.com
Route: Northern Line to Highgate then 10 min walk. Buses 143, 210, 214, 271

WAREHOUSE THEATRE
Contact: Ted Craig (Artistic Director)
Dingwall Road
Croydon CR0 2NF
F 020 8688 6699
BO 020 8680 4060   T 020 8681 1257
E info@warehousetheatre.co.uk
W www.warehousetheatre.co.uk
Route: Adjacent to East Croydon (Main Line). Direct from Victoria (15 min), Clapham Junction (10 min) or by First Capital Connect from West Hampstead, Kentish Town, Kings Cross (25 Mins) & London Bridge (10 mins)

WATERLOO EAST THEATRE
3 Wooton Street
London E15 3DX   T 020 7928 0060
E info@waterlooeast.co.uk
W www.waterlooeast.co.uk

WATERMANS
40 High Street
Brentford TW8 0DS
F 020 8232 1030
BO 020 8232 1010   T 020 8232 1020
E info@watermans.org.uk
W www.watermans.org.uk
Route: Buses: 237, 267, 65, N9. Tube: Gunnersbury or South Ealing. Main Line: Kew Bridge then 5 min walk, Gunnersbury then 10 min walk, or Brentford

WESTRIDGE (OPEN CENTRE)
Drawing Room Recitals
Star Lane, Highclere
Nr Newbury
Berkshire RG20 9PJ   T 01635 253322

WHITE BEAR THEATRE
Favours New Writing
138 Kennington Park Road
London SE11 4DJ   T 020 7793 9193 (Admin/BO)
E info@whitebeartheatre.co.uk
W www.whitebeartheatre.co.uk
Route: Northern Line to Kennington (2 min walk)

WILTONS MUSIC HALL
Graces Alley
Off Ensign Street
London E1 8JB
F 0871 2532424   T 020 7702 9555
W www.wiltons.org.uk
Route: Tube: Under 10 minutes walk from Aldgate East (exit for Leman Street)/Tower Hill. DLR: Shadwell or Tower Gateway. Car: Follow the yellow AA signs to Wiltons Music Hall from the Highway, Aldgate or Tower Hill

WIMBLEDON STUDIO THEATRE
See NEW WIMBLEDON THEATRE & STUDIO

WYCOMBE SWAN
St Mary Street
High Wycombe
Buckinghamshire HP11 2XE
BO 01494 512000   T 01494 514444
E enquiries@wycombeswan.co.uk
W www.wycombeswan.co.uk

ABERDEEN
His Majesty's Theatre
Rosemount Viaduct, Aberdeen AB25 1GL
SD 01224 337673
BO 01224 641122   T 0845 2708200
E hmtinfo@aberdeenperformingarts.com
W www.boxofficeaberdeen.com

ABERYSTWYTH
Aberystwyth Arts Centre
University of Wales, Aberystwyth SY23 3DE
SD 01970 624239
BO 01970 623232   T 01970 622882
E ggo@aber.ac.uk
W www.aber.ac.uk/artscentre

BACUP
Royal Court Theatre
Rochdale Road, Bacup OL13 9NR   BO 01706 874080

BASINGSTOKE
The Haymarket Theatre
Wote Street, Basingstoke RG21 7NW
BO 01256 844244   T 01256 819797 (Admin/SD)
E box.office@anvilarts.org.uk
W www.anvilarts.org.uk

BATH
Theatre Royal
Sawclose, Bath BA1 1ET
BO 01225 448844   T 01225 448815 (Admin/SD)
E forename.surname@theatreroyal.org.uk
W www.theatreroyal.org.uk

BELFAST
Grand Opera House
Great Victoria Street, Belfast BT2 7HR
BO 028 9024 1919   T 028 9024 0411 (Admin/SD)
E info@goh.co.uk
W www.goh.co.uk

BILLINGHAM
Forum Theatre
Town Centre
Billingham TS23 2LJ   T 01642 217504 (Admin/BO)
E forumtheatre@btconnect.com
W www.forumtheatrebillingham.co.uk

BIRMINGHAM
Alexandra Theatre
Station Street, Birmingham B5 4DS
SD 0121 230 9102
BO 0844 8472301   T 0121 643 5536
W www.alexandratheatre.org.uk

BIRMINGHAM
Hippodrome
Hurst Street, Birmingham B5 4TB
SD 0121 689 3020
BO 0844 3385000   T 0870 7305555
W www.birminghamhippodrome.com

BLACKPOOL
Grand Theatre
33 Church Street, Blackpool FY1 1HT
SD 01253 743218
BO 01253 290190   T 01253 290111
E box@blackpoolgrand.co.uk
W www.blackpoolgrand.co.uk

BLACKPOOL
Opera House
Church Street, Blackpool FY1 1HW
SD 01253 629732
BO 0844 8561111   T 01253 625252
W www.blackpoollive.com

BOURNEMOUTH
Pavilion Theatre
Westover Road, Bournemouth BH1 2BU
SD 01202 451863
BO 0844 5763000   T 01202 456400
W www.bic.co.uk

BRADFORD
Alhambra Theatre
Morley Street, Bradford BD7 1AJ
BO 01274 432000   T 01274 432375 (Admin/SD)
E administration@ces.bradford.gov.uk
W www.bradford-theatres.co.uk

BRADFORD
Theatre in The Mill
University of Bradford
Shearbridge Road, Bradford BD7 1DP
SD 01274 233187
BO 01274 233200   T 01274 233185
E theatre@bradford.ac.uk
W www.bradford.ac.uk/theatre

BRIGHTON
The Dome, Corn Exchange & Pavilion Theatres
12A Pavilion Buildings
Castle Square, Brighton BN1 1EE
SD 01273 261550
BO 01273 709709   T 01273 700747
E info@brightondome.org
W www.brightondome.org

BRIGHTON
Theatre Royal
New Road, Brighton BN1 1SD
BO 0844 8717650   T 01273 764400 (Admin/SD)
E brightontheatremanager@theambassadors.com
W www.ambassadortickets.com/brighton

BRISTOL
Bristol Hippodrome
St Augustines Parade, Bristol BS1 4UZ
SD 0117 302 3251
BO 0844 8472325   T 0117 302 3310
W www.bristolhippodrome.org.uk

BROXBOURNE (Herts)
Broxbourne Civic Hall
High Street, Hoddesdon, Herts EN11 8BE
BO 01992 441946   T 01992 441931
E civic.leisure@broxbourne.gov.uk
W www.broxbourne.gov.uk/whatson

BURY ST EDMUNDS
Theatre Royal
Westgate Street, Bury St Edmunds IP33 1QR
BO 01284 769505   T 01284 755127
E admin@theatreroyal.org
W www.theatreroyal.org

BUXTON
Buxton Opera House
Water Street, Buxton SK17 6XN
SD 01298 72524
BO 0845 1272190   T 01298 72050
E admin@boh.org.uk
W www.buxtonoperahouse.org.uk

CAMBERLEY
The Camberley Theatre
Knoll Road, Camberley
Surrey GU15 3SY
BO 01276 707600   T 01276 707512
E camberleytheatre@surreyheath.gov.uk
W www.camberleytheatre.biz

CAMBRIDGE
Cambridge Arts Theatre Trust Ltd
6 St Edward's Passage
Cambridge CB2 3PJ
SD 01223 578933
BO 01223 503333   T 01223 578904
E info@cambridgeartstheatre.com
W www.cambridgeartstheatre.com

CAMBRIDGE
Mumford Theatre
Anglia Ruskin University
East Road, Cambridge CB1 1PT
BO 0845 1962320
T 0845 1962848 (Admin/SD)   T 01223 417748 (Admin/SD)
E mumford@anglia.ac.uk

CANTERBURY
Gulbenkian Theatre
University of Kent, Canterbury CT2 7NB
BO 01227 769075   T 01227 827861
E gulbenkian@kent.ac.uk
W www.gulbenkiantheatre.co.uk

CANTERBURY
The Marlowe Theatre
Closed until September 2011 for redevelopment
E marlowetheatre@canterbury.gov.uk   BO 01227 787787
W www.newmarlowetheatre.org.uk

CARDIFF
New Theatre
Park Place, Cardiff CF10 3LN
SD 029 2087 8900
BO 029 2087 8889   T 029 2087 8787
E ntmailings@cardiff.gov.uk
W www.newtheatrecardiff.co.uk

CARDIFF
Wales Millennium Centre
Bute Place, Cardiff CF10 5AL
SD 029 2063 4630
BO 029 2063 6464   T 029 2063 6400
E stagedoor@wmc.org.uk
W www.wmc.org.uk

CHELTENHAM
Everyman Theatre
Regent Street, Cheltenham GL50 1HQ
BO 01242 572573   T 01242 512515 (Admin/SD)
E admin@everymantheatre.org.uk
W www.everymantheatre.org.uk

CHICHESTER
Festival Theatre
Oaklands Park, Chichester PO19 6AP
BO 01243 781312   T 01243 784437 (Admin/SD)
E admin@cft.org.uk
W www.cft.org.uk

CRAWLEY
The Hawth
Hawth Avenue, Crawley
West Sussex RH10 6YZ
BO 01293 553636   T 01293 552941
E info@hawth.co.uk
W www.hawth.co.uk

CREWE
Lyceum Theatre
Heath Street, Crewe CW1 2DA
SD 01270 537321
BO 01270 537333   T 01270 537243
E lyceum.theatre@cheshireeast.gov.uk

DARLINGTON
Civic Theatre
Parkgate, Darlington DL1 1RR
BO 01325 486555   T 01325 387775
W www.darlingtonarts.co.uk

DUBLIN
Gaiety Theatre
South King Street, Dublin 2
BO 00 353 1 6771717   T 00 353 1 6795622 (Admin/SD)
E info@gaietytheatre.com
W www.gaietytheatre.com

DUBLIN
Gate Theatre
1 Cavendish Row, Dublin 1
BO 00 353 1 8744045   T 00 353 1 8744368
E info@gate-theatre.ie
W www.gate-theatre.ie

DUBLIN
Olympia Theatre
72 Dame Street, Dublin 2
SD 00 353 1 6771400
BO 00 353 1 6793323   T 00 353 1 6725883
E info@olympia.ie
W www.olympia.ie

EASTBOURNE
Congress Theatre
Admin Office: Winter Garden
Compton Street, Eastbourne BN21 4BP
SD 01323 410048
BO 01323 412000   T 01323 415500
E theatres@eastbourne.gov.uk
W www.eastbournetheatres.co.uk

EASTBOURNE
Devonshire Park Theatre
Admin Office: Winter Garden
Compton Street, Eastbourne BN21 4BP
SD 01323 410074
BO 01323 412000   T 01323 415500
E theatres@eastbourne.gov.uk
W www.eastbournetheatres.co.uk

EDINBURGH
King's Theatre
2 Leven Street, Edinburgh EH3 9LQ
SD 0131 662 1112
BO 0131 529 6000   T 0131 662 1112
E empire@eft.co.uk
W www.fctt.co.uk

EDINBURGH
Playhouse Theatre
18-22 Greenside Place
Edinburgh EH1 3AA
SD 0131 524 3324
BO 0844 8471660   T 0131 524 3333
W www.livenation.co.uk/edinburgh

GLASGOW
King's Theatre
297 Bath Street, Glasgow G2 4JN
BO 0844 8717648   T 0141 240 1300 (Admin/SD)
E glasgowstagedoor@theambassadors.com
W www.ambassadortickets.com

GLASGOW
Theatre Royal
282 Hope Street, Glasgow G2 3QA
BO 0844 8717648   T 0141 332 3321 (Admin/SD)
W www.ambassadortickets.com/glasgow

GRAYS THURROCK
Thameside Theatre
Orsett Road
Grays Thurrock RM17 5DX
BO 0845 3005264   T 01375 413981
E thameside.theatre@thurrock.gov.uk
W www.thurrock.gov.uk/theatre

HARLOW
Harlow Playhouse
Playhouse Square, Harlow CM20 1LS
BO 01279 431945   T 01279 446704
E playhouse@harlow.gov.uk
W www.playhouseharlow.com

HARROGATE
Harrogate International Centre
Kings Road, Harrogate HG1 5LA
BO 0845 1308840   T 01423 500500
E sales@harrogateinternationalcentre.co.uk
W www.harrogateinternationalcentre.co.uk

HASTINGS
White Rock Theatre
White Rock, Hastings TN34 1JX
BO 01424 462288   T 01424 462283
E info@whiterocktheatre.org.uk
W www.whiterocktheatre.org.uk

HAYES (Middlesex)
Beck Theatre
Grange Road, Hayes, Middlesex UB3 2UE
BO 020 8561 8371   T 020 8561 7506
E enquiries@becktheatre.org.uk
W www.becktheatre.org.uk

HIGH WYCOMBE
Wycombe Swan
St Mary Street
High Wycombe HP11 2XE
BO 01494 512000   T 01494 514444 (Admin/SD)
E enquiries@wycombeswan.co.uk
W www.wycombeswan.co.uk

HUDDERSFIELD
Lawrence Batley Theatre
Queen's Square, Queen Street
Huddersfield HD1 2SP
BO 01484 430528   T 01484 425282
E theatre@thelbt.org
W www.thelbt.org

HULL
Hull New Theatre
Kingston Square, Hull HU1 3HF
SD 01482 318300
BO 01482 226655   T 01482 613818
E theatre.management@hullcc.gov.uk
W www.hullcc.gov.uk

HULL
Hull Truck Theatre
50 Ferensway, Hull HU2 8LB
BO 01482 323638   T 01482 224800
E admin@hulltruck.co.uk
W www.hulltruck.co.uk

ILFORD
Kenneth More Theatre
Oakfield Road, Ilford IG1 1BT
SD 020 8553 4465
BO 020 8553 4466   T 020 8553 4464
E kmtheatre@aol.com
W www.kmtheatre.co.uk

IPSWICH
Sir John Mills Theatre
Hire only
Gatacre Road, Ipswich IP1 2LQ
BO 01473 211498   T 01473 218202
E admin@easternangles.co.uk
W www.easternangles.co.uk

JERSEY
Jersey Opera House
Gloucester Street, St Helier, Jersey JE2 3QR
BO 01534 511115   T 01534 511100
E admin@jerseyoperahouse.co.uk
W www.jerseyoperahouse.co.uk

KIRKCALDY
Adam Smith Theatre
Bennochy Road, Kirkcaldy KY1 1ET
BO 01592 583302   T 01592 583301

LEATHERHEAD
The Leatherhead Theatre
7 Church Street, Leatherhead, Surrey KT22 8DN
BO 01372 365141   T 01372 365130
E info@the-theatre.org
W www.the-theatre.org

LEEDS
City Varieties Music Hall
Swan Street, Leeds LS1 6LW
BO 0845 6441881   T 0845 1260696
E info@cityvarieties.co.uk
W www.cityvarieties.co.uk

LEEDS
Grand Theatre & Opera House
46 New Briggate, Leeds LS1 6NZ
BO 0844 8482705   T 0113 245 6014 (Admin/SD)
E boxoffice@leedsgrandtheatre.com
W www.leedsgrandtheatre.com

LICHFIELD
The Lichfield Garrick
Castle Dyke, Lichfield WS13 6HR
BO 01543 412121   T 01543 412110
E garrick@lichfieldgarrick.com
W www.lichfieldgarrick.com

LINCOLN
Theatre Royal
Clasketgate, Lincoln LN2 1JJ
BO 01522 525555   T 01522 519999
E trl@dial.pipex.com
W www.lincolntheatreroyal.com

LIVERPOOL
Empire Theatre
Lime Street, Liverpool L1 1JE
BO 0844 8472525   T 0151 708 3200 (Admin/SD)
W www.liverpoolempire.org.uk

LLANDUDNO
Venue Cymru
Promenade, Llandudno
Conwy, North Wales LL30 1BB
BO 01492 872000   T 01492 879771
E info@venuecymru.co.uk
W www.venuecymru.co.uk

MALVERN
Malvern Theatres (Festival & Forum Theatres)
Grange Road, Malvern WR14 3HB
BO 01684 892277   T 01684 569256
E post@malvern-theatres.co.uk
W www.malvern-theatres.co.uk

MANCHESTER
Manchester Apollo
Stockport Road, Ardwick Green
Manchester M12 6AP
SD 0161 273 2416
BO 0844 4777677   T 0161 273 6921
E manchester.apollo@livenation.co.uk
W www.livenation.co.uk

MANCHESTER
Opera House
Quay Street
Manchester M3 3HP
BO 0844 8472484   T 0161 828 1700 (Admin/SD)
W www.palaceandoperahouse.org.uk

MANCHESTER
Palace Theatre
Oxford Street
Manchester M1 6FT
BO 0844 8472484   T 0161 245 6600 (Admin/SD)
W www.palaceandoperahouse.org.uk

MARGATE
Theatre Royal
Addington Street
Margate, Kent CT9 1PW
BO 0845 1301786   T 01843 293397 (Admin/SD)
W www.theatreroyalmargate.com

MILTON KEYNES
Milton Keynes Theatre
500 Marlborough Gate
Central Milton Keynes MK9 3NZ
BO 0870 0606652   T 01908 547500 (Admin/SD)
W www.ambassadortickets.com/miltonkeynes

NEWARK
Palace Theatre
Appletongate, Newark NG24 1JY
BO 01636 655755   T 01636 655750
E kevan.jackson@nsdc.info
W www.palacenewark.com

NEWCASTLE UPON TYNE
Northern Stage
Barras Bridge, Haymarket
Newcastle upon Tyne NE1 7RH
BO 0191 230 5151   T 0191 232 3366
E info@northernstage.co.uk
W www.northernstage.co.uk

NEWCASTLE UPON TYNE
Theatre Royal
Grey Street
Newcastle upon Tyne NE1 6BR
BO 0844 8112121   T 0191 244 2500 (Admin/SD)
W www.theatreroyal.co.uk

NORTHAMPTON
Royal & Derngate Theatres
19-21 Guildhall Road
Northampton NN1 1DP
BO 01604 624811   T 01604 626222 (Admin/SD)
E postbox@royalandderngate.co.uk
W www.royalandderngate.co.uk

NORWICH
Theatre Royal
Theatre Street
Norwich NR2 1RL
BO 01603 630000   T 01603 598500 (Admin/SD)
W www.theatreroyalnorwich.co.uk

NOTTINGHAM
Theatre Royal & Royal Concert Hall
Theatre Square
Nottingham NG1 5ND
BO 0115 989 5555   T 0115 989 5500 (Admin/SD)
E enquiry@royalcentre-nottingham.co.uk
W www.royalcentre-nottingham.co.uk

OXFORD
New Theatre
George Street, Oxford OX1 2AG
BO 0844 8440662   T 01865 320760 (Admin/SD)

OXFORD
Oxford Playhouse
11-12 Beaumont Street, Oxford OX1 2LW
SD 01865 305301
BO 01865 305305   T 01865 305300
E admin@oxfordplayhouse.com
W www.oxfordplayhouse.com

POOLE
Lighthouse, Poole's Centre for the Arts
Kingland Road
Poole BH15 1UG   BO 0844 4068666
W www.lighthousepoole.co.uk

READING
The Hexagon
Queen's Walk, Reading RG1 7UA
SD 0118 937 2018
BO 0118 960 6060   T 0118 937 2123
E boxoffice@readingarts.com
W www.readingarts.com

RICHMOND (N Yorks)
Georgian Theatre Royal
Victoria Road, Richmond
North Yorkshire DL10 4DW
BO 01748 825252   T 01748 823710
E admin@georgiantheatreroyal.co.uk
W www.georgiantheatreroyal.co.uk

RICHMOND (Surrey)
Richmond Theatre
The Green, Richmond
Surrey TW9 1QJ
BO 0844 8717651   T 020 8332 4500 (Admin/SD)
E richmondstagedoor@theambassadors.com
W www.ambassadortickets.com/richmond

SHEFFIELD
Sheffield Theatres (Crucible, Lyceum & Crucible Studio)
55 Norfolk Street, Sheffield S1 1DA
BO 0114 249 6000   T 0114 249 5999 (Admin/SD)
E info@sheffieldtheatres.co.uk
W www.sheffieldtheatres.co.uk

SHERINGHAM
The Little Theatre
2 Station Road
Sheringham, Norfolk NR26 8RE
BO 01263 822347   T 01263 822117
E enquiries@sheringhamlittletheatre.com
W www.sheringhamlittletheatre.com

SOUTHAMPTON
The Mayflower
Commercial Road, Southampton SO15 1GE
BO 023 8071 1811   T 023 8071 1800
E info@mayflower.org.uk
W www.mayflower.org.uk

SOUTHEND
Southend Theatres (Cliffs Pavilion, Palace Theatre & Dixon Studio)
Cliffs Pavilion
Station Road
Westcliff-on-Sea, Essex SS0 7RA
SD 01702 347394
BO 01702 351135   T 01702 390657
E info@southendtheatres.org.uk
W www.southendtheatres.org.uk

ST ALBANS
Abbey Theatre
Holywell Hill, St Albans AL1 2DL
BO 01727 857861   T 01727 847472
E manager@abbeytheatre.org.uk
W www.abbeytheatre.org.uk

ST ALBANS
Alban Arena
Civic Centre
St Albans AL1 3LD
BO 01727 844488   T 01727 861078
E alban.arena@leisureconnection.co.uk
W www.alban-arena.co.uk

ST HELENS
Theatre Royal
Corporation Street
St Helens WA10 1LQ
BO 01744 756000   T 01744 756333
E info@sthelenstheatreroyal.co.uk
W www.sthelenstheatreroyal.com

STAFFORD
Stafford Gatehouse Theatre
Eastgate Street
Stafford ST16 2LT
BO 01785 254653   T 01785 253595
E gatehouse@staffordbc.gov.uk
W www.staffordgatehousetheatre.co.uk

STEVENAGE
Gordon Craig Theatre
Arts & Leisure Centre, Lytton Way
Stevenage SG1 1LZ
SD 01438 242629
BO 0870 0131030   T 01438 242679
E gordoncraig@stevenage-leisure.co.uk
W www.gordon-craig.co.uk

SUNDERLAND
Sunderland Empire
High Street West
Sunderland SR1 3EX
SD 0191 566 1057
BO 0844 8472499   T 0191 566 1040
W www.sunderlandempire.org.uk

SWANAGE
Mowlem Theatre
Shore Road
Swanage BH19 1DD   BO 01929 422239
E briantraversmowlem@yahoo.co.uk

TAMWORTH
Assembly Rooms
Corporation Street
Tamworth B79 7DN
BO 01827 709618   T 01827 709619
E assemblyrooms@tamworth.gov.uk
W www.tamworthassemblyrooms.gov.uk

TEWKESBURY
The Roses
Sun Street, Tewkesbury GL20 5NX
BO 01684 295074   T 01684 290734
E admin@rosestheatre.org
W www.rosestheatre.org

TORQUAY
Babbacombe Theatre
Babbacombe Downs, Torquay TQ1 3LU
T 01803 328385 (SD/BO)   T 01803 322233
E info@babbacombe-theatre.com
W www.babbacombe-theatre.com

TORQUAY
Princess Theatre
Torbay Road, Torquay TQ2 5EZ
SD 01803 290068
BO 0844 8472315   T 01803 290288
E wendybennett@theambassadors.com
W www.princesstheatre.org.uk

TRURO
Hall For Cornwall
Lemon Quay, Truro
Cornwall TR1 2LL
BO 01872 262466   T 01872 262465 (Admin/SD)
E admin@hallforcornwall.org.uk
W www.hallforcornwall.co.uk

WINCHESTER
Theatre Royal
21-23 Jewry Street
Winchester SO23 8SB
BO 01962 840440   T 01962 844600
E comms@theatreroyalwinchester.co.uk
W www.theatreroyalwinchester.co.uk

WOLVERHAMPTON
Grand Theatre
Lichfield Street
Wolverhampton WV1 1DE
BO 01902 429212   T 01902 573320 (Admin/SD)
E marketing@grandtheatre.co.uk
W www.grandtheatre.co.uk

WORCESTER
Swan Theatre
The Moors, Worcester WR1 3ED
BO 01905 611427   T 01905 726969
E chris@worcesterlive.co.uk
W www.worcesterlive.co.uk

WORTHING
Connaught Theatre
Union Place, Worthing BN11 1LG
BO 01903 206206   T 01903 231799
E theatres@worthing.gov.uk
W www.worthingtheatres.co.uk

YEOVIL
Octagon Theatre
Hendford
Yeovil BA20 1UX
BO 01935 422884   T 01935 845900
E octagontheatre@southsomerset.gov.uk
W www.octagon-theatre.co.uk

YORK
Grand Opera House
Cumberland Street, York YO1 9SW
BO 0844 8472322   T 01904 678700
E yorkboxoffice@theambassadors.com
W www.grandoperahouseyork.org.uk

AUTHENTIC PUNCH & JUDY
Contact: John Styles. Booths. Presentations. Puppets
42 Christchurch Road, Sidcup
Kent DA15 7HQ   T/F 020 8300 3579
W www.johnstylesentertainer.co.uk

BUCKLEY Simon
Freelance Puppeteer/Presenter
E puppet.buckley@virgin.net
W www.simonbuckley.co.uk

COMPLETE WORKS CREATIVE COMPANY LTD THE
Contact: Phil Evans (Artistic Director)
The Old Truman Brewery, 91 Brick Lane
London E1 6QL
F 020 7247 7405   T 020 7377 0280
E info@tcw.org.uk
W www.tcw.org.uk

CORNELIUS & JONES
49 Carters Close, Sherington
Newport Pagnell
Buckinghamshire MK16 9NW   T/F 01908 612593
E admin@corneliusjones.com
W www.corneliusjones.com

DYNAMIC NEW ANIMATION
Unit 13, The Watermark
Ribbleton Lane
Preston PR1 5EZ   T 0161 408 1720
E info@dynamicnewanimation.co.uk
W www.dynamicnewanimation.co.uk

INDIGO MOON THEATRE
35 Waltham Court, Beverley
East Yorkshire HU17 9JF   M 07855 328552
E info@indigomoontheatre.com
W www.indigomoontheatre.com

JACOLLY PUPPET THEATRE
Kirkella Road, Yelverton
West Devon PL20 6BB   T 01822 852346
E theatre@jacolly-puppets.co.uk
W www.jacolly-puppets.co.uk

LITTLE ANGEL THEATRE
14 Dagmar Passage, Cross Street
London N1 2DN   T 020 7226 1787
E info@littleangeltheatre.com
W www.littleangeltheatre.com

MAJOR MUSTARD'S TRAVELLING SHOW
1 Carless Avenue, Harborne
Birmingham B17 9EG   T 0121 426 4329
E mm@majormustard.com

NORWICH PUPPET THEATRE
St James, Whitefriars
Norwich NR3 1TN
F 01603 617578   T 01603 615564
E info@puppettheatre.co.uk
W www.puppettheatre.co.uk

PEKKO'S PUPPETS
Contact: Stephen Novy (Director)
92 Stanley Avenue, Greenford
Middlesex UB6 8NP   T 020 8575 2311
E enquiries@pekkospuppets.co.uk

PROFESSOR PATTEN'S PUNCH & JUDY
Magic. Puppetry
14 The Crest, Goffs Oak
Herts EN7 5NP   T 01707 873262
W www.dennispatten.co.uk

PUPPET THEATRE WALES
22 Starling Road, St Athan
Vale of Glamorgan CF62 4NJ   T 01446 790634
E info@puppettheatrewales.co.uk
W www.puppettheatrewales.co.uk

TALK TO THE HAND PRODUCTIONS
Custom Characters Created & Performed
Studio 277, Wimbledon Art Studios
Riverside Yard, Earlsfield, London SW17 0BB
M 07813 682293   M 07855 421454
E info@talktothehandpuppets.com
W www.talktothehandpuppets.com

TICKLISH ALLSORTS SHOW
57 Victoria Road
Wilton, Salisbury
Wiltshire SP2 0DZ   T/F 01722 744949
E garynunn@ntlworld.com
W www.ticklishallsorts.co.uk

TOPPER Chris PUPPETS
Puppets & Costume Characters. Created & Performed
75 Barrows Green Lane, Widnes
Cheshire WA8 3JH   T 0151 424 8692
E christopper@ntlworld.com
W www.christopperpuppets.co.uk

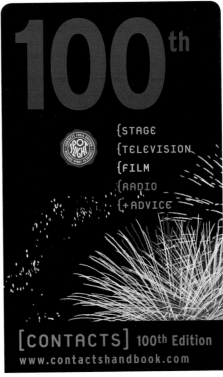

ALDEBURGH
Summer Theatre (July & August) The Jubilee Hall
Crabbe Street, Aldeburgh IP15 5BW
BO 01728 453007/454022 (Evening)
T 020 7724 5432 (Oct-May)   T 01502 726642 (June-Sept)
W www.southwoldtheatre.org

BELFAST
Lyric Theatre
Contact: Richard Croxford (Artistic Director), Conor McGivern
(Head of Production & Technical Services), Neil Edwards
(Theatre Administrator), Ciaran McAuley (Chief Executive),
Deírdre Ferguson (Finance Manager)
88A Stranmillis Road, Belfast BT9 5AD
F 028 9038 1395   T 028 9038 5674
E info@lyrictheatre.co.uk
W www.lyrictheatre.co.uk

BIRMINGHAM
Birmingham Stage Company
Contact: Neal Foster (Actor/Manager)
The Old Rep Theatre, Station Street, Birmingham B5 4DY
BO 0121 303 2323   T 0121 643 9050
E info@birminghamstage.com
W www.birminghamstage.com

BIRMINGHAM
Birmingham Stage Company
Contact: Neal Foster (Actor/Manager), Philip Compton
(Executive Producer)
London Office:, Suite 228 The Linen Hall
162 Regent Street, London W1B 5TB
F 020 7437 3395   T 020 7437 3391
E info@birminghamstage.com
W www.birminghamstage.com

BIRMINGHAM
Repertory Theatre
Contact: Rachel Kavanaugh (Artistic Director), Stuart Rogers
(Executive Director)
Centenary Square, Broad Street, Birmingham B1 2EP
T 0121 245 2072 (Press Office)
BO 0121 236 4455   T 0121 245 2000
E info@birmingham-rep.co.uk

BOLTON
Octagon Theatre
Contact: David Thacker (Artistic Director), John Blackmore
(Executive Director), Lesley Etherington (Head of
Administration), Oliver Seviour (Head of Production)
Howell Croft South, Bolton BL1 1SB
F 01204 556502
BO 01204 520661   T 01204 529407
E info@octagonbolton.co.uk
W www.octagonbolton.co.uk

BRISTOL
Theatre Royal & Studio
Contact: Tom Morris (Artistic Director), Emma Stenning
(Executive Director)
Bristol Old Vic, King Street, Bristol BS1 4ED
F 0117 949 3996
BO 0117 987 7877   T 0117 949 3993
E admin@bristol-old-vic.co.uk
W www.bristololdvic.org.uk

CARDIFF
Sherman Cymru
Contact: Chris Ricketts (Director), Margaret Jones (General
Manager)
Senghennydd Road, Cardiff CF24 4YE
F 029 2064 6902
T 029 2064 6900   T 029 2064 6901
E kate.perridge@shermancymru.co.uk

CHICHESTER
Chichester Festival Theatre
Contact: Jonathan Church (Artistic Director), Alan Finch
(Executive Director), Janet Bakose (Theatre Manager)
Oaklands Park, Chichester
West Sussex PO19 6AP
F 01243 787288
BO 01243 781312   T 01243 784437 (Admin/SD)
E admin@cft.org.uk
W www.cft.org.uk

CHICHESTER
Minerva Theatre at Chichester Festival Theatre
Contact: Jonathan Church (Artistic Director), Alan Finch
(Executive Director), Janet Bakose (Theatre Manager)
Oaklands Park, Chichester
West Sussex PO19 6AP
F 01243 787288
BO 01243 781312   T 01243 784437 (Admin/SD)
E admin@cft.org.uk
W www.cft.org.uk

COLCHESTER
Mercury Theatre
Contact: Dee Evans (Chief Executive), Adrian Grady
(Executive Director)
Balkerne Gate, Colchester
Essex CO1 1PT
F 01206 769607
BO 01206 573948   T 01206 577006
E info@mercurytheatre.co.uk
W www.mercurytheatre.co.uk

COVENTRY
Belgrade Main Stage & B2 Auditorium
Contact: Hamish Glen (Artistic Director/CEO), Joanna
Reid (Executive Director), Nicola Young (Director of
Communications)
Belgrade Square, Coventry
West Midlands CV1 1GS
BO 024 7655 3055   T 024 7625 6431
E admin@belgrade.co.uk
W www.belgrade.co.uk

DUBLIN
Abbey Theatre Amharclann na Mainistreach
Contact: Fiach MacConghail (Director)
26 Lower Abbey Street, Dublin 1
Ireland F 00 353 1 872 9177
BO 00 353 1 878 7222   T 00 353 1 887 2200
E info@abbeytheatre.ie
W www.abbeytheatre.ie

DUNDEE
Dundee Repertory Theatre
Contact: James Brining (Artistic Director/Chief Executive),
Jemima Levick (Associate Director), Ian Alexander (General
Manager)
Tay Square, Dundee DD1 1PB
F 01382 228609
BO 01382 223530   T 01382 227684
W www.dundeereptheatre.co.uk

EDINBURGH
Royal Lyceum Theatre Company
Contact: Mark Thomson (Artistic Director)
30B Grindlay Street
Edinburgh EH3 9AX
F 0131 228 3955
BO 0131 248 4848   T 0131 248 4800 (Admin/SD)
E info@lyceum.org.uk
W www.lyceum.org.uk

EDINBURGH
Traverse Theatre
Contact: Dominic Hill (Artistic Director), Linda Crooks
(Administrative Director). New Writing. Own Productions.
Touring & Visiting Companies
10 Cambridge Street, Edinburgh EH1 2ED
F 0131 229 8443
BO 0131 228 1404   T 0131 228 3223
E admin@traverse.co.uk
W www.traverse.co.uk

EXETER
Exeter Northcott Theatre
Contact: Kate Tyrrell (Chief Executive)
Stocker Road, Exeter, Devon EX4 4QB
F 01392 255835
BO 01392 493493   T 01392 223999
E info@exeternorthcott.co.uk
W www.exeternorthcott.co.uk

FRINTON
Frinton Summer Theatre
Contact: Edward Max (Producer/Artistic Director) July-Sept
The McGrigor Hall, Fourth Avenue
Frinton-on-Sea
Essex CO13 9EB   BO 07905 589792 (July-Sept only)
E ed.max@frintonsummertheatre.co.uk

GLASGOW
Citizens Theatre
Contact: Jeremy Raison, Guy Hollands (Artistic Directors),
Anna Stapleton (Administrative Director)
Gorbals, Glasgow G5 9DS
F 0141 429 7374
BO 0141 429 0022   T 0141 429 5561
E info@citz.co.uk
W www.citz.co.uk

GUILDFORD
Yvonne Arnaud Theatre
Contact: James Barber (Director)
Millbrook, Guildford, Surrey GU1 3UX
F 01483 564071
BO 01483 440000   T 01483 440077
E yat@yvonne-arnaud.co.uk   W www.yvonne-arnaud.co.uk

HARROGATE
Harrogate Theatre
Contact: David Bown (Chief Executive)
Mainly Co-productions. Touring & Visiting Companies
Oxford Street, Harrogate HG1 1QF
F 01423 563205
BO 01423 502116   T 01423 502710
E info@harrogatetheatre.co.uk
W www.harrogatetheatre.co.uk

HULL
Hull Truck Theatre
Contact: John Godber, Gareth Tudor Price (Artistic
Directors), Paul Marshall (Executive Director), Nick Lane
(Associate Director)
50 Ferensway, Hull HU2 8LB
F 01482 581182   T 01482 224800
E admin@hulltruck.co.uk   W www.hulltruck.co.uk

IPSWICH
The New Wolsey Theatre
Contact: Peter Rowe (Artistic Director), Sarah Holmes (Chief
Executive)
Civic Drive, Ipswich, Suffolk IP1 2AS
F 01473 295910
BO 01473 295900   T 01473 295911
E info@wolseytheatre.co.uk   W www.wolseytheatre.co.uk

KESWICK
Theatre by The Lake
Contact: Ian Forrest (Artistic Director)
Lakeside, Keswick
Cumbria CA12 5DJ
F 01768 774698
BO 01768 774411   T 01768 772282
E enquiries@theatrebythelake.com
W www.theatrebythelake.com

LANCASTER
The Dukes
Contact: Joe Sumsion (Director)
Moor Lane, Lancaster
Lancashire LA1 1QE
F 01524 598519
BO 01524 598500   T 01524 598505
E info@dukes-lancaster.org
W www.dukes-lancaster.org

LEEDS
West Yorkshire Playhouse
Contact: Ian Brown (Artistic Director/Chief Executive),
Sheena Wrigley (Joint Chief Executive), Henrietta Duckworth
(Producer)
Playhouse Square, Quarry Hill
Leeds LS2 7UP
F 0113 213 7250
BO 0113 213 7700   T 0113 213 7800
W www.wyp.org.uk

LEICESTER
Curve
Contact: Juliette Stark (Assistant Producer), Paul Kerryson
(Artistic Director), Stella McCabe (Deputy Chief Executive),
Iain Gille (Executive Producer)
Rutland Street, Leicester LE1 1SB   T 0116 242 3560
E j.stark@curvetheatre.co.uk
W www.curveonline.co.uk

LIVERPOOL
Everyman & Playhouse Theatres
Contact: Gemma Bodinetz (Artistic Director), Deborah Aydon
(Executive Director)
Everyman: 13 Hope Street
Liverpool L1 9BH
Playhouse: Williamson Square
Liverpool L1 1EL
F 0151 709 0398
BO 0151 709 4776   T 0151 708 3700
E info@everymanplayhouse.com
W www.everymanplayhouse.com

MANCHESTER
Contact Theatre Company
Contact: Baba Israel (Chief Executive/Artistic Director)
Oxford Road, Manchester M15 6JA
F 0161 274 0640
BO 0161 274 0600   T 0161 274 0623
E info@contact-theatre.org
W www.contact-theatre.org

MANCHESTER
Library Theatre Company
Contact: Chris Honer (Artistic Director), Adrian J. P. Morgan
(General Manager)
Zion Arts, 335 Stretford Road
Manchester M15 5ZA
F 0161 228 6481
BO 0161 236 7110   T 0161 234 1913
E ltcadmin@manchester.gov.uk
W www.librarytheatre.com

MANCHESTER

Royal Exchange Theatre
Contact: Braham Murray, Gregory Hersov, Sarah Frankcom (Artistic Directors), Richard Morgan (Producer/Studio), Jerry Knight-Smith (Casting Director)
St Ann's Square
Manchester M2 7DH
F 0161 832 0881
BO 0161 833 9833
E [no email]
W www.royalexchange.co.uk
T 0161 833 9333

MILFORD HAVEN

Torch Theatre
Contact: Peter Doran (Artistic Director)
St Peter's Road, Milford Haven
Pembrokeshire SA73 2BU
F 01646 698919
BO 01646 695267
E info@torchtheatre.co.uk
W www.torchtheatre.co.uk
T 01646 694192

MOLD

Clwyd Theatr Cymru
Repertoire. 4 Weekly. Also touring
Mold, Flintshire
North Wales CH7 1YA
F 01352 701558
BO 0845 3303565
E admin@clwyd-theatr-cymru.co.uk
W www.clwyd-theatr-cymru.co.uk
T 01352 756331

MUSSELBURGH

The Brunton Theatre
Contact: Lesley Smith (General Manager). Annual programme of Theatre, Dance, Music, Comedy & Children's Work
Ladywell Way
Musselburgh EH21 6AA
F 0131 653 5265
BO 0131 665 2240
W www.bruntontheatre.co.uk
T 0131 665 9900

NEWBURY

Watermill Theatre
Contact: Hedda Beeby (Artistic & Executive Director), Clare Lindsay (General Manager). 4-8 Weekly. Feb-Jan
Bagnor, Nr Newbury
Berkshire RG20 8AE
F 01635 523726
BO 01635 46044
E admin@watermill.org.uk
W www.watermill.org.uk
T 01635 45834

NEWCASTLE UNDER LYME

New Vic Theatre
Contact: Theresa Heskins (Artistic Director), Nick Jones (Managing Director). 3-4 Weekly
Etruria Road, Newcastle-under-Lyme
Staffordshire ST5 0JG
F 01782 712885
BO 01782 717962
E casting@newvictheatre.org.uk
W www.newvictheatre.org.uk
T 01782 717954

NEWCASTLE UPON TYNE

Northern Stage (Theatrical Productions) Ltd
Contact: Erica Whyman (Chief Executive)
Barras Bridge, Newcastle upon Tyne NE1 7RH
F 0191 242 7256
BO 0191 230 5151
E info@northernstage.co.uk
W www.northernstage.co.uk
T 0191 232 3366

NORTHAMPTON

Royal & Derngate
Contact: Martin Sutherland (Chief Executive), Laurie Sansom (Artistic Director), Dani Parr (Associate Director)
19-21 Guildhall Road, Northampton
Northamptonshire NN1 1DP
BO 01604 624811
E postbox@royalandderngate.co.uk
W www.royalandderngate.co.uk
T 01604 626222

NOTTINGHAM

Nottingham Playhouse
Contact: Stephanie Sirr (Chief Executive), Giles Croft (Artistic Director), Andrew Breakwell (Director, Roundabout and Education). 3-4 Weekly
Nottingham Playhouse Trust Ltd, Wellington Circus
Nottingham NG1 5AL
F 0115 947 5759
BO 0115 941 9419
E enquiry@nottinghamplayhouse.co.uk
W www.nottinghamplayhouse.co.uk
T 0115 947 4361

OLDHAM

Coliseum Theatre
Contact: Kevin Shaw (Chief Executive). 3-4 Weekly
Fairbottom Street, Oldham, Lancashire OL1 3SW
F 0161 624 5318
BO 0161 624 2829
E mail@coliseum.org.uk
W www.coliseum.org.uk
T 0161 624 1731

PERTH

Perth Theatre
Contact: Ian Grieve (Artistic Director), Paul Hackett (Head of Planning & Resources), Jane Spiers (Chief Executive) 2-3 Weekly
Horsecross Arts, 185 High Street
Perth PH1 5UW
F 01738 624576
BO 01738 621031
E info@horsecross.co.uk
W www.horsecross.co.uk
T 01738 472700

PETERBOROUGH

Key Theatre
Touring & Occasional Seasonal
Embankment Road, Peterborough
Cambridgeshire PE1 1EF
F 01733 567025
BO 01733 207239
E key.theatre@vivacity-peterborough.com
T 01733 207237

PITLOCHRY

Pitlochry Festival Theatre
Contact: John Durnin (Chief Executive/Artistic Director)
Pitlochry, Perthshire PH16 5DR
F 01796 484616
BO 01796 484626
E admin@pitlochry.org.uk
W www.pitlochry.org.uk
T 01796 484600

PLYMOUTH

Theatre Royal & Drum Theatre
Contact: Simon Stokes (Artistic Director), Adrian Vinken (Chief Executive)
Royal Parade, Plymouth
Devon PL1 2TR
F 01752 230506
BO 01752 267222
E info@theatreroyal.com
W www.theatreroyal.com
T 01752 668282

READING
The Mill at Sonning Theatre
Contact: Sally Hughes (Artistic Director), Ann Seymour (Assistant Administrator). 5-6 Weekly
Sonning Eye, Reading RG4 6TY
BO 0118 969 8000   T 0118 969 6039
W www.millatsonning.com

SALISBURY
Playhouse & Salberg Studio
Contact: Philip Wilson (Artistic Director), Michelle Carwardine-Palmer (Executive Director). 3-4 Weekly
Malthouse Lane, Salisbury
Wiltshire SP2 7RA
F 01722 421991
BO 01722 320333   T 01722 320117
E info@salisburyplayhouse.com
W www.salisburyplayhouse.com

SCARBOROUGH
Stephen Joseph Theatre
Contact: Chris Monks (Artistic Director), Stephen Wood (Executive Director). Repertoire/Repertory
Westborough, Scarborough
North Yorkshire YO11 1JW
F 01723 360506
BO 01723 370541   T 01723 370540
E enquiries@sjt.uk.com

SHEFFIELD
Crucible, Studio & Lyceum Theatres
Contact: Dan Bates (Chief Executive)
55 Norfolk Street
Sheffield S1 1DA
F 0114 249 6003
BO 0114 249 6000   T 0114 249 5999
E info@sheffieldtheatres.co.uk
W www.sheffieldtheatres.co.uk

SHERINGHAM
Summer Repertory
Contact: Sheringham Little Theatre (Producer), Debbie Thompson (Artistic Director)
The Little Theatre
2 Station Road
Sheringham, Norfolk NR26 8RE   BO 01263 822347
E enquiries@sheringhamlittletheatre.com
W www.sheringhamlittletheatre.com

SIDMOUTH
Manor Pavilion Theatre
Weekly. July-Sept
Manor Road, Sidmouth
Devon EX10 8RP   BO 01395 579977 (June-Sept)

SOUTHAMPTON
Nuffield Theatre
Contact: Patrick Sandford (Artistic Director), Kate Anderson (Executive Director). Sept-July. Sunday Night Concerts. Tours
University Road
Southampton SO17 1TR
F 023 8031 5511
BO 023 8067 1771   T 023 8031 5500
W www.nuffieldtheatre.co.uk

SOUTHWOLD
Summer Theatre
Contact: The Jill Freud Company (Producer)
June-Sept: St Edmund's Hall
Cumberland Road, Southwold IP18 6JP   T 01502 724462
E enquiries@southwoldtheatre.org
W www.southwoldtheatre.org

SOUTHWOLD
Summer Theatre
Sept-May: 14 York House
39 Upper Montagu Street
London W1H 1FR   T 020 7724 5432
E enquiries@southwoldtheatre.org
W www.southwoldtheatre.org

ST ANDREWS
Byre Theatre
Contact: Jacqueline McKay (Chief Executive). Not producing. Co-productions only
Abbey Street
St Andrews KY16 9LA
F 01334 475370   T 01334 475000 (Admin/BO)
E enquiries@byretheatre.com
W www.byretheatre.com

STRATFORD-UPON-AVON
Royal Shakespeare Company & Courtyard Theatre
Southern Lane
Stratford-upon-Avon CV37 6BB
F 01789 272560
BO 0844 8001110   T 01789 296655
E info@rsc.org.uk
W www.rsc.org.uk

WATFORD
Watford Palace Theatre
Contact: Brigid Larmour (Artistic Director/Chief Executive), Mathew Russell (Executive Director)
20 Clarendon Road
Watford
Hertfordshire WD17 1JZ
F 01923 819664
BO 01923 225671   T 01923 810300
E enquiries@watfordpalacetheatre.co.uk
W www.watfordpalacetheatre.co.uk

WINDSOR
Theatre Royal
Contact: Simon Pearce (Director)
Thames Street
Windsor
Berkshire SL4 1PS
F 01753 831673
BO 01753 853888   T 01753 863444
E info@theatreroyalwindsor.co.uk
W www.theatreroyalwindsor.co.uk

WOKING
New Victoria Theatre
The Ambassadors
Peacocks Centre
Woking GU21 6GQ
SD 01483 545855
BO 0844 8717645   T 01483 545800
E wokingboxoffice@theambassadors.com
W www.theambassadors.com/woking

YORK
Theatre Royal
Contact: Damian Cruden (Artistic Director), Liz Wilson (Chief Executive)
St Leonard's Place
York YO1 7HD
F 01904 550164
BO 01904 623568   T 01904 658162
E admin@yorktheatreroyal.co.uk
W www.yorktheatreroyal.co.uk

U

Unions, Professional Guilds and Associations

UNITED KINGDOM

BROADCASTING ENTERTAINMENT CINEMATOGRAPH & THEATRE UNION (BECTU)
Formerly BETA & ACTT
373-377 Clapham Road
London SW9 9BT
F 020 7346 0901
E smacdonald@bectu.org.uk
T 020 7346 0900

CASTING DIRECTORS' GUILD
PO Box 64973, London SW20 2AW
E info@thecdg.co.uk
W www.thecdg.co.uk

DIRECTORS GUILD OF GREAT BRITAIN
Studio 24
The Royal Victoria Patriotic Building
John Archer Way
London SW18 3SX
F 020 8870 3585
E info@dggb.org
W www.dggb.org
T 020 8871 1660

EQUITY inc Variety Artistes' Federation
Guild House, Upper St Martin's Lane
London WC2H 9EG
F 020 7379 7001
E info@equity.org.uk
W www.equity.org.uk
T 020 7379 6000

EQUITY inc Variety Artistes' Federation (Midlands)
Office 1, Steeple House
Percy Street
Coventry CV1 3BY
E tjohnson@midlands-equity.org.uk
T/F 024 7655 3612

EQUITY inc Variety Artistes' Federation (North West & Isle of Man)
Express Networks
1 George Leigh Street
Manchester M4 5DL
F 0161 244 5971
E info@manchester-equity.org.uk
T 0161 244 5995

EQUITY inc Variety Artistes' Federation (Scotland & Northern Ireland)
114 Union Street
Glasgow G1 3QQ
F 0141 248 2473
E mcurren@glasgow.equity.org.uk
T 0141 248 2472

EQUITY inc Variety Artistes' Federation (Wales & South West)
Transport House
1 Cathedral Road
Cardiff CF11 9SD
F 029 2023 0754
E info@cardiff-equity.org.uk
T 029 2039 7971

FILM ARTISTS ASSOCIATION
Amalgamated with BECTU
373-377 Clapham Road, London SW9 9BT
F 020 7346 0925
W www.bectu.org.uk
T 020 7346 0900

[CONTACTS 2011]

What are performers' unions?

The unions listed over the next few pages exist to protect and improve the rights, interests and working conditions of performers. They offer very important services to their members, such as advice on pay and conditions, help with contracts and negotiations, legal support and welfare advice. To join a performers' union there is usually a one-off joining fee and then an annual subscription fee calculated in relation to an individual's total yearly earnings. Equity is the main actors' union in the UK. See www.equity.org.uk and their article on the following pages for more details.

Do similar organisations exist for other sectors of the entertainment industry?

In addition to representation by trade unions, some skills also have professional bodies, guilds and associations which complement the work of trade unions. These include directors, producers, stage managers, designers and casting directors. These are also listed over the following pages.

What is the FIA?

The FIA (International Federation of Actors) www.fia-actors.com is an organisation which represents performers' trade unions, guilds and associations from all around the world. It tackles the same issues as individual actors' unions, but on an international rather than local level. Please see their article on the following pages for further information.

I'm a professionally trained actor from overseas and I want to work in the UK. How do I get started?

As with all forms of employment, to work as an actor in the UK you will need to have a relevant work permit/working visa. You might want to visit www.bia.homeoffice.gov.uk/workingintheuk for full information. You may also wish to join the UK's actors' union, Equity. For more information please visit their website www.equity.org.uk. If you can prove that you have relevant professional acting training and/or experience, you can also apply to join Spotlight to promote yourself to casting opportunities.

I am a UK resident and I want to work as an actor elsewhere in Europe. Where do I start?

A good starting point would be to contact the actors' union in the country in which you are hoping to work for information on their employment legislation. Contact details for performers' unions in Europe can be found over the next few pages or obtained from the FIA www.fia-actors.com, who in most cases will be able to advise on what criteria you need to fulfil to be eligible for work.

As a UK national, you have the right to work in any country which is a member of the European Union (EU) without a work permit. You will be given the same employment rights as nationals of the country you are working in, but these rights will change according to the country you choose to work in and may not be the same as the UK.

For more general advice, the Foreign and Commonwealth Office (FCO) offers advice on living overseas and provides information on contacting the UK embassy in and relevant entry requirements for the country of your choice. Please see www.fco.gov.uk/en/travelling-and-living-overseas for details. You could also visit Directgov's website www.direct.gov.uk/en/BritonsLivingAbroad/index.htm for further useful guidance for British citizens living abroad.

You should also go further and start researching agents, casting directors, production companies and so on which are based in the country you wish to live and work in. Begin your search online and then decide whether to approach a person or company for further information once you have found out more about them. Learning the culture and becoming as fluent as possible in the language of your chosen country would be advisable, as this opens up a far wider range of job opportunities.

infopage

What are English Speaking Theatres?

English Speaking Theatres can provide British actors with an opportunity to work abroad in theatre. These companies vary greatly in terms of the plays they put on and the audiences they attract: they may aim to teach English to schoolchildren; help audiences develop an appreciation of English plays; or may exist simply because there is a demand for English speaking entertainment. Some are based in one venue while others tour round the country. Actors may be employed for an individual production or, especially if touring, for a series of plays. Performers interested in the possibility of working for this type of theatre company should refer to the 'Theatre – English Speaking in Europe' section for listings.

I am a UK resident and I want to work as an actor in the USA. Where do I start?

To work in America you will need a Green Card – a visa which entitles the holder to live and work there permanently as an immigrant – but you will not qualify for one unless you are sponsored by a prospective employer in the US or a relative who is a US citizen. It would be worth visiting the US Embassy's website http://london.usembassy.gov/visas.html or the US Department of State's Bureau of Consular Affairs' website http://travel.state.gov/visa/visa_1750.html for information about the criteria you must meet and the fees you will have to pay. Relocation companies and legal services tailored to helping performers move to America can be found in the 'Accountants, Insurance & Law' section of Contacts.

Don't expect to be granted immediate entry to the USA. There is a limit to the number of people who can apply for immigrant status every year, so you could be on the waiting list for several years depending on the category of your application. You could enter the Green Card Lottery at www.greencard.co.uk for a chance to fast-track the processing of your application, although your visa will still have to be approved.

Finding employment from outside the USA will be difficult. You might want to try signing with an American talent agent to submit you for work, although there is huge competition for agents. Try the Association of Talent Agents (ATA) www.agentassociation.com for US agent details. The most effective way to gain an American agent's interest would be to get a personal referral from an industry contact, such as a casting director or acting coach. You should also promote yourself as you would with Spotlight by signing up with casting directories such as www.breakdownservices.com.

Acting employment in America is divided into union work and non-union work. The major actors' unions are SAG www.sag.org, AEA www.actorsequity.org, and AFTRA www.aftra.com. As with any other union they protect and enhance the rights of their members and offer various services and benefits. You will only become eligible for membership once you have provided proof of a contract for a job which comes under a particular union's jurisdiction. Non-members can work on union jobs if a producer is willing to employ them. You can join more than one union, but once you have joined at least one you will be unable to accept any non-union work.

You may have to begin your career in America with non-union work, as experience or union membership in the UK does not make you eligible to join a union in the US. Work ungoverned by the unions could include student and independent films, small stage productions, commercials, voice-overs, extra work, and so on. You are unlikely to be paid well as non-union contracts are not governed by the minimum wages set by the unions, but you will be able to build on your CV and begin making yourself known in the US acting industry.

Phil Pemberton is the Campaigns & Publications Officer at Equity, the trade union for the UK entertainment industry. He works to provide a voice of authority for performers and the industry in general.

There are lots of good reasons to join a performers' union. The issues that impact most upon you as a performer will depend on your personal circumstances and your career, amongst other things, but the one thing that performers can be sure of is that Equity is the union that best represents your interests.

So, why should you join Equity? Here are ten good reasons to get you thinking...

1. PAY: Equity contracts set the minimum rates for employment throughout the entertainment industry and the provisions in our contracts protect members from exploitation and deliver minimum standards.
The stronger we become, the more we push for improved deals. When members come together we can make real progress. In the last twelve months we've achieved a minimum wage of £500 in West End theatres.

2. DECENT TREATMENT AT WORK: On everything from holiday entitlement to meal breaks and from health and safety protection to maximum working time, Equity has negotiated agreements across the industry to protect you from exploitation by unscrupulous employers and to increase awareness of best practice.

3. EQUAL TREATMENT: Regardless of your gender, your race or your sexuality, Equity works for equal opportunities across the entertainment industry and to end discrimination. Recent campaigns for greater opportunities for older women and for a media that is more representative of all sectors of the community have been high profile and continue to attract considerable support.

4. PROTECTION: If your employers, managers or agents are treating you unfairly, Equity will be by your side to ensure that your rights are protected. Equity has a team of specialist organisers working full-time to represent your needs and we have strong legal support for when you need it.

5. PUBLIC LIABILITY: For many performers, Equity's public liability insurance (which provides coverage of up to £10million) is an essential protection for their working lives and provides unbeatable value. If someone gets hurt during your act or if something gets damaged, then the knowledge that full insurance comes with your membership can help take the drama out of a crisis.

6. COMPENSATION: If you are injured or get ill because of your working conditions our legal services can ensure you get proper compensation. We have specialist legal support and a 24 hour helpline if you need to make a personal injury claim.

7. BELONGING: By becoming an Equity member you make a statement about your commitment to your vocation and your place within our industry. For almost 80 years Equity membership has been a symbol of unity in an industry where work is often transitory and geographically diverse. Your Equity card is a symbol of your professionalism.

8. CONTRIBUTE: If you are serious about making a contribution to improving conditions for yourself and those you work with, the best way to help is to get involved in your union. In Equity our democratic structures mean your voice can be heard and that you can genuinely make a difference to your own working life and that of your fellow performers.

9. INFLUENCE: Equity is a major voice in the entertainment industry, contributing to public debate at local, regional, national and international levels. Our influence comes from the strength of our membership. Although we are not affiliated to any political party, we work with other entertainment unions to influence politicians and to protect your interests and the interests of the arts and media in general.

10. PRIDE: By being part of Equity you can be proud of your contribution to making your industry a safer and more rewarding place for everyone who works. Your membership makes our union stronger; your involvement gives your union greater influence. Working together we can make Equity a union we can all be proud of.

For more information about Equity contact:
Post: Equity, Guild House, Upper St Martin's Lane, London WC2H 9EG
T 020 7379 6000 W www.equity.org.uk E info@equity.org.uk

infopage

The International Federation of Actors (FIA) is the umbrella organisation representing performers' unions, guilds and professional associations beyond national borders. Set up in 1952 by Equity and the French Actors' Union (SFA), it has spread to gather more than 100 affiliates in about 80 countries around the world. Together with its sister federation FIM (International Federation of Musicians) it is the only international trade body voicing the professional interests of performers at global level. It enjoys consultative status with the World Intellectual Property Organisation, the International Labour Organisation, UNESCO and the Council of Europe.

Increasingly, decisions are taken at supranational level that may have serious repercussions for the daily lives of hundreds of thousands of professional performers. Our remit at FIA is to anticipate change and ensure that performers' legitimate concerns are duly taken into account. Whether the focus is on intellectual property, core labour rights, cultural diversity, mobility, new media or any other issue that is relevant to them, we bring performers and their livelihoods right to the heart of the decision-making process. As other industrial players also actively foster their own interests at international level, our presence is essential to preserve an equitable level playing field for all. We work closely with other interested parties and their trade bodies across the industry to seek solutions to common problems, wherever possible, through dialogue and negotiation.

Our ability to speak with an authoritative voice relies on the collective strength of our members. To this aim, we relentlessly work to help performers around the world build knowledgeable and effective trade unions. Unions are a vital tool for performers as they secure them decent working conditions and a minimum safety net for them to make a living. They are resourceful contributors to the entertainment industry, as they structure dialogue, help prevent and solve conflicts, raise professional standards, promote excellence and campaign for the industry to continue to be successful and fairly reward its creative talent. Our committed work carries us to countries where our knowledge can truly make a difference and bring local performers hope for a better future. To this end, FIA is particularly active in Africa, Latin America and Asia where we organise regular workshops and grow partnerships to reduce the divide between creative industries in developed and developing countries. We organise several regional meetings each year where unions in North America and in Europe can share experience, coordinate policies and respond to industrial developments.

We are committed to raising professional standards in the industry and regularly publish researches, guidelines and basic advice for performers. With the cooperation of the International Labour Organisation, we recently completed a Health & Safety brief for performers working in live shows as well as in television and film production. We also released a collection of minimum terms of reference for dancers working in countries where there are no collective agreements in place as well as a pan-European study on gender portrayal in the entertainment industry.

We always strongly encourage performers to join and support their unions and offer our services to strengthen their network. We channel solidarity and expertise to our members and create mechanisms to extend assistance to performers when their work brings them far from their union's jurisdiction. Active membership in one of our affiliated unions gives performers privileged access to advice and counselling in many other countries where FIA affiliates are established.

FIA is the voice of performers in the world. By joining local unions, they can help us protect their interests more effectively beyond national borders. They can also help us make a real difference to many other fellow performers who still face very difficult conditions as they struggle to live by their creative work in less fortunate countries.

For more information about FIA contact:
Post: International Federation of Actors (FIA), 31, rue de l'Hôpital, Box 9, 1000 Brussels, Belgium
T +32 2 234 5653   F +32 2 235 0861   W www.fia-actors.com   E office@fia-actors.com

MUSICIANS' UNION
60-62 Clapham Road, London SW9 0JJ
F 020 7582 9805   T 020 7582 5566
W www.musiciansunion.org.uk

NASAA - NATIONAL ASSOCIATION OF SUPPORTING ARTISTES AGENTS
E info@nasaa.org.uk
W www.nasaa.org.uk

NORTH AMERICAN ACTORS ASSOCIATION
Contact: By Telephone/e-mail only
E admin@naaa.org.uk   M 07873 371891
W www.naaa.org.uk

PERSONAL MANAGERS' ASSOCIATION LTD
PO Box 63819, London N1P 1HL   T 0845 6027191
E info@thepma.com
W www.thepma.com

WRITERS' GUILD OF GREAT BRITAIN THE
40 Rosebery Avenue, London EC1R 4RX   T 020 7833 0777
E admin@writersguild.org.uk
W www.writersguild.org.uk

BELGIUM
ACV/TRANSCOM - CULTUUR
Galerij Agora
Grasmarkt 105 bus 40, 1000 Brussels
F 00 32 2 512 8591   T 00 32 2 289 0830
E info@acvcultuur.be
W www.acvcultuur.be

CENTRALE GÉNÉRALE DES SERVICES PUBLICS
Place Fontainas 9-11, 1000 Brussels
F 00 32 2 508 5902   T 00 32 2 508 5811
E mylene.paon@cgsp.be
W www.acod.be

INTERNATIONAL FEDERATION OF ACTORS (FIA)
31 rue de l'Hopital, Box 9, 1000 Brussels
F 00 32 2 235 0861   T 00 32 2 234 5653
E office@fia-actors.com
W www.fia-actors.com

DENMARK
DAF - DANSK ARTIST FORBUND
Dronningensgade 68, 1420 Copenhagen K
F 00 45 33 33 73 30   T 00 45 33 32 66 77
E artisten@artisten.dk
W www.artisten.dk

DANSK SKUESPILLERFORBUND
Sankt Knuds Vej 26, 1903 Frederiksberg C
F 00 45 33 24 81 59   T 00 45 33 24 22 00
E dsf@skuespillerforbundet.dk
W www.skuespillerforbundet.dk

FINLAND
SUOMEN NÄYTTELIJÄLIITTO
Meritullinkatu 33, 00170 Helsinki, Finland
F 00 358 9 2511 2139   T 00 353 9 2511 2135
E office@nayttelijaliitto.fi
W www.nayttelijaliitto.fi

FRANCE
SYNDICAT FRANÇAIS DES ARTISTES-INTERPRÈTES
1 rue Janssen, 75019 Paris
F 00 33 1 53 25 09 01   T 00 33 1 53 25 09 09
E info@sfa-cgt.fr
W www.sfa-cgt.fr

GERMANY
GENOSSENSCHAFT DEUTSCHER BUEHNENANGEHOERIGER
Feldbrunnenstrasse 74
20148 Hamburg
F 00 49 40 45 93 52   T 00 49 40 44 51 85
E gdba@buehnengenossenschaft.de
W www.buehnengenossenschaft.de

GREECE
HAU - HELLENIC ACTORS' UNION
33 Kaniggos Street
106 82 Athens
F 00 30 210 380 8651   T 00 30 210 383 3742
E sei@sei.gr
W www.sei.gr

IRELAND
IEG - IRISH EQUITY GROUP
SIPTU
Liberty Hall, Dublin 1
F 00 353 1 874 3691   T 00 353 1 858 6403
E equity@siptu.ie
W www.irishequity.ie

ITALY
SINDACATO ATTORI ITALIANO
Via Ofanto 18, 00198 Rome
F 00 39 06 854 6780   T 00 39 06 841 7303
E sai@scl.cgil.it
W www.cgil.it/sai-slc

LUXEMBOURG
ONOFHANGEGE GEWERKSCHAFTSBOND LETZEBUERG
60 bd. Kennedy
B.P. 149, L-4002 Esch/Alzette
F 00 352 541 620   T 00 352 540 545 1
E ogbl@ogbl.lu
W www.ogb-l.lu

NETHERLANDS
FNV - KUNSTEN INFORMATIE EN MEDIA
Jan Tooropstraat 1
Postbus 9354
1006 AJ Amsterdam
F 00 31 20 355 3737   T 00 31 20 355 3636
E algemeen@fnv-kiem.nl
W www.fnv.nl/kiem

NORWAY
NSF - NORSK SKUESPILLERFORBUND
Welhavensgate 1
0166 Oslo
F 00 47 21 02 71 91   T 00 47 21 02 71 90
E nsf@skuespillerforbund.no
W www.skuespillerforbund.no

PORTUGAL
STE - SINDICATO DOS TRABALHADORES DE ESPECTÁCULOS
Rua da Fe 23, 2do Piso
1150-149 Lisbon
F 00 351 21 885 3787   T 00 351 21 885 2728
E startistas@mail.telepac.pt

SPAIN
CC.OO. COMISIONES OBRERAS - SERVICIOS A LA CIUDADANÍA SECTOR DE MEDIOS, ARTES, CULTURA Y DEPORTE
Plaza Cristino Martos 4
6A Planta
28015 Madrid
F 00 34 91 548 1613   T 00 34 91 540 9295
E medios@fsc.ccoo.es
W www.fsc.ccoo.es/webfscmedios

FAEE - FEDERACIÓN DE ARTISTAS DEL ESTADO ESPAÑOL
C/ Montera 34
1ro Piso, 28013 Madrid
F 00 34 91 522 6055   T 00 34 91 522 2804
E federaciondeartistas@faee.es
W www.faee.es

SWEDEN
TF TEATERFÖRBUNDET
Kaplansbacken 2A
Box 12 710, 112 94 Stockholm
F 00 46 8 653 9507   T 00 46 8 441 1300
E info@teaterforbundet.se
W www.teaterforbundet.se

UNITED STATES OF AMERICA
AFTRA
(American Federation of Television & Radio Artists)
260 Madison Avenue
New York, NY 10016
F (212) 545 1238   T (212) 532 0800
W www.aftra.com

AFTRA
(American Federation of Television & Radio Artists)
5757 Wilshire Boulevard
9th Floor, Los Angeles CA 90036
F (323) 634 8246   T (323) 634 8100
W www.aftra.com

S A G (Screen Actors Guild)
7th Floor
5757 Wilshire Boulevard
Los Angeles, CA 90036-3600   T (323) 954 1600
W www.sag.org

S A G (Screen Actors Guild)
360 Madison Avenue
12th Floor
New York NY 10017
F (212) 944 6774   T (212) 944 1030
E nymember@sag.org
W www.sag.org

Index To Advertisers

PHOTOGRAPHERS

THEATRE PRODUCERS

TRAINING (Private Coaches)

TRAINING
(Schools, Companies & Workshops)

WIG SUPPLIERS